STATISTICAL MECHANICS OF ELASTICITY

STATISTICAL MECHANICS OF ELASTICITY

J. H. WEINER

Brown University

A Wiley-Interscience Publication

JOHN WILEY & SONS

New York • Chichester • Brisbane • Toronto • Singapore

Library of Congress Cataloging in Publication Data:

Weiner, Jerome Harris, 1923–
  Statistical mechanics of elasticity.

  "A Wiley-Interscience publication."
  Includes index.
  1. Elasticity. 2. Statistical mechanics. I. Title.

QC191.W39 1983   531′.3823   82-20056
ISBN 0-471-09773-X

To Ponnie

PREFACE

In the writing of this book, I have had particularly in mind the research worker or advanced graduate student in solid mechanics who, with a thorough background in the mechanical behavior of solids from a continuum viewpoint, would like to gain some insight into the atomistic aspects of the subject. I have tried to make the treatment reasonably self-contained for this kind of reader and have included, for example, a chapter on the basic concepts of quantum mechanics which assumes no previous exposure to the subject. At the same time, the book is written on a fairly advanced and detailed level since it is my belief that, for readers accustomed to the mathematical literature of continuum solid mechanics, this will prove more congenial than an elementary account. Although the overall structure of the book is shaped with this particular audience in mind, it is my hope that portions of it will prove of interest to others as well: To those physicists, chemists, and research workers in materials science who are concerned with the mechanical behavior of either crystalline or polymeric solids and to graduate students who are taking a general course in statistical mechanics.

Part One of the book is based solely on classical mechanics. After an introductory chapter, which provides a summary of thermoelasticity from the continuum viewpoint, it develops the principles of classical statistical mechanics and then applies these principles to the study of the thermoelastic behavior of both crystalline and polymeric solids. Although the main emphasis of the book is on elastic behavior, Part One concludes with a chapter on the theory of thermally activated rate processes in solids; a subject that finds important application in the study of some aspects of the inelastic behavior of solids.

Part Two is based on quantum mechanics. It provides a discussion of the role of this subject in the development of interatomic force laws, the manner in which quantum statistical effects modify the low-temperature mechanical behavior of solids, and the nature of quantum effects on the rates of thermally activated processes.

This book is an outgrowth of a course that I have taught a number of times both at Columbia University and at Brown University for graduate students in solid mechanics and for those in materials science primarily concerned with the mechanical behavior of solids. The course was intended to provide an alternative to the usual course in statistical mechanics in which the major emphasis of application is to gases and liquids and to electronic and magnetic phenomena.

The primary purpose of this book is didactic and it does not pretend by any means to present a complete treatment of all aspects of this very large subject and the current research activity in it. Although much of the material is standard, some recent research results have been included to illustrate the general principles. Also, some of the methods of presentation and derivations (for example, the treatment of the stress ensemble in Sections 3.7 and 4.7) are new and have not been previously published.

I am indebted to J. L. Ericksen, H. J. Maris, and W. T. Sanders for reading portions of the manuscript and for helpful comments. My research dealing with the mechanical behavior of crystalline and polymeric solids from the atomistic viewpoint, some of which is discussed in this book, has been supported for a number of years both by the National Science Foundation through the Materials Research Laboratory at Brown University and by the Gas Research Institute. Most of the drawings were prepared by Mrs. Muriel Anderson and Miss Elisabeth Marx. The manuscript went through several drafts and Mrs. Debra Firth typed them all, cheerfully and rapidly.

J. H. WEINER

Providence, Rhode Island
January 1983

CONTENTS

STATISTICAL MECHANICS OF ELASTICITY

Classical Theory

Classical Theory

CHAPTER ONE

Thermoelasticity from the Continuum Viewpoint

1.1 INTRODUCTION

The subject of this book is the mechanical behavior of solids, both crystalline and polymeric, studied from the atomistic viewpoint. We will be particularly concerned with the role of temperature and with understanding its effect in terms of the thermal motion of the atoms of the solids.

To clarify the area of concern, consider two solids under tension, one crystalline, for example, nickel, and the other polymeric, for example, rubber. The first difference one would notice in the behavior of the materials would be the much greater elastic extensibility of the rubber, of the order of 10^3–10^4 times that of a crystalline solid. Even more striking would be the effect of a rise in temperature while the tensile force is maintained constant. Under these conditions, the crystalline solid expands slightly while the polymeric solid undergoes a substantial contraction. The type of question that concerns us is: What goes on at the atomic level that explains this contrasting behavior?

The discipline that has as its primary goal the explication of the macroscopic behavior of matter in terms of its atomic structure is statistical mechanics. A substantial portion of this book, therefore, will be devoted to the presentation of the basic principles of statistical mechanics and in most of the remaining portions these principles will be applied to the understanding of the elasticity of solids. Also, in Chapter 7, an application of the principles of statistical mechanics to the theory of rate processes in solids will be considered.

Our discussion of statistical mechanics will begin in Chapter 2. In this introductory chapter, we first present a brief summary[1] of the relevant con-

---

[1]A similar summary, restricted to the deformation regime underlying the linear theory of elasticity, may be found in Chapter 1 of Boley and Weiner (1960). The present treatment does not make this restriction.

cepts of continuum mechanics, those dealing with the kinematics, mechanics, and thermodynamics of continua, which are needed for the discussion of the thermoelastic behavior of solids on the continuum level. The material of this chapter, therefore, serves to provide a summary, from the continuum viewpoint, of the phenomena that we will be studying from the atomistic viewpoint in the remainder of the book. For example, we will introduce in this chapter such continuum concepts as the stress and strain tensors, temperature, internal energy, entropy, and the macroscopic thermodynamic basis of the thermoelastic stress–strain relations. In succeeding chapters, we will consider the same concepts from the atomistic viewpoint. Therefore, in our presentation of the continuum concepts, particularly those of macroscopic or continuum thermodynamics, we are particularly concerned to do so in a manner that lends itself most naturally to an atomistic reinterpretation; this sometimes leads to a certain artificial appearance to the sequence and manner in which concepts are introduced.

1.2 KINEMATICS OF CONTINUA

From the continuum viewpoint, a given portion of matter is treated as a collection of elements, called material particles, which at any given instant can be placed in a one-to-one correspondence with the points of a closed region[2] of three-dimensional Euclidean space.

It is important to emphasize that the concept of a material particle in continuum mechanics does not at all correspond to a single atom or molecule but rather to a set of a large number of atoms. To emphasize the distinction, we will sometimes use the term "continuum particle."

The one-to-one correspondence between material particles and points of space varies with time as the body moves and deforms, and we speak of that particle that occupies a given point or place in space at time t_0 and occupies some other place at time t; that is, the continuum particle retains its identity as it moves. We denote the position of a given particle at a reference time t_0 by its coordinates X_L, $L = 1, 2, 3$, with respect to a rectangular Cartesian coordinate system (Figure 1.1). The position of the same particle at a later instant t is denoted by x_i, $i = 1, 2, 3$, its coordinates with respect to the same coordinate system. The coordinates X_L are called material or Lagrangian while the coordinates x_i are called spatial or Eulerian. The equations

$$x_i = x_i(t; X_1, X_2, X_3) = x_i(t; X), \qquad (1.2.1)$$

where X_L ranges over the region D_0 occupied by the body at the reference time

---

[2]A definition may be found, for example, in Kellogg (1953, p. 93).

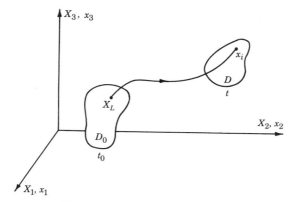

Figure 1.1   Deformation of a body.

t_0 (Figure 1.1) describe its motion completely. The inverse of Eq. (1.2.1)

$$X_L = X_L(t; x_1, x_2, x_3) = X_L(t; x), \quad x \in D \tag{1.2.2}$$

is also needed.

Particle Velocity

The velocity of a particle is obtained from Eq. (1.2.1) as

$$\dot{x}_i(t; X) \triangleq \frac{\partial}{\partial t} x_i(t; X) \tag{1.2.3}$$

and is the velocity of the particle which was at X_L at the reference time t_0. Here, the superposed dot denotes the material derivative, that is, the derivative of a quantity with respect to time for a given particle (or with X_L fixed).[3] The particle velocity may be expressed as a function of x_i, the particle's position at the current time t, by means of Eq. (1.2.2); in this case the notation

$$v_i(x, t) \triangleq \dot{x}_i\big(t; X(t; x)\big) \tag{1.2.4}$$

is used.

---

[3] We will also use the superposed dot for time differentiation of different types in other parts of the book. In each case, the local usage will be defined and the context of the discussion should prevent confusion.

Deformation Measures

Consider a pair of neighboring particles whose material coordinates differ by dX_L. The square of the distance between these particles at t_0 is given by

$$(dS)^2 = dX_L \, dX_L \tag{1.2.5}$$

with the summation convention on repeated indices applying as usual.[4] The difference in coordinates between the same pair of particles at time t is

$$dx_i = x_{i,L} \, dX_L \tag{1.2.6}$$

where the partial derivatives

$$x_{i,L} \triangleq \frac{\partial}{\partial X_L} x_i(t; X) \tag{1.2.7}$$

are computed from Eq. (1.2.1). Therefore the square of the distance between the same pair of particles at t is given by

$$(ds)^2 = dx_i \, dx_i = x_{i,L} x_{i,M} \, dX_L \, dX_M \tag{1.2.8}$$

and

$$(ds)^2 - (dS)^2 = (x_{i,L} x_{i,M} - \delta_{LM}) \, dX_L \, dX_M$$

$$= 2 E_{LM} \, dX_L \, dX_M, \tag{1.2.9}$$

where δ_{LM} is the Kronecker delta ($\delta_{LM} = 1$ if $L = M$, $\delta_{LM} = 0$ if $L \neq M$) and

$$E_{LM} = \tfrac{1}{2}(x_{i,L} x_{i,M} - \delta_{LM}) \tag{1.2.10}$$

is the material strain tensor. As seen from Eq. (1.2.9), it provides a measure of the change in distance between a pair of neighboring particles in terms of their material coordinates. Alternatively, by use of Eq. (1.2.2),

$$(dS)^2 = dX_L \, dX_L = X_{L,i} X_{L,j} \, dx_i \, dx_j. \tag{1.2.11}$$

Therefore,

$$(ds)^2 - (dS)^2 = (\delta_{ij} - X_{L,i} X_{L,j}) \, dx_i \, dx_j$$

$$= 2 e_{ij} \, dx_i \, dx_j \tag{1.2.12}$$

---

[4]Summation convention: Repeated indices in an expression imply summation over the indicated range of the indices. Thus, $(dS)^2 = dX_L \, dX_L \triangleq \sum_{L=1}^{3} dX_L \, dX_L$, $(ds)^2 = x_{i,L} x_{i,M} \, dX_L \, dX_M \triangleq \sum_{i=1}^{3}\sum_{L=1}^{3}\sum_{M=1}^{3} x_{i,L} x_{i,M} \, dX_L \, dX_M$. We use the summation convention throughout; the suspension of the convention in a given expression is indicated by underlining the indices or by an explicit statement.

where

$$e_{ij} = \tfrac{1}{2}\left(\delta_{ij} - X_{L,i}X_{L,j}\right) \tag{1.2.13}$$

is the spatial strain tensor. It provides a measure of the change in distance between a pair of neighboring particles in terms of their spatial coordinates.

Change in Area Elements

Consider two noncolinear infinitesimal fibers[5] with one point in common, corresponding at t_0 to the vectors $dX_L^{(1)}$, $dX_M^{(2)}$. These fibers span a parallelogram element of area (Figure 1.2) given by the cross product of the vectors[6] $dX_L^{(1)}$, $dX_M^{(2)}$,

$$dA_L = e_{LMN}\,dX_M^{(1)}\,dX_N^{(2)} \tag{1.2.14}$$

where e_{LMN} is the alternating tensor[7] and dA_L is a vector normal to the area element with magnitude equal to its area. At time t, the corresponding area is

$$da_r = e_{rst}\,dx_s^{(1)}\,dx_t^{(2)}$$

$$= e_{rst}x_{s,M}x_{t,N}\,dX_M^{(1)}\,dX_N^{(2)}. \tag{1.2.15}$$

Consider next

$$x_{r,L}\,da_r = e_{rst}x_{r,L}x_{s,M}x_{t,N}\,dX_M^{(1)}\,dX_N^{(2)}. \tag{1.2.16}$$

From the definition of a determinant[8]

$$e_{rst}x_{r,L}x_{s,M}x_{t,N} = e_{LMN}|x_{i,K}| \tag{1.2.17}$$

where $|x_{i,K}|$ is the 3×3 determinant whose elements are $x_{i,K}$, $i, K = 1,\ldots, 3$. Therefore, Eq. (1.2.16) takes the form

$$x_{r,L}\,da_r = e_{LMN}|x_{i,K}|\,dX_M^{(1)}\,dX_N^{(2)}$$

$$= |x_{i,K}|\,dA_L \tag{1.2.18}$$

[5] By this terminology we mean sets of material particles lying on straight lines whose lengths are infinitesimal.

[6] We use as equivalent terminology "the vector F_L" and "the vector $\mathbf{F}$ with components F_L."

[7] $e_{LMN} = 1$ if LMN is an even permutation of the sequence 123.

   $= -1$ if LMN is an odd permutation of 123.

   $= 0$ otherwise, that is, if LMN contains a repeated integer.

[8] For a discussion of determinants in this notation see, for example, McConnell (1957, p. 10).

Figure 1.2   Deformation of area elements.

by use of Eq. (1.2.14). By use of the relation

$$x_{r,L} X_{L,s} = \delta_{rs} \tag{1.2.19}$$

we obtain finally

$$da_s = X_{L,s} |x_{i,K}| dA_L = X_{L,s} J dA_L \tag{1.2.20}$$

where we have introduced the notation

$$J = J(X_1, X_2, X_3) = |x_{i,K}|. \tag{1.2.21}$$

The kinematic significance of J is considered next. .

Change in Volume Elements

Consider three noncoplanar infinitesimal fibers with one point in common, corresponding at t_0 to the vectors $d\mathbf{X}^{(1)}$, $d\mathbf{X}^{(2)}$, $d\mathbf{X}^{(3)}$. They span a parallelepiped of volume $d\mathscr{V}$,

$$d\mathscr{V} = d\mathbf{X}^{(1)} \cdot d\mathbf{X}^{(2)} \times d\mathbf{X}^{(3)} = e_{LMN} dX_L^{(1)} dX_M^{(2)} dX_N^{(3)} \tag{1.2.22}$$

where we assume the orientation of the three vectors is such that the triple product is positive. At t, the same material fibers span a volume dv,

$$dv = e_{rst} dx_r^{(1)} dx_s^{(2)} dx_t^{(3)}$$

$$= e_{rst} x_{r,L} x_{s,M} x_{t,N} dX_L^{(1)} dX_M^{(2)} dX_N^{(3)}$$

$$= e_{LMN} |x_{i,K}| dX_L^{(1)} dX_M^{(2)} dX_N^{(3)}$$

$$= |x_{i,K}| d\mathscr{V}. \tag{1.2.23}$$

Therefore,[9]

$$J = |x_{i,K}| = \frac{dv}{d\mathscr{V}} \quad . \tag{1.2.24}$$

[9] We assume throughout that $|x_{i,K}| > 0$.

Homogeneous Deformation

For the purpose of the comparison of the concepts of statistical and continuum mechanics, we will be concerned only with homogeneous deformations[10] defined by

$$x_i(t; X) = a_{iL}(t)X_L + b_i(t). \tag{1.2.25}$$

A homogeneous deformation is also referred to sometimes as an affine transformation. Clearly, in this case, straight lines of finite length remain straight under the deformation and the results previously derived for the change in distance between neighboring points, and in infinitesimal elements of area and volume, will apply for the corresponding finite quantities. For this case

$$x_{i,L}(t; X) = a_{iL}(t), \quad X_{L,i}(t; x) = A_{Li}(t) \tag{1.2.26}$$

and the preceding formulas will be transcribed in terms of the deformation matrix a_{iL} and its inverse A_{Li} when needed. Thus, for example, the material strain tensor E_{LM} takes the form

$$E_{LM} = \tfrac{1}{2}(a_{iL}a_{iM} - \delta_{LM}) \tag{1.2.27}$$

for a homogeneous deformation.

1.3   MECHANICS

Laws of Motion

Newton's laws of the conservation of linear and angular momentum, originally formulated for a system of discrete particles, are extended by postulate to apply as well to any portion of matter regarded as a continuum. For a body occupying at time t the region D with boundary S, subjected to surface forces $\mathbf{t}$ per unit area (referred to as surface tractions) and body forces $\mathbf{b}$ per unit mass (as, for example, those due to gravity), these laws take the form

$$\int_D (\mathbf{b} - \dot{\mathbf{v}})\rho_m \, dv + \int_S \mathbf{t} \, da = 0 \tag{1.3.1}$$

$$\int_D (\mathbf{b} - \dot{\mathbf{v}}) \times \mathbf{r}\rho_m \, dv + \int_S \mathbf{t} \times \mathbf{r} \, da = 0 \tag{1.3.2}$$

where ρ_m is the mass density, $\dot{\mathbf{v}}$ is the material derivative of the particle velocity,

---

[10] This is because the goal of our use of statistical mechanics is to provide an atomistic basis for the constitutive relations of elastic solids. For this purpose it is only necessary to consider homogeneous deformations. These constitutive relations are, of course, applicable to nonuniform processes as well, as discussed in Section 3.10.

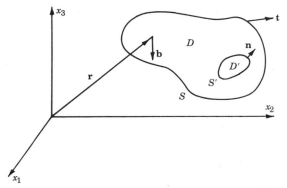

Figure 1.3 Forces acting on body.

that is, its acceleration, and **r**, the variable of integration, is the position of a generic particle in the body with respect to a fixed origin (Figure 1.3).

Stress Principle

Consider any subregion of D, say D' with boundary S' (Figure 1.3). It is postulated that surface tractions **t** act on this interior boundary as well as on S, the exterior boundary of the body. Physically, these interior tractions are regarded as exerted by the material of the body exterior to D' on the material in D'. Furthermore, it is postulated that the laws of motion, Eqs. (1.3.1) and (1.3.2), originally stated for the entire body, apply as well to the material in any subregion D' when the effect of these interior surface tractions are included.

Let $\mathbf{t}(\mathbf{n})$ be the traction at a point of S' where the exterior unit normal is **n**. By taking D' in the shape of a pillbox with faces normal to **n** and height h, using Eq. (1.3.1) and letting $h \to 0$, it may be shown[11] that at any interior point of the body in a region in which body and inertia forces are bounded

$$\mathbf{t}(\mathbf{n}) = -\mathbf{t}(-\mathbf{n}). \qquad (1.3.3)$$

By taking D' in the shape of a tetrahedron in a region of bounded body and inertia forces it may be shown further that a stress tensor, t_{ij} (referred to as the Cauchy stress tensor), is defined at each point in such a region so that at that point

$$\big(\mathbf{t}(\mathbf{n})\big)_i \triangleq t_i(\mathbf{n}) = t_{ij}n_j. \qquad (1.3.4)$$

[11] Details may be found, for example, in Truesdell and Toupin (1960, p. 536–543).

In the absence of body moments or couple stresses[11], it follows, by application of the law of conservation of angular momentum, that the stress tensor is symmetric,

$$t_{ij} = t_{ji}. \tag{1.3.5}$$

Thus far, surface tractions, whether on exterior or interior surfaces, have been defined per unit of present area. If da_j is an element of area of present magnitude da and present unit normal n_j, then the total force, f_i, acting on that element is

$$f_i = t_i(\mathbf{n})\, da = t_{ij} n_j\, da = t_{ij}\, da_j. \tag{1.3.6}$$

The material, which presently forms the area element da_j, occupied at t_0 the area element dA_L, and we introduce next the (first) Piola–Kirchhoff stress tensor T_{iL} which permits the computation of the force f_i in terms of dA_L,

$$f_i = t_{ij}\, da_j = T_{iL}\, dA_L. \tag{1.3.7}$$

By use of Eq. (1.2.20) relating da_j and dA_L, we find that

$$T_{iL} = J X_{L,j} t_{ij} \tag{1.3.8}$$

and

$$t_{ij} = J^{-1} x_{j,L} T_{iL}. \tag{1.3.9}$$

Note that the Piola–Kirchhoff stress tensor T_{iL} (sometimes referred to as a double vector) is not symmetric in its indices. The physical significance of its components is of importance: T_{iL} is the ith component of force presently acting on an area element which, in its reference state, was one unit of area in magnitude and had its normal in the direction of the coordinate axis X_L (Figure 1.4).[12] It represents the stated component of force exerted by the material on the positive side of the normal on the material on the negative side of the normal. Alternatively, it also represents, by Eq. (1.3.3), the negative of the force exerted by the material on the negative side of the normal on the material on the positive side of the normal. It is the latter interpretation that carries over most naturally to the microscopic interpretation of stress in a crystal (Section 4.3) or in a polymeric solid (Section 6.10).

In addition to the Piola–Kirchhoff stress tensor, we will also have need of the material stress tensor,[13] T_{LM}, defined as

$$T_{LM} = X_{L,i} T_{iM} = J X_{L,i} X_{M,j} t_{ij}. \tag{1.3.10}$$

It is seen that the symmetry of T_{LM} follows from that of t_{ij}.

---

[12]As in this figure, we sometimes use Roman numerals I, II, III to denote particular values of the material subscripts L, M; for example, X_I, T_{III}, etc.

[13]T_{LM} is also termed the second Piola–Kirchhoff stress tensor; see Thurston (1964, p. 33) and Truesdell and Toupin (1960, Eq. 210.9).

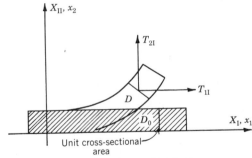

Figure 1.4   Significance of Piola–Kirchhoff stress components.

Work and Power

Consider a body occupying a region D with bounding surface S (Figure 1.3) subjected to prescribed time-dependent surface tractions $\mathbf{t}(t)$ for $t_1 \leqslant t \leqslant t_2$ at all points of S and free of body forces. Then, if the particle velocity $\mathbf{v}(x, t)$ is known for all points on S in the same time interval, $\dot{W}$, the rate[14] at which the external agency imposing the traction does work on the body is

$$\dot{W}(t) = \int_S t_i v_i \, da, \qquad t_1 \leqslant t \leqslant t_2, \qquad (1.3.11)$$

and, ΔW, the total work done on the body in this time interval is obtained by integration,

$$\Delta W = \int_{t_1}^{t_2} \dot{W}(t)\, dt = \int_{t_1}^{t_2} dt \int_S t_i(t) v_i(x, t)\, da. \qquad (1.3.12)$$

These considerations apply as well to a portion of a body, such as that occupying D' in Figure 1.3; in this case the external agency is the material surrounding D'.

We next specialize the above discussion to the case[15] in which during the time interval $t_1 < t < t_2$, the body is undergoing a homogeneous, time-dependent deformation, as defined by Eq. (1.2.25). We assume further that during this process there exists a homogeneous time-dependent state of stress $t_{ij}(t)$ throughout the body corresponding to imposed surface tractions $t_i(t)$ obtained

---

[14] For a function that depends solely on time, such as $W(t)$, we use the notation $\dot{W}(t) = dW(t)/dt$.
[15] The type of process we are describing here is referred to as quasi-static and will be treated in greater detail in our discussion of continuum thermodynamics. It is an idealization of a real process, one that may be approached as closely as one likes by varying the applied loads at a sufficiently slow rate.

from $t_{ij}(t)$ by means of Eq. (1.3.4). Then,

$$\dot{W} = \int_S t_{ij} v_i n_j \, da = \int_D (t_{ij} v_i)_{,j} \, dv$$

$$= \int_D t_{ij} v_{i,j} \, dv = t_{ij} v_{i,j} v \tag{1.3.13}$$

where v is the volume of D and we have used the divergence theorem and the fact that the state of stress is homogeneous. By use of Eqs. (1.3.9), (1.2.4), (1.2.24), and (1.2.26), Eq. (1.3.13) may be written in the form

$$\dot{W} = J^{-1} T_{iL} x_{j,L} v_{i,j} v = T_{iL} \dot{x}_{i,L} \mathscr{V}$$

or

$$\dot{W} = T_{iL} \dot{a}_{iL} \mathscr{V} \tag{1.3.14}$$

where $\mathscr{V}$ is the original volume of the body and $\dot{a}_{iL} = (d/dt) a_{iL}(t)$.

The expression for $\dot{W}$ may also be written in terms of the material stress tensor by use of the inverse of Eq. (1.3.10), namely, $T_{iL} = x_{i,M} T_{ML}$, and the material derivative of the material strain tensor which, from Eq. (1.2.10), is

$$\dot{E}_{LM} = \tfrac{1}{2} (\dot{x}_{i,L} x_{i,M} + x_{i,L} \dot{x}_{i,M}). \tag{1.3.15}$$

Substitution in Eq. (1.3.14) then yields

$$\dot{W} = T_{iL} \dot{x}_{i,L} \mathscr{V} = T_{ML} x_{i,M} \dot{x}_{i,L} \mathscr{V}$$

$$= T_{LM} \dot{E}_{LM} \mathscr{V}, \tag{1.3.16}$$

where we have used the symmetry of T_{LM}.

A special case of importance is that in which

$$t_{ij} = -p \delta_{ij} \tag{1.3.17}$$

as occurs, for example, in an inviscid fluid; p is called the pressure. In this case Eq. (1.3.13) becomes

$$\dot{W} = -p v_{i,i} v = -p \dot{v} \tag{1.3.18}$$

where we have used the familiar property[16] of the divergence of the velocity field, $v_{i,i} = \dot{v}/v$. Another example of interest is a one-dimensional linear string

[16] This result will be derived in Section 2.5 as part of the proof of Liouville's theorem.

of length ℓ subject to a tensile force f. In this case

$$\dot{W} = f\dot{\ell}. \tag{1.3.19}$$

We will frequently find it convenient to introduce a generalized notation with $\mathscr{A}_1, \ldots, \mathscr{A}_\nu$ as kinematical variables and $\mathscr{F}_1, \ldots, \mathscr{F}_\nu$ as their conjugate forces, so that $\dot{W}$, the rate of doing work during a quasi-static process can be written

$$\dot{W} = \sum_{\alpha=1}^{\nu} \mathscr{F}_\alpha \dot{\mathscr{A}}_\alpha. \tag{1.3.20}$$

Thus, for an elastic solid we may take the $\mathscr{A}_\alpha$ as representing E_{LM} and the corresponding $\mathscr{F}_\alpha$ are therefore $\mathscr{V}T_{LM}$, as seen from Eq. (1.3.16). In this case $\nu = 6$, if we take into account the symmetry of E_{LM} and T_{LM}. The correspondence between the single index and the symmetric pair of indices (LM) is generally made in accordance with the convention known as Voigt notation.

α	1	2	3	4	5	6	
LM	11	22	33	23 = 32	31 = 13	12 = 21	(1.3.21)

Care must be taken in the correspondence between $\mathscr{A}_\alpha$, $\mathscr{F}_\alpha$ and E_{LM}, $\mathscr{V}T_{LM}$ for the off-diagonal terms. The expression $\dot{W} = \mathscr{V}T_{LM}\dot{E}_{LM}$ of Eq. (1.3.16) includes terms of the form $\mathscr{V}T_{12}\dot{E}_{12} + \mathscr{V}T_{21}\dot{E}_{21} = 2\mathscr{V}T_{12}\dot{E}_{12}$, but only a single term of the form $\mathscr{V}T_{11}\dot{E}_{11}$. Therefore, a suitable correspondence is

$$\mathscr{A}_1 = E_{11}, \mathscr{A}_2 = E_{22}, \mathscr{A}_3 = E_{33}, \mathscr{A}_4 = 2E_{23}, \mathscr{A}_5 = 2E_{13}, \mathscr{A}_6 = 2E_{12}$$

$$\tag{1.3.22}$$

$$\mathscr{F}_1 = \mathscr{V}T_{11}, \mathscr{F}_2 = \mathscr{V}T_{22}, \mathscr{F}_3 = \mathscr{V}T_{33},$$

$$\mathscr{F}_4 = \mathscr{V}T_{23}, \mathscr{F}_5 = \mathscr{V}T_{13}, \mathscr{F}_6 = \mathscr{V}T_{12}. \tag{1.3.23}$$

We may also use the quantities a_{iL} as kinematical variables $\mathscr{A}_\alpha$ together with $\mathscr{V}T_{iL}$ as corresponding generalized forces $\mathscr{F}_\alpha$ [Eq. (1.3.14)]. In this case $\nu = 9$, a larger number because the variables a_{iL} include the description of the rigid rotation superimposed on the deformation of the body, whereas the variables E_{LM} describe only the latter. Finally, for an inviscid fluid or a linear string, $\nu = 1$, with $\mathscr{A}_1 = v$, $\mathscr{F}_1 = -p$ for the fluid, and with $\mathscr{A}_1 = \ell$, $\mathscr{F}_1 = f$ for the string. In a general context we will refer to the quantities $\mathscr{F}_\alpha$ and $\mathscr{A}_\alpha$ as generalized forces and displacements that are conjugate to each other in the sense that the rate of doing work is given by Eq. (1.3.20). When we are dealing with deformable bodies we will frequently refer to the $\mathscr{F}_\alpha$ and $\mathscr{A}_\alpha$ simply as stresses and strains.

1.4 THERMODYNAMICS

Although the scope of equilibrium macroscopic thermodynamics is very broad, in this brief review of its principles we will be concerned primarily with those thermodynamic systems that consist of a fixed collection of matter of constant chemical composition regarded as a continuum, that is, with bodies on which mechanical processes, such as described in Sections 1.2 and 1.3, are performed. Nevertheless, we will use the term "thermodynamic system" or simply "system" in this discussion in order to conform with common usage as well as to emphasize the generality of the subject.

Uniform State of Thermodynamic Equilibrium

The subjects of kinematics and mechanics, which we have just reviewed, serve to introduce various properties of this class of systems. From the subject of kinematics come properties such as volume v, and material strain tensor E_{LM}, whereas properties such as pressure p or stress tensor T_{LM} come from the concepts of mechanics. Some of these quantities, such as strain and pressure, are intensive (their values do not change if two identical systems are joined to form a new one), whereas others, such as volume and mass, are extensive (their values are doubled). A system is said to be in a state of uniform thermodynamic equilibrium if all of its properties are independent of time and, in addition, all of its intensive properties are independent of position.

State Variables

The basis for continuum thermodynamics is described as a summary of empirical observations. These generally refer to idealized experiments, which it is believed could be approached arbitrarily closely by real experiments. In some cases, however, it is not clear how the idealized experiments could, in fact, be performed in reality. For this reason, the reference to experimental results in this section should not be taken literally. Nevertheless, the consequences of the theory developed in this way are subject to experimental verification.

As our first summary of empirical data, we note that it is not possible to specify arbitrarily the values of all of the properties of a system in a state of uniform thermodynamic equilibrium. Rather, under these conditions, only a certain number (which is characteristic of the given system) of properties may be specified independently while the remaining properties are determined as functions of these. The two classes are referred to as independent and dependent state variables, and there is considerable flexibility as to which properties are put in each class. As an example, an elastic solid with a specified reference configuration has seven independent state variables. We may choose as independent variables the six components of the material stress tensor, T_{LM}, together with the mean material strain, $\varepsilon = \frac{1}{3}E_{LL}$. In this case, the deviatoric material strain components, $E'_{LM} = E_{LM} - \delta_{LM}\varepsilon$, would be determined as functions of the independent state variables, $E'_{LM} = E'_{LM}(T_{RS}, \varepsilon)$. Such functional relations are referred to as state functions; they are applicable only when the system is in a state of uniform thermodynamic equilibrium. Alternatively, we may take the independent state variables for an elastic solid as the six components of the material strain tensor, E_{LM}, together with the mean material stress, $\tau = \frac{1}{3}T_{LL}$. We would then have state functions of the form $T'_{LM} = T'_{LM}(E_{RS}, \tau)$, where $T'_{LM} = T_{LM} - \delta_{LM}\tau$ are the deviatoric material stress components. Still other combinations are possible. In terms of the corresponding physical situation, we may think of the independent state variables as imposed on the system by a suitable apparatus, with the state functions predicting the result of measurement of the other variables.

Thermal Equilibrium

Two systems, each in a state of uniform thermodynamic equilibrium, are said to be in thermal equilibrium if they each remain in thermodynamic equilibrium after being placed in contact while maintaining, by suitable experimental design, all but one[17] of the independent state variables of each system constant.

This definition of thermal equilibrium is an attempt to introduce the concept of equality of temperature while using purely kinematical and mechanical terminology, and the thrust of the definition—together with the difficulties in making it precise—will be clearer if this is kept in mind.[18] For example, consider two cylinders containing gas which are in states of thermodynamic equilibrium characterized by state variables p_1, v_1 and p_2, v_2, respectively (Figure 1.5a). If these two cylinders are brought into contact while maintaining the imposed pressures p_1 and p_2 constant (Figure 1.5b) the systems will each remain in thermodynamic equilibrium if and only if the quantities p_1, v_1 and p_2, v_2 satisfy a certain functional relation. (If the gases obey the ideal or perfect gas law, the relation is $p_1 v_1/n_1 = p_2 v_2/n_2$, where n_1, n_2 are the number of moles of gas in each cylinder.)

It is seen that one of the difficulties of the definition of thermal equilibrium as given above lies in making the concept of "brought into contact" precise while maintaining the discussion completely within the context of macroscopic

[17]That is, one of the independent state variables for each system is free to change in the given experiment; it will not do so if the systems are in thermal equilibrium.
[18]A definition of equality of temperature involving purely kinematical and mechanical terminology will be required when we seek to determine the corresponding concept in statistical mechanics (Section 3.2).

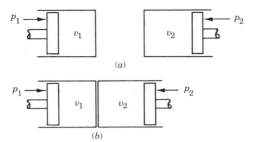

Figure 1.5   Test of thermal equilibrium.

equilibrium thermodynamics.[19] More extended treatments of this question will be found in the works of Falk (1959) and of Landsberg (1961).

Zeroth Law of Thermodynamics

The zeroth[20] law of thermodynamics states that if two systems A and B are each in thermal equilibrium with a third system C, then A is in thermal equilibrium with B. By the phrase "system A" is meant a given system in a particular state of uniform thermodynamic equilibrium, that is, characterized by a set of values $\mathscr{A}_1, \ldots, \mathscr{A}_{s_A}$ of independent state variables[21] of system A. In what follows in this section, we use the term "system A" and a particular set of values $\{\mathscr{A}_1, \ldots, \mathscr{A}_{s_A}\}$, referred to simply as a state, interchangeably. We also use the symbol "$\sim$" to describe the relation of thermal equilibrium between two systems. From the nature of the concept of thermal equilibrium and the zeroth law of thermodynamics, it is clear that this relation satisfies the properties

  (i) $A \sim A$ (reflexive)
 (ii) $A \sim B \Rightarrow B \sim A$ (symmetric)
(iii) $A \sim B$ and $B \sim C \Rightarrow A \sim C$ (transitive)

Therefore, the relation of thermal equilibrium between systems is, in set-theoretic terms, an equivalence relation.[22] As an equivalence relation it divides

---

[19] The phrase "brought into contact" will be clarified in our study of statistical mechanics; in the language of that subject, it means that the two systems are placed in weak interaction while the controlled parameters are maintained constant (Section 3.2).

[20] So called, presumably, because the importance of the concept was recognized and it was elevated to the level of a law after the labels of the first and second laws had become firmly established in the literature.

[21] In this discussion of the zeroth law, the notation $\mathscr{A}_1, \ldots, \mathscr{A}_{s_A}$ refers to an arbitrary set of independent state variables for system A. Elsewhere, we reserve the notation $\mathscr{A}_1, \ldots, \mathscr{A}_\nu$ for kinematic state variables.

[22] See for example, the discussion in Birkhoff and MacLane (1944, p. 160 et seq.).

$$
\boxed{\begin{array}{l}
\{\mathscr{A}_1^{(1)}, \ldots, \mathscr{A}_{s_A}^{(1)}\} \\
\{\mathscr{A}_1^{\prime(1)}, \ldots, \mathscr{A}_{s_A}^{\prime(1)}\} \\
\quad\text{———}\qquad\text{———} \\
\{\mathscr{B}_1^{(1)}, \ldots, \mathscr{B}_{s_B}^{(1)}\} \\
\quad\text{———}\qquad\text{———} \\
\{\mathscr{R}_1^{(1)}, \ldots, \mathscr{R}_{s_R}^{(1)}\}
\end{array}}
\quad \cdots \quad
\boxed{\begin{array}{l}
\{\mathscr{A}_1^{(r)}, \ldots, \mathscr{A}_{s_A}^{(r)}\} \\
\{\mathscr{A}_1^{\prime(r)}, \ldots, \mathscr{A}_{s_A}^{\prime(r)}\} \\
\quad\text{———}\qquad\text{———} \\
\{\mathscr{B}_1^{(r)}, \ldots, \mathscr{B}_{s_B}^{(r)}\} \\
\quad\text{———}\qquad\text{———} \\
\{\mathscr{R}_1^{(r)}, \ldots, \mathscr{R}_{s_R}^{(r)}\}
\end{array}}
$$

Figure 1.6 Equivalence classes of systems in thermal equilibrium with each other.

the set of all thermodynamic systems existing in all possible states[23] into equivalence classes so that two systems are in the same class if and only if they are in thermal equilibrium with each other (Figure 1.6).

Among the various types of thermodynamic systems there are some which are adequately characterized by a single state variable, for example, a sealed glass thermometer with state defined by the length of the mercury column. Select one such system, which we will call system E, and denote its single state variable by θ. Then given a particular value of θ there is determined the values of all s-tuples $\{\mathscr{A}_1, \ldots, \mathscr{A}_{s_A}\}$, $\{\mathscr{B}_1, \ldots, \mathscr{B}_{s_B}\}$, etc., of systems in thermal equilibrium with system E in the state θ and conversely, given a value of the s-tuple $\{\mathscr{A}_1, \ldots, \mathscr{A}_{s_A}\}$ there is determined the value of θ for which system E is in thermal equilibrium with system A. Therefore, there is a functional relationship for each type of thermodynamic system, for example,

$$
\begin{aligned}
\theta &= \theta_A(\mathscr{A}_1, \ldots, \mathscr{A}_{s_A}) \\
\theta &= \theta_B(\mathscr{B}_1, \ldots, \mathscr{B}_{s_B}) \\
&\text{————} \\
\theta &= \theta_R(\mathscr{R}_1, \ldots, \mathscr{R}_{s_R})
\end{aligned}
\tag{1.4.1}
$$

such that two systems A and B are in thermal equilibrium with each other if and only if

$$
\theta = \theta_A(\mathscr{A}_1, \ldots, \mathscr{A}_{s_A}) = \theta_B(\mathscr{B}_1, \ldots, \mathscr{B}_{s_B}). \tag{1.4.2}
$$

[23] That is, it is the set of all s_A-tuples $\{\mathscr{A}_1, \ldots, \mathscr{A}_{s_A}\}$ for systems of type A, the set of all s_B-tuples $\{\mathscr{B}_1, \ldots, \mathscr{B}_{s_B}\}$ for systems of type B, etc., which are all collectively subdivided into equivalence classes. The appearance of the two s_A-tuples $\{\mathscr{A}_1^{(1)}, \ldots, \mathscr{A}_{s_A}^{(1)}\}$ and $\{\mathscr{A}_1^{\prime(1)}, \ldots, \mathscr{A}_{s_A}^{\prime(1)}\}$ in the same equivalence class in Figure 1.6 signifies that two identical systems of type A would be in thermal equilibrium with each other if they were, respectively, in these two states.

In this way, the zeroth law of thermodynamics has led to the introduction of a new state variable, θ, which is appropriate to all thermodynamic systems. It is an intensive variable, by the nature of its definition, and is called an empirical temperature, with many different empirical temperature scales possible depending on the particular type of system chosen and the detailed method of definition of θ.[24]

The empirical temperature θ has been introduced as a dependent state variable. We will now find it convenient to use θ as an independent state variable and regard one of the kinematical or mechanical state variables as a dependent state variable in its place. For example, for system A we can solve Eq. (1.4.2) for $\mathscr{A}_{s_A}$ in terms of θ and the other variables to obtain the state function

$$\mathscr{A}_{s_A} = \mathscr{A}_{s_A}\left(\mathscr{A}_1, \ldots, \mathscr{A}_{s_A-1}, \theta\right). \tag{1.4.3}$$

First Law of Thermodynamics

The zeroth law of thermodynamics has served to introduce the concept of empirical temperature. The first law will provide the concepts of internal energy and heat. In order to do so, we first need the idea of an adiabatic wall, which is defined as follows:

Bring two systems, each in thermodynamic equilibrium but not in thermal equilibrium with each other (i.e., not at the same empirical temperature), into contact through an intermediate layer or wall while maintaining the imposed kinematical and mechanical independent state variables constant;[25] the wall is said to be adiabatic if the systems remain in thermodynamic equilibrium.[26] Consider a system surrounded by a flexible (so work can be done through it) adiabatic envelope which is brought from one uniform state of thermodynamic equilibrium, state 1, to a second uniform state of thermodynamic equilibrium, state 2. (The system need not be uniform or in thermodynamic equilibrium during the process.) Then, from experimental observation, the amount of work ΔW [computed by means of Eq. (1.3.12)] required to go from state 1 to 2 in this manner—briefly, the adiabatic work—depends only on the two equilibrium terminal states but is independent of any other aspects of the process. Furthermore, it is found experimentally that an adiabatic process exists which connects any two states of a given system, at least in one direction. The internal energy U of a system in any state is then defined as the adiabatic work done on the system in taking it from an arbitrary fixed reference state to the

[24] For example, even if a mercury-in-glass thermometer is chosen for system E, there is still flexibility in the choice of the unit of length for measurement of the mercury column and the choice of reference level.

[25] No constraint is imposed on the empirical temperature of each system.

[26] The concept of an adiabatic wall is an idealization, corresponding to a wall with infinite thermal resistance.

state in question (or the work done by the system in going from the state in question to the reference state). It follows that U is a state function whose value is determined by the values of the independent state variables.

A further experimental observation is that the internal energy is an extensive quantity. These two empirical observations, the lack of dependence of the adiabatic work on the nature of the process, and its extensive character, embody what is known as the first law of thermodynamics. However, it is customary and more useful to state this law with the aid of the concept of heat; this is introduced next.

We have stated that for an adiabatic process linking two states,

$$\Delta U = \Delta W. \qquad (1.4.4)$$

Both quantities in this equation are defined as well for a nonadiabatic process connecting two equilibrium states: ΔW by the laws of mechanics [(Eq. (1.3.12)] and ΔU by use of its state function. However, for an arbitrary process they need not be equal and their difference is defined as ΔQ. That is,

$$\Delta Q = \Delta U - \Delta W \qquad (1.4.5)$$

for any process and we speak of ΔQ as the heat supplied to the system during the process. (Note that ΔQ is zero for an adiabatic process.)

If the two states are neighboring, that is, if the independent state variables characterizing them are arbitrarily close in value, Eq. (1.4.5) is written

$$dQ = dU - dW \qquad (1.4.6)$$

with no implication intended that dW or dQ are differentials of a state function. (Sometimes the notation dW and dQ is used to emphasize this fact.)

We wish to show next that ΔQ has the familiar characterization of energy transferred from one system to another by virtue of a temperature difference between them. For this purpose, consider the idealized experiment on a system of gas in two cylinders separated by a flexible nonadiabatic wall, with the composite system surrounded by adiabatic walls (Figure 1.7). The composite system $A + B$ is brought from one equilibrium state to a second one by an adiabatic process during which, however, system A and system B separately

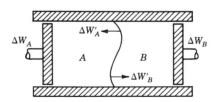

Figure 1.7 Idealized experiment illustrating concept of heat transferred between systems.

undergo nonadiabatic processes. Therefore, for each system we may write

$$\Delta U_A = \Delta W_A + \Delta W_A' + \Delta Q_A$$

$$\Delta U_B = \Delta W_B + \Delta W_B' + \Delta Q_B \qquad (1.4.7)$$

where ΔW_A is the adiabatic work done by the piston, $\Delta W_A'$ is the work done across the flexible, nonadiabatic wall, ΔQ_A is the heat supplied to system A as required by Eq. (1.4.5), and similarly for system B. By the laws of mechanics

$$\Delta W_A' = -\Delta W_B'. \qquad (1.4.8)$$

Therefore, addition of Eqs. (1.4.7) leads to

$$\Delta U_A + \Delta U_B = \Delta W_A + \Delta W_B + \Delta Q_A + \Delta Q_B. \qquad (1.4.9)$$

Since the composite system $A + B$ undergoes an adiabatic process,

$$\Delta U_{A+B} = \Delta W_{A+B} = \Delta W_A + \Delta W_B. \qquad (1.4.10)$$

But, by the extensive nature of U,

$$\Delta U_{A+B} = \Delta U_A + \Delta U_B. \qquad (1.4.11)$$

Therefore,

$$\Delta Q_A = -\Delta Q_B \qquad (1.4.12)$$

and we may speak of heat as energy transferred from one system to the other. Also, if systems A and B had been at the same empirical temperature throughout the process, then the wall between them could have been replaced by an adiabatic wall without any change in the systems' behavior. In that case $\Delta Q_A = -\Delta Q_B = 0$. In other words, ΔQ is energy transferred from one system to another by virtue of the temperature difference between them.

Second Law of Thermodynamics

The second law serves to introduce the concepts of an absolute thermodynamic temperature scale and of entropy. The form of its statement which is most readily translated into statistical mechanical terms is that due to Carathéodory. We refer to the extensive literature[27] for detailed discussions of this approach and outline only the results we will need later.

The discussion of the first law dealt with two states linked by an arbitrary process during which the system was not necessarily in uniform thermody-

[27]See Buchdahl (1966), Wilson (1957), and Born (1949).

namic equilibrium. We now wish to discuss linking states by means of a quasi-static process. As independent state variables we use the ν generalized displacements $\mathscr{A}_1, \ldots, \mathscr{A}_\nu$ introduced at the end of Section 1.3, together with the empirical temperature θ. A quasi-static process during $t_1 \leqslant t \leqslant t_2$ is defined in macroscopic thermodynamics as follows:

1 The values of the functions $\mathscr{A}_1(t), \ldots, \mathscr{A}_\nu(t), \theta(t)$ are specified and characterize a state of uniform thermodynamic equilibrium of the system for $t_1 \leqslant t \leqslant t_2$.

2 All dependent state variables may be computed for $t_1 \leqslant t \leqslant t_2$ by means of the appropriate state functions. In particular,

$$\mathscr{F}_\alpha(t) = \mathscr{F}_\alpha\big(\mathscr{A}_1(t), \ldots, \mathscr{A}_\nu(t), \theta(t)\big), \quad \alpha = 1, \ldots, \nu \qquad (1.4.13)$$

where $\mathscr{F}_\alpha$ is the generalized force conjugate to $\mathscr{A}_\alpha$, and the internal energy

$$U(t) = U\big(\mathscr{A}_1(t), \ldots, \mathscr{A}_\nu(t), \theta(t)\big). \qquad (1.4.14)$$

As we discussed in Section 1.3, where only mechanical variables were involved, a quasi-static process is an idealization that can be approached in reality as closely as one likes by varying imposed conditions arbitrarily slowly. For a quasi-static process, we may rewrite the first law, using Eq. (1.4.6), for a pair of neighboring[28] states corresponding respectively to t and $t + dt$ and to state variables $\{\mathscr{A}_1, \ldots, \mathscr{A}_\nu, \theta\}$ and $\{\mathscr{A}_1 + d\mathscr{A}_1, \ldots, \mathscr{A}_\nu + d\mathscr{A}_\nu, \theta + d\theta\}$, as

$$dQ = dU - dW = \sum_{\alpha=1}^{\nu} \frac{\partial U}{\partial \mathscr{A}_\alpha} d\mathscr{A}_\alpha + \frac{\partial U}{\partial \theta} d\theta - \sum_{\alpha=1}^{\nu} \mathscr{F}_\alpha d\mathscr{A}_\alpha$$

$$= \sum_{\alpha=1}^{\nu} \left(\frac{\partial U}{\partial \mathscr{A}_\alpha} - \mathscr{F}_\alpha \right) d\mathscr{A}_\alpha + \frac{\partial U}{\partial \theta} d\theta \qquad (1.4.15)$$

where $\mathscr{F}_\alpha = \mathscr{F}_\alpha(\mathscr{A}_1, \ldots, \mathscr{A}_\nu, \theta)$ from Eq. (1.4.13) and similarly the partial derivatives $\partial U/\partial \mathscr{A}_\alpha$, $\partial U/\partial \theta$ are computed from Eq. (1.4.14) as functions of the independent state variables. For a quasi-static process, therefore, the quantity dQ, as defined by Eq. (1.4.15), is a linear differential form in the independent state variables; that is, it is a linear combination of the differentials $d\mathscr{A}_1, \ldots, d\mathscr{A}_\nu, d\theta$ with coefficients that are functions of $\mathscr{A}_1, \ldots, \mathscr{A}_\nu, \theta$.

---

[28]Neighboring states are those whose independent state variables differ by an arbitrarily small quantity from those of the given state.

Having completed this discussion of the nature of quasi-static processes, we may now state Carathéodory's form of the second law as follows:

Given an arbitrary state of a thermodynamic system, there exist neighboring states which cannot be linked to this state, in either direction, by means of a quasi-static adiabatic process.

Note the relationship to the first law, which stated that any two states could be linked by an adiabatic process at least in one direction. The second law states that some pairs of states can be linked by an adiabatic process only if it is not quasi-static.

For a quasi-static adiabatic process between neighboring states, $dQ = 0$, and Eq. (1.4.15) becomes the total differential equation

$$0 = \sum_{\alpha=1}^{\nu} \left(\frac{\partial U}{\partial \mathscr{A}_{\alpha}} - \mathscr{F}_{\alpha} \right) d\mathscr{A}_{\alpha} + \frac{\partial U}{\partial \theta} d\theta. \qquad (1.4.16)$$

Carathéodory's statement of the second law implies, therefore, the mathematical statement that there are neighboring states inaccessible along solutions of Eq. (1.4.16). Carathéodory has shown that this in turn implies that the differential form dQ defined by Eq. (1.4.15) is integrable, that is, that there exist functions $F(\mathscr{A}_{\alpha}, \theta)$, $G(\mathscr{A}_{\alpha}, \theta)$ such that

$$\frac{dQ}{F} = dG \qquad (1.4.17)$$

or, written out in greater detail, such that

$$\frac{1}{F} \left\{ \sum_{\alpha=1}^{\nu} \left(\frac{\partial U}{\partial \mathscr{A}_{\alpha}} - \mathscr{F}_{\alpha} \right) d\mathscr{A}_{\alpha} + \frac{\partial U}{\partial \theta} d\theta \right\} = \sum_{\alpha=1}^{\nu} \frac{\partial G}{\partial \mathscr{A}_{\alpha}} d\mathscr{A}_{\alpha} + \frac{\partial G}{\partial \theta} d\theta.$$

$$(1.4.18)$$

The function $F(\mathscr{A}_1, \ldots, \mathscr{A}_{\nu}, \theta) = F(\mathscr{A}, \theta)$ is referred to as an integrating factor for the differential form and $G(\mathscr{A}, \theta)$ is termed its associated function.

It is clear that if one integrating factor exists, then an infinite number of integrating factors may be found. For example, consider the function $H = G^2$. Then, by use of Eq. (1.4.17),

$$dH = 2G\,dG = 2G\frac{dQ}{F}, \qquad (1.4.19)$$

from which we deduce that $F/(2G)$ is also an integrating factor of dQ, with H as its associated function.

By consideration of a composite system consisting of two sub-systems which remain in thermal equilibrium with each other during a quasi-static process, it is shown[29] that among all possible integrating factors $F(\mathscr{A}, \theta)$ there is one, unique up to a constant multiplicative factor, which depends only on θ. This integrating factor is designated by $T(\theta)$ and is called an absolute thermodynamic temperature scale. It is a universal[30] state function, that is, it is applicable to all thermodynamic systems. Its associated function is designated by $S(\mathscr{A}, \theta) = S(\mathscr{A}, T)$ and is called the entropy of the system in question. (Here, and in the remainder of this chapter, we use T in place of θ as the temperature state variable.) Eq. (1.4.17) then takes the form

$$dQ = TdS = dU - dW = \sum_{\alpha=1}^{\nu} \left(\frac{\partial U}{\partial \mathscr{A}_\alpha} - \mathscr{F}_\alpha \right) d\mathscr{A}_\alpha + \frac{\partial U}{\partial T} dT,$$

(1.4.20)

an equation valid for any quasi-static process between neighboring states.

1.5 VARIOUS THERMODYNAMIC POTENTIALS

Internal Energy

We rewrite Eq. (1.4.20) in the form

$$dU = T dS + \mathscr{F}_\alpha d\mathscr{A}_\alpha \qquad (1.5.1)$$

where we are using the summation convention, $\alpha = 1, \ldots, \nu$. We now regard $U = U(\mathscr{A}, S)$; that is, we are using the kinematic variables $\mathscr{A}_\alpha, \alpha = 1, \ldots, \nu,$ together with the entropy S as independent state variables. Then

$$dU = \frac{\partial U}{\partial \mathscr{A}_\alpha} d\mathscr{A}_\alpha + \frac{\partial U}{\partial S} dS. \qquad (1.5.2)$$

Comparison of Eqs. (1.5.1) and (1.5.2) leads[31] to the results

$$\mathscr{F}_\alpha = \frac{\partial U}{\partial \mathscr{A}_\alpha}, \qquad T = \frac{\partial U}{\partial S}. \qquad (1.5.3)$$

---

[29] See, for example, Buchdahl (1966) or Wilson (1957).

[30] The form of the function $T(\theta)$ will depend, of course, on which empirical temperature scale is employed.

[31] The formal argument is as follows: Subtract Eq. (1.5.1) from Eq. (1.5.2) yielding

$$0 = \sum_{\alpha=1}^{\nu} \left(\frac{\partial U}{\partial \mathscr{A}_\alpha} - \mathscr{F}_\alpha \right) d\mathscr{A}_\alpha + \left(\frac{\partial U}{\partial S} - T \right) dS.$$

Since $d\mathscr{A}_\alpha, \alpha = 1, \ldots, \nu$ and dS are independent, set all but one to zero. The coefficient of the nonzero increment must then be zero.

Enthalpy

The enthalpy H is defined as[32]

$$H = U - \mathscr{F}_\alpha \mathscr{A}_\alpha. \tag{1.5.4}$$

Then

$$d\mathrm{H} = dU - \mathscr{F}_\alpha \, d\mathscr{A}_\alpha - \mathscr{A}_\alpha \, d\mathscr{F}_\alpha, \tag{1.5.5}$$

so that, by use of Eq. (1.5.1),

$$d\mathrm{H} = T dS - \mathscr{A}_\alpha \, d\mathscr{F}_\alpha. \tag{1.5.6}$$

Use $\mathscr{F}_\alpha$, S as independent variables so that $\mathrm{H} = \mathrm{H}(\mathscr{F}, S)$. Then

$$d\mathrm{H} = \frac{\partial \mathrm{H}}{\partial \mathscr{F}_\alpha} d\mathscr{F}_\alpha + \frac{\partial \mathrm{H}}{\partial S} dS. \tag{1.5.7}$$

By comparison of Eqs. (1.5.6) and (1.5.7)

$$\mathscr{A}_\alpha = -\frac{\partial \mathrm{H}}{\partial \mathscr{F}_\alpha}, \qquad T = \frac{\partial \mathrm{H}}{\partial S}. \tag{1.5.8}$$

Helmholtz Free Energy

The Helmholtz free energy F is defined as

$$F = U - TS. \tag{1.5.9}$$

Then

$$dF = dU - T dS - S dT, \tag{1.5.10}$$

so that, by use of Eq. (1.5.1),

$$dF = \mathscr{F}_\alpha \, d\mathscr{A}_\alpha - S dT. \tag{1.5.11}$$

Use $\mathscr{A}_\alpha$, T as independent variables so that $F = F(\mathscr{A}, T)$. Then

$$dF = \frac{\partial F}{\partial \mathscr{A}_\alpha} d\mathscr{A}_\alpha + \frac{\partial F}{\partial T} dT. \tag{1.5.12}$$

[32] The roman H is used for enthalpy since the italic H is reserved for the system Hamiltonian.

By comparison of Eqs. (1.5.11) and (1.5.12)

$$\mathscr{F}_\alpha = \frac{\partial F}{\partial \mathscr{A}_\alpha}, \qquad S = -\frac{\partial F}{\partial T}. \qquad (1.5.13)$$

Gibbs Free Energy

The Gibbs free energy G is defined as

$$G = F - \mathscr{F}_\alpha \mathscr{A}_\alpha. \qquad (1.5.14)$$

Then

$$dG = dF - \mathscr{F}_\alpha d\mathscr{A}_\alpha - \mathscr{A}_\alpha d\mathscr{F}_\alpha, \qquad (1.5.15)$$

so that, by use of Eq. (1.5.11),

$$dG = -\mathscr{A}_\alpha d\mathscr{F}_\alpha - S\,dT. \qquad (1.5.16)$$

Use $\mathscr{F}_\alpha$, T as independent variables so that $G = G(\mathscr{F}, T)$. Then

$$dG = \frac{\partial G}{\partial \mathscr{F}_\alpha} d\mathscr{F}_\alpha + \frac{\partial G}{\partial T} dT. \qquad (1.5.17)$$

By comparison of Eqs. (1.5.16) and (1.5.17)

$$\mathscr{A}_\alpha = -\frac{\partial G}{\partial \mathscr{F}_\alpha}, \qquad S = -\frac{\partial G}{\partial T}. \qquad (1.5.18)$$

Fundamental Thermodynamic Equations

Consider the $2\nu + 2$ variables $\mathscr{A}_\alpha$, $\mathscr{F}_\alpha$, S, and T. As we have seen, knowledge of the internal energy function $U = U(\mathscr{A}, S)$ is sufficient, by Eqs. (1.5.3), to determine the remaining $\nu + 1$ variables $(\mathscr{F}_\alpha, T)$ in terms of the $\nu + 1$ independent variables $(\mathscr{A}_\alpha, S)$. Therefore, $U = U(\mathscr{A}, S)$ is referred[33] to as a fundamental thermodynamic equation. Similarly, the enthalpy $H(\mathscr{F}, S)$, the Helmholtz free energy $F(\mathscr{A}, T)$, and the Gibbs free energy, $G(\mathscr{F}, T)$, when expressed as functions of the indicated variables are fundamental equations. They are also described as thermodynamic potentials.

Partial Derivative Notation

If, as in the previous discussion, the choice of independent state variables is made explicit, then the nature of the partial derivatives as in Eq. (1.5.3), for example, is unambiguous. In the thermodynamics literature, it is customary to

---

[33] See, for example, Wilson (1957, p. 44) and Callen (1960, p. 25). Recall that we are restricting attention to systems of constant chemical composition.

make explicit the variables held fixed in partial differentiation by rewriting Eq. (1.5.3) as

$$\mathscr{F}_\alpha = \left.\frac{\partial U}{\partial \mathscr{A}_\alpha}\right|_{\mathscr{A}'_\beta, S}, \qquad T = \left.\frac{\partial U}{\partial S}\right|_{\mathscr{A}_\alpha}, \qquad (1.5.19)$$

where the subscripts $\mathscr{A}'_\beta, S$ in the first equation indicate that S and all the variables $\mathscr{A}_\beta, \beta = 1,\ldots, \nu$ with $\beta = \alpha$ omitted, are held fixed in the differentiation. Since in our discussions the nonthermodynamic arguments of any function will always be either all kinematical or all mechanical, we will simplify Eq. (1.5.19), writing

$$\mathscr{F}_\alpha = \left.\frac{\partial U}{\partial \mathscr{A}_\alpha}\right|_{S}, \qquad T = \left.\frac{\partial U}{\partial S}\right|_{\mathscr{A}_\alpha}, \qquad (1.5.20)$$

or, if the set of independent variables is clear and it is notationally convenient, we will omit subscripts completely as in Eq. (1.5.3).

1.6 THERMOELASTIC STRESS – STRAIN RELATIONS

We now specialize the discussion of the previous section to the case of an elastic solid. As kinematical variables $\mathscr{A}_\alpha$, $\alpha = 1,\ldots, 6$, we use the components $E_{LM} = E_{ML}$ of the material strain tensor describing the homogeneous deformation of the solid from a specified reference configuration $\mathscr{R}$. It then follows from Eq. (1.3.16) that the conjugate mechanical variables $\mathscr{F}_\alpha$, $\alpha = 1,\ldots, 6$, are $\mathscr{V} T_{LM}$, where $\mathscr{V}$ is the volume of the solid in the reference configuration $\mathscr{R}$ and T_{LM} is the material (or second Piola–Kirchhoff) stress tensor. The correspondence between the variables $\mathscr{A}_\alpha$, $\mathscr{F}_\alpha$ and the variables E_{LM}, $\mathscr{V} T_{LM}$ is given in Eqs. (1.3.22) and (1.3.23).

As part of our definition of an elastic solid, we assume that the seven variables E_{LM} and S constitute a complete set of independent variables[34] and that the internal energy U of the solid may be given as a function of these variables, $U = U(E_{LM}, S; \mathscr{R})$. We have included the designation of the reference configuration $\mathscr{R}$ in the specification of the function $U(E_{LM}, S; \mathscr{R})$ in order to emphasize that the variables E_{LM} have full meaning only when $\mathscr{R}$ is specified and that the choice of the reference configuration affects the functional dependence of U on the variables E_{LM} and S.

Then, Eq. (1.5.20), specialized to the present case, takes the form

$$\mathscr{V} T_{LM} = \left.\frac{\partial U}{\partial E_{LM}}\right|_{S}, \qquad T = \left.\frac{\partial U}{\partial S}\right|_{E_{NK}}. \qquad (1.6.1)$$

[34] We are thus ruling out, for example, the possibility that the internal energy depends on only a portion of the strain tensor E_{LM}, as in some theories of viscoelastic behavior; see, for example, Boley and Weiner (1960, pp. 32–34).

The partial derivative notation used in the first of Eqs. (1.6.1) requires clarification. The direct transcription of $\mathscr{F}_6 = \partial U / \partial \mathscr{A}_6$ is, according to Eqs. (1.3.22) and (1.3.23), $\mathscr{V} T_{12} = \partial U / \partial (2 E_{12})$ when U is regarded as a function of the six independent strain variables E_{LM}, $L \leqslant M$. To avoid this awkward factor of 2, we set $2 E_{LM} = E_{LM} + E_{ML}$ in this function and now regard U, for the purpose of our partial derivative notation only, as a function of the nine components E_{LM}. Then

$$\frac{\partial U}{\partial (2 E_{12})}\bigg|_6 = \frac{\partial U}{\partial E_{12}}\bigg|_9$$

where the subscript 6 denotes partial differentiation with the six variables E_{LM}, $L \leqslant M$, as independent variables and the subscript 9 indicates that the nine components E_{LM} are taken as formal independent variables in the partial derivative notation. We adopt the latter convention throughout our discussions leading, in particular, to the first of Eqs. (1.6.1); this equation provides the stress–strain–entropy relation for the solid,

$$T_{LM} = T_{LM}(E_{NK}, S; \mathscr{R}). \qquad (1.6.2)$$

Given the function $U(E_{LM}, S; \mathscr{R})$, the Helmholtz free energy of the solid, $F(E_{LM}, T; \mathscr{R})$, may be defined as in Eq. (1.5.9). Then, by application of Eq. (1.5.13) specialized to this case,

$$\mathscr{V} T_{LM} = \frac{\partial F}{\partial E_{LM}}\bigg|_T, \qquad S = -\frac{\partial F}{\partial T}\bigg|_{E_{NK}}. \qquad (1.6.3)$$

The first of these equations provides the stress–strain–temperature relation for the solid,

$$T_{LM} = T_{LM}(E_{NK}, T; \mathscr{R}). \qquad (1.6.4)$$

Similarly, the Gibbs free energy, $G(T_{LM}, T; \mathscr{R})$, is

$$G = F - \mathscr{V} T_{LM} E_{LM} \qquad (1.6.5)$$

and leads, by Eq. (1.5.18), to

$$E_{LM} = -\frac{1}{\mathscr{V}} \frac{\partial G}{\partial T_{LM}}\bigg|_T, \qquad S = -\frac{\partial G}{\partial T}\bigg|_{T_{NK}}, \qquad (1.6.6)$$

where the first of these yields the relation

$$E_{LM} = E_{LM}(T_{NK}, T; \mathscr{R}). \qquad (1.6.7)$$

Specification of Reference Configuration

Remaining within the confines of the continuum viewpoint, we may specify the reference configuration $\mathscr{R}$ by the statement that when the solid is in this configuration and at the temperature T_0, the stress in the solid is T_{LM}^0. Then, Eq. (1.6.4) must satisfy the relation

$$T_{LM}^0 = T_{LM}(0, T_0; \mathscr{R}),\qquad(1.6.8)$$

and Eq. (1.6.7) must satisfy

$$0 = E_{LM}(T_{NK}^0, T_0; \mathscr{R}).\qquad(1.6.9)$$

In most discussions devoted exclusively to the continuum viewpoint, it is customary to take the reference state (that is the reference configuration $\mathscr{R}$ plus the reference temperature T_0) as one corresponding to zero stress. For the purpose of future comparison with atomistic models of solids, where other means of specification of the reference configuration $\mathscr{R}$ become available, it is necessary to keep open the more general possibility of nonzero initial stress.

Use of Deformation Matrix Elements

In place of the material strain tensor components, we may use as kinematic variables the deformation matrix elements a_{iL} which describe the deformation from the reference configuration $\mathscr{R}$. From Eq. (1.3.14), the corresponding mechanical variables are $\mathscr{V}T_{iL}$. Then, for example, the Helmholtz free energy $F = F(a_{iL}, T; \mathscr{R})$ and Eqs. (1.6.3) become

$$\mathscr{V}T_{iL} = \left.\frac{\partial F}{\partial a_{iL}}\right|_T ; \quad S = -\left.\frac{\partial F}{\partial T}\right|_{a_{jK}} .\qquad(1.6.10)$$

It is understood that the nine variables a_{iL} appear as arguments of F in combinations, such as those yielding E_{LM}, Eq. (1.2.27), so that the scalar function F is invariant to rigid body rotations.

Other Systems

For future reference, we also note here the equations analogous to the first of Eqs. (1.6.10) for the cases (Section 1.3) of an inviscid fluid ($\mathscr{A}_1 = v$ and $\mathscr{F}_1 = -p$) and a linear string ($\mathscr{A}_1 = \ell, \mathscr{F}_1 = f$):

$$p = -\left.\frac{\partial F}{\partial v}\right|_T ;\qquad(1.6.11)$$

$$f = \left.\frac{\partial F}{\partial \ell}\right|_T .\qquad(1.6.12)$$

1.7 THERMOELASTIC RELATIONS FOR SMALL CHANGES FROM REFERENCE STATE

Consider the stress–strain–temperature relation of Eq. (1.6.4). If we confine ourselves to small strains from the reference configuration, $E_{NK} \ll 1$, and small temperature changes ΔT from the reference temperature T_0, $\Delta T / T_0 \ll 1$, then this relation may be approximated by its Taylor series expansion, retaining only linear terms:[35]

$$T_{LM}(E_{NK}, T_0 + \Delta T; \mathcal{R}) = T_{LM}|^0 + \frac{\partial T_{LM}}{\partial E_{NK}}\bigg|_T^0 E_{NK} + \frac{\partial T_{LM}}{\partial T}\bigg|_{E_{PQ}}^0 \Delta T$$

$$(1.7.1)$$

where the superscript 0 denotes evaluation at the reference state, $E_{NK} = 0$, $T = T_0$.

The stress–strain–entropy relation of Eq. (1.6.2) may be approximated for small changes in a similar manner:

$$T_{LM}(E_{NK}, S_0 + \Delta S; \mathcal{R}) = T_{LM}|^0 + \frac{\partial T_{LM}}{\partial E_{NK}}\bigg|_S^0 E_{NK} + \frac{\partial T_{LM}}{\partial S}\bigg|_{E_{PQ}}^0 \Delta S.$$

$$(1.7.2)$$

From Eq. (1.6.8), $T_{LM}|^0 = T_{LM}^0$, the specified initial stress in the reference state. Equations (1.7.1) and (1.7.2) can be rewritten as

$$T_{LM} = T_{LM}^0 + C_{LMNK}^T E_{NK} + b_{LM} \Delta T, \qquad (1.7.3)$$

and

$$T_{LM} = T_{LM}^0 + C_{LMNK}^S E_{NK} + a_{LM} \Delta S, \qquad (1.7.4)$$

where

$$C_{LMNK}^T(T_0; \mathcal{R}) = \frac{\partial T_{LM}}{\partial E_{NK}}\bigg|_T^0 = \frac{1}{\mathcal{V}} \frac{\partial^2 F}{\partial E_{LM} \partial E_{NK}}\bigg|_0, \qquad (1.7.5)$$

$$C_{LMNK}^S(S_0; \mathcal{R}) = \frac{\partial T_{LM}}{\partial E_{NK}}\bigg|_S^0 = \frac{1}{\mathcal{V}} \frac{\partial^2 U}{\partial E_{LM} \partial E_{NK}}\bigg|_0, \qquad (1.7.6)$$

$$b_{LM}(T_0; \mathcal{R}) = \frac{\partial T_{LM}}{\partial T}\bigg|_{E_{PQ}}^0 = \frac{1}{\mathcal{V}} \frac{\partial^2 F}{\partial T \partial E_{LM}}\bigg|_0, \qquad (1.7.7)$$

---

[35] We do not pursue here the important question of the stability of the reference state. For a recent discussion, see Ericksen (1978).

and

$$a_{LM}(S_0; \mathcal{R}) = \left.\frac{\partial T_{LM}}{\partial S}\right|^0_{E_{PQ}} = \frac{1}{\mathcal{V}} \left.\frac{\partial^2 U}{\partial S \partial E_{LM}}\right|_0. \qquad (1.7.8)$$

In the derivation of Eqs. (1.7.5)–(1.7.8) we have used Eqs. (1.6.1) and (1.6.3). We take the natural variables $F = F(E_{NK}, T)$, $U = U(E_{NK}, S)$ as understood and use the subscript $_0$ to denote evaluation at the reference state.

From their definition, C^T_{LMNK} and b_{LM} describe tangents to the general $T_{LM}(E_{NK}, T; \mathcal{R})$ relation at the reference state $(T_0; \mathcal{R})$ and, as indicated, their values depend on this state. It is also possible to evaluate all derivatives at the general state $(E_{NK}, T; \mathcal{R})$ to obtain the tangent moduli at that point. However, since the reference state $(T_0; \mathcal{R})$ is itself arbitrary, this would not result in any increase in generality.

The quantities C^T_{LMNK} are known as the isothermal elastic constants while C^S_{LMNK} are referred to as the adiabatic elastic constants.[36] The terminology is unfortunate because it has given the impression that the former can be used only when isothermal conditions prevail and the latter only when the process is adiabatic. As can be seen from their derivation, the isothermal constants can be used for the analysis of a general thermoelastic process with E_{LM} and T used as independent variables and the adiabatic constants can be used for the same process with the use of E_{LM} and S as independent variables. Of course, if it is known *a priori* that the particular elastic process to be studied is isothermal to a good degree of approximation, then it is convenient to use the isothermal constants and treat the constant temperature as a parameter. In this way, one field equation can be eliminated from the problem formulation. A corresponding simplification can be made when it is known[37] that a particular process is adiabatic.

---

[36]Other terms used for C_{LMNK} are elastic moduli and elastic stiffnesses. In this work we use the terms elastic constants and elastic moduli interchangeably although some usage (see Nye, 1957, p. 131) reserves the term elastic moduli to refer to the tensor inverse to C_{LMNK}. There does not appear to be a consistent terminology for these and other closely related quantities (Section 1.9) particularly when the reference state involves initial stress. For a discussion of this latter point see Barron and Klein (1965).

[37]*A priori* judgments in this area may be misleading. A good example is provided by Newton's calculation of the speed of sound in air based on the use of isothermal constants with results in disagreement with experimental results. The difficulty was apparently resolved by Laplace who pointed out that since the vibrations are so rapid, there is not time for heat conduction to take place and therefore the adiabatic constants should be employed. This observation removed the disagreement with experiment. However, although Laplace's conclusion was correct, his reasoning, which omitted consideration of the distance between rarefied and compressed regions over which heat transfer must take place, was faulty; it is because the frequency of ordinary sound waves is low (and wave lengths large) that the adiabatic constants must be employed. At ultrahigh frequencies (and very short wave lengths) the process is more nearly isothermal. For a further discussion, see Tabor (1979), pp. 76–78).

The quantities C_{LMNK}^T and C_{LMNK}^S are also termed second-order elastic moduli since they are defined in terms of second-order derivatives of the functions F and U, respectively, Eqs. (1.7.5) and (1.7.6). Higher-order elastic moduli, to be used in a stress–strain relation which is nonlinear in the strains E_{LM}, are defined by corresponding derivatives as may be seen by continuing the Taylor series expansions of Eqs. (1.7.1) and (1.7.2). Thus, third-order isothermal elastic moduli are defined as

$$C_{LMNKPQ}^T = \left. \frac{\partial^2 T_{LM}}{\partial E_{NK} \partial E_{PQ}} \right|_{E_{RS,T}}^0 = \frac{1}{\mathscr{V}} \left. \frac{\partial^3 F}{\partial E_{LM} \partial E_{NK} \partial E_{PQ}} \right|_0 . \qquad (1.7.9)$$

Voigt Symmetry

Consider the set of either isothermal or adiabatic elastic constants C_{LMNK}. As a fourth rank tensor in three-dimensional space, it has 3^4 or 81 components. However, because of inherent[38] symmetries in this tensor, only a fraction of this number can be assigned values independently. These inherent symmetries state that the elastic moduli C_{LMNK} are invariant[39] under the following index interchanges:

(i) $(LM) \leftrightarrow (ML)$
(ii) $(NK) \leftrightarrow (KN)$
(iii) $(LM) \leftrightarrow (NK)$

The first two properties follow from the stress–strain relation in which the moduli appear, Eqs. (1.7.3) or (1.7.4), or from their definition as tangent moduli,

$$C_{LMNK} = \frac{\partial T_{LM}}{\partial E_{NK}}$$

as in Eqs. (1.7.5) and (1.7.6): symmetry (i) reflects the symmetry of T_{LM}, (ii) follows from the symmetry of E_{NK}. Symmetry (iii) follows from the definition of the elastic constants, Eqs. (1.7.5) or (1.7.6), as mixed second partial derivatives of either F or U.

A set of elastic constants obeying all of the symmetries (i) to (iii) is said to have complete Voigt symmetry. Because of symmetries (i) and (ii), the first and second pair of indices can each assume only six independent values. Therefore, C_{LMNK}, the fourth rank tensor in three-dimensional space, can be represented

---

[38] These symmetries are present regardless of the particular material involved; if there are material symmetries present in the reference state, these will further reduce the number of independent components. See, for example, Gurtin (1972, pp. 87–89).

[39] For example, property (i) implies that the components C_{1234} and C_{2134} must be numerically equal.

as a 6×6 matrix which, by property (iii), is symmetric. It follows that the tensor C_{LMNK} with complete Voigt symmetry has only $6 \times (6 + 1)/2 = 21$ independent components.

Because of symmetries (i) and (ii), Voigt notation, Eq. (1.3.21), may be employed to write the elastic moduli C_{LMNK} in a two-index form as $C_{\alpha\beta}$. For example, the modulus C_{1132} would be written as C_{14} in Voigt notation.

Elastic Compliances

The discussion of tangent moduli may be paralleled to obtain tangent compliances by beginning, for example, with the strain–stress–temperature relation of Eq. (1.6.7). For small changes from the reference state,

$$E_{LM} = S^T_{LMNK}(T_{NK} - T^0_{NK}) + \alpha_{LM}\Delta T \qquad (1.7.10)$$

where

$$S^T_{LMNK}(T_0; \mathscr{R}) = \left.\frac{\partial E_{LM}}{\partial T_{NK}}\right|^0_T = -\frac{1}{\mathscr{V}}\left.\frac{\partial^2 G}{\partial T_{NK}\partial T_{LM}}\right|_0 \qquad (1.7.11)$$

$$\alpha_{LM}(T_0; \mathscr{R}) = \left.\frac{\partial E_{LM}}{\partial T}\right|^0_{T_{PQ}} = -\frac{1}{\mathscr{V}}\left.\frac{\partial^2 G}{\partial T\partial T_{LM}}\right|_0 \qquad (1.7.12)$$

The quantities S^T_{LMNK} are known as the isothermal elastic compliances and α_{LM} is the thermal expansion tensor.

From Eqs. (1.7.5) and (1.7.11),

$$S^T_{LMNK}C^T_{NKPQ} = \left.\frac{\partial E_{LM}}{\partial T_{NK}}\right|^0_T \left.\frac{\partial T_{NK}}{\partial E_{PQ}}\right|^0_T = \tfrac{1}{2}(\delta_{LP}\delta_{MQ} + \delta_{LQ}\delta_{MP}) \qquad (1.7.13)$$

by the chain rule of differentiation and our convention on the notation for partial derivatives discussed following Eq. (1.6.1). By application of Eq. (1.7.13) to Eq. (1.7.3), we find

$$E_{LM} = S^T_{LMPQ}(T_{PQ} - T^0_{PQ}) - S^T_{LMPQ}b_{PQ}\Delta T. \qquad (1.7.14)$$

Comparison of Eqs. (1.7.10) and (1.7.14) yields the alternate expression for the thermal expansion tensor,

$$\alpha_{LM} = -S^T_{LMPQ}b_{PQ} = -\frac{1}{\mathscr{V}}S^T_{LMPQ}\left.\frac{\partial^2 F}{\partial E_{PQ}\partial T}\right|_0, \qquad (1.7.15)$$

where, in the final form, we have used Eq. (1.7.7).

1.8   RELATED THERMODYNAMIC FUNCTIONS

In the previous section we considered various quantities such as C^T_{LMNK} and b_{LM} which arise from the consideration of derivatives of the thermoelastic relation. In this section we introduce some new thermodynamic functions and derive some of the interrelations between these new quantities and those introduced in Section 1.7. As before we consider all functions evaluated at the reference state[40] $(T; \mathscr{R})$. As with the quantities previously introduced, we could equally well evaluate the new functions at the state $(E_{LM}, T; \mathscr{R})$, but since $\mathscr{R}$ is an arbitrary configuration, this adds no generality.

Specific Heat at Constant Configuration

The specific heat at constant configuration of a solid, C_ε, is the heat supplied per unit change of temperature when its configuration is kept constant.[41] Since in this case $dW = 0$, it follows from Eq. (1.4.20) that $dQ = T\,dS = dU$ and therefore

$$C_\varepsilon = T \left. \frac{\partial S}{\partial T} \right|_{E_{LM}} = \left. \frac{\partial U}{\partial T} \right|_{E_{LM}} \qquad (1.8.1)$$

with the derivatives here, and throughout this section, evaluated at the reference state $(T; \mathscr{R})$ or, equivalently, at $E_{LM} = 0$ and T. Therefore, $C_\varepsilon = C_\varepsilon(T; \mathscr{R})$.

Specific Heat at Constant Stress

The specific heat at constant stress of a solid, C_σ, is the heat supplied per unit change of temperature when the stress is kept constant.[42] In this case $dQ = T\,dS = d\mathrm{H}$, as seen from Eq. (1.5.6), and

$$C_\sigma = T \left. \frac{\partial S}{\partial T} \right|_{T_{LM}} = \left. \frac{\partial \mathrm{H}}{\partial T} \right|_{T_{LM}}. \qquad (1.8.2)$$

Grüneisen Tensor

The Grüneisen tensor of a solid, γ_{LM}, is defined as

$$\gamma_{LM} = \frac{1}{C_\varepsilon} \left. \frac{\partial S}{\partial E_{LM}} \right|_T . \qquad (1.8.3)$$

---

[40] It is convenient, henceforth, to denote the reference temperature by T instead of by T_0.

[41] The specific heat at constant configuration is also described as the specific heat at constant strain. If only volume changes of the solid are under consideration, it is called the specific heat at constant volume.

[42] If only states of hydrostatic stress are under consideration, it is called the specific heat at constant pressure.

Relation between Grüneisen and Thermal Expansion Tensors

By use of Eq. (1.6.3), we can write

$$\gamma_{LM} = -\frac{1}{C_\varepsilon}\frac{\partial^2 F}{\partial E_{LM}\partial T}. \tag{1.8.4}$$

From Eq. (1.5.14),

$$G = F - \mathcal{V} T_{LM} E_{LM}, \tag{1.8.5}$$

so that, with $G = G(T_{PQ}, T)$, $F = F(E_{PQ}, T)$,

$$\frac{\partial G}{\partial T}\Big|_{T_{PQ}} = \frac{\partial F}{\partial T}\Big|_{E_{PQ}} + \frac{\partial F}{\partial E_{LM}}\Big|_T \frac{\partial E_{LM}}{\partial T}\Big|_{T_{PQ}} - \mathcal{V} T_{LM}\frac{\partial E_{LM}}{\partial T}\Big|_{T_{PQ}}. \tag{1.8.6}$$

By use of the first of Eqs. (1.6.3), we conclude that

$$\frac{\partial F}{\partial T}\Big|_{E_{PQ}} = \frac{\partial G}{\partial T}\Big|_{T_{PQ}}, \tag{1.8.7}$$

a result which also follows from Eqs. (1.6.3) and (1.6.6). Therefore

$$\frac{\partial^2 F}{\partial E_{LM}\partial T} = \frac{\partial^2 G}{\partial T_{PQ}\partial T}\frac{\partial T_{PQ}}{\partial E_{LM}}\Big|_T = -\mathcal{V}\alpha_{PQ}C^T_{PQLM} \tag{1.8.8}$$

by use of Eqs. (1.7.12) and (1.7.5). Combining Eqs. (1.8.4) and (1.8.8), we obtain

$$\gamma_{LM} = \frac{\mathcal{V}}{C_\varepsilon}\alpha_{PQ}C^T_{PQLM}, \tag{1.8.9}$$

a relation that may be solved for the thermal expansion tensor, by use of Eq. (1.7.13), as

$$\alpha_{PQ} = \frac{C_\varepsilon}{\mathcal{V}}S^T_{PQLM}\gamma_{LM}. \tag{1.8.10}$$

The Grüneisen tensor is a generalization to anisotropic solids of the parameter introduced by Grüneisen (1912) for isotropic solids. In the latter case, $\alpha_{PQ} = \alpha\delta_{PQ}$, $\gamma_{LM} = \gamma\delta_{LM}$, and Eq. (1.8.10) reduces to the form

$$\alpha = \frac{1}{3}\left(\frac{C_\varepsilon}{\mathcal{V}}\right)S^T_{PPLL}\gamma$$

$$= \frac{1}{3}\left(\frac{C_\varepsilon}{\mathcal{V}}\right)x^T\gamma \tag{1.8.11}$$

or

$$\gamma = \frac{3\alpha \mathcal{V}}{C_\varepsilon \chi_T} \qquad (1.8.12)$$

where $\chi_T = S^T_{PPLL}$ is the isothermal compressibility of the solid.[43] The initial simplified model adopted by Grüneisen led to γ approximately independent of temperature and the parameter is still sometimes referred to as Grüneisen's constant. Although it is now clear that the Grüneisen tensor components may have substantial temperature dependence for some materials, they remain useful for reporting and correlating experimental data. We will return to their consideration on the basis of atomistic models in Section 10.3.

Relation between Isothermal and Adiabatic Constants[44]

From Eqs. (1.6.3) and the equality of the mixed second partial derivatives follows

$$\left.\frac{\partial T_{LM}}{\partial T}\right|_{E_{NK}} = -\frac{1}{\mathcal{V}} \left.\frac{\partial S}{\partial E_{LM}}\right|_T . \qquad (1.8.13)$$

By use of Eq. (1.5.1) we see that

$$\left.\frac{\partial U}{\partial E_{LM}}\right|_T = T\left.\frac{\partial S}{\partial E_{LM}}\right|_T + \mathcal{V}T_{LM},$$

which may be rewritten, by use of Eq. (1.8.13), as

$$\left.\frac{\partial U}{\partial E_{LM}}\right|_T = -\mathcal{V}T\left.\frac{\partial T_{LM}}{\partial T}\right|_{E_{NK}} + \mathcal{V}T_{LM}$$

and, by use of Eq. (1.7.7), as

$$\left.\frac{\partial U}{\partial E_{LM}}\right|_T = \mathcal{V}(T_{LM} - Tb_{LM}). \qquad (1.8.14)$$

Also by use of Eq. (1.5.1) we see that

$$T\,dS = dU - \mathcal{V}T_{LM}\,dE_{LM}$$

$$= \left(\frac{\partial U}{\partial E_{LM}}\right)_T dE_{LM} + \left(\frac{\partial U}{\partial T}\right)_{E_{NK}} dT - \mathcal{V}T_{LM}\,dE_{LM}.$$

[43]At constant temperature, $E_{LM} = S^T_{LMRS}(T_{RS} - T^0_{RS})$. If $T_{RS} - T^0_{RS} = -p\delta_{RS}$, then $E_{LL} = -S^T_{LLRR}p$. For small strains, $E_{LL} = (v - \mathcal{V})/\mathcal{V}$ so that $v = (E_{LL} + 1)\mathcal{V} = (1 - S^T_{LLRR}p)\mathcal{V}$. Therefore,

$$S^T_{LLRR} = -\frac{1}{\mathcal{V}}\left.\frac{\partial v}{\partial p}\right|_T \triangleq \chi_T.$$

[44]The derivation follows that given by Thurston (1964, p. 39).

By use of Eqs. (1.8.1) and (1.8.14), this takes the form

$$T\,dS = C_\varepsilon\,dT - \mathcal{V}\,Tb_{LM}\,dE_{LM},\tag{1.8.15}$$

which leads to the result

$$\left.\frac{\partial T}{\partial E_{LM}}\right|_S = \frac{\mathcal{V}\,Tb_{LM}}{C_\varepsilon}.\tag{1.8.16}$$

We now regard $T_{LM} = T_{LM}(E_{NK}, T(E_{NK}, S))$. Then

$$C_{LMNK}^S = \left.\frac{\partial T_{LM}}{\partial E_{NK}}\right|_S = \left.\frac{\partial T_{LM}}{\partial E_{NK}}\right|_T + \left.\frac{\partial T_{LM}}{\partial T}\right|_{E_{PQ}}\left.\frac{\partial T}{\partial E_{NK}}\right|_S.\tag{1.8.17}$$

By use of Eqs. (1.7.5), (1.7.7), and (1.8.16), we then arrive at the desired relationship:

$$C_{LMNK}^S - C_{LMNK}^T = \frac{\mathcal{V}\,Tb_{LM}b_{NK}}{C_\varepsilon}.\tag{1.8.18}$$

From Eqs. (1.7.7) and (1.8.4)

$$b_{LM} = -\frac{C_\varepsilon}{\mathcal{V}}\gamma_{LM}.\tag{1.8.19}$$

Therefore, Eq. (1.8.18) may be put in the form,

$$C_{LMNK}^S - C_{LMNK}^T = \frac{C_\varepsilon\gamma_{LM}\gamma_{NK}T}{\mathcal{V}}.\tag{1.8.20}$$

Relation between C_ε and C_σ

By writing $S = S(E_{LM}(T_{PQ}, T), T)$ we see that

$$\left.\frac{\partial S}{\partial T}\right|_{T_{PQ}} = \left.\frac{\partial S}{\partial E_{LM}}\right|_T\left.\frac{\partial E_{LM}}{\partial T}\right|_{T_{PQ}} + \left.\frac{\partial S}{\partial T}\right|_{E_{LM}}.\tag{1.8.21}$$

It then follows by use of Eqs. (1.8.1)–(1.8.3) and (1.7.12) that

$$C_\sigma = C_\varepsilon\gamma_{LM}\alpha_{LM}T + C_\varepsilon.\tag{1.8.22}$$

By use of Eq. (1.8.9), this may be put in the form

$$C_\sigma - C_\varepsilon = \mathcal{V}\alpha_{LM}\alpha_{NK}C_{LMNK}^T\,T.\tag{1.8.23}$$

1.9 ELASTIC CONSTANTS IN TERMS OF DISPLACEMENT GRADIENTS

The use of the deformation measures E_{LM} provides the clearest conceptual basis for the definition of elastic constants, particularly when initial stress is present in the reference state.[45] There are three reasons, however, for reconsidering the question in terms of displacement gradients:

1 Much work on atomistic models for crystal elasticity has been based on displacement formulations.

2 A widely used experimental method for determining elastic constants in the presence of initial stress uses ultrasonic wave-propagation techniques and is best described in terms of displacements.

3 The theory of linear elasticity is based on an unstressed reference configuration and uses displacements as primary variables.

The concept of the general deformation of a continuum has been discussed in Section 1.2. In terms of that notation, the displacement u_i of the continuum particle which was at X_L in the reference configuration and is at x_i in the deformed configuration is

$$u_i = x_i - \delta_{iL} X_L, \qquad (1.9.1)$$

where the Kronecker delta δ_{iL} serves to translate between the two coordinate indexing notations. In a general deformation, the displacement gradients are

$$u_{i,L} = x_{i,L} - \delta_{iL}, \qquad (1.9.2)$$

which, for a homogeneous or affine deformation we will write as

$$u_{iL} = a_{iL} - \delta_{iL}. \qquad (1.9.3)$$

By the substitution of Eq. (1.9.3) into Eq. (1.2.27), we can express the material strain tensor E_{LM} in terms of the displacement gradients as follows:

$$E_{LM} = \tfrac{1}{2}(\delta_{iL} u_{iM} + \delta_{iM} u_{iL} + u_{iL} u_{iM}). \qquad (1.9.4)$$

The thermodynamic independent variable, T or S, plays no role in the following discussion and we will write[46] $F = F(E_{LM})$ as representing either $F(E_{LM}, T)$ or $U(E_{LM}, S)$. The discussion, therefore, applies equally well to isothermal or to adiabatic moduli and we omit those designations.

Because of Eq. (1.9.4), we can use the displacement gradients u_{iL} as kinematical variables and regard $F = F(u_{iL})$. Then, by use of the first of Eqs.

[45] See, for example, the discussion in Barron and Klein (1965).

[46] For simplicity, we are also omitting the designation of the reference configuration $\mathscr{R}$ from the arguments of F.

(1.6.10),

$$\mathscr{V} T_{iL} = \frac{\partial F}{\partial a_{iL}} = \frac{\partial F}{\partial u_{iL}}, \tag{1.9.5}$$

leading to the stress–displacement gradient relation

$$T_{iL} = T_{iL}(u_{jM}). \tag{1.9.6}$$

We next confine attention to small displacement gradients, $u_{jM} \ll 1$, and expand the relation of Eq. (1.9.6) up to linear terms.

$$T_{iL} = T_{iL}^{0} + \mathscr{S}_{iLjM} u_{jM} \tag{1.9.7}$$

where T_{iL}^{0} is the initial stress in the reference configuration and we will term $\mathscr{S}_{iLjM}$ the displacement-gradient moduli. (Note that the distinction between the three forms of the stress tensor t_{ij}, T_{iL}, and T_{LM} arises because, in the general case, two distinct configurations of the body are involved. The stress acts in the deformed configuration but, in the case of T_{iL} and T_{LM}, is referred to some aspects of the reference configuration. The initial stress, however, acts in the reference configuration and therefore $t_{ij}^{0} = T_{iL}^{0} \delta_{Lj} = T_{LM}^{0} \delta_{iL} \delta_{jM}$. This may also be seen from the formal equations relating the different stress tensors by taking the deformed and reference configurations to be identical so that $x_{i,L} = \delta_{iL}$.)

From Eq. (1.9.5)

$$T_{iL}^{0} = \frac{1}{\mathscr{V}} \left. \frac{\partial F}{\partial u_{iL}} \right|_{0} \tag{1.9.8}$$

$$\mathscr{S}_{iLjM} = \left. \frac{\partial T_{iL}}{\partial u_{jM}} \right|_{0} = \frac{1}{\mathscr{V}} \left. \frac{\partial^2 F}{\partial u_{iL} \partial u_{jM}} \right|_{0} \tag{1.9.9}$$

where the subscript denotes evaluation at the reference state, $u_{jM} \equiv 0$. Therefore, the expansion of $F(u_{jM})$ through terms of second order takes the form

$$F = F_0 + \mathscr{V} T_{iL}^{0} u_{iL} + \tfrac{1}{2} \mathscr{V} \mathscr{S}_{iLjM} u_{iL} u_{jM}. \tag{1.9.10}$$

Similarly, as seen from the developments of Section 1.7, the expansion of $F(E_{LM})$ through terms of second-order takes the form

$$F = F_0 + \mathscr{V} T_{LM}^{0} E_{LM} + \tfrac{1}{2} \mathscr{V} C_{LMNK} E_{LM} E_{NK}. \tag{1.9.11}$$

We may now obtain a relation between the two types of moduli C_{LMNK} and $\mathscr{S}_{iLjM}$ by substituting for E_{LM} in Eq. (1.9.11) its expression in terms of u_{iL} as given in Eq. (1.9.4). When this is done, and the coefficients of $u_{iL}u_{jM}$ are compared, we find that

$$\mathscr{S}_{iLjM} = \delta_{ij}T^0_{LM} + \delta_{iN}\delta_{jK}C_{NLKM}$$

or

$$\mathscr{S}_{iLjM} = \delta_{ij}T^0_{LM} + C_{iLjM}. \qquad (1.9.12)$$

Note that the initial stress appears in Eq. (1.9.12) because E_{LM} contains the second-order terms $u_{iL}u_{iM}$. We conclude that the two types of moduli are equal only if the initial stress vanishes.

Ultrasonic Measurements of Elastic Moduli

The equations of motion for an elastic body assume a particularly simple form[47] when the Piola–Kirchhoff stress tensor T_{iL} is used, namely

$$\rho_0\ddot{u}_i = T_{iL,L} \qquad (1.9.13)$$

where body forces are assumed absent, ρ_0 is the mass density in the reference configuration and u_i, T_{iL} are expressed as functions of (X_M, t). If we assume small displacement gradients we may substitute for T_{iL} by the use of Eq. (1.9.7), where we now write $u_{j,M}$ in place of u_{jM}, in order to treat inhomogeneous deformations. The result is

$$\rho_0\ddot{u}_i = T^0_{iL,L} + \mathscr{S}_{iLjM}u_{j,ML} \qquad (1.9.14)$$

or

$$\rho_0\ddot{u}_i = \mathscr{S}_{iLjM}u_{j,ML}$$

since $T^0_{iL,L} = 0$ because the initial stress corresponds to an equilibrium configuration. We see, therefore, that the displacement gradient moduli $\mathscr{S}_{iLjM}$ appear naturally in the equations of motion and that these are the moduli determined experimentally by the measurement of wave speeds in the solids. Moreover, since the second partial derivatives $u_{j,ML}$ are symmetric in L and M, it is seen that only the symmetric part

$$\hat{C}_{iLjM} = \tfrac{1}{2}\left[\mathscr{S}_{iLjM} + \mathscr{S}_{iMjL}\right] \qquad (1.9.15)$$

of the $\mathscr{S}_{iLjM}$ tensor is determined by such experiments. This poses the following translation problem: Given the tensor $\hat{C}_{iLjM}$, find the tensor C_{iLjM} of elastic constants based on the strain tensor E_{LM}. This problem is solved as follows.[48]

---

[47]See, for example, Truesdell and Toupin (1960, p. 554).
[48]We are following the discussion of Lax (1965, p. 587).

From Eqs. (1.9.12) and (1.9.15), we find

$$C_{iLjM} + C_{iMjL} = 2\left[\hat{C}_{iLjM} - \delta_{ij}T^0_{LM}\right]. \qquad (1.9.16)$$

By interchange of i and L,

$$C_{LijM} + C_{LMji} = 2\left[\hat{C}_{LijM} - \delta_{Lj}T^0_{iM}\right], \qquad (1.9.17)$$

and by interchange of i and j in the latter,

$$C_{LjiM} + C_{LMij} = 2\left[\hat{C}_{LjiM} - \delta_{Li}T^0_{jM}\right]. \qquad (1.9.18)$$

Subtract Eq. (1.9.18) from the sum of Eqs. (1.9.16) and (1.9.17) and use the Voigt symmetry of C_{iLjM} to find

$$C_{iLjM} = \left[\hat{C}_{iLjM} + \hat{C}_{LijM} - \hat{C}_{LjiM} - \delta_{ij}T^0_{LM} - \delta_{Lj}T^0_{iM} + \delta_{Li}T^0_{jM}\right]. \qquad (1.9.19)$$

Born – Huang Relations

As we see from Eq. (1.9.12), the Voigt symmetry of the strain moduli C_{LMNK} or C_{iLjM} implies Voigt symmetry of the displacement moduli $\mathscr{S}_{iLjM}$ only when the initial stress T^0_{LM} vanishes.[49] We can, however, use the Voigt symmetry of C_{iLjM} to derive relations which must be satisfied by $\hat{C}_{iLjM}$, the symmetric part in LM of $\mathscr{S}_{iLjM}$. It follows directly from this definition that

$$\hat{C}_{iLjM} = \hat{C}_{iMjL}. \qquad (1.9.20)$$

From Eq. (1.9.16) we find

$$\hat{C}_{iLjM} = \delta_{ij}T^0_{LM} + \tfrac{1}{2}\left(C_{iLjM} + C_{iMjL}\right). \qquad (1.9.21)$$

By use of the Voigt symmetry of C_{iLjM}, we then conclude that

$$\hat{C}_{iLjM} = \hat{C}_{jLiM}. \qquad (1.9.22)$$

By the simultaneous interchange of indices i and L and of j and M in Eq. (1.9.21) and the use of the Voigt symmetry of C_{iLjM}, we conclude that

$$\hat{C}_{iLjM} - \delta_{ij}T^0_{LM} = \hat{C}_{LiMj} - \delta_{LM}T^0_{ij}. \qquad (1.9.23)$$

---

[49]As noted, this result applies no matter how small the displacement gradients. Therefore, it is necessary to assume a stress-free reference configuration to arrive at the usual theory of linear elasticity.

Equations (1.9.23), together with those that follow by use of Eqs. (1.9.20) and (1.9.22), were first considered in terms of elastic moduli based on atomistic models (see Section 4.9) and are known as the Born–Huang relations.[50]

1.10 ISOTROPIC SOLIDS

The previous three sections dealt with small deformations from a specified reference configuration and were intended to provide a continuum background for our discussion of crystal elasticity in Chapters 4 and 10. The theory was presented for the general anisotropic solid. Discussions of further symmetries imposed on the various tensors by material symmetries in the reference configuration will be found in the literature.[51]

In our discussion of rubber elasticity in Chapters 5 and 6 we will be dealing with the large deformations of a solid whose properties are isotropic in its undeformed reference configuration. We develop in this section some of the continuum concepts which will be useful for this purpose.

We return first to our study of the kinematics of continua of Section 1.2 and add some general concepts which are needed in this connection.

The material Cauchy–Green tensor C_{LM} corresponding to a general deformation $x_i(X)$ or to an affine deformation a_{iL} is defined as

$$C_{LM} = x_{i,L}x_{i,M} = a_{iL}a_{iM};$$ (1.10.1)

the corresponding spatial tensor c_{ij} is

$$c_{ij} = X_{L,i}X_{L,j} = A_{Li}A_{Lj},$$ (1.10.2)

where A_{Li} is the matrix inverse of a_{iL}, $A_{Li}a_{iM} = \delta_{LM}$, $a_{iM}A_{Mj} = \delta_{ij}$.

We confine attention to the case of an affine deformation, although the results are readily transcribed as locally applicable in the general case. Consider a fiber that corresponds to the vector $\mathbf{F}$ with components F_L in the reference configuration and to the vector $\mathbf{f}$ with components $f_i = a_{iL}F_L$ in the deformed configuration. Then, from Eq. (1.10.1),

$$f^2 = \mathbf{f} \cdot \mathbf{f} = f_i f_i = C_{LM}F_L F_M.$$ (1.10.3)

It is seen that C_{LM} is a real, symmetric and, from Eq. (1.10.3), positive-definite matrix. It follows that it has three real characteristic directions $\mathbf{N}^{(\alpha)}$, $\alpha = 1, 2, 3$, with components $N_L^{(\alpha)}$, to which correspond three positive characteristic values λ_α^2 such that

$$C_{LM}N_M^{(\alpha)} = \lambda_\alpha^2 N_L^{(\alpha)}, \qquad \alpha = 1, 2, 3.$$ (1.10.4)

---

[50] Begbie and Born (1947), Huang (1950), Born and Huang (1954).

[51] See, for example, Nye (1957), Thurston (1964), and Gurtin (1972).

If the characteristic values λ_α^2 are distinct, then it is readily demonstrated that the three directions $\mathbf{N}^{(\alpha)}$ are mutually orthogonal; if they are not distinct, then the characteristic directions are not unique but may be chosen to be mutually orthogonal.

Let $\mathbf{n}^{(\alpha)}$ be the vectors with components[52]

$$n_i^{(\alpha)} = a_{iL} N_L^{(\alpha)}. \tag{1.10.5}$$

Then, by use of Eqs. (1.10.1), (1.10.2), (1.10.4), and (1.10.5),

$$c_{ij} n_j^{(\alpha)} = A_{Li} A_{Lj} n_j^{(\alpha)} = A_{Li} N_L^{(\alpha)}$$

$$= A_{Li} \lambda_\alpha^{-2} C_{LM} N_M^{(\alpha)}$$

$$= \lambda_\alpha^{-2} A_{Li} a_{kL} a_{kM} N_M^{(\alpha)}$$

$$= \lambda_\alpha^{-2} n_i^{(\alpha)}. \tag{1.10.6}$$

That is, the characteristic vectors $\mathbf{N}^{(\alpha)}$ of the material tensor C_{LM} are transformed, under the affine deformation a_{iL}, into the characteristic vectors $\mathbf{n}^{(\alpha)}$ of the spatial tensor c_{ij} with characteristic values λ_α^{-2}. By application of Eqs. (1.10.3) and (1.10.4), it is seen that

$$\lambda_\alpha = \frac{n^{(\alpha)}}{N^{(\alpha)}} \tag{1.10.7}$$

where $n^{(\alpha)} = |\mathbf{n}^{(\alpha)}|$, $N^{(\alpha)} = |\mathbf{N}^{(\alpha)}|$. The directions $\mathbf{N}^{(\alpha)}, \mathbf{n}^{(\alpha)}$ are called, respectively, the material and spatial principal axes of the deformation and λ_α are known as the principal stretches since, from Eq. (1.10.7), λ_α is the ratio of the final to the original length of a fiber in the α principal direction.

Polar Decomposition Theorem

A special class of affine deformations is that for which $a_{iL} = R_{iL}$ where R_{iL} is called a rotation matrix and corresponds to a rigid rotation of the body which leaves lengths and angles invariant. That is, consider any set of vectors $\mathbf{F}^{(\alpha)}$ with components $F_L^{(\alpha)}$ which are transformed by R_{iL} into vectors $\mathbf{f}^{(\alpha)}$ with components $f_i^{(\alpha)}$; then

$$\mathbf{f}^{(\alpha)} \cdot \mathbf{f}^{(\beta)} = \mathbf{F}^{(\alpha)} \cdot \mathbf{F}^{(\beta)}. \tag{1.10.8}$$

We return to the consideration of an arbitrary deformation matrix a_{iL}. By the polar decomposition theorem[53] of linear algebra, it is possible to write it in

---

[52] Note that we do not require that $\mathbf{N}^{(\alpha)}, \mathbf{n}^{(\alpha)}$ be unit vectors.

[53] Halmos (1958, p. 170).

the form

$$a_{iL} = R_{iK}S_{KL}$$

where R_{iK} is a rotation matrix and S_{KL} is a real symmetric matrix. From Eq. (1.10.1) it follows that

$$S_{LK}S_{KM} = C_{LM}$$

so that we can write[54] $S_{LM} = C^{\frac{1}{2}}_{LM}$ and express the polar decomposition theorem in the form

$$a_{iL} = R_{iK}C^{\frac{1}{2}}_{KL}. \tag{1.10.9}$$

It is readily verified that the characteristic directions of $C^{\frac{1}{2}}_{LM}$ are $\mathbf{N}^{(\alpha)}$, the same as they are for C_{LM}, and that the corresponding characteristic values are λ_α. The polar decomposition theorem, Eq. (1.10.9), therefore describes a general affine transformation $x_i = a_{iL}X_L + b_i$ as taking place in three steps: (i) Deformation by $C^{\frac{1}{2}}_{KM}$; fibers in the principal directions $\mathbf{N}^{(\alpha)}$ undergo stretches λ_α but do not rotate; fibers in other directions, in general, undergo both stretch and rotation. (ii) Rigid rotation of the deformed body by R_{iK}. In this step fibers originally in the material principal directions $\mathbf{N}^{(\alpha)}$ are carried into the spatial principal directions $\mathbf{n}^{(\alpha)}$. (iii) Translation by b_i.

It is also possible to write the polar decomposition theorem in the form

$$a_{iL} = c^{\frac{1}{2}}_{ij}R_{jL} \tag{1.10.10}$$

and to express the sequence of steps in the affine transformations in the reverse order.

From the definition of C_{LM}, Eq. (1.10.1), its determinant

$$|C_{LM}| = |a_{iL}|^2 = J^2 \tag{1.10.11}$$

where we have used Eq. (1.2.24) transcribed to the case $x_{i,L} = a_{iL}$. It follows that

$$J = \frac{v}{\mathcal{V}} = \lambda_1\lambda_2\lambda_3 \tag{1.10.12}$$

where $\mathcal{V}$ is the original and v the deformed volume of the body. This result is also easily derived by considering a unit cube with edges in the material principal directions which is deformed into a rectangular parallelelepiped with edges λ_α, $\alpha = 1, 2, 3$.

---

[54] The definition of this notation is provided by the previous equation.

From the definitions of C_{LM}, Eq. (1.10.1), and E_{LM}, Eq. (1.2.10), we see that

$$E_{LM} = \tfrac{1}{2}(C_{LM} - \delta_{LM}). \tag{1.10.13}$$

It follows that E_{LM} and C_{LM} have the same characteristic directions and that E_α, the characteristic values of E_{LM}, are

$$E_\alpha = \tfrac{1}{2}(\lambda_\alpha^2 - 1). \tag{1.10.14}$$

Since E_{LL} has the same value in all rectangular cartesian coordinate systems, that is, it is a Cartesian tensor invariant, we conclude that

$$E_{LL} = \sum_{\alpha=1}^{3} E_\alpha = \tfrac{1}{2} \sum_{\alpha=1}^{3} (\lambda_\alpha^2 - 1). \tag{1.10.15}$$

Scalar Functions of a_{iL}

We consider next $F(a_{iL})$, any scalar-valued function of the elements of the deformation matrix a_{iL}. It will be convenient for this discussion to use a notation in which we denote this matrix by A, the polar decomposition theorem of Eq. (1.10.9) by $A = R\sqrt{C}$, etc. The matrix A represents the affine deformation of the body for a particular choice of coordinate system X_L or X used for its reference configuration and a particular choice x_i or x used for its deformed configuration; for this choice, the deformation is given by the equation

$$x = AX. \tag{1.10.16}$$

We now change the coordinate system used for the deformed configuration by means of an orthogonal transformation Q:

$$\bar{x} = Qx \tag{1.10.17}$$

so that

$$\bar{x} = QAX = \bar{A}X; \quad \bar{A} = QA. \tag{1.10.18}$$

The matrix $\bar{A}$ describes the same deformation when coordinate systems X and $\bar{x}$ are employed as does A when coordinate systems X and x are employed. Since F is a scalar-valued function, its value must be independent of the coordinate systems used; therefore

$$F(A) = F(\bar{A}). \tag{1.10.19}$$

This result applies for any orthogonal transformation Q. By the polar decomposition theorem, $A = R\sqrt{C}$. Take $Q = R^{-1}$. Then $\bar{A} = \sqrt{C}$ and Eq.

(1.10.19) becomes

$$F(\mathbf{A}) = F(\sqrt{\mathbf{C}}); \qquad (1.10.20)$$

that is, a scalar-valued function of the deformation matrix a_{iL} must be expressible as a function of $C_{LM}^{\frac{1}{2}}$. This is clear on physical grounds: for a given deformation of the body, a_{iL} depends both on the coordinate systems X_L and x_i while C_{LM} depends only on the coordinate system X_L, and a change in coordinate system x_i is equivalent to the rigid rotation of the body after it has been deformed.

Isotropy

For a given coordinate system X_L, the six elements of the symmetric C_{LM} are determined by its three characteristic values λ_α and the three angles θ_α which describe the orientation of the set of mutually orthogonal characteristic directions $\mathbf{N}^{(\alpha)}$ with respect to the coordinate system X_L. Therefore, an alternate set of arguments for a scalar-valued function of a_{iL} are the six variables, $\lambda_\alpha, \theta_\alpha$, $\alpha = 1, 2, 3$. However, if the body is isotropic in its reference configuration then the scalar property F must be independent of the orientation of the coordinate system X_L, that is, independent of the angles θ_α, $\alpha = 1, 2, 3$ and must be expressible as a function $F(\lambda_1, \lambda_2, \lambda_3)$.

Stress – Strain Relations

It follows that for a body which is isotropic in its reference configuration[55] we can write its Helmholtz free energy as $F(\lambda_1, \lambda_2, \lambda_3, T)$. We can describe an arbitrary deformation of the body, in its simplest form by taking the coordinate system $\overline{X}_L$ in the material principal directions and $\overline{x}_i$ in the spatial principal directions. With this choice of coordinate systems, the deformation is described by

$$\overline{x}_i = \sum_{L=1}^{3} \delta_{iL} \lambda_L \overline{X}_L = \overline{a}_{iL} \overline{X}_L \qquad (1.10.21)$$

where

$$\overline{a}_{iL} = \delta_{iL} \lambda_L, \qquad (1.10.22)$$

and where we have written λ_L, $L = 1, 2, 3$ in place of λ_α, $\alpha = 1, 2, 3$. The Piola–Kirchhoff stress tensor $\overline{T}_{iL}$ in these coordinate systems is, from Eq. (1.6.10),

$$\overline{T}_{iL} = \frac{1}{\mathscr{V}} \frac{\partial F}{\partial \overline{a}_{iL}} = \delta_{iL} \frac{1}{\mathscr{V}} \frac{\partial F}{\partial \lambda_L} \qquad (1.10.23)$$

---

[55]Its properties may be anisotropic in its deformed state.

That is, in these coordinate systems, the Piola–Kirchhoff stress tensor is described by a diagonal matrix with diagonal elements

$$T_L = \frac{1}{\mathscr{V}} \frac{\partial F}{\partial \lambda_L}. \tag{1.10.24}$$

From the significance of the Piola–Kirchhoff stress tensor components and the choices of the coordinate systems $\overline{X}_L$, $\bar{x}_i$, we see that T_L is the force per unit of original area acting across a plane given by $\overline{X}_L$ = constant in the reference configuration and which is normal to a principal direction of the deformation; the force acts in a direction $\bar{x}_i$, $i = L$, which is normal to the same plane in the deformed configuration. There are no tangential components of the force acting on these planes.

We have gone through this somewhat lengthy derivation of Eq. (1.10.24) in order to place it within the general context of Eq. (1.6.10), to emphasize both its applicability to an arbitrary deformation and the fact that it is only the isotropy of the body in its reference configuration that is needed in order to arrive at a free energy function of the form $F(\lambda_1, \lambda_2, \lambda_3, T)$. Granted these points, we can motivate Eq. (1.10.24) much more directly by considering a cube of material with its faces X_L = constant subject to normal forces T_L per unit original area and undergoing stretches λ_L in the X_L directions, with no rotations. Then it is readily verified that $\dot{W}$, the rate of doing work on the body, is

$$\dot{W} = \mathscr{V} T_L \dot{\lambda}_L \tag{1.10.25}$$

from which Eq. (1.10.24) follows by the same reasoning as used in Section 1.6.

APPENDIX: NOTATION OF THURSTON (1964)

A summary of continuum thermoelasticity is given by Thurston (1964) in a notation which is employed in some recent research papers on the subject. We tabulate here the relation between our notation and his.

		Weiner (1983)	Thurston (1964)
(1)	Material coordinates	$X_L, L = 1, 2, 3$	$a_i, i = 1, 2, 3$
(2)	Spatial coordinates	$x_i, i = 1, 2, 3$	x_i
(3)	Affine transformation matrix	$x_{i,L} = a_{iL}$	$\dfrac{\partial x_p}{\partial a_q}$
(4)	Volume ratio	$J = \dfrac{dv}{d\mathscr{V}}$	$J = \dfrac{dV}{dV_0}$
(5)	Spatial strain tensor	e_{ij}	ε_{ij}
(6)	Material strain tensor	E_{LM}	η_{ij}

(7)	Cauchy stress tensor	t_{ij}	T_{ij}
(8)	First Piola–Kirchhoff stress tensor	T_{iL}	P_{ik}
(9)	Second Piola–Kirchhoff stress tensor	T_{LM}	t_{ij}
(10)	Helmholtz free energy	F	A
(11)	Elastic moduli (isothermal)	C^T_{LMNK}	c^T_{ijkl}
(12)	Elastic moduli (adiabatic)	C^S_{LMNK}	c^S_{ijkl}
(13)	Elastic compliances	S_{LMNK}	s_{ijkm}
(14)	Displacement gradient moduli	$\mathscr{S}_{iLjM}$	A_{kmij}
(15)	Stress–temperature derivatives	b_{LM}	$-\lambda_{ij}$
(16)	Thermal expansion tensor	α_{LM}	α_{km}

CHAPTER TWO

Concepts of Classical Statistical Mechanics

2.1 INTRODUCTION

In the previous chapter, we presented a summary of the kinematics, mechanics, and thermodynamics of elastic solids from the continuum viewpoint. In the remainder of the book we will be treating the same phenomena from the atomistic viewpoint. That is, we will treat the body as a collection of discrete mass points, representing atoms, which interact with each other according to some specified force law.[1] In addition, the atoms of the body interact with those of its environment. These external interactions serve to impose surface tractions or deformations on the body and also to set its atoms into thermal motion. This chapter is primarily concerned with the latter effect; the role of imposed surface tractions or deformations is discussed in Chapter 3 and the manner in which they are imposed will be discussed, for crystalline solids, in Chapter 4 and, for polymeric solids, in Chapter 6.

For the description and analysis of the thermal motion of the atoms of the body, the concepts of statistical mechanics are needed. If one is concerned with the mechanical behavior of solids at very low temperature levels, it is necessary to employ quantum statistical mechanics for its description. At ordinary temperature levels, however, classical statistical mechanics provide an accurate description of most of these phenomena and we begin our discussion with the classical theory since the physical picture it provides is so much closer to the experience and intuition of most of those concerned with the mechanical behavior of solids. The principles of quantum statistical mechanics and the ways in which they modify the classical results are discussed in Chapter 10. We further restrict our discussion to systems that are, from the continuum thermo-

---

[1] The quantum mechanical background of these laws is discussed in Chapter 9.

dynamics viewpoint, in states of uniform thermodynamic equilibrium. From the atomistic viewpoint this means, therefore, that we are restricting ourselves here to the domain of classical equilibrium statistical mechanics.

As Fowler has remarked, "Statistical mechanics may... be regarded as consisting of two almost distinct subjects: the theory of the equilibrium properties of matter based on... assumptions which can be introduced in a way which makes them *a priori* eminently reasonable, and the deeper theory of these assumptions themselves."[2] It is with the first of these subjects that we are concerned. The second, the examination of the foundations of statistical mechanics, continues to be a very active area of research.[3] Although there is little question regarding the validity of the final mathematical formalism for the calculation of equilibrium properties, there are several distinct paths for basing this formalism on more fundamental principles, with proponents and critics for each approach. In order to provide an underlying physical picture to the formalism, we follow the approach that relates the quantities calculated by the methods of equilibrium statistical mechanics to time averages of observed properties. This approach is based on a concrete and easily visualized physical model of processes on the microscopic level, and therefore appears best suited for a first meeting with the subject. It is also well adapted to the treatment of different boundary conditions on elastic bodies. On the other hand, from the foundations viewpoint, it is the most difficult to carry through and serious gaps remain. Our treatment is heuristic[4] and omits discussion of some of the deeper mathematical and philosophical questions studied by those concerned with the foundations of the subject. After completing our account of this approach, we return, in Section 2.8, to a short discussion of some of the fundamental difficulties this path entails, and describe some of the alternate paths which have been followed.

2.2 HAMILTONIAN MECHANICS

As indicated by its name, classical equilibrium statistical mechanics is a combination of the principles of classical mechanics and statistical reasoning. In the development of the subject, Hamiltonian mechanics is the appropriate formulation of classical mechanics to be employed and we begin with a brief exposition.

Consider a single particle of mass m constrained to move in a single direction x, subject to a potential $V(x)$. In the Newtonian formulation of this problem, we seek a function $x(t)$ satisfying the second-order ordinary differen-

---

[2] Fowler (1936, p. 7).

[3] For a recent review, see Penrose (1979).

[4] A rigorous presentation of the approach we have followed is found in Khinchin (1949); a clear summary of Khinchin's derivations is given by Grad (1950).

tial equation

$$m\ddot{x} = -\frac{dV}{dx}$$ (2.2.1)

satisfying specified initial conditions

$$x(0) = x_0,$$

$$\dot{x}(0) = \dot{x}_0.$$ (2.2.2)

We may replace the single second order differential equation, Eq. (2.2.1), by a pair of first-order equations, Eqs. (2.2.3) and (2.2.4), by introducing the particle momentum p defined as

$$m\dot{x} = p$$ (2.2.3)

which, from Eq. (2.2.1), satisfies

$$\dot{p} = -\frac{dV}{dx}.$$ (2.2.4)

The motion is now described in terms of two functions $x(t)$ and $p(t)$ which satisfy the respective initial conditions

$$x(0) = x_0$$

$$p(0) = p_0 = m\dot{x}_0.$$ (2.2.5)

One advantage of this expanded description is that it provides a better overview of the nature of the solutions for a given mechanical system for a variety of initial conditions. Consider, as an example, the simple harmonic oscillator $V(x) = \frac{1}{2}\kappa x^2$. A plot of $x(t)$ of solutions to Eq. (2.2.1) for various initial conditions leads to a jumble in x–t space (Figure 2.1a), whereas the plot in x–p space of the solutions to Eqs. (2.2.3) and (2.2.4) (Figure 2.1b) shows a clear pattern. The plane with coordinates x and p is referred to as the phase space of the system, which in this example has one degree of freedom. The solution curve passing through a given point of the phase space is referred to as a trajectory of the system. The direction in which the system traverses a given trajectory (shown by arrows in Figure 2.1b) is clear from the sign of p.

The non-intersecting character of the set of trajectories for the harmonic oscillator will be retained in essence for more complex systems, since from existence and uniqueness theorems for systems of ordinary differential equations it follows that, for well-behaved potential functions $V(x)$, there will be one and only one[5] trajectory through each point in phase space.

[5] Except for isolated points that represent equilibrium configurations of the system.

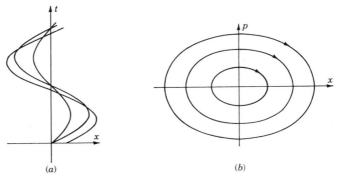

Figure 2.1 Motion of a simple harmonic oscillator shown in x–t plane (a) and in x–p plane (b).

To complete the transition to the Hamiltonian formulation, let

$$H(x, p) = K(p) + V(x) = \frac{p^2}{2m} + V(x), \qquad (2.2.6)$$

where $K(p)$ is the kinetic energy of the particle and $H(x, p)$, the Hamiltonian of the system, is in this case[6] the total energy of the system. Then, Eqs. (2.2.3) and (2.2.4) can be rewritten

$$\dot{x} = \frac{p}{m} = \frac{\partial H}{\partial p} \qquad (2.2.7)$$

$$\dot{p} = -\frac{dV}{dx} = -\frac{\partial H}{\partial x} \qquad (2.2.8)$$

and are Hamilton's equations for this system.

The extension of this formulation to the case of a single particle of mass m with three degrees of freedom is straightforward. The particle position is referred to rectangular Cartesian coordinates x_1, x_2, x_3 or x_i, $i = 1, 2, 3$, and the potential energy is now $V(x_1, x_2, x_3)$. The Newtonian equations of motion are[7]

$$m\ddot{x}_i = -\frac{\partial V}{\partial x_i}; \qquad (2.2.9)$$

[6]In more complicated situations involving, for example, systems with moving geometrical constraints, the Hamiltonian is not necessarily the total energy of the system. See, for example, Goldstein (1980, pp. 349–351). We will not be concerned with such systems here.

[7]Here, and in the following, the range of indices is determined by the context of the discussion.

the components of the momentum, or the momenta, are

$$p_i = m\dot{x}_i \qquad (2.2.10)$$

and these satisfy the first order differential equations

$$\dot{p}_i = -\frac{\partial V}{\partial x_i}. \qquad (2.2.11)$$

With the introduction of the Hamiltonian

$$H(x_1, x_2, x_3, p_1, p_2, p_3) = \sum_{i=1}^{3} p_i^2/(2m) + V(x_1, x_2, x_3), \qquad (2.2.12)$$

Eqs. (2.2.10) and (2.2.11) may be written in Hamiltonian form as

$$\dot{x}_i = \frac{\partial H}{\partial p_i}, \qquad (2.2.13)$$

$$\dot{p}_i = -\frac{\partial H}{\partial x_i}. \qquad (2.2.14)$$

This development and notation may also be extended to a system of N particles by the device of labeling the coordinates of the first particle, x_1, x_2, x_3, the coordinates of the second particle, x_4, x_5, x_6, and so on through the coordinates of the Nth particle which are labeled x_{n-2}, x_{n-1}, x_n, where $n = 3N$. It is important to note that all of these coordinates refer to the same rectangular Cartesian coordinate system. It is also possible to incorporate particles of differing mass into this scheme by using the notation $m_1 = m_2 = m_3$ for the mass of particle 1, $m_4 = m_5 = m_6$ for the mass of particle 2, etc. Then, the Hamiltonian of the system may be written as

$$H(x_1, \ldots, x_n; p_1, \ldots, p_n) = \sum_{i=1}^{n} \frac{p_i^2}{2m_i} + V(x_1, \ldots, x_n) \qquad (2.2.15)$$

and the corresponding set of Hamilton's equations again take the form of Eqs. (2.2.13) and (2.2.14), with the new range of indices, $i = 1, \ldots, n$ to be understood.

For a system with n degrees of freedom, the phase space in which the system moves along trajectories $x_i(t)$, $p_i(t)$ becomes $2n$-dimensional. For $n > 1$, it is no longer possible to draw pictures as in Figure 2.1b. Nevertheless, the conceptual simplicity of a single trajectory passing through each point of phase space remains, and is enormously valuable to our visualization of the motion.

As we have seen, the replacement of the Newtonian formulation of mechanics by the Hamiltonian formulation for a system of particles is a straightforward matter when there are no geometrical constraints and therefore the particle positions may be described by their rectangular Cartesian coordinates. The Hamiltonian formulation applies as well in the presence of geometric constraints, although it is then more difficult to derive from the Newtonian formulation.[8] In that case, the rectangular Cartesian coordinates x_i are replaced by q_i, $i = 1, \ldots, n$, the generalized coordinates which embody the geometrical constraints, and p_i are the corresponding momenta. Here n still represents the number of degrees of freedom of the system, but $n < 3N$, where N is the number of particles. Hamilton's equations still take the form

$$\dot{q}_i = \frac{\partial H}{\partial p_i}, \tag{2.2.16}$$

$$\dot{p}_i = -\frac{\partial H}{\partial q_i}. \tag{2.2.17}$$

Since classical equilibrium statistical mechanics depends only on these equations, the subject retains the same form for systems described by generalized coordinates. We will, hereafter, use the q, p notation instead of x, p notation, in order to conform to general usage, although rectangular Cartesian coordinates are intended in most cases.[9]

In addition to depending on the coordinates and the momenta of the system, the Hamiltonian of systems discussed in statistical mechanics will also depend on a small number of controllable parameters. An example of a controllable parameter is the volume of a gas in a cylinder closed by a moveable piston, and in this case the controllable parameter is a kinematic variable of the type considered in Section 1.3 and represents a constraint of a macroscopic character imposed by the environment (the cylinder) on the atomistic system (the gas). In general these macroscopic constraints will be kinematical[10] variables $\mathscr{A}_1, \ldots, \mathscr{A}_\nu$ of the type discussed in Section 1.3. When we wish to make this dependence explicit we write $H = H(q, p; \mathscr{A}_1, \ldots, \mathscr{A}_\nu)$ $= H(q, p; \mathscr{A})$. Since the controllable parameters are regarded as fixed in value throughout this chapter, we will simply write $H = H(q, p)$ in its developments. Variations in the controllable parameters play a key role in later chapters.

2.3 USE OF STATISTICS IN STATISTICAL MECHANICS

Thus far, we have been dealing solely with the mechanics portion of the subject of statistical mechanics. We turn next to a brief examination of its statistical aspect. The use of statistics in the analysis of a situation is indicated when two

---

[8] For a discussion of this derivation see, for example, Goldstein (1980, Chap. 8).

[9] Curvilinear coordinates and the imposition of geometric constraints are considered in the treatment of polymer molecules in Chapter 6.

[10] We will also consider on occasion the use of the conjugate forces $\mathscr{F}_1, \ldots, \mathscr{F}_\nu$ (Section 1.3) as controllable parameters; cf. Sections 3.7 and 4.7.

criteria are satisfied: (a) The absence of complete information defining the problem prevents its complete solution. (b) Incomplete solutions suffice for the purposes at hand. A familiar example is provided by the analysts of an insurance company who certainly lack the information to compute the lifetime of their individual clients, but are completely satisfied by accurate calculations of the statistical distribution of these lifetimes.

Consider next an example that is closer to our subject, namely a collection of like atoms at rest in an array corresponding (from a purely classical[11] viewpoint) to a perfect crystal at zero temperature. Given the interatomic potential $V(q_1, \ldots, q_n)$ for this particular collection of atoms, we can compute a_0, the interatomic spacing in a given direction at which this collection of atoms will all be in stable equilibrium.[12]

We now visualize placing this crystal in an ambient consisting of a gas at temperature T (Figure 2.2) and allowing sufficient time for the crystal to arrive at macroscopic equilibrium. Because of the interaction between the atoms of the crystal and the atoms of the gas flying by, those of the crystal will be set into motion and the spacing, for some typical pair of atoms, which was formerly a_0 will now become some complicated function of time, $a(t)$. It is clear that we cannot compute this function precisely. One obvious difficulty is that we are dealing with a mechanical system with an enormous number of degrees of freedom. In addition, we clearly cannot, at the initial instant of observation of the crystal, determine the initial conditions, that is, coordinates and momenta, of all of the atoms of the crystal. Furthermore, we do not know the precise nature of the interaction between the crystal atoms and the gas atoms, so that this, along with the initial conditions, constitutes missing information.[13] To compensate, however, we are generally not interested in the detailed nature of the atomic motion, as typified by the fluctuating interatomic spacing $a(t)$, but rather in some time-averaged value $\hat{a}$, where the average is taken over a time interval that is very short on a macroscopic time scale, for example, 10^{-6} seconds. Furthermore, we know from experience that this average value, and other aspects of the macroscopic behavior of the crystal, will not depend, for a crystal in macroscopic equilibrium, on the particular instant at which observation begins or on the detailed nature of the crystal atom–gas atom interaction. For example, the macroscopic behavior of a crystal will be the same whether it is placed in an ambient of nitrogen, argon, or air, so long as all three are at the same temperature.

To summarize, therefore, the use of statistics in the phenomena treated by equilibrium statistical mechanics is dictated by the great complexity of the mechanics problems involved and by the absence of complete information

---

[11]From the quantum viewpoint, zero-point motion is present even at zero temperature (Section 8.9).

[12]We neglect, in this illustration, surface effects, which will require slightly different spacing near the crystal boundary.

[13]That is, as will be discussed further in later developments, we do not wish to include this information (which would require also the study of the motion of the gas atoms) in our problem description.

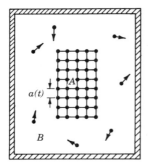

Figure 2.2 Crystal A surrounded by gaseous ambient B.

defining these problems. These difficulties are balanced by the facts that only average aspects of the full solution are needed, and these averages are independent of the missing information.

2.4 PHASE FUNCTIONS AND TIME AVERAGES

Given a system of particles with n degrees of freedom. The term "phase function of the system" is used to describe any of its properties whose instantaneous value at time t is completely determined by the $2n$ values of its coordinates and momenta, that is, by the system's position in its phase space or, as it is termed, by its microstate at that time. A phase function can be expressed therefore[14] as $F(q_1, \ldots, q_n; p_1, \ldots, p_n) = F(q, p)$. Examples of phase functions are: the distance between a given pair of atoms, $|\mathbf{q}_i - \mathbf{q}_j|$, as considered in the last section; the kinetic energy of the system, $K = \frac{1}{2} \sum_{i=1}^{n} p_i^2 / m_i$; the total energy of the system, $H(q, p)$, etc.

As the system follows a trajectory $(q(t), p(t))$ in phase space, the value of a particular phase function will be correspondingly time dependent, $F(t) = F(q(t), p(t))$. The rate of variation of phase functions for atomic systems will generally be very rapid on a macroscopic time scale, that is, with respect to the time intervals required for macroscopic measurements. For example, the period of lattice vibrations in a crystal is of the order of 10^{-12} seconds. What we are interested in, therefore, and what is measured in a macroscopic measurement, is the time average

$$F(t, t_0) = \frac{1}{t} \int_{t_0}^{t + t_0} F(q(\tau), p(\tau)) \, d\tau. \qquad (2.4.1)$$

In fact, in view of the enormous ratio between macroscopic and microscopic

---

[14] The phase function will also generally depend on the values of the controllable parameters $\mathscr{A}_1, \ldots, \mathscr{A}_\nu$ as discussed in Section 2.2. Again we omit explicit reference to these in this chapter.

time scales, it may be expected that the value of $F(t, t_0)$ will be almost independent of t for these very large values of t and therefore may be replaced by the limit of $F(t, t_0)$ as $t \to \infty$. It can be shown, under very general conditions, that such limits exist, are independent of t_0 and of the initial microstate, excluding possibly some exceptional initial conditions.[15] We then write

$$\hat{F} = \lim_{T \to \infty} \frac{1}{T} \int_0^T F\big(q(t), p(t)\big) \, dt. \qquad (2.4.2)$$

The computation of the trajectory in phase space, $\big(q(t), p(t)\big)$ is a hopeless task for a macroscopic system because of its huge number of degrees of freedom. Furthermore, as we noted in the discussion in Section 2.3 of the example of a crystal in a gaseous ambient at elevated temperature, there is missing information as to the exact nature of the initial conditions and the interaction between the crystal atoms and the gas atoms so the computation of the exact trajectory is impossible not only in practice but in principle as well.

In order to circumvent this difficulty, we adopt the postulate that it is possible to find, for any given system with coordinates and momenta (q, p) and associated phase space Γ, a function $\rho(q, p)$ (known as a distribution function) with the following properties:

(i)
$$\rho \geqslant 0 \qquad (2.4.3)$$

(ii)
$$\int_\Gamma \rho(q, p) \, dq \, dp = 1 \qquad (2.4.4)$$

and, for *any* phase function $F(q, p)$ of the system,

(iii)
$$\bar{F} \triangleq \int_\Gamma F(q, p) \rho(q, p) \, dq \, dp = \hat{F}. \qquad (2.4.5)$$

The quantity $\bar{F}$ defined by the volume integral over Γ in Eq. (2.4.5) is referred to as the phase average of the phase function $F(q, p)$. Postulate (iii), therefore, declares the equality of phase averages and time averages for all phase functions of the system. A system for which this is true is said to be ergodic.[16] For an ergodic system it is possible to derive the following interpretation of $\rho(q, p)$:

Consider any region D in Γ. Define the phase function $F_D(q, p)$ as

$$F_D(q, p) = 1 \qquad \text{if } (q, p) \in D$$
$$= 0 \qquad \text{if } (q, p) \notin D. \qquad (2.4.6)$$

---

[15] This result is contained in Birkhoff's theorem. For a precise statement and proof see Khinchin (1949).

[16] The term was introduced by Boltzmann (1887); see Section 2.5. The term ergodic is currently used in several different contexts. In particular it describes the hypothesis of equality of phase and time averages and ergodic theory deals with the difficult question of delineating precise conditions under which this holds. For extensive studies, see Farquhar (1964), Mackey (1974), and Penrose (1979). We return briefly to this question in Section 2.8.

Then,

$$\bar{F}_D = \int_\Gamma F_D(q, p)\rho(q, p)\, dq\, dp = \int_D \rho(q, p)\, dq\, dp \qquad (2.4.7)$$

and

$$\hat{F}_D = \lim_{T \to \infty} \frac{1}{T} \int_0^T F_D\big(q(t), p(t)\big)\, dt = \lim_{T \to \infty} \frac{t(D; T)}{T} \qquad (2.4.8)$$

where $t(D; T)$ is the total time spent by the system in D in the time interval $0 \leqslant t \leqslant T$. Since the system is ergodic, $\hat{F}_D = \bar{F}_D$ or

$$\int_D \rho(q, p)\, dq\, dp = f_D \qquad (2.4.9)$$

where f_D is the limiting fraction of time that the system spends in the region D. For an ergodic system, therefore, f_D is independent of the starting point of the trajectory.

We can gain additional insight into Eq. (2.4.9) and the property of $\rho(q, p)$ which it implies by considering a hypothetical meter which measures the fluctuating values of $F_D\big(q(t), p(t)\big)$, leading to a record tape as shown in Figure 2.3.

If the detailed time variation of F_D is desired, it is necessary to retain the tape intact. However, if only the time average $\hat{F}_D$ is of interest, the tape may be cut into segments in each of which F_D is either 1 or 0 and the fraction of the total tape length with the former value determined. This is the procedure corresponding to Eq. (2.4.9). In carrying out this experiment, it is clear that the pieces of tape may be scrambled and need not be retained in their original sequence; that is, the precise knowledge of $q(t)$, $p(t)$ is not needed.

We have obtained Eq. (2.4.9) as a consequence of Eq. (2.4.5). We can also proceed in the reverse direction. That is, we can describe $\rho(q, p)$ as a function with the property, as stated in Eq. (2.4.9), that its integral over any arbitrary

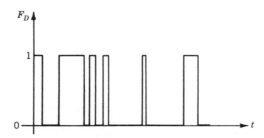

Figure 2.3 Time variation of phase function F_D, Eq. (2.4.6).

set D is the limiting fraction of time that the system spends in that set. Then clearly Eqs. (2.4.3) and (2.4.4) follow directly from this description. Consider next the computation of the time average $\hat{F}$ of a phase function $F(q, p)$. Subdivide the phase space Γ into a large number of regions D_i and let $t_i(T)$ be the total elapsed time spent in D_i (not necessarily in a single continuous interval) during the time T. Then

$$\hat{F} = \lim_{T \to \infty} \frac{1}{T} \int_0^T F\big(q(\tau), p(\tau)\big) \, d\tau = \lim_{T \to \infty} \frac{1}{T} \sum_i \int_{t_i(T)} F(q(\tau), p(\tau)) \, d\tau$$

$$= \lim_{T \to \infty} \sum_i \bar{F}_i \frac{t_i}{T} = \sum_i \bar{F}_i f_{D_i} = \sum_i \bar{F}_i \int_{D_i} \rho(q, p) \, dq \, dp = \sum_i \bar{F}_i \bar{\rho}_i V_i \qquad (2.4.10)$$

where we have made use of Eq. (2.4.9) in the penultimate step, $\bar{F}_i, \bar{\rho}_i$ are suitable mean values of $F(q, p)$ and $\rho(q, p)$ in D_i and

$$V_i = \int_{D_i} dq \, dp \qquad (2.4.11)$$

is the volume of the region D_i. If we now refine the subdivision of Γ into smaller and smaller sets D_i, we are led to the conclusion that

$$\hat{F} = \bar{F} \qquad (2.4.12)$$

with the phase average F defined as in Eq. (2.4.5).

We see from the above considerations that the distribution function $\rho(q, p)$ gives a partial description of the motion in phase space of a system with specified Hamiltonian and for given values of the controllable parameters[17] that describe the effect on it of its environment. The description is partial in that it gives only the fraction of time that the system spends in any region of phase space, not its detailed trajectory. However, under the ergodic hypothesis, it permits us to compute the time average of any phase function, and therefore the macroscopic value of any physical property of the system, solely in terms of a volume integral as in Eq. (2.4.5). Our next concern, therefore, and one which will occupy us for the remainder of this chapter, is the determination of the explicit form of the distribution function for a system under specified macroscopic conditions.

To fix ideas, consider a crystal (system A) surrounded by a gaseous ambient (system B) as shown in Figure 2.2. We assume further that the gas is

---

[17]The function $\rho(q, p)$ will therefore also depend upon these parameters. Since these controllable parameters are constant in this chapter, we do not make this dependence explicit until the discussion of Chapter 3 and what follows.

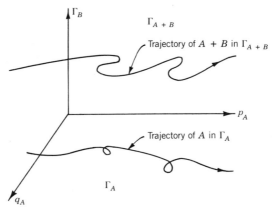

Figure 2.4 Projection of trajectory of isolated system $A + B$ onto the phase space Γ_A of component A.

surrounded by an isolating container so that the combined system $A + B$ is isolated and described by a Hamiltonian $H_{A+B}(q_A, q_B; p_A, p_B)$. (An isolated system has a Hamiltonian that depends only on the coordinates and momenta of the particles of the system itself, and is independent of the coordinates and momenta of any particles outside the system.) The phase space, Γ_{A+B}, of the combined system $A + B$ has coordinates and momenta q_A, p_A, q_B, p_B and is therefore the Cartesian product[18] of the phase spaces Γ_A and Γ_B. This is shown schematically in Figure 2.4. As noted previously, there passes through any point of Γ_{A+B} a unique trajectory of the combined system as determined by the Hamiltonian $H_{A+B}(q_A, q_B; p_A, p_B)$. Therefore, as shown in Figure 2.4 a trajectory of $A + B$ cannot cross itself. On the other hand, the projection of this trajectory onto Γ_A, leading to a description of the motion of system A in its phase space, will be more complex, showing many crossing points. In the specific example we are discussing, a crossing point is one in which the coordinates and momenta of all of the atoms in the crystal are identical, but the coordinates and momenta of the atoms in the gas differ.

Our primary interest is in the distribution function for a system, such as the crystal in this example, which interacts with a surrounding ambient. Because of the greater conceptual simplicity of an isolated system, however, we start first with the study of the phase space dynamics of such systems and derive the form of the distribution function for this case. Given the fraction of time which an isolated system spends in any region of its space, we can then compute the fraction of time which any component of it (such as the crystal in this example) spends in any region of the component's phase space.

---

[18]For the concept of a cartesian product see, for example, Rudin (1966, p. 7).

2.5 PHASE SPACE DYNAMICS OF ISOLATED SYSTEMS

In accord with the program just outlined, we start with an examination of the nature of the motion in its phase space of an isolated dynamical system with n degrees of freedom. It is described by a Hamiltonian $H(q_1, \ldots, q_n, p_1, \ldots, p_n)$, and its motion obeys the equations

$$\dot{q}_i = \frac{\partial H}{\partial p_i},$$

$$\dot{p}_i = -\frac{\partial H}{\partial q_i}. \tag{2.5.1}$$

As noted previously, the motion of an isolated system in its $2n$-dimensional phase space Γ is conceptually simple, since through each point of Γ passes a unique trajectory of the system (Figure 2.5). We can rephrase this situation in a somewhat more picturesque fashion by saying that the entire phase space Γ is filled with a collection of replicas of the given system, with each point in Γ occupied by a unique replica at a given instant of time. By the term replica is simply meant a mechanical system governed by the same Hamiltonian as is the given system. We can interpret the motion of the replicas as the flow of a fluid in $2n$-dimensional space with the velocity $(\dot{q}, \dot{p})$ of the replica at (q, p) given by Hamilton's equations, Eqs. (2.5.1). Since, for the systems with which we are concerned, the Hamiltonian $H = H(q, p)$ has no explicit time dependence, the flow of this "fluid" is steady state and therefore trajectories and streamlines are identical.

This collection of replicas has been termed an ensemble by Gibbs. It is important to note that each replica of the ensemble moves, according to Hamilton's equations, in a manner that depends only on its own coordinates and momenta; there is no interaction between neighboring replicas as there is between the particles of a real fluid.

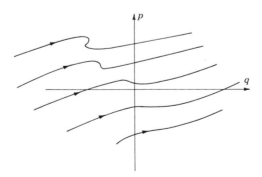

Figure 2.5 Family of trajectories of an isolated system.

To describe the motion of the ensemble more compactly, we introduce the coordinates y_j, $j = 1, \ldots, 2n$ in place of q_i, p_i, $i = 1, \ldots, n$; that is, $y_i = q_i$, $i = 1, \ldots, n$ and $y_{i+n} = p_i$, $i = 1, \ldots, n$. It is also convenient to employ some of the terminology of continuum mechanics, referring to the material or Lagrangian coordinates,[19] Y_j, of a given replica as the place in phase space occupied by the replica at time $t = 0$ and y_j, the spatial or Eulerian coordinates, as the place occupied by the same replica at the present time t. The relation between the two coordinates is obtained by solution of Hamilton's equations subject to the initial conditions that $y_j = Y_j$ at $t = 0$ in the form

$$y_j = y_j(Y, t) \tag{2.5.2}$$

with inverse

$$Y_j = Y_j(y, t). \tag{2.5.3}$$

The velocity of a given replica at time t is obtained from Eq. (2.5.2) as

$$\dot{y}_j \triangleq \frac{\partial y_j}{\partial t}(Y, t)$$

and gives the replica velocity in terms of its Lagrangian coordinates. It may be expressed in terms of the Eulerian designation of a replica by means of Eq. (2.5.3); in this case the notation $v_j(y, t)$ is used for the velocity components. That is,

$$\dot{y}_j(Y, t) \triangleq \frac{\partial y_j}{\partial t}(Y, t) = v_j(y, t) \tag{2.5.4}$$

where Y and y are the Lagrangian and Eulerian coordinates, respectively, of the same replica, that is, they are related by Eqs. (2.5.2) and (2.5.3).

Liouville's Theorem

Consider the collection of replicas which at time t occupy the region D_t whose volume is V_t,

$$V_t = \int_{D_t} dy. \tag{2.5.5}$$

At a later time t', the same collection of replicas will occupy a different region

---

[19] We are paralleling, to some degree, the kinematic terminology and notation of three-dimensional continuum mechanics as outlined in Section 1.2. [The utility of this terminology and viewpoint in this connection has been noted by Grad (1950).] A complete parallel would require the notation Y_L for the Lagrangian coordinates, but this added complexity is not helpful here.

D_t, with volume V_t. We wish to compute dV_t/dt. The computation proceeds along the same lines as in ordinary three-dimensional continuum mechanics. In order to avoid the differentiation of an integral with the variable range of integration D_t, it is convenient to first change the variables of integration from Eulerian to Lagrangian. Then,

$$\frac{dV_t}{dt} = \frac{d}{dt}\int_{D_t} dy = \frac{d}{dt}\int_{D_0}\left|\frac{\partial y}{\partial Y}\right| dY = \int_{D_0}\frac{\partial}{\partial t}\left|\frac{\partial y}{\partial Y}\right| dY \qquad (2.5.6)$$

where $|\partial y/\partial Y|$ is the $2n \times 2n$ Jacobian determinant between the y_i and Y_j coordinates. Note that the Lagrangian coordinates Y_j always range over the fixed region D_0 and therefore the time derivative may be brought under the integral sign. The time derivative of the Jacobian may be computed by the usual rules for the differentiation of a determinant whose elements are functions of a parameter,

$$\frac{\partial}{\partial t}\left|\frac{\partial y}{\partial Y}\right| = \frac{\partial^2 y_i}{\partial t\,\partial Y_j} A_{ij} \qquad (2.5.7)$$

where A_{ij} is the cofactor of $\partial y_i/\partial Y_j$ in the determinant and where, as previously noted, the summation convention (with range of indices $i, j = 1,\dots, 2n$) is employed. We may now interchange the order of differentiation and change to Eulerian coordinates,

$$\frac{\partial^2 y_i}{\partial t\,\partial Y_j} A_{ij} = \frac{\partial}{\partial Y_j}\left(\frac{\partial y_i}{\partial t}(Y,t)\right)A_{ij} = \frac{\partial}{\partial Y_j}v_i(y,t)A_{ij} = \frac{\partial v_i}{\partial y_k}\frac{\partial y_k}{\partial Y_j}A_{ij} \qquad (2.5.8)$$

where Eq. (2.5.4) has been employed to relate the Lagrangian and Eulerian velocity descriptions. However, from the rule for expansion of a determinant in terms of cofactors,[20]

$$\frac{\partial y_k}{\partial Y_j}A_{ij} = \delta_{ik}\left|\frac{\partial y}{\partial Y}\right| \qquad (2.5.9)$$

and therefore,

$$\frac{\partial}{\partial t}\left|\frac{\partial y}{\partial Y}\right| = \frac{\partial v_i}{\partial y_i}\left|\frac{\partial y}{\partial Y}\right|. \qquad (2.5.10)$$

Substitution into Eq. (2.5.6) leads to the result:

$$\frac{dV_t}{dt} = \frac{d}{dt}\int_{D_t} dy = \int_{D_0}\frac{\partial v_i}{\partial y_i}\left|\frac{\partial y}{\partial Y}\right| dY = \int_{D_t}\frac{\partial v_i}{\partial y_i} dy \qquad (2.5.11)$$

---

[20] McConnell (1957, p. 17).

where in the last step we have reverted to Eulerian coordinates. We are thus led to the result, familiar in three-dimensional continuum mechanics, that $\partial v_i / \partial y_i$, the divergence of the velocity field, is the rate of change of volume per unit volume. In fact, with the use of the summation convention, the appearance of the derivation is identical to that of the three-dimensional case, although in this case the range of summation is from 1 to $2n$, and n may be of the order of 10^{23}.

To conclude Liouville's theorem, we next compute the divergence $\partial v_i / \partial y_i$ for the present case in which the velocity components v_i are determined by Hamilton's equations. We return, therefore, to (q, p) notation, recalling that $y_i = q_i$, $y_{i+n} = p_i$, $i = 1, \ldots, n$ and correspondingly, $v_i = \dot{q}_i$, $v_{i+n} = \dot{p}_i$, $i = 1, \ldots, n$. Therefore, making summations explicit,

$$\frac{\partial v_i}{\partial y_i} = \sum_{i=1}^{2n} \frac{\partial v_i}{\partial y_i} = \sum_{i=1}^{n} \left[\frac{\partial \dot{q}_i}{\partial q_i} + \frac{\partial \dot{p}_i}{\partial p_i} \right]$$

$$= \sum_{i=1}^{n} \left[\frac{\partial^2 H}{\partial q_i \partial p_i} - \frac{\partial^2 H}{\partial p_i \partial q_i} \right] = 0, \tag{2.5.12}$$

where we have used Hamilton's equations Eqs. (2.5.1), and the assumption of sufficiently regular H so that the mixed partials are equal.

This completes the proof of Liouville's theorem: The motion in its phase space of an ensemble of replicas of an isolated Hamiltonian system is volume preserving.

Liouville's Theorem in Terms of the Distribution Function ρ

Liouville's theorem may also be recast in terms of the distribution function ρ. As before, consider a given collection of replicas which at time t_1 occupy the region D_{t_1} and at time t_2 occupy the region D_{t_2} (Figure 2.6). In choosing the two regions D_{t_1} and D_{t_2} we have been following a given collection of replicas. We now recall, however, that the flow in phase space of an ensemble of replicas of an isolated system is steady, so that trajectories and streamlines are identical. We can regard the same two regions as fixed in phase space and consider the flow of a typical replica through these regions, letting a (Figure 2.6) be the point at which it enters D_{t_1}, b the point at which it leaves D_{t_1}, etc. Then, letting t_{ac} denote the time required for the replica to travel from a to c, etc., we see that

$$t_{ac} = t_{bd} = t_2 - t_1. \tag{2.5.13}$$

If we subtract t_{bc} from both sides of this equation, we obtain

$$t_{ab} = t_{cd}, \tag{2.5.14}$$

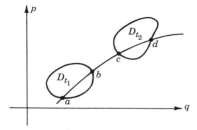

Figure 2.6 Motion of replicas.

that is, the fraction of time spent in D_{t_1} and D_{t_2} is the same. Therefore, from the property of $\rho(q, p)$ expressed in Eq. (2.4.9),

$$\frac{d}{dt} \int_{D_t} \rho(q, p) \, dq \, dp = 0, \qquad (2.5.15)$$

which may be restated in the compact y notation as

$$\frac{d}{dt} \int_{D_t} \rho(y) \, dy = 0. \qquad (2.5.16)$$

Eq. (2.5.16) has the appearance of the principle of the conservation of mass in three-dimensional continuum mechanics. By calculations which are identical to those in continuum mechanics, we are led to the equation of continuity for ρ:

$$\frac{\partial \rho}{\partial t} + \frac{\partial}{\partial y_r}(\rho v_r) = 0 \qquad (2.5.17)$$

or

$$\frac{d\rho}{dt} + \rho \frac{\partial v_r}{\partial y_r} = 0 \qquad (2.5.18)$$

where

$$\frac{d\rho}{dt} = \frac{\partial \rho}{\partial t} + v_r \frac{\partial \rho}{\partial y_r} \qquad (2.5.19)$$

is the material derivative.[21]

We now use the result that $\partial v_r / \partial y_r = 0$ for an ensemble of replicas of an isolated system. Therefore, from Eq. (2.5.19),

$$\frac{d\rho}{dt} = 0, \qquad (2.5.20)$$

[21] In order to retain the familiar appearance of these equations, we have retained the term $\partial \rho / \partial t$ in them, although it vanishes for the distribution function $\rho(q, p)$ of equilibrium statistical mechanics. See also the discussion of the ensemble viewpoint in Section 2.8 in which another interpretation is given to Eq. (2.5.16).

that is, ρ is constant along the trajectory of an isolated system. This is an alternate statement of Liouville's theorem.

Constant Energy Surfaces

Consider the variation of $H(q, p)$ along the trajectory of an isolated system:

$$\frac{dH}{dt} = \sum_{i=1}^{n} \left[\frac{\partial H}{\partial q_i} \dot{q}_i + \frac{\partial H}{\partial p_i} \dot{p}_i \right] = \sum_{i=1}^{n} \left[\frac{\partial H}{\partial q_i} \frac{\partial H}{\partial p_i} - \frac{\partial H}{\partial p_i} \frac{\partial H}{\partial q_i} \right] = 0 \quad (2.5.21)$$

by the use of Hamilton's equations, Eqs. (2.5.1). Therefore $H(q, p) = E$, a constant, along the trajectory of an isolated system. Furthermore, for the systems we are considering, E is the total energy of the system.

It follows that an isolated system with n degrees of freedom (and therefore a $2n$-dimensional phase space Γ) follows a trajectory which is confined to the $2n - 1$ dimensional hypersurface $S = S(E)$ defined by the equation $H(q, p) = E$.

$\rho = C$ on S

We would like to conclude next that, for an isolated system with energy E, the distribution function ρ is constant on S.

It is easy to provide a heuristic basis for this conclusion. By Liouville's theorem, ρ is constant along a trajectory of the system. If, because of the system's size and complexity, we assume that any of its trajectories will, in some sense, wander all over S, then the invariance of ρ on any trajectory should imply its invariance on S.

Two difficulties arise in a rigorous treatment:

1 The precise characterization of the wandering character of the system trajectories on S so that this behavior implies the conclusion that $\rho = C$ on S.

2. The demonstration that broad classes of mechanical systems, including those of physical interest, have trajectories which satisfy this characterization.

The first attempt at part **1** was made by Boltzmann (1871a, b) who postulated that the system trajectory passed through every point of S, that is, that there is only a single trajectory and the surface S consists of the set of points of this trajectory. This postulate, termed the ergodic hypothesis by Boltzmann (1887), was proved false on topological grounds by Rosenthal (1913) and by Plancherel (1913).

A satisfactory characterization was provided by the work of Birkhoff, von Neumann, and Koopman[22] in the early 1930s which led to the concept of a metrically indecomposable energy surface. For brevity, we will speak of the volume of a $2n - 1$ dimensional region in the hypersurface S as an area. S is said to be metrically indecomposable[23] if it is not possible to express it as the sum of two regions S_1 and S_2, each with nonzero area,[24] such that a trajectory that begins in S_1 always stays in S_1 and a trajectory that begins in S_2 always stays in S_2.

To simplify the demonstration that this characterization serves the desired purpose, we add the assumption that the distribution function is continuous on S. It then follows that $\rho(y)$ is constant on S. To prove this result, assume the contrary, that is, assume that there exist points P_1' and P_2' on S with the property that $\rho(P_1') \neq \rho(P_2')$. By the continuity of ρ we may express S as the sum $S = S_1 + S_2$ with $P_1' \in S_1$ and $P_2' \in S_2$ and with S_1, S_2 of nonzero area, such that $\rho(P_1) \neq \rho(P_2)$ for P_1 any point interior to S_1 and P_2 any point interior to S_2. Since, by hypothesis, S is metrically indecomposable, a trajectory starting from P_1' will pass through S_2. However, by Liouville's theorem, ρ is constant along a trajectory. Therefore, a contradiction has been reached and we can conclude that $\rho(y)$ is, in fact, a constant on S.

We turn next to part **2**: to what extent do mechanical systems satisfy the characterization of metric indecomposability?

As a very simple, but trivial, example of a mechanical system with a metrically indecomposable constant energy surface, consider a harmonic oscillator with Hamiltonian

$$H(q, p) = \frac{p^2}{2m} + \tfrac{1}{2}\kappa q^2. \tag{2.5.22}$$

In this case $n = 1$, and the constant energy "hypersurface" S has dimension $2n - 1 = 1$, that is, it is a curve, namely, an ellipse (Figure 2.8). Since every trajectory, no matter where it starts, must travel completely around the ellipse, S is clearly metrically indecomposable. The same argument applies to any system with one degree of freedom and closed, periodic orbits.

On the other hand, consider the system consisting of two, uncoupled, harmonic oscillators,

$$H(q_1, q_2, p_1, p_2) = H_1(q_1, p_1) + H_2(q_2, p_2) \tag{2.5.23}$$

with

$$H_i(q_i, p_i) = \frac{p_i^2}{2m_i} + \tfrac{1}{2}\kappa_i q_i^2 \text{(no sum)}, \qquad i = 1, 2. \tag{2.5.24}$$

---

[22] See, for example, the account in Mackey (1974, pp. 178–179).
[23] The term metrically transitive is also used.
[24] A mathematically rigorous treatment requires the concept of an appropriate measure (see Khinchin, 1949); hence, the terminology metrically indecomposable.

In this case the hypersurface S corresponding to $H(q, p) = E$ is three-dimensional and is not metrically undecomposable. It can be decomposed by writing, for example, $S = S_1 + S_2$ where (in usual set-theoretic notation)

$$S_1 = \{y: H_1(y) \leqslant E^*, H_2(y) = E - H_1(y)\}$$

$$S_2 = \{y: E^* < H_1(y) \leqslant E, H_2(y) = E - H_1(y)\} \qquad (2.5.25)$$

where $0 < E^* < E$ is arbitrary, but fixed. Since the oscillators are uncoupled, the energy of each is conserved and it is clear, therefore, that a trajectory which begins in S_1 will stay in S_1, and similarly for S_2.

We see from this simple example that there must be some interaction between the components of a compound system if the energy surfaces of the latter are to be metrically indecomposable. However, this is not sufficient and the formulation of general conditions on mechanical systems for which this property follows remains a difficult and open problem. We will return to a brief discussion of some recent work in this area in Section 2.8. For the present, we continue on the basis of the assumption that we are dealing with systems for which the conclusion $\rho = C$ on S is valid.

Microcanonical Distribution

It must be recalled at this time that the ergodic interpretation of the distribution function $\rho(q, p) = \rho(y)$ referred to the fraction of time that the system spent per unit *volume* at any point in the $2n$-dimensional phase space. The fact that $\rho(y)$ is constant on the constant energy surface S does not imply, therefore, that the isolated system spends equal times in equal *areas* of S. To see that this is not the case, consider an isolated system with Hamiltonian $H(y)$ and energy E_0. Its trajectory is then confined to the $2n - 1$ dimensional hypersurface $S(E_0)$ defined by the equation $H(y) = E_0$. In order to make use of the volume interpretation of $\rho(y)$, we regard the given system as part of an ensemble of replicas with energy in the interval $E_0 \leqslant E \leqslant E_0 + \Delta$. This ensemble will move in the shell $\Sigma(E_0, \Delta)$ confined between the surfaces $S(E_0)$ and $S(E_0 + \Delta)$, that is,

$$\Sigma(E_0, \Delta) = \{y: E_0 \leqslant H(y) \leqslant E_0 + \Delta\} \qquad (2.5.26)$$

as shown schematically in Figure 2.7. Consider the collection of replicas of this ensemble which at time t_1 occupies the region D_{t_1} and at time t_2 occupies the region D_{t_2}. Let a_1 be the area of the portion of $S(E_0)$ which forms a boundary of D_{t_1} and a_2 the corresponding boundary of D_{t_2}. By Liouville's theorem, the volumes of D_{t_1} and D_{t_2} are equal and the system spends equal time in each. It follows that it will spend more time per unit *area* of $S(E_0)$ at a point (such as at a_2 in Figure 2.7) where the surfaces $S(E_0)$ and $S(E_0 + \Delta)$ are far apart, than at a point (such as at a_1) where they are close together.

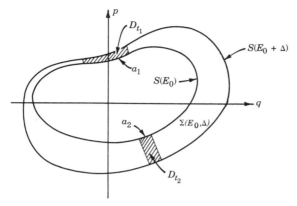

Figure 2.7 Shell $\Sigma(E_0, \Delta)$ between two constant-energy surfaces.

In order to produce a $(2n - 1)$-dimensional distribution function which is defined on $S(E_0)$ and which varies in this manner, it is easiest to start with a $2n$-dimensional distribution function $\rho(y)$ defined as uniform over the shell $\Sigma(E_0, \Delta)$ defined in Eq. (2.5.26) (and zero elsewhere in Γ) and then let $\Delta \to 0$. Let ΔV be the volume of the shell $\Sigma(E_0, \Delta)$. Then, in order that $\rho(y)$ be normalized to unity over Γ, we define

$$\rho(y) = \frac{1}{\Delta V}, \qquad y \in \Sigma(E_0, \Delta)$$

$$= 0, \qquad y \notin \Sigma(E_0, \Delta). \tag{2.5.27}$$

We can now give the prescription for computing the phase average $\bar{F}$ for any phase function $F(y)$ appropriate to the given isolated system:

$$\bar{F} = \lim_{\Delta \to 0} \int_{\Gamma} \rho(y) F(y) \, dy = \lim_{\Delta \to 0} \int_{\Sigma(E_0, \Delta)} \rho(y) F(y) \, dy$$

$$= \lim_{\Delta \to 0} \frac{1}{\Delta V} \int_{\Sigma(E_0, \Delta)} F(y) \, dy. \tag{2.5.28}$$

The distribution function defined on $S(E_0)$ by this limiting process has been termed microcanonical by Gibbs. The limiting process may be carried further. In all of our work we assume that the energy of the system under consideration is bounded from below and the reference level chosen so that $E \geqslant 0$. Choose the origin of the phase space Γ so that $H(0) = 0$ and define the set V_E as

$$V_E = \{y : H(y) \leqslant E\} \tag{2.5.29}$$

and further denote the volume of the region V_E as $V(E)$. Then Eq. (2.5.28) for the phase average based on the microcanonical distribution corresponding to energy E can be rewritten as follows:

$$\bar{F} = \lim_{\Delta \to 0} \frac{\int_{V_{E+\Delta}} F(y)\, dy - \int_{V_E} F(y)\, dy}{\int_{V_{E+\Delta}} dy - \int_{V_E} dy}$$

$$= \frac{\lim_{\Delta \to 0} \frac{1}{\Delta}\left[\int_{V_{E+\Delta}} F(y)\, dy - \int_{V_E} F(y)\, dy\right]}{\lim_{\Delta \to 0} \frac{1}{\Delta}[V(E + \Delta) - V(E)]}$$

$$= \frac{\frac{d}{dE} \int_{V_E} F(y)\, dy}{V'(E)} = \frac{1}{\Omega(E)} \frac{d}{dE} \int_{V_E} F(y)\, dy \qquad (2.5.30)$$

where $V' = dV/dE$ and

$$\Omega(E) = V'(E) \qquad (2.5.31)$$

has been termed by Khinchin the *structure function* of the system. It plays an important role in subsequent computations. We note here, for example, that it may be used to simplify the evaluation of volume integrals for phase functions $F(y)$ that depend on y only through $H(y)$, that is, $F(y) = f(H(y)) = f(E)$, where we have written $H(y) = E$. Then, in computing the integral

$$\int_{V_E} F(y)\, dy,$$

we can subdivide V_E into shells in each of which $H(y)$ is constant and write (as in using spherical coordinates in the integration of a function of the radial distance r alone),

$$\int_{V_E} F(y)\, dy = \int_0^E f(E)V'(E)\, dE = \int_0^E f(E)\Omega(E)\, dE. \qquad (2.5.32)$$

Example:

As a simple example to help make the formalism of this section more concrete, consider the microcanonical distribution for a harmonic oscillator corresponding to the Hamiltonian of Eq. (2.5.22) and energy E. Then the region V_E is the interior of the ellipse (Figure 2.8) defined by the equation $H(q, p) = E$ and, since the area of an ellipse with major and minor axes

a, b is πab, $V(E) = 2\pi\sqrt{m/\kappa}\, E$ so that $\Omega(E) = V'(E) = 2\pi\sqrt{m/\kappa} = 2\pi/\omega$ $= t_p$, its period of oscillation. Consider next a property of the system described by a phase function $F(q)$. From Eq. (2.5.30), its microcanonical phase average is

$$\bar{F} = \frac{1}{\Omega(E)} \frac{d}{dE} \int_{V_E} F(q)\, dq\, dp = \frac{1}{t_p}\frac{d}{dE} 2\int_{-\sqrt{2E/\kappa}}^{\sqrt{2E/\kappa}} F(q) p(q)\, dq \quad (2.5.33)$$

where

$$p(q) = +\left[2m\left(E - \frac{\kappa}{2}q^2\right)\right]^{1/2} \quad (2.5.34)$$

and where we are using the symmetry of the integral about $p = 0$. By carrying out the indicated differentiation we find

$$\bar{F} = \frac{2}{t_p}\int_{-\sqrt{2E/\kappa}}^{+\sqrt{2E/\kappa}} \frac{F(q)}{\left[2m^{-1}\left(E - \frac{\kappa}{2}q^2\right)\right]^{1/2}}\, dq. \quad (2.5.35)$$

For this simple example we may show directly that the phase average $\bar{F} = \hat{F}$, the time average. By virtue of periodicity and symmetry, we can confine attention to the time average of $F(q)$ when q goes from $-\sqrt{2E/\kappa}$ (when we set $t = 0$) to $+\sqrt{2E/\kappa}$ at time $t = t_p/2$, so that

$$\hat{F} = \frac{2}{t_p}\int_0^{t_p/2} F(q(t))\, dt. \quad (2.5.36)$$

This time integral may be rewritten as one with respect to q as

$$\hat{F} = \frac{2}{t_p}\int_{-\sqrt{2E/\kappa}}^{+\sqrt{2E/\kappa}} \frac{F(q)}{\dot{q}}\, dq, \quad (2.5.37)$$

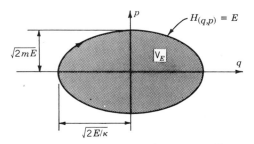

Figure 2.8   Region V_E for harmonic oscillator.

and since $\dot{q} = [2m^{-1}(E - (\kappa/2)q^2)]^{1/2}$, we see that $\hat{F} = \bar{F}$. This argument may be generalized readily to other systems with one degree of freedom and periodic closed orbits.

2.6 SYSTEMS IN WEAK INTERACTION

We next consider an isolated system $A + B$, which is composed of two separate systems A and B. An example is provided by a crystal A surrounded by a gas B with the combination surrounded in turn by an isolating envelope (Figure 2.2). Let y_A denote the coordinates and momenta of system A, etc. Then, the Hamiltonian $H_{A+B}(y_A, y_B)$ can be written in the form

$$H_{A+B}(y_A, y_B) = H_A(y_A) + H_B(y_B) + H_{AB}(y_A, y_B) \qquad (2.6.1)$$

where $H_A(y_A)$ is the Hamiltonian which would control system A if it were isolated and similarly for $H_B(y_B)$. $H_{AB}(y_A, y_B)$ describes the interaction between A and B. Generally $H_{AB}(y_A, y_B) = V_{AB}(q_A, q_B)$; that is, it is the potential energy of interaction between the two systems and does not involve the momenta.[25]

The two systems A and B are said to be in *weak interaction* if H_{AB} may be neglected in the computation of any integral over phase space and if, for this purpose alone, we may write

$$H_{A+B}(y_A, y_B) = H_A(y_A) + H_B(y_B). \qquad (2.6.2)$$

For example, for the case of crystal A surrounded by gas B, there are configurations in which many of the gas atoms are very close to the crystal's surface and interact strongly with it. However, such configurations occupy a very small volume in the phase space Γ_{A+B} and may be neglected in a volume integration. Furthermore, if we plan to focus attention on subsystem A, it is only necessary that the part of the interaction energy between A and B which depends explicitly on the (time-dependent) coordinates y_B be small;[26] any portion of the interaction energy which is independent of the y_B may be incorporated in H_A.

It must be emphasized that although the interaction H_{AB} is omitted in volume integrations, it is essential from a conceptual viewpoint that H_{AB} not be zero identically; for then, systems A and B would be completely uncoupled and the constant energy surfaces for the combined system $A + B$ would not be

---

[25] An example of kinematical coupling which does involve the momenta is provided by a model of a polymer chain. See Section 9.4.

[26] The point that only the variable portion of H_{AB} must be small has been emphasized by Gibbs (1902, p. 37), and plays an important role in the discussion of controllable parameters (Sections 4.3 and 4.7).

metrically indecomposable.[27] That is, even though H_{AB} may be neglected in the computation of phase integrals, it has a significant effect on the trajectory of the combined system $A + B$. This point is discussed further in Section 7.6.

Structure Function of Systems in Weak Interaction

As previously discussed (Section 2.4), the phase space Γ_{A+B} (with coordinates[28] (y_A, y_B)) of the combined system $A + B$ is the Cartesian product of space Γ_A (with coordinates y_A) and space Γ_B (with coordinates y_B). In the space Γ_{A+B} consider the region

$$V_E^{A+B} = \{(y_A, y_B): H_{A+B}(y_A, y_B) \leqslant E\}. \qquad (2.6.3)$$

If systems A and B are in weak interaction, we may write equivalently:

$$V_E^{A+B} = \{(y_A, y_B): H_A(y_A) + H_B(y_B) \leqslant E\} \qquad (2.6.4)$$

since we will be using these regions only for purposes of volume integration. We may express $V_{A+B}(E)$, the volume of the region V_E^{A+B} in Γ_{A+B}, as (see Figure 2.9):

$$V_{A+B}(E) = \int_{V_E^A}\left(\int_{V_{E-H_A(y_A)}^B} dy_B\right) dy_A = \int_{V_E^A} V_B(E - H_A(y_A)) \, dy_A. \qquad (2.6.5)$$

Equation (2.6.5) provides an example of a volume integral whose integrand depends on y_A only through $H_A(y_A)$. Therefore, as discussed on p. 70, the structure function $\Omega_A(E_A)$ may be used to rewrite the volume integral as the one-dimensional integral,

$$V_{A+B}(E) = \int_0^E V_B(E - E_A)\Omega_A(E_A) \, dE_A. \qquad (2.6.6)$$

Differentiate Eq. (2.6.6) with respect to E. The derivative with respect to the upper limit vanishes since $V_B(0) = 0$, and the result is

$$\Omega_{A+B}(E) = \int_0^E \Omega_B(E - E_A)\Omega_A(E_A) \, dE_A. \qquad (2.6.7)$$

We have, therefore, the elegant relation (Khinchin, 1949) that the structure function of a composite system consisting of two systems in weak interaction is the convolution of the structure functions of the subsystems.

[27]See the discussion of uncoupled harmonic oscillators on p. 67.
[28]When the abbreviated notation y is employed instead of (q, p), we refer simply to the coordinates y, although they represent, of course, both coordinates and momenta of the mechanical system.

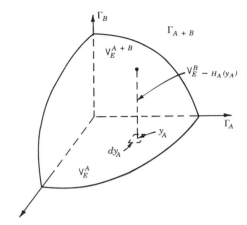

Figure 2.9 Schematic illustration for Eq. (2.6.5).

Distribution Function for Component of an Isolated System

We continue with our discussion of the composite system $A + B$ which is isolated with a total fixed energy E. Since it is an isolated system we know (Section 2.5) that its distribution function $\rho_{A+B}(y_A, y_B)$ is microcanonical. It is defined by Eq. (2.5.30) through the relation

$$\int_{\Gamma_{A+B}} F_{A+B}(y_A, y_B) \rho_{A+B}(y_A, y_B)\, dy_A\, dy_B$$

$$\triangleq \frac{1}{\Omega_{A+B}(E)} \frac{d}{dE} \int_{V_E^{A+B}} F_{A+B}(y_A, y_B)\, dy_A\, dy_B \qquad (2.6.8)$$

where $F_{A+B}(y_A, y_B)$ is an arbitrary phase function. The function $\rho_{A+B}(y_A, y_B)$ describes the fraction of time which the composite system $A + B$ spends in any portion of the phase space Γ_{A+B}. Therefore, the fraction of time that the component A spends in a region Γ_A can be obtained by integration over Γ_B:

$$\rho_A(y_A) = \int_{\Gamma_B} \rho_{A+B}(y_A, y_B)\, dy_B. \qquad (2.6.9)$$

Since in place of a specific functional form for the microcanonical distribution ρ_{A+B}, we have the prescription for computing phase averages of Eq. (2.6.8), we do not evaluate $\rho_A(y_A)$ directly by means of Eq. (2.6.9) but use the following indirect procedure.

It is clear that $\rho_A(y_A) = 0$ for $y_A \notin V_E^A$, since system A cannot have[29] more energy than the combined system $A + B$. Let M_A be an arbitrary region in V_E^A

---

[29]Recall that the energy datum for any system is chosen so that energy values are nonnegative.

and let $\phi(y_A)$ be its characteristic function, that is:

$$\phi(y_A) = 1 \text{ for } y_A \in M_A$$

$$= 0 \text{ for } y_A \notin M_A. \qquad (2.6.10)$$

Then

$$\int_{M_A} \rho_A(y_A) \, dy_A = \int_{\Gamma_A} \phi(y_A)\rho_A(y_A) \, dy_A$$

$$= \int_{\Gamma_A} \phi(y_A) \int_{\Gamma_B} \rho_{A+B}(y_A, y_B) \, dy_B \, dy_A$$

$$= \int_{\Gamma_{A+B}} \phi(y_A)\rho_{A+B}(y_A, y_B) \, dy_B \, dy_A \qquad (2.6.11)$$

where we have used Eq. (2.6.9). Since ρ_{A+B} corresponds to a microcanonical ensemble with energy E, the phase average of $\phi(y_A)$ in Eq. (2.6.11) is computed as in Eq. (2.6.8):

$$\int_{M_A} \rho_A(y_A) \, dy_A = \frac{1}{\Omega_{A+B}(E)} \frac{d}{dE} \int_{V_E^{A+B}} \phi(y_A) \, dy_A \, dy_B. \qquad (2.6.12)$$

However (see Figure 2.9),

$$\int_{V_E^{A+B}} \phi(y_A) \, dy_A \, dy_B = \int_{V_E^{A}} \phi(y_A) \, dy_A \int_{V_{E-E_A}^{B}} dy_B$$

$$= \int_{V_E^{A}} \phi(y_A) V_B(E - E_A) \, dy_A = \int_{M_A} V_B(E - E_A) \, dy_A,$$

$$(2.6.13)$$

where $E_A(y_A) = H_A(y_A)$. Substituting Eq. (2.6.13) into Eq. (2.6.12) and carrying out the indicated differentiation, we obtain

$$\int_{M_A} \rho_A(y_A) \, dy_A = \frac{1}{\Omega_{A+B}(E)} \int_{M_A} \Omega_B(E - E_A) \, dy_A. \qquad (2.6.14)$$

Since Eq. (2.6.14) applies for an arbitrary region M_A we conclude that

$$\rho_A(y_A) = \frac{\Omega_B(E - E_A)}{\Omega_{A+B}(E)} = \frac{\Omega_B(E - H_A(y_A))}{\Omega_{A+B}(E)} \qquad \text{for } y_A \in V_E^A$$

$$= 0 \qquad \text{for } y_A \notin V_E^A. \qquad (2.6.15)$$

It is seen that $\rho_A(y_A)$ depends on y_A only through the function $H_A(y_A)$; therefore, it may be verified easily as follows that it is normalized to unity over Γ_A.

$$\int_{\Gamma_A} \rho_A(y_A)\, dy_A = \int_{V_E^A} \rho_A(y_A)\, dy_A = \frac{1}{\Omega_{A+B}(E)} \int_0^E \Omega_B(E - E_A)\Omega_A(E_A)\, dE_A$$

$$= 1 \tag{2.6.16}$$

where Eq. (2.5.32), to convert the volume integral to an integral over E_A, and Eq. (2.6.7), the convolution property of the structure functions, have been employed.

2.7 CANONICAL DISTRIBUTION

The discussion of the previous section did not depend on the relative sizes or numbers of degrees of freedom of the two components A and B. We now assume that B has a very large number of degrees of freedom. In fact we will ultimately let $n_B \to \infty$. We will also draw on the experience that a system, such as crystal A, in weak interaction with an ambient such as gas B, has macroscopic equilibrium properties that do not depend on all the atomistic features of B. For example, the macroscopic properties of a given crystal in an ambient of air at 70°C will be same if the air is replaced by a bath of argon at the same temperature.[30] To arrive at the distribution function for system A in the simplest manner, therefore, we take[31] the ambient B as an ideal simple monatomic gas of $n/3$ atoms confined in a cube of edge L. An ideal gas is one that is sufficiently dilute that the energy of interaction between atoms may be neglected, that is, the individual atoms themselves may be regarded as systems in weak interaction with each other in the sense of Section 2.6. The only potential energy term in the Hamiltonian of B, therefore, is that representing the effect of the confining container on the atoms of the gas:

$$V_B(q) = 0 \text{ for all particles in box,}$$

$$= \infty \text{ if any particle outside of box,} \tag{2.7.1}$$

---

[30] Note that this indifference to the exact nature of the ambient applies only when the interaction between the component and the ambient may be properly characterized as weak. For example, the behavior of a crystal of sodium in an ambient of argon and one of oxygen will be radically different, even though both ambients are at the same temperature.

[31] We introduce physical experience as a guide here in order to simplify the presentation. Khinchin (1949) has shown that it is possible to arrive at the same distribution for a much more general class of ambients B, ambients that consist of an arbitrarily large number of subsystems of quite general character which are in weak interaction with each other. His derivation makes use of the convolution property of subsystems in weak interaction, (Eq. 2.6.7), and the central limit theorem of probability (Section 5.4).

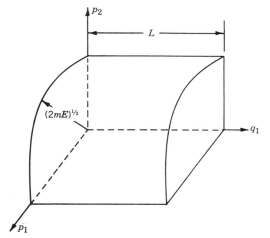

Figure 2.10 Schematic of region V_E for perfect gas.

which is the statement that it requires an infinite amount of work to remove an atom from the box.[32] The kinetic energy of the gas B is

$$K_B(p) = \frac{1}{2m} \sum_{i=1}^{n} p_i^2 \qquad (2.7.2)$$

where m is the atomic mass. By definition, the region V_E^B in the phase space Γ_B is that in which $H_B(q, p) = V_B(q) + K_B(p) \leqslant E$ and is seen to be the Cartesian product of an n-dimensional hypercube with side L in q-space and an n-dimensional hypersphere of radius $(2mE)^{1/2}$ in p-space (Figure 2.10). The volume of the hypercube is L^n and the volume of the hypersphere[33] is proportional to $E^{n/2}$. Since only the nature of the dependence on E concerns us here we may write

$$V_B(E) = C'E^{n/2} \qquad (2.7.3)$$

and therefore

$$\Omega_B(E) = CE^{(n/2)-1}. \qquad (2.7.4)$$

It is convenient at this point to recast Eq. (2.6.15) for $\rho_A(y_A)$ in the form

$$\rho_A(y_A) = \frac{\Omega_B(E)}{\Omega_{A+B}(E)} \frac{\Omega_B(E - E_A)}{\Omega_B(E)}$$

$$= C \frac{\Omega_B(E - E_A)}{\Omega_B(E)} \qquad (2.7.5)$$

[32] Note that this definition of V_B introduces the imposed volume v into the Hamiltonian of the gas.

[33] The volume of a hypersphere of dimension n and radius R is $\dfrac{2\pi^{n/2}R^n}{n\Gamma(n/2)}$.

where

$$C = \frac{\Omega_B(E)}{\Omega_{A+B}(E)} \qquad (2.7.6)$$

is independent of E_A and may be regarded as a parameter to be determined subsequently by the requirement that $\rho_A(y_A)$ is normalized to unity[34] over Γ_A. Substitution of Eq. (2.7.4) into Eq. (2.7.5) leads to

$$\rho_A(y_A) = C\left(1 - \frac{E_A}{E}\right)^{(n/2)-1}. \qquad (2.7.7)$$

Let

$$\frac{E}{n} = \frac{\theta}{2}; \qquad (2.7.8)$$

that is, $\theta/2$ is the energy of $A + B$ per number of degrees of freedom (or number of p_i^2 terms) of B. Then

$$\rho_A(y_A) = C\left(1 - \frac{2E_A}{n\theta}\right)^{(n/2)-1}. \qquad (2.7.9)$$

We now take the limit of this expression as $n \to \infty$ with θ maintained constant. In this limit

$$\rho_A(y_A) = Ce^{-E_A/\theta}, \qquad (2.7.10)$$

which, since $E_A = H_A(y_A)$, may be written also as

$$\rho_A(y_A) = Ce^{-H_A(y_A)/\theta} \qquad (2.7.11)$$

and describes what Gibbs has termed the canonical distribution. It applies to an arbitrary system A in weak interaction with a large ambient B. There is no restriction on the size of system A.

The canonical distribution forms the basis of much of our later work. Several remarks concerning it are in order here:

1 As originally introduced, the parameter $\theta/2$ was the energy of $A + B$ divided by n, the number of degrees of freedom, or of p_i^2 terms, in B. As $n \to \infty$ with θ fixed, the energy of B becomes infinite and the parameter $\theta/2$ represents the energy of B per degree of freedom of B.

---

[34]As we have seen earlier [Eq. (2.6.16)], the definition of C given in Eq. (2.7.6) leads automatically to the proper normalization of ρ_A. However, it is simpler in the following to determine the value of C directly by the normalization requirement.

2 It may appear strange at first glance that $\rho_A(y_A)$ decays monotonically with $E_A = H_A(y_A)$, seeming to imply that the system spends progressively less time in regions corresponding to higher energies. However, it must be emphasized that ρ_A is the fraction of time spent in a region, *per unit volume* of that region of phase space, and account must be taken of the fact that the volume of phase space corresponding to a given energy interval increases with energy in a manner described by the structure function of the system. Since $\rho_A(y_A)$ depends on y_A only through $H_A(y_A)$, the fraction of time spent by system A in the interval $E_1 \leqslant E_A \leqslant E_2$ is

$$\int_{V_{E_2}} \rho_A(y_A)\, dy_A - \int_{V_{E_1}} \rho_A(y_A)\, dy_A = \int_{E_1}^{E_2} \rho_A(E_A)\Omega_A(E_A)\, dE_A = \int_{E_1}^{E_2} W_A(E_A)\, dE_A$$

$$(2.7.12)$$

where

$$W_A(E_A) = \rho_A(E_A)\Omega_A(E_A) \qquad (2.7.13)$$

is the fraction of time *per unit energy* that system A spends in a given energy interval. The functional form of the structure function depends on the detailed nature of the system, but in general it will be an increasing function of energy with the rate of increase depending on the number of degrees of freedom. For example, if system A is also an ideal gas with n_A degrees of freedom, then $\Omega_A(E) = CE^{(n_A/2)-1}$ and

$$W_A(E_A) = CE_A^{(n_A/2)-1}e^{-E_A/\theta} \qquad (2.7.14)$$

with derivative with respect to E_A given by

$$W_A'(E_A) = \left[\left(\frac{n_A}{2} - 1\right)E_A^{-1} - \theta^{-1}\right]W_A(E_A). \qquad (2.7.15)$$

Therefore, the maximum value of $W_A(E_A)$ occurs at

$$E_A = \left(\frac{n_A}{2} - 1\right)\theta, \qquad (2.7.16)$$

so that for large n_A, the energy per degree of freedom of system A which occurs with maximum probability is equal to the energy per degree of freedom of system B. The form of $W_A(E_A)$ is shown in Figure 2.11 for large and small values of n_A. It is seen that for large n_A, the function W_A is very sharply peaked so that the system A spends most of its time in the vicinity of the maximum probability energy, while for small n_A the fluctuations in energy of system A are much larger.[35]

---

[35] Fluctuations are discussed further in Section 3.9.

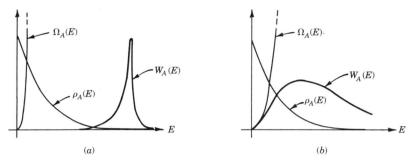

(a)   *(b)*

Figure 2.11 Schematic behavior of $W_A(E)$, Eq. (2.7.13), for n_A large (*a*) and for n_A small (*b*).

2.8 TIME AVERAGES VERSUS ENSEMBLE AVERAGES

We have arrived, in Eq. (2.7.11), at the general form of the canonical distribution function which describes a system in macroscopic equilibrium in weak interaction with a large ambient. By its use we can predict the observed values of any macroscopic property of the system by computing the phase average of the appropriate phase function corresponding to this property.

While there is no disagreement as to the fundamental correctness of this calculation procedure, there are conflicting ways in which the phase average is interpreted, and to these different interpretations correspond, as well, different paths for arriving at the final result. In our development, we have identified the phase average with the time average of the corresponding property as determined by a measurement on the system over a time interval that is short on a macroscopic time scale but is very long on the microscopic time scale, and we have used this interpretation in order to motivate the reasoning by which the canonical distribution was obtained.

As noted in the introduction to this chapter, our work does not deal with the foundations of statistical mechanics but with one of its applications, and our account of the path to the canonical distribution is intended primarily for the purpose of providing a valuable physical picture underlying the calculation procedure. Nevertheless, it is appropriate to consider briefly[36] here some of the difficulties that, at this time, are seen to stand in the way of a rigorous development of the basic principles of the subject based on this time-average viewpoint.

(a) Ergodic Behavior of Isolated Systems

The replacement, for isolated systems, of time averages by phase averages based on the microcanonical distribution is a key step in the development of the canonical distribution as we have presented it. We arrived at the micro-

---

[36]A more extensive recent account will be found in Penrose (1979) and in the numerous references cited therein.

canonical ensemble by assuming that the constant energy surfaces of the system were metrically indecomposable. When this concept was introduced by Birkhoff in the early 1930s, it was believed by him and others[37] that it would be possible in due course to prove that broad classes of mechanical systems have this property. Not only was such a proof not forthcoming, but this optimistic view received severe setbacks in the mid-1950s by the computer experiments of Fermi, Pasta, and Ulam (1955), which showed nonergodic behavior in a system of nonlinearly coupled oscillators, and by the theoretical work of Kolmogoroff, Arnold, and Moser over the period 1954–1962, work that is now often referred to as the KAM theorem.[38] This theorem shows that for broad classes of Hamiltonians the constant energy surfaces $S(E)$ will not be metrically indecomposable for sufficiently low values of the system energy E.

There have, however, been more recent developments on the positive side. One of these is the proof announced by Sinai (1963) that a system of N hard spheres[39] enclosed in a cube with perfectly reflecting walls is ergodic. Also, greater insight has been obtained into another attribute of the motion of some mechanical systems, an attribute described as mixing. A simple example[40] will serve to illustrate this property.

Consider a single particle constrained to move in the x direction, confined between perfectly reflecting walls at $x = 0$ and $x = L$ but otherwise free of imposed forces. As in Section 2.5, we consider a collection of replicas of the particle which are contained between two constant energy surfaces which in this case we can describe equally well as corresponding to constant momentum with absolute values $|p_0|$ and $|p_0 + \Delta|$. The region, $\Sigma(p_0, \Delta)$, in which the replicas move is the interior of the two rectangles, $0 < x < L$, $p_0 < |p| < p_0 + \Delta$; see Figure 2.12, which may be compared with Figure 2.7.

We next focus attention on a subset of replicas that at time t_0 occupy the rectangle D_{t_0}: $a \leqslant x \leqslant a + \delta$, $p_0 \leqslant p \leqslant p_0 + \Delta$. It is easy to verify that at later instants of time, t_i, this same collection of replicas will occupy the regions D_{t_i} shown in Figure 2.12 for a few representative times. Note that Liouville's theorem is satisfied in that the areas of D_{t_i} are all equal.

Of particular interest is the region D_{t_4} at a time t_4 after many collisions with the wall have occurred. We see that the original region D_{t_0}, although its area remains unchanged, has been spread almost uniformly over the region $\Sigma(p_0, \Delta)$. If we select any rectangle M in Σ, then in the limit as $t \to \infty$ we have

$$\lim_{t \to \infty} \frac{D_t \cap M}{M} = \frac{D_0}{\Sigma} \qquad (2.8.1)$$

---

[37]See, for example, the brief discussion by Smale (1980).
[38]See Penrose (1979) for a brief discussion and for further references.
[39]This term refers to a model for a gas in which the atoms are regarded as spheres which undergo elastic collisions; there is no attractive potential between the atoms.
[40]This example appears as a problem in Kotkin and Serbo (1971).

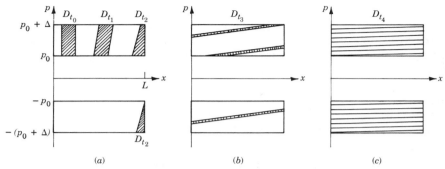

Figure 2.12 Motion of collection of replicas confined between reflecting walls at $x = 0$ and $x = L$. (a) Regions D_{t_0}, D_{t_1}, D_{t_2} occupied by collection of replicas at initial time t_0, at time t_1 before any collisions with walls have occurred, and at time t_2 when some of the replicas have collided with wall at $x = L$. (b) Region D_{t_3} at time t_3 when collisions with both walls have occurred. (c) Region D_{t_4} at time t_4 when many collisions have occurred.

where we are using the notation D_t, M, Σ, etc., both for the sets of points they represent and for their areas (or, more precisely, for their measures); $D_t \cap M$ denotes the intersection of these sets.

The property described in Eq. (2.8.1) is referred to as mixing. Its importance in statistical mechanics was recognized by Gibbs (1902) who described it heuristically in terms of the example of mixing a blob of ink in water. A rigorous definition was given by Hopf (1934) but only in the 1960s has the concept assumed a central role.[41] It may be shown (the measure-theoretic demonstration requires only four lines[42]) that a system that satisfies the mixing condition has constant energy surfaces that are metrically indecomposable and is, therefore, ergodic.

Recent work[43] has clarified the properties of systems and their trajectories which give rise to the mixing property. This work, together with computer experiments, has again led to an optimistic view on the part of some[44] that broad classes of mechanical systems, including models suitable for the study of solids, will be found to be ergodic, although general rigorous proofs are still lacking.

(b) Further Objections to the Time-Average Viewpoint

In addition to the question of the ergodic behavior of isolated systems, other objections have been raised to the time-average view-point. These objections, which are still the subject of some controversy, include such questions as the use of infinite-time averages in the theory whereas real measurements always take place over finite time intervals. They are discussed briefly by Penrose

[41] See Arnold and Avez (1968) and Wightman (1971).
[42] Arnold and Avez (1968, p. 19).
[43] A review is given by Ford (1973).
[44] See, for example, Ford (1973, p. 164).

(1979, p. 1944), who also gives further references to both sides of the various discussions.

Ensemble Viewpoint

The result of a long-time observation of some property of a system under fixed macroscopic conditions, the central concept in the time-average viewpoint, may be regarded as the average of a sequence of many short-time observations performed on the same system as its microstate varies rapidly over the many possibilities consistent with imposed macroscopic conditions. In place of using a single system and performing the measurements sequentially, we may instead, from the ensemble viewpoint, think of performing the large number of observations simultaneously on an ensemble of replicas of the given system, with the microstates of the replicas distributed throughout phase space according to an appropriate distribution function $\rho(q, p)$. The phase average $\bar{F}$ of any phase function $F(q, p)$ as defined in Eq. (2.4.5) is then regarded as an average over the ensemble of replicas (and referred to as an ensemble average) rather than identified with a long time average for a single system.

The time-average and the ensemble viewpoints carry with them different interpretations of the distribution function $\rho(q, p) = \rho(y)$. From the time-average viewpoint, $\int_D \rho(y)\,dy$ is the long-time fraction of time spent by the system in the region D; as we have shown, this interpretation leads to the equality of phase averages and time averages. From the ensemble viewpoint, the same integral is the fraction of the total number of replicas of the ensemble which is contained in D; this interpretation leads to the equality of phase averages and ensemble averages. If we are dealing with an isolated system then, as we have seen, from the time-average viewpoint, Eq. (2.5.15) represents the statement that the fraction of time spent by the system in a convected volume D_t is constant. From the ensemble viewpoint, Eq. (2.5.15) is the statement that the set of replicas that occupy the region D_t remains the same fraction of the total ensemble as they all change their microstates according to the Hamiltonian that describes the isolated system.

The ensemble viewpoint is perceived to have some conceptual advantages relative to the time-average viewpoint[45] although the physical picture it provides is less direct. One of its advantages is that it lends itself more readily to the treatment of nonequilibrium processes by the use of time-dependent distribution functions $\rho(y, t)$. For example, the simple case treated in Figure 2.12 may be regarded as illustrating the approach to equilibrium of the single-particle system whose microstate at time t_0 is known to be located in D_{t_0}. In the absence of further information, it appears reasonable to set

$$\rho(x, p, t_0) = \frac{1}{\delta\Delta} \qquad \text{for } (x, p) \in D_{t_0}$$

$$= 0 \qquad \text{otherwise.} \tag{2.8.2}$$

---

[45]See Penrose (1979, p. 1944), and Münster (1969, Chapter I).

The equilibrium, microcanonical distribution for this case corresponds to

$$\rho_{mc}(x, p) = \frac{1}{2\Delta L} \quad \text{for } (x, p) \text{ in } \Sigma(p_0, \Delta)$$

$$= 0 \quad\quad \text{otherwise.} \quad\quad (2.8.3)$$

The evolution of $\rho(x, p, t)$, subject to the initial condition of Eq. (2.8.2), according to Liouville's theorem ($\dot{\rho} = 0$ on a replica trajectory) is shown in Figure 2.12. It is seen that $\rho(x, p, t)$ does not converge pointwise to $\rho_{mc}(x, p)$. However there is weak convergence in the sense that for any continuous phase function $F(x, p)$,

$$\bar{F} = \lim_{t \to \infty} \int_{\Gamma} F(x, p)\rho(x, p, t) \, dx \, dp = \int_{\Gamma} F(x, p)\rho_{mc}(x, p) \, dx \, dp.$$

$$(2.8.4)$$

Returning to our discussion of equilibrium statistical mechanics, if the ensemble viewpoint is adopted, there still remains the problem of how to motivate the correct definition of the distribution function for different physical situations from the ensemble viewpoint. One approach (Jaynes, 1957) is to regard the definition of ρ as a problem in statistical inference and to use concepts from information theory for its solution. This method is quick and completely bypasses the underlying dynamics of the system. We discuss the necessary information theory concepts in Section 3.11 and apply them in Section 10.2 to obtain the canonical distribution in quantum statistical mechanics.

The information theory approach is still subject to debate on philosophical grounds[46] and much of the effort on the foundations of statistical mechanics from the ensemble viewpoint is based on the dynamics of the members of the ensemble in phase space. When this is done, ergodic theory and associated questions again play a central role.[47]

Although we stress the time-average viewpoint in our presentation, we will also employ the ensemble concept when convenient. The terms canonical distribution and canonical ensemble will be used interchangeably and similarly for other distribution functions.

[46]Penrose (1979, p. 1943).
[47]Penrose (1979).

CHAPTER THREE

Corresponding Concepts in Thermodynamics and Statistical Mechanics

3.1 INTRODUCTION

A summary of the basic concepts of continuum thermodynamics was presented in Chapter 1 and some of the basic concepts of statistical mechanics were introduced in Chapter 2. In this chapter we consider the relationship between these two subjects.

We may think of the subject of statistical mechanics as supplying us with mathematical models on which may be performed some[1] of the idealized experiments referred to in the development of continuum thermodynamics. By noting the outcome of these mathematical experiments, we can determine the corresponding concepts in the two theories.

Consider an atomistic system representing either a gas or an elastic solid and described by a Hamiltonian $H(q_1, \ldots, q_n, p_1, \ldots, p_n; \mathscr{A}_1, \ldots, \mathscr{A}_\nu) = H(q, p; \mathscr{A})$ where $\mathscr{A}_1, \ldots, \mathscr{A}_\nu$ are kinematical parameters of the type described in Section 1.3, Eq. (1.3.20). For example, for a gas, $\nu = 1$ and $\mathscr{A}_1 = v$, the volume of the gas, while for an elastic solid we may take the $\mathscr{A}_\alpha$ to correspond to the material strain components, E_{LM}, so that $\nu = 6$. We regard the values of these quantities as deterministic and imposed on the system by its environment, and therefore speak of them as controllable kinematical parameters. We have seen in Section 2.7 an example which illustrates how v enters the Hamiltonian in that case. We will discuss later how the controllable kinemati-

---

[1] Recall that we are using the term statistical mechanics to connote equilibrium statistical mechanics. Therefore, some of the experiments referred to in the development of continuum thermodynamics, for example, those involving an arbitrary (not necessarily quasi-static) process connecting two states, lie outside the scope of this subject, although they are treated in the context of nonequilibrium statistical mechanics.

cal parameters, for example, E_{LM} or a_{iL}, enter the Hamiltonian for a deformed crystal (Section 4.3) or for a deformed amorphous polymeric network (Section 6.10). (It is also possible to use the conjugate generalized forces $\mathscr{F}_\alpha$ as controllable parameters and formulations of this type are discussed in Section 3.7. However, formulations involving the generalized displacements $\mathscr{A}_\alpha$ as controllable parameters are more widely used and are slightly more natural. Therefore, we emphasize these to begin with in this chapter.)

In Chapter 2, we derived both the microcanonical distribution function appropriate for discussing an isolated system, and the canonical distribution function appropriate for the discussion of such a system in an ambient (or heat bath as it is sometimes termed) characterized by the parameter θ. The canonical distribution takes the form

$$\rho(q, p) = \exp\left\{ \frac{\psi - H(q, p; \mathscr{A})}{\theta} \right\} \qquad (3.1.1)$$

where ψ is to be determined by the normalization condition

$$\int_\Gamma \rho(q, p)\, dq\, dp = 1. \qquad (3.1.2)$$

Equation (3.1.2) determines ψ as a function of the parameters $\mathscr{A}_1, \ldots, \mathscr{A}_\nu, \theta$ and therefore the canonical distribution function also depends on these parameters, that is, $\rho = \rho(q, p; \mathscr{A}, \theta)$.

By a fundamental premise of statistical mechanics, Section 2.4, for every observable property of the system there exists a phase function whose phase average is equal to the macroscopic value of the property which will be observed under the given conditions. In Section 2.4, a generic phase function was denoted by $F(q, p)$ and its phase average was denoted by $\bar{F}$. We will continue to use this notation when convenient. However, when we are concerned with a specific macroscopic property, for example, $\mathscr{F}_\alpha$, the generalized force conjugate to $\mathscr{A}_\alpha$, we will frequently adopt the alternate notation of designating the corresponding phase function by $\mathscr{F}_\alpha^m(q, p)$, where the superscript m refers to microscopic, and designate the phase average of this function by $\mathscr{F}_\alpha$. Thus, we write

$$\int_\Gamma \mathscr{F}_\alpha^m(q, p)\rho(q, p; \mathscr{A}, \theta)\, dq\, dp = \mathscr{F}_\alpha(\mathscr{A}, \theta). \qquad (3.1.3)$$

By use of this notation, we identify directly the statistical mechanics phase average with the corresponding macroscopic continuum quantity. In doing so, we assume, as we will throughout most of our discussions, that the system is sufficiently large, that is, it is composed of a sufficiently large number of particles, so that temporal fluctuations in the observed property will be negligible and so that this identification is permissible. When this is the case we refer to the body as macroscopic. We will also speak of this regime as the thermodynamic limit.[2]

We see, from relations such as Eq. (3.1.3), that $\rho(q, p; \mathscr{A}, \theta)$ describes a system that, from the viewpoint of continuum thermodynamics, is in uniform thermodynamic equilibrium (all its macroscopic properties are independent of space and time) and that the variables $\mathscr{A}_1, \ldots, \mathscr{A}_\nu, \theta$ are an appropriate set of independent state variables. We have already identified the $\mathscr{A}_\alpha$ as kinematical variables and we will show next that θ represents an empirical temperature scale.

3.2 EMPIRICAL TEMPERATURE

In order to identify the parameter θ, which appears in the canonical distribution, with an empirical temperature scale, we consider the statistical mechanics analog of the experiments described in Section 1.4 which are used to define this concept.

Consider two separate systems A and B, each in equilibrium with its ambient, and described by the canonical distributions

$$\rho_A(y_A; \mathscr{A}_A, \theta_A) = \exp\left(\frac{\psi_A - H_A(y_A; \mathscr{A}_A)}{\theta_A}\right),$$

$$\rho_B(y_B; \mathscr{A}_B, \theta_B) = \exp\left(\frac{\psi_B - H_B(y_B; \mathscr{A}_B)}{\theta_B}\right), \qquad (3.2.1)$$

where, as in Chapter 2, we are using the abbreviated notation, $y = (q, p)$. As noted in Section 1.4, from the viewpoint of macroscopic thermodynamics, the two systems are in thermal equilibrium if, when brought into contact,[3] they each remain in the same states of uniform thermodynamic equilibrium they were in prior to contact. This will be the case, from the viewpoint of statistical mechanics, if the composite system $A + B$ has a distribution function

$$\rho_{A+B} = \rho_A \rho_B = \exp\left(\frac{\psi_A - H_A(y_A; \mathscr{A}_A)}{\theta_A} + \frac{\psi_B - H_B(y_B; \mathscr{A}_B)}{\theta_B}\right)$$

$$(3.2.2)$$

---

[2] The relation of the magnitude of fluctuations to the size of the system was discussed briefly in Section 2.7 and will be discussed at greater length in Section 3.9.

[3] Note that this process requires that ambients of the respective systems are coalesced into a single ambient for the two systems in contact.

for then all the properties of A and of B remain unchanged.[4] However, the composite system $A + B$ is, in itself, a system in equilibrium with an ambient and therefore must be described by a canonical distribution.

$$\rho_{A+B} = \exp\left(\frac{\psi_{A+B} - H_{A+B}(y_A, y_B; \mathscr{A}_A, \mathscr{A}_B)}{\theta_{A+B}}\right). \qquad (3.2.3)$$

We now make the requirement that systems A and B interact only weakly with each other when they are placed in contact.[5] Then Eq. (3.2.3) may be rewritten as

$$\rho_{A+B} = \exp\left\{\frac{\psi_{A+B} - \left[H_A(y_A; \mathscr{A}_A) + H_B(y_B; \mathscr{A}_B)\right]}{\theta_{A+B}}\right\}. \qquad (3.2.4)$$

The two expressions for ρ_{A+B}, Eqs. (3.2.2) and (3.2.4), are consistent for all values of y_A and y_B if and only if

$$\theta_A^{-1}H_A + \theta_B^{-1}H_B \equiv \theta_{A+B}^{-1}(H_A + H_B). \qquad (3.2.5)$$

The functions $H_A(y_A; \mathscr{A}_A)$ and $H_B(y_B; \mathscr{A}_B)$ are clearly independent and therefore consistency requires

$$\theta_A = \theta_B = \theta_{A+B}. \qquad (3.2.6)$$

This completes the demonstration that the parameter θ in the canonical distribution plays the role of an empirical temperature scale.

3.3   QUASI-STATIC PROCESS

Consider a quasi-static process (Section 1.4) in which the functions $\mathscr{A}_1(t),\ldots,$ $\mathscr{A}_\nu(t)$, $\theta(t)$ are defined for $t_1 \leqslant t \leqslant t_2$. The statistical mechanics analog of this process is obtained by making the assumption that the canonical distribution

$$\rho\big(q, p; \mathscr{A}(t), \theta(t)\big) = \exp\left(\frac{\psi - H(q, p; \mathscr{A}(t))}{\theta(t)}\right) \qquad (3.3.1)$$

---

[4] Consider, for example, the computation of the phase average on the basis of ρ_{A+B} of a function $F(y_A)$ which represents a property of A. The integration over the variables y_B then simply leads to unity since ρ_B is normalized.

[5] This assumption is essential if equality of empirical temperature is to imply that the two systems will remain in thermodynamic equilibrium after they are placed in contact; for example, consider systems of sodium and oxygen at the same temperature. This point is emphasized by Gibbs (1902, p. 37).

applies for $t_1 \leqslant t \leqslant t_2$. (Normalization of ρ is required for all t so that $\psi = \psi(\mathscr{A}(t), \theta(t))$. It then follows from the procedure of taking phase averages, as in Eq. (3.1.3), that during the process all dependent state variables, for example, $\mathscr{F}_\alpha(t) = \mathscr{F}_\alpha(\mathscr{A}(t), \theta(t))$, are determined by the state functions used in uniform thermodynamic equilibrium, as required by the thermodynamic definition of a quasi-static process given in Section 1.4.

It is important to emphasize that the variable t used in the definition of a quasi-static process is simply a label for a continuous sequence of states of uniform thermodynamic equilibrium. If it is interpreted as time, it must be recognized that it represents an arbitrarily slow process on a *macroscopic* time scale. We may get some feeling for how slow a process has to be in order to approximate a quasi-static process if we recall (Section 2.4) that ρ represents the fraction of time (per unit of phase space volume) that the system spends in any region of phase space. Therefore, if ρ as given by Eq. (3.3.1) is to have meaning, $\mathscr{A}_\alpha(t)$ and $\theta(t)$ must change little in a macroscopic time interval Δt which is large enough so that the system has sufficiently sampled the region of phase space accessible to it. Since the volume of accessible regions in phase space grows rapidly with the number of degrees of freedom of the system [see, e.g., Eq. (2.7.3)], we again come to the conclusion that the larger the system, the slower must be the variation in imposed conditions in order to approximate a quasi-static process.

3.4 PHASE FUNCTIONS FOR GENERALIZED FORCES

Consider a system with Hamiltonian $H(q, p; \mathscr{A}_1, \ldots, \mathscr{A}_\nu)$ and a thought experiment in which the controllable kinematical parameters imposed on the system by its environment are given prescribed arbitrary increments $d\mathscr{A}_\alpha$ while all the coordinates and momenta (q, p) of the system are held fixed. By the laws of mechanics, the change in total energy[6] of the system must be equal to the work done on it by the generalized forces $\mathscr{F}_\alpha{}^m$ which are conjugate to the $\mathscr{A}_\alpha$ and are exerted on the system by its environment. Therefore,

$$dH|_{(q,\,p)} = \sum_{\alpha=1}^{\nu} \frac{\partial H}{\partial \mathscr{A}_\alpha}\bigg|_{(q,\,p)} d\mathscr{A}_\alpha = \sum_{\alpha=1}^{\nu} \mathscr{F}_\alpha{}^m \, d\mathscr{A}_\alpha. \qquad (3.4.1)$$

Since the increments $d\mathscr{A}_\alpha$ are arbitrary, it follows that

$$\mathscr{F}_\alpha{}^m(q, p; \mathscr{A}) = \frac{\partial H}{\partial \mathscr{A}_\alpha}(q, p; \mathscr{A}), \qquad \alpha = 1, \ldots, \nu. \qquad (3.4.2)$$

[6] We recall that we are restricting attention to those cases in which the Hamiltonian corresponds to the total energy of the system.

The functions $\mathcal{F}_\alpha{}^m(q, p; \mathcal{A})$ defined by Eq. (3.4.2) are therefore the appropriate phase functions to be used for computing the generalized forces $\mathcal{F}_\alpha$.

In particular, for a gas[7]

$$p^m(q, p; v) = \frac{-\partial H}{\partial v}(q, p; v) \tag{3.4.3}$$

and for an elastic solid, when the material strains E_{LM} are used as controllable kinematic parameters,

$$\mathcal{V} T_{LM}^m(q, p; E_{RS}) = \frac{\partial H}{\partial E_{LM}}(q, p; E_{RS}), \tag{3.4.4}$$

or when the deformation matrix elements a_{iL} are used,

$$\mathcal{V} T_{iL}^m(q, p; a_{jK}) = \frac{\partial H}{\partial a_{iL}}(q, p; a_{jK}). \tag{3.4.5}$$

3.5 FIRST LAW OF THERMODYNAMICS

The thermodynamic concept of a system surrounded by an adiabatic envelop has, as its statistical mechanics analog, an isolated system with prescribed total energy E; it is described, therefore, by a microcanonical ensemble $\rho_{mc}(q, p; \mathcal{A}, E)$. Here the, notation ρ_{mc} denotes the function which is zero throughout the phase space Γ except on the energy surface $S(E; \mathcal{A})$ defined by the equation

$$H(q, p; \mathcal{A}) = E, \tag{3.5.1}$$

and is normalized to unity when integrated over S,

$$\int_{S(E; \mathcal{A})} \rho_{mc}(q, p; \mathcal{A}, E) \, dS = 1. \tag{3.5.2}$$

The precise form of ρ_{mc} may be obtained[8] from Eq. (2.5.30) but is not needed here. The generalized force $\mathcal{F}_\alpha$ acting on the isolated system is then

$$\mathcal{F}_\alpha(\mathcal{A}, E) = \int_{S(E; \mathcal{A})} \mathcal{F}_\alpha{}^m(q, p; \mathcal{A}) \rho_{mc}(q, p; \mathcal{A}, E) \, dS$$

$$= \int_{S(E; \mathcal{A})} \frac{\partial H}{\partial \mathcal{A}_\alpha}(q, p; \mathcal{A}) \rho_{mc}(q, p; \mathcal{A}, E) \, dS \tag{3.5.3}$$

where Eq. (3.4.2) has been employed.

---

[7] We are using the notation p for the pressure in a gas and as a collective designation of the momenta in an atomistic system; the context should make clear which use is intended.

[8] See, for example, Khinchin (1949) where it is shown that $\rho_{mc}(q, p; \mathcal{A}, E) = (\Omega(E; \mathcal{A})|\nabla H|)^{-1}$ where $\Omega(E; \mathcal{A})$ is the structure function of the system and $|\nabla H| = [\Sigma_{i=1}^n (\partial H/\partial q_i)^2 + (\partial H/\partial p_i)^2]^{1/2}$.

Consider next[9] $\dot{W}$, the rate of doing work on the isolated system during a quasi-static process specified by the functions $\mathscr{A}_\alpha(t)$, $E(t)$.

$$\dot{W} = \sum_{\alpha=1}^{\nu} \mathscr{F}_\alpha \dot{\mathscr{A}}_\alpha = \sum_{\alpha=1}^{\nu} \left(\int_{S(E;\,\mathscr{A})} \mathscr{F}_\alpha^m \rho_{mc}\, dS \right) \dot{\mathscr{A}}_\alpha$$

$$= \sum_{\alpha=1}^{\nu} \int_{S(E;\,\mathscr{A})} \frac{\partial H}{\partial \mathscr{A}_\alpha} \dot{\mathscr{A}}_\alpha \rho_{mc}\, dS = \int_{S(E;\,\mathscr{A})} \dot{H} \rho_{mc}\, dS, \qquad (3.5.4)$$

where

$$\dot{H}(q, p; \mathscr{A}) = \sum_{\alpha=1}^{\nu} \frac{\partial H}{\partial \mathscr{A}_\alpha} (q, p; \mathscr{A}) \dot{\mathscr{A}}_\alpha \qquad (3.5.5)$$

is the rate of change of H at fixed (q, p) due to change in the controllable parameters.

On the other hand, let

$$\bar{H}(\mathscr{A}, E) = \int_{S(E;\,\mathscr{A})} H(q, p; \mathscr{A}) \rho_{mc}\, dS$$

be the phase average of H with respect to the microcanonical ensemble. Then, during the quasi-static process,

$$\frac{d}{dt}\bar{H} = \dot{\bar{H}} = \frac{d}{dt} \int_{S(E;\,\mathscr{A})} H \rho_{mc}\, dS$$

$$= \int_{S(E;\,\mathscr{A})} \dot{H} \rho_{mc}\, dS + E \frac{d}{dt} \int_{S(E;\,\mathscr{A})} \rho_{mc}\, dS \qquad (3.5.6)$$

where we have separated the differentiation with respect to t into two parts: the first accounts for the variation of $\mathscr{A}_\alpha$ in the arguments of H while in the second part, these parameters are held fixed in H but $\mathscr{A}_\alpha$ and E vary everywhere else they appear. In the second part we have also used the fact that $H = E$ on $S(E; \mathscr{A})$ in order to take H outside the integral. It then follows from the normalization condition, Eq. (3.5.2), that

$$E \frac{d}{dt} \int_{S(E;\,\mathscr{A})} \rho_{mc}\, dS = 0 \qquad (3.5.7)$$

[9]Here, and subsequently in similar discussions, the superposed dot refers to differentiation with respect to the variable t which acts as a label for the quasi-static process (Section 3.3). The differentiation, therefore, only affects the argument t in the controllable parameters, here $\mathscr{A}_\alpha(t)$, $E(t)$. Put another way, the variable t represents a macroscopic time scale for the description of the quasi-static process. The microscopic time scale does not appear in these calculations since all integrations are over phase space with (q, p) as independent variables.

and we have, from Eqs. (3.5.4) and (3.5.6), that

$$\dot{W} = \dot{\bar{H}} \tag{3.5.8}$$

for work done during an adiabatic quasi-static process. We conclude that the Hamiltonian $H(q, p; \mathcal{A})$ is the appropriate phase function for the computation of the internal energy, that is, that $U^m(q, p; \mathcal{A}) = H(q, p; \mathcal{A})$.

Consider next the same system, no longer isolated, but in equilibrium with an ambient at empirical temperature θ and undergoing a quasi-static process given by $\mathcal{A}_\alpha(t)$, $\theta(t)$. The canonical ensemble now applies and the internal energy of the system is,[10] since $U^m(q, p; \mathcal{A}) = H(q, p; \mathcal{A})$,

$$U(\mathcal{A}, \theta) = \int_\Gamma H(q, p; \mathcal{A}) \rho(q, p; \mathcal{A}, \theta) \, dq \, dp \tag{3.5.9}$$

where $\rho(q, p; \mathcal{A}, \theta)$, describing a canonical ensemble, is defined by Eq. (3.1.1). Then

$$\dot{U} = \frac{d}{dt} \int_\Gamma H\rho \, dq \, dp = \int_\Gamma \dot{H}\rho \, dq \, dp + \int_\Gamma H\dot{\rho} \, dq \, dp. \tag{3.5.10}$$

The first integral in this equation,

$$\int_\Gamma \dot{H}\rho \, dq \, dp = \int_\Gamma \sum_{\alpha=1}^\nu \frac{\partial H}{\partial \mathcal{A}_\alpha} \dot{\mathcal{A}}_\alpha \rho \, dq \, dp = \sum_{\alpha=1}^\nu \left(\int_\Gamma \mathcal{F}_\alpha^m \rho \, dq \, dp \right) \dot{\mathcal{A}}_\alpha$$

$$= \sum_{\alpha=1}^\nu \mathcal{F}_\alpha \dot{\mathcal{A}}_\alpha = \dot{W} \tag{3.5.11}$$

by use of Eqs. (3.5.5) and (3.4.2). It follows from the first law of thermodynamics, $\dot{U} = \dot{W} + \dot{Q}$, that the second integral in Eq. (3.5.10) represents $\dot{Q}$, the heat flow into the system from the ambient; that is

$$\dot{Q} = \int_\Gamma H\dot{\rho} \, dq \, dp. \tag{3.5.12}$$

The distinction between work and heat, from the viewpoint of statistical mechanics, is noteworthy. From Eq. (3.5.11) it is seen that work is done on the system because the value of the Hamiltonian changes at a given point in phase space, that is, because of $\dot{H}$, while the statistical character of the motion of the system through phase space, as described by ρ, remains unchanged. For heat

---

[10] Note that it follows from the discussion of Section 2.4 that the definition of a phase function is independent of the type of ensemble employed.

flow, as seen from Eq. (3.5.12), the situation is reversed, and it is the change, $\dot{\rho}$, in the statistical character of the motion which is significant. The statistical nature of heat flow is thus emphasized.

It is also of interest to compare Eq. (3.5.12) for $\dot{Q}$ in a canonical ensemble with the corresponding expression [see Eq. (3.5.7)] for the microcanonical ensemble; that is, heat flow into an isolated system is zero, as it should be.

3.6 SECOND LAW OF THERMODYNAMICS

Equation (3.5.12) provides an explicit formula, in the framework of statistical mechanics, for the heat flow $\dot{Q}$ into a system undergoing a quasi-static process while interacting with an ambient at empirical temperature θ. We wish next to show that $\dot{Q} = f(\theta)\bar{F}(\mathscr{A}, \theta)$ where $\bar{F}(\mathscr{A}, \theta)$ is the phase average of a suitably chosen phase function, $F(q, p; \mathscr{A})$. It will then follow from the second law of thermodynamics (Section 1.4) that $f(\theta)$ represents an absolute temperature scale and the function $\bar{F}(A, \theta)$ corresponds to the entropy of the system.

It is first convenient to rewrite the canonical distribution function as

$$\rho(q, p; \mathscr{A}, \theta) = e^{\eta(q, p; \mathscr{A}, \theta)}, \qquad (3.6.1)$$

where

$$\eta(q, p; \mathscr{A}, \theta) = \frac{\psi(\mathscr{A}, \theta) - H(q, p; \mathscr{A})}{\theta}. \qquad (3.6.2)$$

Since the distribution function is normalized throughout the quasistatic process specified by the functions $\mathscr{A}_a(t)$, $\theta(t)$, that is,

$$\int_\Gamma e^\eta \, dq \, dp = 1, \qquad (3.6.3)$$

it follows that

$$\frac{d}{dt} \int_\Gamma e^\eta \, dq \, dp = \int_\Gamma \dot{\eta} e^\eta \, dq \, dp = 0. \qquad (3.6.4)$$

We may, therefore, write

$$\dot{Q} = \int_\Gamma H\dot{\rho} \, dq \, dp = \int_\Gamma H\dot{\eta} e^\eta \, dq \, dp = \int_\Gamma (H - \psi)\dot{\eta} e^\eta \, dq \, dp \qquad (3.6.5)$$

where we have used the fact that $\psi = \psi(\mathscr{A}, \theta)$ is independent of (q, p) and therefore

$$\int_\Gamma \psi\dot{\eta} e^\eta \, dq \, dp = \psi \int_\Gamma \dot{\eta} e^\eta \, dq \, dp = 0 \qquad (3.6.6)$$

by Eq. (3.6.4). By use of Eq. (3.6.2), the expression for $\dot{Q}$, Eq. (3.6.5), may be rewritten

$$\dot{Q} = -\theta \int_\Gamma \eta \dot{\eta} e^\eta \, dq \, dp. \qquad (3.6.7)$$

Consider next

$$\dot{\bar{\eta}} = \frac{d}{dt} \int_\Gamma \eta e^\eta \, dq \, dp = \int_\Gamma \dot{\eta} e^\eta \, dq \, dp + \int_\Gamma \eta \dot{\eta} e^\eta \, dq \, dp$$

$$= \int_\Gamma \eta \dot{\eta} e^\eta \, dq \, dp \qquad (3.6.8)$$

by use of Eq. (3.6.4). The combination of Eqs. (3.6.7) and (3.6.8) leads to the expression for $\dot{Q}$ in the desired form, namely:

$$\dot{Q} = -\theta \dot{\bar{\eta}}. \qquad (3.6.9)$$

It follows from the second law of thermodynamics that the parameter θ, which was formerly shown to correspond to an empirical temperature scale, corresponds in fact to an absolute temperature scale. Since the absolute temperature scale is unique up to a multiplicative factor, we may write

$$\theta = kT \qquad (3.6.10)$$

where k is known as Boltzman's constant and T is an absolute temperature. We recall (Section 2.7) that θ is twice the energy per degree of freedom of the heat bath (when the latter is a perfect gas). If this energy is measured in ergs and T is measured in degrees Kelvin, then

$$k = 1.380 \times 10^{-16} \text{ ergs deg}^{-1}. \qquad (3.6.11)$$

(The smallness of k in these units simply reflects the fact that the erg is a unit chosen to measure conveniently macroscopic quantities of energy.)

Since the scale of the entropy function $S(\mathscr{A}, T)$ is chosen in thermodynamics so that

$$\dot{Q} = T\dot{S} \qquad (3.6.12)$$

it follows from Eq. (3.6.9) that

$$\bar{\eta}(\mathscr{A}, T) = -\frac{S(\mathscr{A}, T)}{k} \qquad (3.6.13)$$

where we are now using $T = \theta/k$ as the temperature variable. If we take the phase average of both sides of Eq. (3.6.2), then

$$\bar{\eta}(\mathscr{A}, T) = \frac{\psi(\mathscr{A}, T) - \bar{H}(\mathscr{A}, T)}{kT} = \frac{\psi(\mathscr{A}, T) - U(\mathscr{A}, T)}{kT}$$

$$(3.6.14)$$

where we have used Eq. (3.5.9) which equates the phase average of the Hamiltonian $H(q, p; \mathscr{A})$ to the macroscopic internal energy function $U(\mathscr{A}, T)$. It follows from Eqs. (3.6.13) and (3.6.14) that

$$\psi(\mathscr{A}, T) = U(\mathscr{A}, T) - TS(\mathscr{A}, T) = F(\mathscr{A}, T) \qquad (3.6.15)$$

where $F(\mathscr{A}, T)$ is the Helmholtz free energy of the system (Section 1.5). We recall [Eq. (3.1.2)] that $\psi = F$ is determined from the normalization condition so that

$$e^{-F/(kT)} = \int_\Gamma e^{-H/(kT)} \, dq \, dp \qquad (3.6.16)$$

or

$$F(\mathscr{A}, T) = -kT \log Z(\mathscr{A}, T) \qquad (3.6.17)$$

where we have introduced the notation

$$Z(\mathscr{A}, T) = \int_\Gamma e^{-H(q, p; \mathscr{A})/kT} \, dq \, dp. \qquad (3.6.18)$$

The function $Z(\mathscr{A}, T)$ is known as the partition function of the system. Since it may be computed directly in terms of the Hamiltonian of the system, $H(q, p; \mathscr{A})$, with $\mathscr{A} = (\mathscr{A}_1, \dots, \mathscr{A}_\nu)$ a set of controllable kinematical parameters, and since the Helmholtz free energy as function of the arguments $\mathscr{A}_1, \dots, \mathscr{A}_\nu, T$ represents a basic equation of state or fundamental relation (Section 1.5), we see that Eq. (3.6.17) provides a basic link between an atomistic model of a system and its macroscopic behavior.

By use of Eq. (2.5.32), the partition function $Z(\mathscr{A}, T)$ can be written as a one-dimensional integral,

$$Z(\mathscr{A}, T) = \int_0^\infty \Omega(E, \mathscr{A}) \exp\left[-\frac{E}{kT}\right] dE \qquad (3.6.19)$$

where $\Omega(E, \mathscr{A})$ is the structure function of the system as determined from the Hamiltonian $H(q, p; \mathscr{A})$.

As a simple example, we use Eq. (3.16.9) to compute the partition function for a harmonic oscillator. As previously shown in Section 2.5 following Eq.

(2.5.32), for a harmonic oscillator with circular frequency ω the structure function $\Omega(E) = 2\pi/\omega$. Therefore

$$Z = \frac{2\pi}{\omega} \int_0^\infty e^{-E/kT} \, dE = \frac{2\pi kT}{\omega}. \tag{3.6.20}$$

Partition Function for Systems in Weak Interaction

Consider two systems A and B in weak interaction so that the composite system $A + B$ has a Hamiltonian

$$H_{A+B}(q_A, q_B, p_A, p_B; \mathscr{A}_A, \mathscr{A}_B) = H_A(q_A, p_A; \mathscr{A}_A) + H_B(q_B, p_B; \mathscr{A}_B). \tag{3.6.21}$$

Then, it follows readily from Eq. (3.6.18) that

$$Z_{A+B}(\mathscr{A}_A, \mathscr{A}_B, T) = Z_A(\mathscr{A}_A, T) Z_B(\mathscr{A}_B, T) \tag{3.6.22}$$

and, from Eq. (3.6.17), that

$$F_{A+B}(\mathscr{A}_A, \mathscr{A}_B, T) = F_A(\mathscr{A}_A, T) + F_B(\mathscr{A}_B, T). \tag{3.6.23}$$

Entropy in terms of ρ

It is important to note that Eq. (3.6.13) provides a definition for the entropy $S(\mathscr{A}, T)$ in terms of $\rho(q, p; \mathscr{A}, T)$. Since, from Eq. (3.6.1), $\eta = \log \rho$, we see that Eq. (3.6.13) becomes

$$S(\mathscr{A}, T) = -k \int_\Gamma \rho(q, p; \mathscr{A}, T) \log \rho(q, p; \mathscr{A}, T) \, dq \, dp. \tag{3.6.24}$$

This relation has been derived by comparison of statistical mechanics and continuum thermodynamics. In Section 3.11 we will reinterpret this relation from the viewpoint of information theory.

3.7   USE OF MECHANICAL VARIABLES AS CONTROLLABLE PARAMETERS

Thus far in this chapter, we have considered the formulation of statistical mechanics with generalized displacements $\mathscr{A}_\alpha$ employed as the controllable parameters. We wish next to develop the corresponding formulation with generalized forces $\mathscr{F}_\alpha$ as controllable parameters. Since we will be dealing with both cases in this section, we use the notation $H_{\mathscr{A}}(q, p; \mathscr{A})$ for the Hamiltonian of a system with the generalized displacements $\mathscr{A}_\alpha$ used as controllable parameters whereas in the previous sections of this chapter we used the simpler notation $H(q, p; \mathscr{A})$.

Legendre transformation

Begin with the Hamiltonian $H_{\mathscr{A}}(q, p; \mathscr{A}_1,\ldots, \mathscr{A}_\nu) = H_{\mathscr{A}}(q, p; \mathscr{A})$. With the microscopic variables (q, p) fixed in the following discussion, we consider the Legendre transform of $H_{\mathscr{A}}$ regarded as a function of $(\mathscr{A}_1,\ldots, \mathscr{A}_\nu)$. That is, define

$$\mathscr{F}_\alpha = \frac{\partial H_{\mathscr{A}}}{\partial \mathscr{A}_\alpha}(q, p; \mathscr{A}), \qquad \alpha = 1,\ldots, \nu, \tag{3.7.1}$$

which provides the functional relationship

$$\mathscr{F}_\alpha = \mathscr{F}_\alpha(q, p; \mathscr{A}) \tag{3.7.2}$$

with inverse

$$\mathscr{A}_\alpha = \mathscr{A}_\alpha(q, p; \mathscr{F}_1,\ldots, \mathscr{F}_\nu), \qquad \alpha = 1,\ldots, \nu. \tag{3.7.3}$$

Then, $H_{\mathscr{F}}$, the Legendre transform of $H_{\mathscr{A}}$, is the function defined as[11]

$$H_{\mathscr{F}}(q, p; \mathscr{F}_1,\ldots, \mathscr{F}_\nu) = H_{\mathscr{A}}(q, p; \mathscr{A}_1,\ldots, \mathscr{A}_\nu) - \mathscr{A}_\alpha \mathscr{F}_\alpha, \tag{3.7.4}$$

with $\mathscr{A}_\alpha = \mathscr{A}_\alpha(q, p; \mathscr{F})$ given by Eq. (3.7.3). (The summation convention $\alpha = 1,\ldots, \nu$ is employed here and throughout this and the following section.) Consider an arbitrary variation $d\mathscr{F}_\alpha$. Then

$$dH_{\mathscr{F}} = \frac{\partial H_{\mathscr{F}}}{\partial \mathscr{F}_\alpha} d\mathscr{F}_\alpha = \frac{\partial H_{\mathscr{A}}}{\partial \mathscr{A}_\alpha} d\mathscr{A}_\alpha - (\mathscr{F}_\alpha d\mathscr{A}_\alpha + \mathscr{A}_\alpha d\mathscr{F}_\alpha)$$

$$= -\mathscr{A}_\alpha d\mathscr{F}_\alpha$$

by use of Eq. (3.7.1). Therefore,

$$\mathscr{A}_\alpha = -\frac{\partial H_{\mathscr{F}}}{\partial \mathscr{F}_\alpha}(q, p; \mathscr{F}), \qquad \alpha = 1,\ldots, \nu \tag{3.7.5}$$

and provides an explicit interpretation of Eq. (3.7.3) in terms of $H_{\mathscr{F}}$.

---

[11]See, for example, Callen (1960, p. 90) and Arnold (1978, p. 61) for discussions of the Legendre transform.

Physical Interpretation

In the preceding discussion the microscopic variables (q, p) have been fixed. We now turn attention to the function $H_{\mathscr{A}}(q, p; \mathscr{A}_1, \ldots, \mathscr{A}_\nu)$ as descriptive of a system of particles I with coordinates and momenta $(q_1, \ldots, q_n; p_1, \ldots, p_n) = (q, p)$ in interaction with an environment E with the state of E, as far as its effect on I is concerned, described[12] in terms of a small number of controlled kinematical parameters $\mathscr{A}_\alpha$, $\alpha = 1, \ldots, \nu$. We next show that, in a certain sense, the Legendre transform $H_{\mathscr{F}}(q, p; \mathscr{F}_1, \ldots, \mathscr{F}_\nu)$ describes the same system I in interaction with the same environment E whose state, as far as its effect on I is concerned, is now described in terms of controlled mechanical parameters $\mathscr{F}_\alpha$. The correspondence follows from the result

$$\frac{\partial H_{\mathscr{F}}}{\partial q_i}(q, p; \mathscr{F}) = \frac{\partial H_{\mathscr{A}}}{\partial q_i}(q, p; \mathscr{A}) + \frac{\partial H_{\mathscr{A}}}{\partial \mathscr{A}_\alpha}\frac{\partial \mathscr{A}_\alpha}{\partial q_i} - \frac{\partial \mathscr{A}_\alpha}{\partial q_i}\mathscr{F}_\alpha$$

$$= \frac{\partial H_{\mathscr{A}}}{\partial q_i}(q, p; \mathscr{A}), \qquad i = 1, \ldots, n \qquad (3.7.6)$$

where Eqs. (3.7.4) and (3.7.1) have been used. Similarly $\partial H_{\mathscr{F}}/\partial p_i = \partial H_{\mathscr{A}}/\partial p_i$. Therefore, if $\mathscr{A}_\alpha$ and $\mathscr{F}_\alpha$ are related as in Eq. (3.7.1) or (3.7.5) at a given point (q, p) in the phase space of I, then $H_{\mathscr{A}}$ and $H_{\mathscr{F}}$ predict the same values of $(\dot{q}, \dot{p})$ at that point; that is, under these conditions the forces acting on all the particles of I are identical. It is in this sense that $H_{\mathscr{A}}$ and $H_{\mathscr{F}}$ are alternate Hamiltonians for the description of I in interaction with E. Note, however, that $H_{\mathscr{A}}$ and $H_{\mathscr{F}}$ do not predict the same trajectory[13] of I through its phase space, for even if $\mathscr{A}_\alpha$ and $\mathscr{F}_\alpha$ are related as in Eq. (3.7.1) at a given point (q, p), this relation will not be maintained when the system moves away from that point. For example, when $H_{\mathscr{A}}$ is employed, the parameters $\mathscr{A}_\alpha$ are kept fixed and the quantities $\mathscr{F}_\alpha$ vary with (q, p) as described by Eq. (3.7.1). To emphasize the dependence on (q, p), we rewrite that equation as

$$\mathscr{F}_\alpha^m(q, p; \mathscr{A}) = \frac{\partial H_{\mathscr{A}}}{\partial \mathscr{A}_\alpha}(q, p; \mathscr{A}), \qquad \alpha = 1, \ldots, \nu \qquad (3.7.7)$$

so that $\mathscr{F}_\alpha^m$ are the microscopic phase functions for the generalized forces as previously introduced. Similarly when $H_{\mathscr{F}}$ is employed, the parameters $\mathscr{A}_\alpha$ vary with (q, p) as described by Eq. (3.7.5) and we rewrite that equation as

$$\mathscr{A}_\alpha^m(q, p; \mathscr{F}) = -\frac{\partial H_{\mathscr{F}}}{\partial \mathscr{F}_\alpha}(q, p; \mathscr{F}). \qquad \alpha = 1, \ldots, \nu. \qquad (3.7.8)$$

---

[12] Since the environment E has, from the atomistic viewpoint, a large number of degrees of freedom, this description is only a partial one, but one that is sufficient for the determination of the statistical or macroscopic behavior of system I. The remaining time-dependent interaction, which is due to the detailed atomic configuration of the environment, is assumed to be a weak interaction in the sense of Section 2.6 and is therefore not described explicitly and neglected in all phase space integrations.

[13] Because of the effect of weak interactions, the actual trajectory followed by the system will not be that computed on the basis of either $H_{\mathscr{A}}$ or $H_{\mathscr{F}}$; see the discussion in Section 7.6.

Here, $\mathscr{A}_\alpha^m$ are the microscopic phase functions for the kinematic parameters to be used when the mechanical parameters are controlled. With this notation we rewrite Eq. (3.7.4) for the Hamiltonian to be employed when the stresses are controlled as

$$H_{\mathscr{F}}(q, p; \mathscr{F}_1, \ldots, \mathscr{F}_\nu) = H_{\mathscr{A}}(q, p; \mathscr{A}_1^m, \ldots, \mathscr{A}_\nu^m) - \mathscr{A}_\alpha^m \mathscr{F}_\alpha$$

in order to make explicit the fluctuating character of $\mathscr{A}_\alpha^m(q, p; \mathscr{F})$. Similarly, we write the Hamiltonian $H_{\mathscr{A}}$ for the strain ensemble as

$$H_{\mathscr{A}}(q, p; \mathscr{A}_1, \ldots, \mathscr{A}_\nu) = H_{\mathscr{F}}(q, p; \mathscr{F}_1^m, \ldots, \mathscr{F}_\nu^m) + \mathscr{A}_\alpha \mathscr{F}_\alpha^m.$$

As a very simple example which may help clarify these ideas, consider the two particle system of Figure 3.1. The particles are constrained to move in the x direction, with particle I of mass m representing system I and particle E representing the environment with which I interacts. We take the springs as linear with unit spring constant. Then

$$H_{\mathscr{A}}(q, p; \mathscr{A}) = \frac{p^2}{2m} + \tfrac{1}{2}\left(q^2 + (q - \mathscr{A})^2\right)$$

is the Hamiltonian of I when E is fixed at distance $\mathscr{A}$ as shown. Following Eq. (3.7.1),

$$\mathscr{F} = \frac{\partial H_{\mathscr{A}}}{\partial \mathscr{A}} = \mathscr{A} - q,$$

with inverse

$$\mathscr{A} = \mathscr{F} + q.$$

Therefore,

$$H_{\mathscr{F}}(q, p; \mathscr{F}) = H_{\mathscr{A}} - \mathscr{A}\mathscr{F}$$

$$\cdot = \frac{p^2}{2m} + \tfrac{1}{2}q^2 - \frac{\mathscr{F}^2}{2} - \mathscr{F}q$$

is the appropriate Hamiltonian when $\mathscr{F}$, the force exerted by E on I is held constant, while the position of E changes as necessary to meet this constraint.

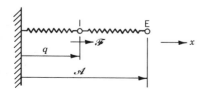

Figure 3.1 Simple model illustrating strain and stress ensembles.

Canonical Strain and Stress Ensembles

Since $H_{\mathscr{A}}$ and $H_{\mathscr{F}}$ are alternate Hamiltonians for the description of the same system I in interaction with environment E, the canonical ensemble takes the same form[14] in both cases:

$$\rho_{\mathscr{A}}(q, p; \mathscr{A}, T) = \exp\left\{ \frac{\psi_{\mathscr{A}} - H_{\mathscr{A}}(q, p; \mathscr{A})}{kT} \right\} \tag{3.7.9}$$

and

$$\rho_{\mathscr{F}}(q, p; \mathscr{F}, T) = \exp\left\{ \frac{\psi_{\mathscr{F}} - H_{\mathscr{F}}(q, p; \mathscr{F})}{kT} \right\}. \tag{3.7.10}$$

We refer to $\rho_{\mathscr{A}}$ as the canonical strain distribution or, alternatively, as describing the canonical strain ensemble or, more simply still, the strain ensemble. Similarly, $\rho_{\mathscr{F}}$ describes the stress ensemble.[15] From the requirement that both $\rho_{\mathscr{A}}$ and $\rho_{\mathscr{F}}$ are normalized to unity when integrated over the phase space Γ it follows that

$$\psi_{\mathscr{A}}(\mathscr{A}, T) = -kT \log Z_{\mathscr{A}}(\mathscr{A}, T)$$

$$\psi_{\mathscr{F}}(\mathscr{F}, T) = -kT \log Z_{\mathscr{F}}(\mathscr{F}, T) \tag{3.7.11}$$

where

$$Z_{\mathscr{A}}(\mathscr{A}, T) = \int_{\Gamma} \exp\left[\frac{-H_{\mathscr{A}}(q, p; \mathscr{A})}{kT} \right] dq \, dp$$

$$Z_{\mathscr{F}}(\mathscr{F}, T) = \int_{\Gamma} \exp\left[\frac{-H_{\mathscr{F}}(q, p; \mathscr{F})}{kT} \right] dq \, dp \tag{3.7.12}$$

are the corresponding partition functions.

The canonical strain ensemble $\rho_{\mathscr{A}}$ has been discussed previously. In particular, we have seen (Section 3.6) that $\psi_{\mathscr{A}} = \psi_{\mathscr{A}}(\mathscr{A}, T)$ corresponds, in continuum thermodynamics, to $F(\mathscr{A}, T)$, the Helmholtz free energy of the system. We consider next the significance of the parameter $\psi_{\mathscr{F}} = \psi_{\mathscr{F}}(\mathscr{F}, T)$ in $\rho_{\mathscr{F}}$.

As determined previously (Section 3.5), $H_{\mathscr{A}}(q, p; \mathscr{A}) = U^m(q, p; \mathscr{A})$, the phase function for the internal energy function. As we have emphasized, the definition of the appropriate phase function for a given property is independent of the nature of the ensemble employed. Therefore, when the system is

---

[14] Note that the reasoning in Chapter 2, which led to the form of the canonical ensemble as given in Eq. (3.7.9), did not depend on the nature of the controllable parameters.

[15] When attention is confined to gases with volume and pressure as conjugate mechanical variables, the term pressure ensemble, or isobaric ensemble, is employed to describe analogous concepts.

described in terms of mechanical controllable parameters,

$$U(\mathscr{F}, T) = \int_\Gamma H_{\mathscr{A}}(q, p; \mathscr{A}^m(q, p; \mathscr{F}))\rho_{\mathscr{F}}(q, p; \mathscr{F}, T)\, dq\, dp.$$

$$(3.7.13)$$

It follows that

$$\bar{H}_{\mathscr{F}}(\mathscr{F}, T) = \int_\Gamma H_{\mathscr{F}}\rho_{\mathscr{F}}\, dq\, dp = \int_\Gamma (H_{\mathscr{A}} - \mathscr{A}^m_\alpha \mathscr{F}_\alpha)\rho_{\mathscr{F}}\, dq\, dp$$

$$= U(\mathscr{F}, T) - \mathscr{A}_\alpha(\mathscr{F}, T)\mathscr{F}_\alpha \triangleq H(\mathscr{F}, T) \qquad (3.7.14)$$

where [Eq. (1.5.4)], $H(\mathscr{F}, T)$ is the enthalpy of the system.[16] We have come to the conclusion, therefore, that $H_{\mathscr{F}}(q, p; \mathscr{F}) = H^m(q, p; \mathscr{F})$, the phase function for the enthalpy, just as $H_{\mathscr{A}}(q, p; \mathscr{A}) = U^m(q, p; \mathscr{A})$ is the phase function for the internal energy.

From the first law of thermodynamics, $\dot{U} = \dot{W} + \dot{Q} = \mathscr{F}_\alpha \dot{\mathscr{A}}_\alpha + \dot{Q}$, and the definition of the enthalpy, $H = U - \mathscr{F}_\alpha \mathscr{A}_\alpha$, it follows that

$$\dot{H} = -\mathscr{A}_\alpha \dot{\mathscr{F}}_\alpha + \dot{Q}. \qquad (3.7.15)$$

We may now find a statistical mechanics interpretation for $\dot{Q}$ in terms of $H_{\mathscr{F}}$ and $\rho_{\mathscr{F}}$ by a procedure analogous to that followed in Section 3.5 for the strain ensemble. Consider a quasi-static process described by $\mathscr{F}_\alpha(t)$, $T(t)$. From Eq. (3.7.14),

$$\dot{H} = \frac{d}{dt}\int_\Gamma H_{\mathscr{F}}\rho_{\mathscr{F}}\, dq\, dp = \int_\Gamma \dot{H}_{\mathscr{F}}\rho_{\mathscr{F}}\, dq\, dp + \int_\Gamma H_{\mathscr{F}}\dot{\rho}_{\mathscr{F}}\, dq\, dp. \quad (3.7.16)$$

The first integral in this equation,

$$\int_\Gamma \dot{H}_{\mathscr{F}}\rho_{\mathscr{F}}\, dq\, dp = \int_\Gamma \frac{\partial H_{\mathscr{F}}}{\partial \mathscr{F}_\alpha}\dot{\mathscr{F}}_\alpha \rho_{\mathscr{F}}\, dq\, dp = -\int_\Gamma \mathscr{A}^m_\alpha \dot{\mathscr{F}}_\alpha \rho_{\mathscr{F}}\, dq\, dp$$

$$= -\mathscr{A}_\alpha \dot{\mathscr{F}}_\alpha. \qquad (3.7.17)$$

by use of Eq. (3.7.8). By comparison with Eq. (3.7.15), we conclude that the second integral in Eq. (3.7.16) represents $\dot{Q}$, that is

$$\dot{Q} = \int_\Gamma H_{\mathscr{F}}\dot{\rho}_{\mathscr{F}}\, dq\, dp. \qquad (3.7.18)$$

---

[16] Recall that the system enthalpy is denoted by roman H while the system Hamiltonian is denoted by italic H.

This is the same form as the expression for heat flow for the strain ensemble [see Eq. (3.5.12)] and therefore the relation to the second law of thermodynamics follows the same lines as in Section 3.6. That is, we define, analogously to Eq. (3.6.2),

$$\eta_{\mathscr{F}}(q, p; \mathscr{F}, T) = \frac{\psi_{\mathscr{F}} - H_{\mathscr{F}}(q, p; \mathscr{F})}{kT} \tag{3.7.19}$$

and find [as in Eqs. (3.6.3)–(3.6.14)] that

$$\bar{\eta}_{\mathscr{F}}(\mathscr{F}, T) = -\frac{S(\mathscr{F}, T)}{k}. \tag{3.7.20}$$

It follows from Eqs. (3.7.14), (3.7.19), and (3.7.20), that

$$\psi_{\mathscr{F}}(\mathscr{F}, T) = U - TS - \mathscr{A}_{\alpha}\mathscr{F}_{\alpha} \triangleq G(\mathscr{F}, T) \tag{3.7.21}$$

where [Eq. (1.5.14)] $G(\mathscr{F}, T)$ is the Gibbs free energy, or by use of Eq. (3.7.11),

$$G(\mathscr{F}, T) = -kT \log Z_{\mathscr{F}}(\mathscr{F}, T). \tag{3.7.22}$$

As in the derivation of Eq. (3.6.20), we see from Eq. (3.7.20) that a corresponding relation applies for $S(\mathscr{F}, T)$, namely

$$S(\mathscr{F}, T) = -k \int_{\Gamma} \rho_{\mathscr{F}}(q, p; \mathscr{F}, T) \log \rho_{\mathscr{F}}(q, p; \mathscr{F}, T) \, dq \, dp.$$

$$\tag{3.7.23}$$

Augmented System Approach to Stress Ensemble

In the development of the stress ensemble as just presented, the Hamiltonians $H_{\mathscr{F}}(q, p; \mathscr{F})$ and $H_{\mathscr{A}}(q, p; \mathscr{A})$ are alternate descriptions of the same atomic system in interaction with the same heat bath. A different approach to the stress ensemble is based on a system consisting of the original atomic system described by coordinates and momenta (q, p), plus the kinematical parameters or generalized displacements $\mathscr{A}_1, \ldots, \mathscr{A}_{\nu}$ regarded as additional coordinates or degrees of freedom of the augmented system. These additional displacements move in a linear potential so that they are subject to the prescribed constant forces $\mathscr{F}_1, \ldots, \mathscr{F}_{\nu}$; the kinetic energy associated with these displacements is neglected. Therefore, the Hamiltonian $\tilde{H}_{\mathscr{F}}(q, p, \mathscr{A}'; \mathscr{F})$ of the augmented system takes the form[17]

$$\tilde{H}_{\mathscr{F}}(q, p, \mathscr{A}'; \mathscr{F}) = H_{\mathscr{A}}(q, p; \mathscr{A}') - \mathscr{A}'_{\alpha}\mathscr{F}_{\alpha} \tag{3.7.24}$$

---

[17]The use of the prime on the strain variables $\mathscr{A}'_{\alpha}$ emphasizes that they are fluctuating variables; we reserve the notation of $\mathscr{A}^m_{\alpha}$ to denote the phase functions $\mathscr{A}^m_{\alpha}(q, p; \mathscr{F})$ as in our previous development of the stress ensemble. For a discussion of a stress ensemble in which, in addition to the stress, enthalpy rather than temperature is held fixed, see Parrinello and Rahman (1982).

in place of Eq. (3.7.4). Furthermore, the augmented system described by $\tilde{H}_{\mathscr{F}}(q, p, \mathscr{A}'; \mathscr{F})$ is regarded as in weak interaction with a heat bath at temperature T. Therefore, it is described by a canonical ensemble

$$\tilde{\rho}_{\mathscr{F}}(q, p, \mathscr{A}'; \mathscr{F}, T) = \exp\left\{\frac{\tilde{\psi}_{\mathscr{F}} - \tilde{H}_{\mathscr{F}}}{kT}\right\} \tag{3.7.25}$$

defined on $\Gamma + \mathscr{A}$, the space consisting of the original phase space together with $-\infty < \mathscr{A}'_{\alpha} < \infty$, $\alpha = 1, \ldots, \nu$.

In terms of the simple model shown in Figure 3.1, the augmented system consists of both particles I and E, with particle E subjected to a constant force $\mathscr{F}$ while both are in weak interaction with a surrounding heat bath. We may give a physical motivation of the neglect of the kinetic energy of E by the assumption that it is very massive since, in the strain ensemble, it represents the environment with which the atomic particle I interacts.

The partition function $\tilde{Z}_{\mathscr{F}}(\mathscr{F}, T)$ for the augmented system is

$$\tilde{Z}_{\mathscr{F}}(\mathscr{F}, T) = \int_{\Gamma+\mathscr{A}} \exp\left[-\frac{\tilde{H}_{\mathscr{F}}(q, p, \mathscr{A}'; \mathscr{F})}{kT}\right] dq\, dp\, d\mathscr{A}'$$

$$= \int_{\Gamma+\mathscr{A}} \exp\left[\frac{-H_{\mathscr{A}}(q, p; \mathscr{A}') + \mathscr{A}'_{\alpha}\mathscr{F}_{\alpha}}{kT}\right] dq\, dp\, d\mathscr{A}'$$

$$\tag{3.7.26}$$

by use of Eq. (3.7.24). By carrying out the integration with respect to (q, p), we find

$$\tilde{Z}_{\mathscr{F}}(\mathscr{F}, T) = \int_{-\infty}^{\infty} \cdots \int_{-\infty}^{\infty} Z_{\mathscr{A}}(\mathscr{A}', T) \exp(\beta \mathscr{A}'_{\alpha}\mathscr{F}_{\alpha})\, d\mathscr{A}'_1 \ldots d\mathscr{A}'_{\nu}.$$

$$\tag{3.7.27}$$

where $\beta = (kT)^{-1}$. For the case of $\nu = 1$, Eq. (3.7.27) describes $\tilde{Z}_{\mathscr{F}}(\mathscr{F}, T)$ as the two-sided Laplace transform of $Z_{\mathscr{A}}(\mathscr{A}, T)$ with $-\beta \mathscr{A}'$ playing the role of the transform parameter. An example of the use of this relation will be found in Weiner and Pear (1977), which treats an idealized model of a polymer chain under tension.

The distribution function $\tilde{\rho}_{\mathscr{F}}$ can also be written in the form

$$\tilde{\rho}_{\mathscr{F}}(q, p, \mathscr{A}'; \mathscr{F}, T) = \tilde{Z}_{\mathscr{F}}^{-1} \exp\left[\frac{-H_{\mathscr{A}}(q, p; \mathscr{A}') + \mathscr{A}'_{\alpha}\mathscr{F}_{\alpha}}{kT}\right].$$

$$\tag{3.7.28}$$

From this form, it is clear that

$$\overline{\mathscr{A}'_\alpha} = \int_{\Gamma + \mathscr{A}} \mathscr{A}'_\alpha \tilde{\rho}_{\mathscr{F}} \, dq \, dp \, d\mathscr{A}' = kT \frac{\partial}{\partial \mathscr{F}_\alpha} \log \tilde{Z}_{\mathscr{F}}(\mathscr{F}, T), \quad (3.7.29)$$

as may be verified by use of Eq. (3.7.26) and the direct calculation of the derivative.

For brevity, we will refer to the ensemble described by $\tilde{\rho}_{\mathscr{F}}(q, p, \mathscr{A}'; \mathscr{F}, T)$ as the augmented stress ensemble and continue to refer to that described by $\rho_{\mathscr{F}}(q, p; \mathscr{F}, T)$ in Eq. (3.7.10) as the stress ensemble.

3.8 FLUCTUATIONS

Thus far in our discussions, we have identified the phase averages of micro-scopic phase functions with the corresponding macroscopic thermodynamic quantities. The notation we have used has been framed for this purpose. For example, in this notation the phase function for the stress tensor would be written $T_{LM}^m(q, p; E_{RS})$ and its phase average with respect to the appropriate canonical ensemble would be denoted by $T_{LM}(E_{RS}, T)$, the same notation used for its macroscopic equivalent.

This identification is valid, and the notation is convenient, in the thermody-namic limit, that is, for systems of macroscopic size in which temporal fluctuations of system properties from their equilibrium values are too small to be observed on a macroscopic scale of measurement. We now wish to consider this question more closely and to obtain estimates of the magnitude of the fluctuations as function of the size of the system. For this purpose, we return here to the use of superposed bars to denote phase averages. Let $\mathscr{F}_\alpha$, $\mathscr{A}_\alpha$, $\alpha = 1, \ldots, \nu$ denote a set of conjugate generalized stresses and strains. When the strains, $\mathscr{A}_\alpha$, are used as controlled parameters, the corresponding micro-scopic phase functions for the stresses are denoted by $\mathscr{F}_\alpha^m(q, p; \mathscr{A})$ as be-fore, but their phase averages with respect to the canonical distribution $\rho_{\mathscr{A}}(q, p; \mathscr{A}, T)$ [Eq. (3.7.9)] are written $\overline{\mathscr{F}_\alpha^m}(\mathscr{A}, T)$, with the understanding that $\overline{\mathscr{F}_\alpha^m}(\mathscr{A}, T) = \mathscr{F}_\alpha(\mathscr{A}, T)$ only for bodies of macroscopic size. Analogous notations are used when the stresses are the controlled parameters.

By the ergodic hypothesis, the phase average $\overline{\mathscr{F}_\alpha^m} = \widehat{\mathscr{F}_\alpha^m}$, where the latter notation represents a time average as discussed in Section 2.4. As a measure of the magnitude of the temporal fluctuations in the stress $\mathscr{F}_\alpha^m$, we take the time average of the square of the deviation from the mean,

$$\widehat{\left(\mathscr{F}^m - \widehat{\mathscr{F}_\alpha^m} \right)^2} = \overline{\left(\mathscr{F}_\alpha^m - \overline{\mathscr{F}_\alpha^m} \right)^2} \triangleq \left(\Delta \mathscr{F}_\alpha^m \right)^2 \qquad (3.8.1)$$

where we have again invoked the ergodic hypothesis to return from time averages to phase averages. The quantity $(\Delta \mathscr{F}_\alpha^m)^2$ is called the mean-square deviation or variance of the fluctuating quantity $\mathscr{F}_\alpha{}^m$. It is sometimes typographically clearer to use enclosing carats in place of superposed bars for phase averages, writing, for example,

$$
\left(\Delta \mathscr{F}_\alpha{}^m \right)^2 = \left\langle \left(\mathscr{F}_\alpha{}^m - \left\langle \mathscr{F}_\alpha{}^m \right\rangle \right)^2 \right\rangle = \left\langle \left(\mathscr{F}_\alpha{}^m \right)^2 - 2 \mathscr{F}_\alpha{}^m \left\langle \mathscr{F}_\alpha{}^m \right\rangle + \left\langle \mathscr{F}_\alpha{}^m \right\rangle^2 \right\rangle
$$

$$
= \left\langle \left(\mathscr{F}_\alpha{}^m \right)^2 \right\rangle - \left\langle \mathscr{F}_\alpha{}^m \right\rangle^2.
$$

In what follows, we will use whichever notation appears clearer in the given context.

We next derive a relation for the mean-square deviation which provides the basis for an estimate of its magnitude. This relation will be derived by three different approaches. The most fundamental is based on the phase space, Γ. If we adopt the augmented system viewpoint for the stress ensemble, fluctuations in the strain components can be discussed in terms of a strain space, $\mathscr{A}$. Finally, if the system is sufficiently large so that the fluctuations are small, the fluctuations in strain may be described in terms of macroscopic thermodynamic functions.

Phase Space Derivation[18]

Consider a system described by the Hamiltonian $H_{\mathscr{A}}(q, p; \mathscr{A})$ and the canonical ensemble

$$
\rho_{\mathscr{A}}(q, p; \mathscr{A}, T) = \exp \left[\frac{\psi_{\mathscr{A}} - H_{\mathscr{A}}(q, p; \mathscr{A})}{kT} \right] \tag{3.8.2}
$$

with the normalization condition

$$
\int_\Gamma \rho_{\mathscr{A}} \, dq \, dp = \int_\Gamma \exp \left[\frac{\psi_{\mathscr{A}} - H_{\mathscr{A}}}{kT} \right] dq \, dp = 1. \tag{3.8.3}
$$

Differentiation of Eq. (3.8.3) with respect to $\mathscr{A}_\alpha$ leads to the result

$$
\int_\Gamma \left[\frac{\partial \psi_{\mathscr{A}}}{\partial \mathscr{A}_\alpha} - \frac{\partial H_{\mathscr{A}}}{\partial \mathscr{A}_\alpha} \right] \exp \left[\frac{\psi_{\mathscr{A}} - H_{\mathscr{A}}}{kT} \right] dq \, dp = 0, \tag{3.8.4}
$$

and differentiation of Eq. (3.8.4) with respect to $\mathscr{A}_\alpha$ yields

$$
\int_\Gamma \left[\frac{\partial^2 \psi_{\mathscr{A}}}{\partial \mathscr{A}_\alpha^2} - \frac{\partial^2 H_{\mathscr{A}}}{\partial \mathscr{A}_\alpha^2} + \frac{1}{kT} \left(\frac{\partial \psi_{\mathscr{A}}}{\partial \mathscr{A}_\alpha} - \frac{\partial H_{\mathscr{A}}}{\partial \mathscr{A}_\alpha} \right)^2 \right] \rho_{\mathscr{A}} \, dq \, dp = 0. \tag{3.8.5}
$$

---

[18]This derivation is given by Gibbs (1902, p. 80). For the use of strain fluctuations for the computation of elastic constants by means of molecular dynamics, see Parinello and Rahman (1982).

We recall that the phase function for $\mathscr{F}_\alpha$ is [Eq. (3.7.7)]

$$\mathscr{F}_\alpha{}^m(q, p; \mathscr{A}) = \frac{\partial H_\mathscr{A}}{\partial \mathscr{A}_\alpha}(q, p; \mathscr{A}). \tag{3.8.6}$$

Since Eq. (3.8.4) implies that the phase average of the quantity in the bracket is zero, it follows that

$$\overline{\mathscr{F}_\alpha{}^m} = \frac{\partial \psi_\mathscr{A}}{\partial \mathscr{A}_\alpha} = -kT \frac{\partial}{\partial \mathscr{A}_\alpha} \log Z_\mathscr{A}. \tag{3.8.7}$$

Similarly, from Eq. (3.8.5) we obtain the relation

$$\frac{\partial^2 \psi_\mathscr{A}}{\partial \mathscr{A}_\alpha^2} - \overline{\frac{\partial^2 H_\mathscr{A}}{\partial \mathscr{A}_\alpha^2}} + \frac{1}{kT}\overline{\left[\frac{\partial \psi_\mathscr{A}}{\partial \mathscr{A}_\alpha} - \frac{\partial H_\mathscr{A}}{\partial \mathscr{A}_\alpha}\right]^2} = 0$$

from which, by use of Eqs. (3.8.6) and (3.8.7), we find the desired relation for the magnitude of fluctuation of the stress $\mathscr{F}$,

$$(\Delta \mathscr{F}_\alpha{}^m)^2 \triangleq \overline{\left(\mathscr{F}_\alpha{}^m - \overline{\mathscr{F}_\alpha{}^m}\right)^2} = \overline{\left(\mathscr{F}_\alpha{}^m\right)^2} - \left(\overline{\mathscr{F}_\alpha{}^m}\right)^2 = kT\left(\overline{\frac{\partial^2 H_\mathscr{A}}{\partial \mathscr{A}_\alpha^2}} - \frac{\partial^2 \psi_\mathscr{A}}{\partial \mathscr{A}_\alpha^2}\right)$$

$$\tag{3.8.8}$$

or

$$(\Delta \mathscr{F}_\alpha{}^m)^2 = kT\left(\overline{\frac{\partial \mathscr{F}_\alpha{}^m}{\partial \mathscr{A}_\alpha}} - \frac{\partial \overline{\mathscr{F}_\alpha{}^m}}{\partial \mathscr{A}_\alpha}\right) = kT\left(\left\langle \frac{\partial \mathscr{F}_\alpha{}^m}{\partial \mathscr{A}_\alpha}\right\rangle - \frac{\partial \langle \mathscr{F}_\alpha{}^m\rangle}{\partial \mathscr{A}_\alpha}\right)$$

$$\tag{3.8.9}$$

with no summation on α.

The correlation in the fluctuations between the stresses $\mathscr{F}_\gamma$ and $\mathscr{F}_\delta$, $\gamma \neq \delta$, is measured by the quantity $\overline{\Delta\mathscr{F}_\alpha{}^m \Delta\mathscr{F}_\delta{}^m}$, referred to as the covariance of $\mathscr{F}_\gamma{}^m$ and $\mathscr{F}_\delta{}^m$, where

$$\overline{\Delta\mathscr{F}_\gamma{}^m \Delta\mathscr{F}_\delta{}^m} \triangleq \overline{\left(\mathscr{F}_\gamma{}^m - \overline{\mathscr{F}_\gamma{}^m}\right)\left(\mathscr{F}_\delta{}^m - \overline{\mathscr{F}_\delta{}^m}\right)} = \overline{\mathscr{F}_\gamma{}^m \mathscr{F}_\delta{}^m} - \overline{\mathscr{F}_\gamma{}^m}\,\overline{\mathscr{F}_\delta{}^m}.$$

By differentiation of Eq. (3.8.4) with respect to $\mathscr{A}_\gamma$ we find, as in the derivation of Eq. (3.8.9), that

$$\overline{\Delta\mathscr{F}_\gamma{}^m \Delta\mathscr{F}_\delta{}^m} = kT\left(\left\langle \frac{\partial \mathscr{F}_\gamma{}^m}{\partial \mathscr{A}_\delta}\right\rangle - \frac{\partial \langle \mathscr{F}_\gamma{}^m\rangle}{\partial \mathscr{A}_\delta}\right). \tag{3.8.10}$$

We may also obtain an estimate for the fluctuation in energy by differentiating Eq. (3.8.3) twice with respect to $\beta = (kT)^{-1}$. The result of the first differentiation is

$$\int_{\Gamma}\left[\psi_{\mathscr{A}} - H_{\mathscr{A}} + \beta\frac{\partial\psi_{\mathscr{A}}}{\partial\beta}\right]\rho_{\mathscr{A}}\,dq\,dp = 0 \qquad (3.8.11)$$

which implies that

$$\overline{H}_{\mathscr{A}} = \psi_{\mathscr{A}} + \beta\frac{\partial\psi_{\mathscr{A}}}{\partial\beta} = \frac{\partial}{\partial\beta}(\beta\psi_{\mathscr{A}}) = -\frac{\partial}{\partial\beta}\log Z_{\mathscr{A}}. \qquad (3.8.12)$$

Substitution of this result into Eq. (3.8.11) and differentiating it with respect to β leads to

$$\int_{\Gamma}\left[\frac{\partial\overline{H}_{\mathscr{A}}}{\partial\beta} + (\overline{H}_{\mathscr{A}} - H_{\mathscr{A}})^2\right]\rho_{\mathscr{A}}\,dq\,dp = 0, \qquad (3.8.13)$$

which leads to the desired result, namely,

$$(\Delta H_{\mathscr{A}})^2 \triangleq \overline{H_{\mathscr{A}}^2} - (\overline{H}_{\mathscr{A}})^2 = -\frac{\partial\overline{H}_{\mathscr{A}}}{\partial\beta} = kT^2\frac{\partial\overline{H}_{\mathscr{A}}}{\partial T}. \qquad (3.8.14)$$

The multiplicative factor kT, which appears in Eqs. (3.8.9), (3.8.10), and (3.8.14), for the various fluctuation magnitudes plays a key role. As we have seen in Section 3.6, $(kT)/2$ is the mean energy per degree of freedom of a perfect gas and, as we shall see, the energy per atom of more general systems is also of the order of magnitude of kT. This factor, therefore, brings in to the discussion of the relative magnitude of fluctuations the ratio of the energy per atom to the total energy of the system and results in the relative fluctuations becoming negligible for macroscopic systems. For example, we may estimate the relative magnitude of energy fluctuations by considering the case in which $H_{\mathscr{A}}$ corresponds to the sum of N harmonic oscillators. This is the case for the Hamiltonian of a crystal of $N/3$ atoms in the harmonic approximation as will be discussed in Section 4.4. Then $\overline{H}_{\mathscr{A}} = NkT$ and Eq. (3.8.14) becomes

$$\frac{\Delta H_{\mathscr{A}}}{\overline{H}_{\mathscr{A}}} = \frac{1}{\sqrt{N}}. \qquad (3.8.15)$$

Similar considerations apply to the relative magnitude of the fluctuations in the stresses $\mathscr{F}_\alpha$, although the estimate is not as clear-cut. We rewrite Eq. (3.8.8) as

$$\frac{\Delta\mathscr{F}_\alpha^m}{\overline{\mathscr{F}}_\alpha^m} = \frac{\left[kT\left(\overline{\frac{\partial^2 H_{\mathscr{A}}}{\partial\mathscr{A}_\alpha^2}} - \frac{\partial^2\psi_{\mathscr{A}}}{\partial\mathscr{A}_\alpha^2}\right)\right]^{1/2}}{\partial\psi_{\mathscr{A}}/\partial\mathscr{A}_\alpha}.$$

If we take $\mathscr{A}_\alpha$ as intensive variables and make the heuristic assumption that $\left\langle \partial^2 H_{\mathscr{A}}/\partial \mathscr{A}_\alpha^2 \right\rangle$, $\partial^2 \psi_{\mathscr{A}}/\partial \mathscr{A}_\alpha^2$, $\partial \psi_{\mathscr{A}}/\partial \mathscr{A}_\alpha$ are all of the order of magnitude of the extensive quantities $\psi_{\mathscr{A}}$ or $\bar{H}$, then we find

$$\frac{\Delta \mathscr{F}_\alpha^m}{\mathscr{F}_\alpha^m} = 0\left(\sqrt{\frac{kT}{\psi_{\mathscr{A}}}} \right) = 0\left(\sqrt{\frac{kT}{\bar{H}_{\mathscr{A}}}} \right) = 0\left(\frac{1}{\sqrt{N}} \right). \qquad (3.8.16)$$

The difficulty in making precise the estimates of the fluctuations in the stresses $\mathscr{F}_\alpha$ lies in the term $\left\langle \partial^2 H_{\mathscr{A}}/\partial \mathscr{A}_\alpha^2 \right\rangle = \left\langle \partial \mathscr{F}_\alpha^m/\partial \mathscr{A}_\alpha \right\rangle$ which has no macroscopic interpretation. Therefore a quantitative estimate requires a specific atomistic model.[19]

Fluctuations in Strains

Completely anlogous considerations apply when mechanical parameters are controlled in a stress ensemble described by

$$\rho_{\mathscr{F}}(q, p; \mathscr{F}, T) = \exp\left[\frac{\psi_{\mathscr{F}} - H_{\mathscr{F}}(q, p; \mathscr{F})}{kT} \right] \qquad (3.8.17)$$

and the strains $\mathscr{A}_\alpha$ can then fluctuate. The calculations proceed as before and lead to the result

$$\Delta \mathscr{A}_\gamma^m \Delta \mathscr{A}_\delta^m = kT\left(\frac{\partial \left\langle \mathscr{A}_\gamma^m \right\rangle}{\partial \mathscr{F}_\delta} - \left\langle \frac{\partial \mathscr{A}_\gamma^m}{\partial \mathscr{F}_\delta} \right\rangle \right) \qquad (3.8.18)$$

analogous to Eqs. (3.8.10). [The difference in sign is due to that between Eqs. (3.7.7) and (3.7.8).] The magnitude of the relative fluctuations may be estimated to be $0(1/\sqrt{N})$ by the heuristic reasoning that lead to Eq. (3.8.16).

State Space Viewpoint

In our discussion of the fluctuations of a quantity such as $\mathscr{F}_\alpha^m$, we considered the phase function $\mathscr{F}_\alpha^m(q, p; \mathscr{A})$ and determined its mean-square deviation in a canonical ensemble described by $\rho_{\mathscr{A}}(q, p; \mathscr{A}, T)$. From the viewpoint of probability theory, the sample space[20] in that discussion was the phase space Γ and $\rho_{\mathscr{A}}$ is the probability distribution function defined on this space. If the stresses $\mathscr{F}_\alpha$ are the controlled parameters and we adopt the augmented stress ensemble, then it is possible to rephrase the problem in terms of a sample space $\mathscr{A}$ spanned by the coordinates $-\infty < \mathscr{A}_\alpha' < \infty$, $\alpha = 1, \ldots, \nu$, which we

---

[19]See, for example, Fowler (1936, p. 756) and Münster (1969, p. 188).

[20]For a discussion of the concept of sample space see, for example, Feller (1950).

will refer to as strain space.[21] For this purpose, it is necessary to determine the probability distribution function $W(\mathscr{A}'; \mathscr{F}, T)$ on strain space. This can be accomplished by the use of the distribution $\tilde{\rho}_{\mathscr{F}}(q, p, \mathscr{A}'; \mathscr{F}, T)$ defined on $\Gamma + \mathscr{A}$ in Eq. (3.7.28) and its integration over Γ:

$$
W(\mathscr{A}'; \mathscr{F}, T) = \int_{\Gamma} \tilde{\rho}_{\mathscr{F}}(q, p, \mathscr{A}'; \mathscr{F}, T)\, dq\, dp
$$

$$
= \tilde{Z}_{\mathscr{F}}^{-1} \int_{\Gamma} \exp\left[\frac{-H_{\mathscr{A}}(q, p; \mathscr{A}') + \mathscr{A}'_{\alpha} \mathscr{F}_{\alpha}}{kT} \right] dq\, dp
$$

$$
= \left[\tilde{Z}_{\mathscr{F}}(\mathscr{F}, T) \right]^{-1} Z_{\mathscr{A}}(\mathscr{A}', T) \exp(\beta \mathscr{A}'_{\alpha} \mathscr{F}_{\alpha}).
$$

$$(3.8.19)$$

We can now compute quantities such as the means $\langle \mathscr{A}'_{\gamma} \rangle$ and the covariance matrix $\Delta \mathscr{A}'_{\gamma} \Delta \mathscr{A}'_{\delta}$ by suitable integrations over the strain space $\mathscr{A}$. Thus,

$$
\langle \mathscr{A}'_{\gamma} \rangle = \int_{-\infty}^{\infty} \cdots \int_{-\infty}^{\infty} \mathscr{A}'_{\gamma} W(\mathscr{A}'; \mathscr{F}, T)\, d\mathscr{A}'_1 \cdots d\mathscr{A}'_{\nu} \quad (3.8.20)
$$

and, by differentiation of this equation,

$$
\frac{\partial \langle \mathscr{A}'_{\gamma} \rangle}{\partial \mathscr{F}_{\delta}} = \int_{-\infty}^{\infty} \cdots \int_{-\infty}^{\infty} \mathscr{A}'_{\gamma} \frac{\partial W}{\partial \mathscr{F}_{\delta}}(\mathscr{A}'; \mathscr{F}, T)\, d\mathscr{A}'_1 \ldots d\mathscr{A}'_{\nu}.
$$

$$(3.8.21)$$

From the definition of W in Eq. (3.8.19),

$$
\frac{\partial W}{\partial \mathscr{F}_{\delta}} = \left(-\frac{\partial}{\partial \mathscr{F}_{\delta}} \log \tilde{Z}_{\mathscr{F}} + \beta \mathscr{A}'_{\delta} \right) W
$$

$$
= \beta \left(\mathscr{A}'_{\delta} - \langle \mathscr{A}'_{\delta} \rangle \right) W \qquad (3.8.22)
$$

by use of Eq. (3.7.29). Substitution of Eq. (3.8.22) into Eq. (3.8.21) yields

$$
\frac{\partial \langle \mathscr{A}'_{\gamma} \rangle}{\partial \mathscr{F}_{\delta}} = \beta \int_{-\infty}^{\infty} \cdots \int_{-\infty}^{\infty} \mathscr{A}'_{\gamma} \left(\mathscr{A}'_{\delta} - \langle \mathscr{A}'_{\delta} \rangle \right) W\, d\mathscr{A}'_1 \ldots d\mathscr{A}'_{\nu}
$$

or

$$
\frac{\partial \langle \mathscr{A}'_{\gamma} \rangle}{\partial \mathscr{F}_{\delta}} = \beta \left(\langle \mathscr{A}'_{\gamma} \mathscr{A}'_{\delta} \rangle - \langle \mathscr{A}'_{\gamma} \rangle \langle \mathscr{A}'_{\delta} \rangle \right) = \beta \Delta \mathscr{A}'_{\gamma} \Delta \mathscr{A}'_{\delta}. \quad (3.8.23)
$$

---

[21] The remaining state variable, temperature, is regarded as fixed in our discussion.

This result may be compared with the result of Eq. (3.8.18) derived for the stress ensemble defined on the phase space Γ and which contains the additional term $\langle \partial \mathscr{A}_{\gamma}^{m} / \partial \mathscr{F}_{\delta} \rangle$. Here, in the augmented stress ensemble, $\mathscr{A}_{\gamma}'$ is an independent fluctuating coordinate, so the corresponding partial derivative vanishes.

Macroscopic Thermodynamics Viewpoint

We continue to use the augmented stress ensemble with stresses $\mathscr{F}_{\alpha}$ and temperature T imposed. If the system is sufficiently large so that macroscopic thermodynamics applies, the corresponding strains are given by the macroscopic equations of state $\mathscr{A}_{\alpha} = \mathscr{A}_{\alpha}(\mathscr{F}, T)$.

We now treat the case in which the system is sufficiently small so that the fluctuations of $\mathscr{A}_{\alpha}'$ from the macroscopic values of $\mathscr{A}_{\alpha}$ are not negligible, yet is sufficiently large so that these fluctuations are small quantities and macroscopic thermodynamics may be expected to apply to the mean quantities.

The strain space probability distribution $W(\mathscr{A}'; \mathscr{F}, T)$ of Eq. (3.8.19) may be rewritten as

$$W(\mathscr{A}'; \mathscr{F}, T) = \exp - \beta R(\mathscr{A}'; \mathscr{F}, T) \tag{3.8.24}$$

where

$$R(\mathscr{A}'; \mathscr{F}, T) = kT \log \tilde{Z}_{\mathscr{F}}(\mathscr{F}, T) - kT \log Z_{\mathscr{A}}(\mathscr{A}', T) - \mathscr{A}_{\alpha}' \mathscr{F}_{\alpha}. \tag{3.8.25}$$

We expand R in a power series up to quadratic terms about $\mathscr{A}_{\alpha}$:

$$R(\mathscr{A}'; \mathscr{F}, T) = R(\mathscr{A}; \mathscr{F}, T) + \left(\frac{\partial R}{\partial \mathscr{A}_{\gamma}'} \right) (\mathscr{A}_{\gamma}' - \mathscr{A}_{\gamma})$$

$$+ \frac{1}{2} \left(\frac{\partial^2 R}{\partial \mathscr{A}_{\gamma}' \partial \mathscr{A}_{\delta}'} \right) (\mathscr{A}_{\gamma}' - \mathscr{A}_{\gamma})(\mathscr{A}_{\delta}' - \mathscr{A}_{\delta}) \tag{3.8.26}$$

where the derivatives are evaluated at $(\mathscr{A}; \mathscr{F}, T)$. From Eq. (3.8.25),

$$\frac{\partial R}{\partial \mathscr{A}_{\gamma}'} = - \frac{\partial}{\partial \mathscr{A}_{\gamma}'} kT \log Z_{\mathscr{A}} - \mathscr{F}_{\gamma}$$

$$= \overline{\mathscr{F}_{\gamma}^{m}} - \mathscr{F}_{\gamma} = 0 \tag{3.8.27}$$

where we have used Eq. (3.8.7) and our assumption that the means are governed by macroscopic thermodynamics. Furthermore,

$$\frac{\partial^2 R}{\partial \mathscr{A}'_\gamma \partial \mathscr{A}'_\delta} = -\frac{\partial^2}{\partial \mathscr{A}'_\gamma \partial \mathscr{A}'_\delta} kT \log Z_\mathscr{A} = \frac{\partial^2 F}{\partial \mathscr{A}'_\gamma \partial \mathscr{A}'_\delta} \triangleq F_{\gamma\delta} \quad (3.8.28)$$

where $F(\mathscr{A}, T) = -kT \log Z_\mathscr{A}(\mathscr{A}, T)$, Eq. (3.6.17), is the Helmholtz free energy of the system and $F_{\gamma\delta}$ denotes the indicated matrix of second partial derivatives, evaluated at $(\mathscr{A}, T)$.

We see therefore that for small fluctuations of $\mathscr{A}'_\alpha$ from the macroscopic equilibrium values $\mathscr{A}_\alpha$,

$$W(\mathscr{A}'; \mathscr{F}, T) \sim \exp\frac{-\beta}{2} F_{\gamma\delta}(\mathscr{A}'_\gamma - \mathscr{A}_\gamma)(\mathscr{A}'_\delta - \mathscr{A}_\delta), \quad (3.8.29)$$

and for a body of moderate size we expect that W will be negligible for large fluctuations.[22] Therefore we may extend the approximate definition of W of Eq. (3.8.29) to apply over all of strain space as

$$W(\mathscr{A}'; \mathscr{F}, T) = \frac{|F_{\gamma\delta}|^{1/2}}{(2\pi kT)^{\nu/2}} \exp - \frac{\beta}{2} F_{\gamma\delta}(\mathscr{A}'_\gamma - \mathscr{A}_\gamma)(\mathscr{A}'_\delta - \mathscr{A}_\delta),$$

$$(3.8.30)$$

where $|F_{\gamma\delta}|$ is the determinant of the matrix $F_{\gamma\delta}$ and the multiplicative constant has been introduced to ensure that this approximate probability distribution function W is normalized over strain space $\mathscr{A}$. In this approximation, therefore, W corresponds to a multivariate Gaussian distribution. It follows as a standard result for this distribution[23] that

$$\Delta\mathscr{A}'_\gamma \Delta\mathscr{A}'_\delta = kT F_{\gamma\delta}^{-1} \quad (3.8.31)$$

where $F_{\gamma\delta}^{-1}$ is the matrix inverse to $F_{\gamma\delta}$. But, by use of Eq. (1.5.13),

$$F_{\gamma\delta} = \frac{\partial^2 F}{\partial \mathscr{A}_\gamma \partial \mathscr{A}_\delta} = \frac{\partial \mathscr{F}_\gamma}{\partial \mathscr{A}_\delta}. \quad (3.8.32)$$

Therefore,

$$\Delta\mathscr{A}'_\gamma \Delta\mathscr{A}'_\delta = kT \frac{\partial \mathscr{A}_\gamma}{\partial \mathscr{F}_\delta} \quad (3.8.33)$$

---

[22] This is consistent with Eq. (3.8.29) since, from the extensive character of the Helmholtz free energy F, the exponent will have large magnitude for large fluctuations.
[23] See, for example, Landau and Lifshitz (1980, p.337).

in agreement with Eq. (3.8.23), since in the present approximation we are equating $\langle \mathscr{A}'_\alpha \rangle = \mathscr{A}_\alpha$.

Consistency of Stress and Strain Ensembles for Macroscopic Systems

From the viewpoint of macroscopic thermodynamics, we can regard the temperature and either the strains or the stresses as independent variables. If the former combination is used, then the stresses are obtained from the relations, Eq. (1.5.13),

$$\mathscr{F}_\alpha = \frac{\partial F}{\partial \mathscr{A}_\alpha}, \qquad \alpha = 1, \ldots, \nu, \tag{3.8.34}$$

where $F = F(\mathscr{A}, T)$ is the Helmholtz free energy. The Gibbs free energy, $G(\mathscr{F}, T)$, is defined as the Legendre transform of $F(\mathscr{A}, T)$, that is, Eq. (1.5.14),

$$G(\mathscr{F}, T) = F(\mathscr{A}, T) - \mathscr{A}_\alpha \mathscr{F}_\alpha, \tag{3.8.35}$$

where the quantities $\mathscr{A}_\alpha$ and $\mathscr{F}_\alpha$ are related as in Eq. (3.8.34). Then, as shown in the discussion of the Legendre transform of Section 3.7, the relations

$$\mathscr{A}_\alpha = -\frac{\partial G}{\partial \mathscr{F}_\alpha}, \qquad \alpha = 1, \ldots, \nu, \tag{3.8.36}$$

in which the stresses are independent variables will be the inverse relations to Eqs. (3.8.34). Either set of relations may be used to describe the same state of the system.

From the viewpoint of equilibrium statistical mechanics, however, the use of strains or of stresses as independent variables corresponds to two different physical situations. The independent variables are imposed, controlled quantities and are strict constants; the dependent variables are fluctuating quantities and only the mean values of the latter are measured. Regardless of the system size, we can compute these means by the relation

$$\overline{\mathscr{F}_\alpha^m} = \frac{\partial \psi_{\mathscr{A}}}{\partial \mathscr{A}_\alpha} = -kT \frac{\partial}{\partial \mathscr{A}_\alpha} \log Z_{\mathscr{A}}(\mathscr{A}, T)$$

derived as Eq. (3.8.7) for the strain ensemble, or by the analogous relation, Eq. (3.7.29),

$$\overline{\mathscr{A}'_\alpha} = -\frac{\partial \tilde{\psi}_{\mathscr{F}}}{\partial \mathscr{F}_\alpha} = kT \frac{\partial}{\partial \mathscr{F}_\alpha} \log \tilde{Z}_{\mathscr{F}}(\mathscr{F}, T) \tag{3.8.37}$$

for the augmented stress ensemble. These will be inverse relations if $\tilde{\psi}_{\mathscr{F}}$ and $\psi_{\mathscr{A}}$

are Legendre transforms of each other. We next present heuristic arguments,[24] which indicate that this will be the case for sufficiently large systems.

Consider the case in which the stresses $\mathscr{F}_\alpha$ are controlled in an augmented stress ensemble and use the relation between the partition functions $\tilde{Z}_\mathscr{F}(\mathscr{F}, T)$ and $Z_\mathscr{A}(\mathscr{A}, T)$ [Eq. (3.7.27)] which we rewrite here as

$$\tilde{Z}_\mathscr{F}(\mathscr{F}, T) = \int_{-\infty}^{\infty} \cdots \int_{-\infty}^{\infty} \exp \beta \big[kT \log Z_\mathscr{A}(\mathscr{A}', T)$$

$$+ \mathscr{A}'_\alpha \mathscr{F}_\alpha \big] d\mathscr{A}'_1 \ldots d\mathscr{A}'_\nu,$$

or, by use of Eq. (3.7.11),

$$\tilde{Z}_\mathscr{F}(\mathscr{F}, T) = \int_{-\infty}^{\infty} \cdots \int_{-\infty}^{\infty} \exp - \beta \big[\psi_\mathscr{A}(\mathscr{A}', T) - \mathscr{A}'_\alpha \mathscr{F}_\alpha \big] d\mathscr{A}'_1 \ldots d\mathscr{A}'_\nu.$$

$$(3.8.38)$$

Let $\mathscr{A}_\alpha$ be the solutions to the equations

$$\mathscr{F}_\alpha = \frac{\partial \psi_\mathscr{A}}{\partial \mathscr{A}_\alpha}(\mathscr{A}, T), \quad \alpha = 1, \ldots, \nu \qquad (3.8.39)$$

for the imposed values of $(\mathscr{F}, T)$ and expand the integrand about $(\mathscr{A}, T)$ up to quadratic terms. Then

$$\psi_\mathscr{A}(\mathscr{A}', T) = \psi_\mathscr{A}(\mathscr{A}, T) + \left(\frac{\partial \psi_\mathscr{A}}{\partial \mathscr{A}_\gamma} \right)(\mathscr{A}'_\gamma - \mathscr{A}_\gamma)$$

$$+ \frac{1}{2} \left(\frac{\partial^2 \psi_\mathscr{A}}{\partial \mathscr{A}_\gamma \partial \mathscr{A}_\delta} \right)(\mathscr{A}'_\gamma - \mathscr{A}_\gamma)(\mathscr{A}'_\delta - \mathscr{A}_\delta)$$

$$= \psi_\mathscr{A}(\mathscr{A}, T) + \mathscr{F}_\gamma(\mathscr{A}'_\gamma - \mathscr{A}_\gamma)$$

$$+ \frac{1}{2} \left(\frac{\partial^2 \psi_\mathscr{A}}{\partial \mathscr{A}_\gamma \partial \mathscr{A}_\delta} \right)(\mathscr{A}'_\gamma - \mathscr{A}_\gamma)(\mathscr{A}'_\delta - \mathscr{A}_\delta) \quad (3.8.40)$$

where the derivatives of $\psi_\mathscr{A}$ are evaluated at $(\mathscr{A}, T)$ and we have made use of Eq. (3.8.39). Substitution of Eq. (3.8.40) into (3.8.38) then leads to the result

$$\tilde{Z}_\mathscr{F}(\mathscr{F}, T) = \exp - \beta \big[\psi_\mathscr{A}(\mathscr{A}, T) - \mathscr{A}_\alpha \mathscr{F}_\alpha \big]$$

$$\times \int_{-\infty}^{\infty} \cdots \int_{-\infty}^{\infty} \exp - \frac{\beta}{2} \frac{\partial^2 \psi_\mathscr{A}}{\partial \mathscr{A}_\gamma \partial \mathscr{A}_\delta}(\mathscr{A}'_\gamma - \mathscr{A}_\gamma)(\mathscr{A}'_\delta - \mathscr{A}_\delta) d\mathscr{A}'_1 \ldots d\mathscr{A}'_\nu,$$

$$(3.8.41)$$

---

[24] Rigorous proofs require assumptions about the nature of the atomistic model and are difficult. An extensive discussion of this question is given in Münster (1969, Chapter IV).

or, by use of Eqs. (3.7.11),

$$\tilde{\psi}_{\mathscr{F}}(\mathscr{F}, T) = \psi_{\mathscr{A}}(\mathscr{A}, T) - \mathscr{A}_\alpha \mathscr{F}_\alpha - kT \log \int_{-\infty}^{\infty}$$

$$\cdots \int_{-\infty}^{\infty} \exp\left[-\frac{\beta}{2} \frac{\partial^2 \psi_{\mathscr{A}}}{\partial \mathscr{A}_\gamma \partial \mathscr{A}_\delta} (\mathscr{A}_\gamma' - \mathscr{A}_\gamma) \right.$$

$$\left. \times (\mathscr{A}_\delta' - \mathscr{A}_\delta) \right] d\mathscr{A}_1' \cdots d\mathscr{A}_\nu'. \qquad (3.8.42)$$

Therefore,

$$\tilde{\psi}_{\mathscr{F}}(\mathscr{F}, T) = \psi_{\mathscr{A}}(\mathscr{A}, T) - \mathscr{A}_\alpha \mathscr{F}_\alpha - kT \log(2\pi kT)^{\nu/2} |\psi_{\gamma\delta}|^{-1/2} \qquad (3.8.43)$$

where $|\psi_{\gamma\delta}|$ is the determinant of the matrix of second partials, $\partial^2 \psi_{\mathscr{A}}/\partial \mathscr{A}_\gamma \partial \mathscr{A}_\delta$. If we now assume the extensive character of $\tilde{\psi}_{\mathscr{F}}$, $\psi_{\mathscr{A}}$, $\mathscr{A}_\alpha \mathscr{F}_\alpha$, and $\psi_{\gamma\delta}$, say all of $0(NkT)$, then it is seen that the Legendre transform relation between $\tilde{\psi}_{\mathscr{F}}$ and $\psi_{\mathscr{A}}$ is approached as N becomes large, since the log term becomes negligible with respect to the other terms in Eq. (3.8.43).

We can now summarize the difference in behavior between small systems and macroscopic systems. Regardless of system size, we can use Eq. (3.8.7) to compute the relation

$$\overline{\mathscr{F}_\alpha^m} = \overline{\mathscr{F}_\alpha^m}(\mathscr{A}, T; N) \qquad (3.8.44)$$

for a strain ensemble, or Eq. (3.8.37) to compute

$$\overline{\mathscr{A}_\alpha'} = \overline{\mathscr{A}_\alpha'}(\mathscr{F}, T; N) \qquad (3.8.45)$$

for an augmented stress ensemble, where N is the number of atoms in the system. When N is small these relations will differ from the concepts of macroscopic thermodynamics in three ways: (1) $\overline{\mathscr{F}_\alpha^m}$, $\overline{\mathscr{A}_\alpha'}$ represent phase or time averages of quantities which undergo large relative fluctuations, whereas in macroscopic thermodynamics these fluctuations are assumed negligible and taken as absent in the theory.[25] (2) We may take both $\mathscr{F}_\alpha$ and $\mathscr{A}_\alpha$ to be intensive variables, dividing by $\mathscr{V}$, the original volume of the system, if necessary. Nevertheless, the relations of Eqs. (3.8.44) and (3.8.45) will be size dependent. (3) The identification of the variables $\overline{\mathscr{F}_\alpha^m}$ and $\mathscr{F}_\alpha$, $\mathscr{A}_\alpha'$ and $\mathscr{A}_\alpha$ is

[25] Hill (1962, p. 3183) makes this point as follows: "Only mean values are of interest [for macroscopic systems] because fluctuations about the mean values are ordinarily negligible in magnitude relative to the mean values themselves. With small systems, fluctuations are larger and hence higher moments of the probability distributions become of interest, as well as do the mean values." For a discussion of the computation of higher moments of energy fluctuations, see Buchdahl (1982).

not permissible; that is, the relations of Eqs. (3.8.44) and (3.8.45) are not inverse relations.[26]

That we can compute relations such as Eqs. (3.8.44) and (3.8.45) for any N emphasizes the point that the scope and the utility of equilibrium statistical mechanics goes beyond the computation of equations of state in the thermodynamic limit. Indeed, with its aid, we can, on the basis of particular atomistic models, compute quantities such as the average energy of a single atom, which are completely without analog in macroscopic thermodynamics.

3.9 PARTITION FUNCTION RELATIONS

For convenience we collect here several relations that connect the partition functions of Eq. (3.7.12) to macroscopic thermodynamic functions. These relations have either been derived previously, or are readily verified by direct computation.

Helmholtz Free Energy

$$F(\mathscr{A},T) = U(\mathscr{A},T) - TS(\mathscr{A},T) = -kT\log Z_{\mathscr{A}}(\mathscr{A},T) \quad (3.9.1)$$

Gibbs Free Energy

$$G(\mathscr{F},T) = U(\mathscr{F},T) - TS(\mathscr{F},T) - \sum_{\alpha=1}^{\nu} \mathscr{A}_\alpha \mathscr{F}_\alpha = -kT\log Z_{\mathscr{F}}(\mathscr{F},T)$$

$$(3.9.2)$$

Internal Energy

$$U(\mathscr{A},T) = -Z_{\mathscr{A}}^{-1}\frac{\partial Z_{\mathscr{A}}}{\partial \beta} = -\frac{\partial}{\partial \beta}\log Z_{\mathscr{A}} \quad (3.9.3)$$

where $\beta = (kT)^{-1}$.

Enthalpy

$$H(\mathscr{F},T) = U(\mathscr{F},T) - \sum_{\alpha=1}^{\nu} \mathscr{A}_\alpha \mathscr{F}_\alpha = -\frac{\partial}{\partial \beta}\log Z_{\mathscr{F}} \quad (3.9.4)$$

[26] For an example, see Weiner and Pear (1977).

Entropy

$$S(\mathscr{A}, T) = -k \int_{\Gamma} \rho_{\mathscr{A}} \log \rho_{\mathscr{A}} \, dq \, dp = k \left[\log Z_{\mathscr{A}} - \beta \frac{\partial}{\partial \beta} \log Z_{\mathscr{A}} \right]$$

(3.9.5)

$$S(\mathscr{F}, T) = -k \int_{\Gamma} \rho_{\mathscr{F}} \log \rho_{\mathscr{F}} \, dq \, dp = k \left[\log Z_{\mathscr{F}} - \beta \frac{\partial}{\partial \beta} \log Z_{\mathscr{F}} \right]$$

(3.9.6)

These relations connect extensive thermodynamic quantities to the appropriate partition functions. They may be converted to intensive quantities by division by the system volume $\mathscr{V}$. As we discussed in Section 3.8, if these relations are applied to small systems, they will lead to state functions for these intensive quantities which are size dependent and represent properties which undergo large fluctuations. For these reasons, the applicability of these relations is generally restricted to macroscopic systems.

With these caveats kept in mind, however, it is sometimes convenient to use the thermodynamic terminology and apply these relations to small systems as well. For example, a large system may consist of many small systems in weak interaction so that, by an extension of Eq. (3.6.22),

$$Z = \prod_{r=1}^{n} Z_r$$

(3.9.7)

where Z is the partition function of the large system and where Z_r, $r = 1, \ldots, n$ are the partition functions of the small component functions. Then, the internal energy U and the entropy S of the large system is found to be

$$U = \sum_{r=1}^{n} U_r,$$

(3.9.8)

$$S = \sum_{r=1}^{n} S_r,$$

(3.9.9)

where U_r, S_r, the internal energy and the entropy of the rth component, are obtained from Z_r by use of Eqs. (3.9.3) and (3.9.5), respectively.

3.10 CONTINUUM FORMULATIONS OF NONUNIFORM PROCESSES

Thus far, we have confined attention to the development of constitutive relations for uniform systems undergoing quasi-static processes. The principal

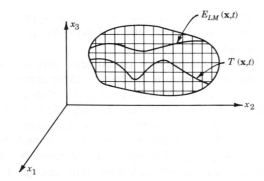

Figure 3.2   Body undergoing nonuniform, transient process.

interest in these constitutive relations, however, lies in their application to material systems undergoing processes which are spatially nonuniform and, frequently, highly transient.

A rigorous discussion of nonuniform, transient processes must be based on the subject of nonequilibrium statistical mechanics.[27] We can, however, discuss the problem on a heuristic basis as follows:

Consider a body undergoing a nonuniform, transient process as indicated in Figure 3.2 in which are shown schematically such variable quantities as strain and temperature, $E_{LM}(\mathbf{x}, t)$ and $T(\mathbf{x}, t)$. We wish to regard the body as subdivided into a set of small elements with each element regarded as undergoing a quasi-static process determined by the local value of E_{LM} and T. For this to be permissible it is necessary that each element is sufficiently small so that:

1   The quantities E_{LM} and T vary negligibly across each element and may be regarded as spatially uniform within it. The more severe the spatial gradients of the functions $E_{LM}(\mathbf{x}, t)$ and $T(\mathbf{x}, t)$, the smaller is the required element size.

2   The time rate of change of E_{LM} and T is sufficiently slow so that each element may be regarded as undergoing a quasistatic process. The more rapid the transients, the smaller the required element since, as discussed in Section 3.3, the time required for equilibration decreases with system size.

Since the subdivision of the body into elements is purely conceptual, there would be no difficulty in meeting these two requirements in all cases—if they were the only ones necessary. However, there is a third requirement, namely:

3   The number of atoms in each element must be sufficiently large so that, as discussed in Section 3.8, the relative fluctuations in its properties are

[27]See also the brief discussion in Boley and Weiner (1960, p. 15) of the difficulty of transition on a continuum basis from the laws for uniform systems to those for nonuniform systems.

negligible and the macroscopic constitutive relations apply to it. This sets a lower limit to the size of the element, one that depends on the number density of atoms in the material.

For the overwhelming majority of phenomena that one would consider formulating in terms of continuum mechanics, these three requirements are easily satisfied simultaneously. If this is the case, it is then concluded that each "continuum particle" (Section 1.2) may be regarded, from the atomistic viewpoint, as representing a macroscopic system undergoing a uniform, quasi-static process.[28] Under these conditions it may be assumed that equations of state such as $T_{LM} = T_{LM}(E_{NK}, T)$, which are derived by the methods of equilibrium statistical mechanics for uniform systems and quasi-static processes, may be applied to spatially nonuniform and time-dependent processes as well. Examples of cases where all three requirements may not be satisfied simultaneously include shock phenomena in highly rarified gases or the consideration of phenomena in solids on the atomic scale, for example, the deformation field in the core of a crystal dislocation.

3.11 EQUIPARTITION THEOREM

Consider a system with a Hamiltonian of the form

$$H(q_1, \ldots, q_n, p_1, \ldots, p_n) = H(y_1, \ldots, y_{2n}) = \sum_{i=1}^{r} a_i y_i^2 + H'(y_{r+1}, \ldots, y_{2n})$$

$$(3.11.1)$$

where a_i, $i = 1, \ldots, r$ are positive constants, the variables y_i, $i = 1, \ldots, r$ may include both coordinates and momenta among them, and all variables y_i, $i = 1, \ldots, 2n$ are taken to have the range $-\infty < y_i < \infty$. We consider phase averages with respect to a canonical distribution

$$\rho = Z^{-1} e^{-\beta H} \qquad (3.11.2)$$

where $\beta = (kT)^{-1}$ and the partition function

$$Z = \int_{\Gamma} e^{-\beta H} \prod_{i=1}^{2n} dy_i = \left(\prod_{i=1}^{r} \int_{-\infty}^{\infty} e^{-\beta a_i y_i^2} dy_i \right) \int_{-\infty}^{\infty} e^{-\beta H'} \prod_{j=r+1}^{2n} dy_j.$$

$$(3.11.3)$$

---

[28] From a continuum thermodynamic viewpoint such processes are frequently described as locally reversible.

Because of the linearity of the operation of taking phase averages,

$$\left\langle \sum_{i=1}^{r} a_i y_i^2 \right\rangle = \sum_{i=1}^{r} \left\langle a_i y_i^2 \right\rangle. \tag{3.11.4}$$

Furthermore,

$$\langle a_i y_i^2 \rangle = Z^{-1} \int_\Gamma a_i y_i^2 e^{-\beta H} \prod_{i=1}^{2n} dy_i$$

$$= Z^{-1} \int_{-\infty}^{\infty} a_i y_i^2 e^{-\beta a_i y_i^2} dy_i \int_{-\infty}^{\infty} e^{-\beta(\Sigma' a_j y_j^2 + H')} \Pi' dy_k \tag{3.11.5}$$

where Σ', Π' denote sum and product from 1 to $2n$ with i omitted. Comparison of Eqs. (3.11.3) and (3.11.5) shows that all integrals, except those with respect to y_i, cancel from numerator and denominator, and

$$\langle a_i y_i^2 \rangle = \int_{-\infty}^{\infty} a_i y_i^2 e^{-\beta a_i y_i^2} dy_i \Big/ \int_{-\infty}^{\infty} e^{-\beta a_i y_i^2} dy_i$$

$$= -\frac{d}{d\beta} \log \int_{-\infty}^{\infty} e^{-\beta a_i y_i^2} dy_i = -\frac{d}{d\beta} \log \left(\frac{\pi}{\beta a_i} \right)^{1/2}$$

$$= \frac{kT}{2}, \tag{3.11.6}$$

and, from Eq. (3.11.4),

$$\left\langle \sum_{i=1}^{r} a_i y_i^2 \right\rangle = \frac{rkT}{2}. \tag{3.11.7}$$

This is the equipartition theorem of classical equilibrium statistical mechanics: Each quadratic term with positive coefficient in the Hamiltonian H contributes $kT/2$ to the mean energy $\overline{H}$, where the mean is taken with respect to the canonical distribution.

Note that the result is independent of the nature of the function H'. Thus, on the basis of classical equilibrium statistical mechanics, the mean kinetic energy of a gas with N atoms is $3NkT/2$, whether the potential energy of interaction between the atoms is neglected, as in a perfect gas, or not. The result is also independent of the value of the positive coefficients a_i. For a one-dimensional harmonic oscillator, for example, the mean kinetic and the mean potential energy is each $kT/2$ and the mean total energy is kT, regardless of the magnitude of the spring constant.

3.12   ENTROPY FROM THE INFORMATION THEORY VIEWPOINT

In Section 3.6 we derived an expression, Eq. (3.6.24), for the entropy $S(\mathscr{A}, T)$ of a system in terms of its distribution function $\rho(q, p; \mathscr{A}, T)$. The concepts of information theory[29] provide increased insight into this relation and into the nature of entropy. We will find this viewpoint particularly valuable in our study of the mechanical behavior of polymeric solids.

Concept of Uncertainty

Consider an experiment A, for example, the toss of a coin, with two possible outcomes A_1 and A_2 with associated probabilities p_1 and p_2, $p_1 + p_2 = 1$. These quantities are sometimes presented in an array

$$A = \begin{pmatrix} A_1 & A_2 \\ p_1 & p_2 \end{pmatrix} \tag{3.12.1}$$

and referred to as a probability scheme. If, for the example of the toss of a coin, we have no information which indicates an unbalanced coin or a biased tossing procedure, we would set

$$A = \begin{pmatrix} A_1 & A_2 \\ 0.5 & 0.5 \end{pmatrix}. \tag{3.12.2}$$

The basis for this assignment of probabilities is sometimes referred to as the Principle of Insufficient Reason[30]—we do not have any reason for the choice of any other probability values. The question we consider next is the development of a basis for probability assignment when some additional information is available.

In this connection, consider experiment B with associated probability scheme

$$B = \begin{pmatrix} B_1 & B_2 \\ 0.99 & 0.01 \end{pmatrix}. \tag{3.12.3}$$

It is clear that there is greater uncertainty—using this term for the present in its loose, psychological sense—regarding the outcome of experiment A than of experiment B. This suggests, as a principle for the assignment of probabili-

---

[29] The subject has its beginnings in the famous work of Shannon (1948) in which he made use of the concept of entropy from statistical mechanics in order to illuminate problems in communications theory. The direction of conceptual flow was later reversed, principally by Jaynes (1957) who used the uncertainty concept of information theory as a basis for the development of equilibrium statistical mechanics. The literature on this approach to the subject is now large. See, for example, Katz (1967), Tribus (1961), Landsberg (1978), and Levine and Tribus (1979). Our development of the uncertainty function follows closely the treatment of Khinchin (1957).

[30] Due to Jacques Bernoulli.

ties, that the resulting uncertainty of the probability scheme for an experiment should be a maximum subject to the constraints of any information available regarding the experiment. In order to make this principle quantitative, it is necessary that we have a mathematical expression for the uncertainty of a probability scheme.

Properties of the Uncertainty Function

Consider a general finite probability scheme[31] A with m outcomes:

$$A = \begin{pmatrix} A_1 & \cdots & A_m \\ p_1 & \cdots & p_m \end{pmatrix}. \tag{3.12.4}$$

We designate the uncertainty associated with A as $\mathscr{H}(A)$ and require that it be a function of the assigned probabilities, that is, $\mathscr{H}(A) = \mathscr{H}(p_1, \ldots, p_m)$. We wish next to develop three properties which it appears natural to require of $\mathscr{H}(\mathscr{A})$ in order that it correspond to the psychological concept of uncertainty. Two of these properties are easily motivated and stated. To begin with, we would not expect a small change in the values of p_i to cause a large change in the uncertainty of the probability scheme. Therefore, the first desired property is:

1. $\mathscr{H}(A) = \mathscr{H}(p_1, \ldots, p_m)$ *is a continuous function of its arguments.*

Second, we recognize that we are not dealing with the development of a single function $\mathscr{H}(p_1, \ldots, p_m)$, but with a class of such functions corresponding to different values of m. If, for example, we consider two probability schemes,

$$A = \begin{pmatrix} A_1 & A_2 \\ \frac{1}{2} & \frac{1}{2} \end{pmatrix} \text{ and } B = \begin{pmatrix} B_1 & B_2 & B_3 \\ \frac{1}{3} & \frac{1}{3} & \frac{1}{3} \end{pmatrix},$$

it is clear that we would regard $\mathscr{H}(B) > \mathscr{H}(A)$; although in each scheme the possible outcomes are equally likely, B has more possibilities. We formalize this as the second property of the uncertainty function:

2. *The quantity* $L(n) = \mathscr{H}\left(\dfrac{1}{n}, \ldots, \dfrac{1}{n}\right)$ *is a monotonically increasing function.*

The third property of the uncertainty function is somewhat more difficult to motivate. Consider two experiments, A with probability scheme as in Eq. (3.12.4) and

$$B = \begin{pmatrix} B_1 & \cdots & B_n \\ q_1 & \cdots & q_n \end{pmatrix}. \tag{3.12.5}$$

---

[31]We are using, as equivalent terminology, the expressions A is a probability scheme and A is an experiment with the given associated probability scheme.

We construct a compound experiment AB in which we first perform experiment A with possible outcomes $A_1 \ldots A_m$ and then perform experiment B with its possible outcomes. The two experiments are independent by hypothesis, since $q_1, \ldots, q_n$, the probabilities of outcomes $B_1, \ldots, B_n$, do not depend on the prior outcome of experiment A. The probability scheme for AB is, therefore,

$$AB = \begin{pmatrix} A_1 B_1 & A_1 B_2 & \cdots & A_m B_n \\ p_1 q_1 & p_1 q_2 & \cdots & p_m q_n \end{pmatrix}. \tag{3.12.6}$$

Since the experiments are independent, it is reasonable to postulate

3'. $$\mathscr{H}(AB) = \mathscr{H}(A) + \mathscr{H}(B) \tag{3.12.7}$$

for the fact that the two experiments are coupled does not serve to change the uncertainty associated with either. Another example to demonstrate the reasonableness of property (3') is provided by the case in which experiment B has only a single outcome. Under this condition we would expect any suitable measure of uncertainty to set $\mathscr{H}(B) = 0$ and therefore $\mathscr{H}(AB) = \mathscr{H}(A)$.

It is necessary, however, to generalize property (3') to compound experiments AB for which the number, nature and probabilities of the outcomes of B depend on the prior outcome of A, that is, we have a different probability scheme B/A_k for each outcome A_k:

$$B/A_k = \begin{pmatrix} B_{k1} & \cdots & B_{kn_k} \\ q_{k1} & \cdots & q_{kn_k} \end{pmatrix}; \qquad k = 1, \ldots, m. \tag{3.12.8}$$

As a prototype of this class of compound experiments, consider a collection of m baskets with n_k objects in the kth basket. Experiment A is the selection of one of these baskets, with outcome A_k being the choice of the kth basket. The succeeding experiment, denoted by B/A_k, is the selection of an object from the kth basket. The compound experiment AB is then the selection of an object from among $\sum_{k=1}^{m} n_k = N$ distinct objects. From the knowledge of the schemes A and B/A_k, $k = 1, \ldots, m$, we can compute the probability scheme AB. We now extend property (3') to these general compound schemes as follows:

3. $$\mathscr{H}(AB) = \mathscr{H}(A) + \sum_{k=1}^{m} p_k \mathscr{H}(B/A_k).$$

This generalization is reasonable since it weights the uncertainties associated with B/A_k according to the probability p_k that this alternative will occur in the compound experiment AB. Note that for the case when A and B are independent experiments, $B/A_k \equiv B$, and property (3) reduces to (3').

Derivation of uncertainty function

We next derive the form of the function $\mathscr{H}(A) = \mathscr{H}(p_1, \ldots, p_m)$ on the basis of properties (1)–(3). Because of (1) it is sufficient to determine the form of the function $\mathcal{H}(A)$ for rational p_k, that is, we set

$$p_k = \frac{n_k}{N}, \quad k = 1, \ldots, m \tag{3.12.9}$$

with

$$\sum_{k=1}^{m} n_k = N \tag{3.12.10}$$

so that $\sum_{k=1}^{m} p_k = 1$.

Along with experiment A with probabilities given by Eqs. (3.12.9) and (3.12.10), we consider the compound experiment AB with

$$B/A_k = \begin{pmatrix} B_{k1} & \cdots & B_{kn_k} \\ \dfrac{1}{n_k} & \cdots & \dfrac{1}{n_k} \end{pmatrix}, \quad k = 1, \ldots, m. \tag{3.12.11}$$

In terms of the basket-selection procedure, we can describe the compound experiment AB as the selection of one of N objects which are contained in m baskets with n_k objects in the kth basket. The outcome A_k is the selection of the kth basket with $p_k = n_k/N$, that is, the probability of selecting a particular basket is proportional to the number of objects in it. Experiment B/A_k is then the selection of one of the n_k objects from the kth basket, all of them having equal probability. It is seen that the probability of selecting the jth object in the kth basket is

$$A_k \cdot B_{kj} = \frac{n_k}{N} \cdot \frac{1}{n_k} = \frac{1}{N}$$

and therefore

$$AB = \begin{pmatrix} (AB)_1 & \cdots & (AB)_N \\ \dfrac{1}{N} & \cdots & \dfrac{1}{N} \end{pmatrix}. \tag{3.12.12}$$

Both AB and B/A_k are probability schemes with all outcomes equally probable. Therefore, the notation of property (2) applies and, for this case, property (3) assumes the form

$$L(N) = \mathcal{H}(A) + \sum_{k=1}^{m} p_k L(n_k). \tag{3.12.13}$$

Thus far, A has been a completely general finite probability scheme with rational p_k. We next consider the special case of equal p_k:

$$p_k = \frac{n}{N} = \frac{1}{m}, \quad k = 1, \ldots, m \tag{3.12.14}$$

so that

$$A = \begin{pmatrix} A_1 & \cdots & A_m \\ \dfrac{1}{m} & \cdots & \dfrac{1}{m} \end{pmatrix}. \tag{3.12.15}$$

Therefore $\mathcal{H}(A) = L(m)$ and Eqs. (3.11.13) takes the form

$$L(mn) = L(m) + L(n) \tag{3.12.16}$$

where we have used the relation [from Eq. (3.12.14)], $n_k \equiv n$ and $N = mn$. A solution to the functional Eq. (3.12.16) is

$$L(m) = K \log m \tag{3.12.17}$$

and, from property (2), $K > 0$. We substitute this expression back into Eq. (3.12.13) to obtain

$$\mathcal{H}(A) = K\left(-\sum_{k=1}^{m} p_k \log n_k + \log N \right)$$

$$= -K \sum_{k=1}^{m} p_r \log \frac{n_k}{N} = -K \sum_{k=1}^{m} p_k \log p_k \tag{3.12.18}$$

by use of Eq. (3.12.9). By property (1), this form of $\mathcal{H}(A)$ applies to arbitrary values of p_k, irrational as well as rational. For a discussion of the uniqueness of the uncertainty function, we refer the reader to Khinchin (1957), who uses a slightly different formulation of its properties.

Thus far, we have confined attention to finite probability schemes. If the experiment A has outcomes x, $-\infty < x < \infty$ with probability density $p(x)$, then Eq. (3.11.18) is generalized to

$$\mathcal{H}(A) = -K \int_{-\infty}^{\infty} p(x) \log p(x) \, dx. \tag{3.12.19}$$

Similar generalizations, involving multiple integrals, are made for probability distributions which depend on several continuous variables.

Consider now the definition [Eq. (3.6.24)] of the entropy $S(\mathcal{A}, T)$ of a system in terms of its distribution function $\rho(q, p; \mathcal{A}, T)$:

$$S(\mathcal{A}, T) = -k \int_{\Gamma} \rho \log \rho \, dq \, dp \tag{3.12.20}$$

We see that the entropy definition is exactly of the form of the uncertainty function and we are led therefore to the following information–theoretic interpretation of entropy:

Consider the thought experiment of observing the given system at an arbitrary instant of time. The possible outcomes of the experiment are the various points in phase space accessible to the system. The entropy of the system is the uncertainty associated with this experiment.

Therefore, the larger the region of phase space over which the trajectory of the system wanders, the greater is its entropy. This is depicted schematically in Figure 3.3.

Configurational Entropy

The thought experiment just described has consisted of the location of the system in phase space, that is, it involved the simultaneous determination of coordinates and momenta. Frequently, it is possible to write $\rho(q, p; \mathscr{A}, T) = \rho_q(q; \mathscr{A}, T)\rho_p(p; \mathscr{A}, T)$ and it is then convenient to normalize each distribution separately:

$$\int_{\Gamma_q} \rho_q \, dq = \int_{\Gamma_p} \rho_p \, dp = 1 \tag{3.12.21}$$

Then

$$S(\mathscr{A}, T) = -k \int_{\Gamma} \rho_q \rho_p \log \rho_q \rho_p \, dq \, dp$$

$$= -k \int_{\Gamma_q} \rho_q \log \rho_q \, dq - k \int_{\Gamma_p} \rho_p \log \rho_p \, dp$$

$$= S_q(\mathscr{A}, T) + S_p(\mathscr{A}, T) \tag{3.12.22}$$

where $S_q(\mathscr{A}, T)$ is called the configurational entropy of the system. Furthermore, if (q, p) correspond to rectangular Cartesian coordinates, then $\rho_p = \rho_p(p; T)$ and $S_p = S_p(T)$, that is, it is independent of the controlled kinematical parameters $\mathscr{A}$. Under these conditions, only the configurational entropy will change with deformation.

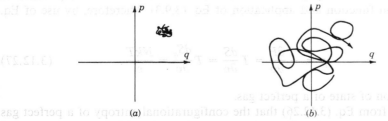

Figure 3.3 (a) System trajectory of low uncertainty and low entropy. (b) System trajectory of high uncertainty and high entropy.

Note that the decomposition of Eq. (3.12.22) is an example of the additivity of uncertainty for independent probability schemes.

Perfect Gas

A simple example of the computation and use of the configurational entropy is provided by the case of a perfect gas of N atoms at temperature T and confined to a region D of volume v. The potential energy of the gas is

$$V(q_1, \ldots, q_N) = 0 \qquad \text{for all } q_j \in D$$

$$= \infty \qquad \text{for any } q_j \notin D \qquad (3.12.23)$$

where q_j is the position of the jth atom. Then

$$\rho_q(q_1, \ldots, q_N) = Ce^{-\beta V(q_1, \ldots, q_N)}$$

$$= \prod_{j=1}^{N} \rho_1(q_j) \qquad (3.12.24)$$

where

$$\rho_1(q_j) = \frac{1}{v} \qquad \text{for } q_j \in D$$

$$= 0 \qquad \text{for } q_j \notin D. \qquad (3.12.25)$$

Therefore, by the additivity of uncertainty for independent schemes,

$$S_q(v) = \sum_{j=1}^{N} - k \int_D \frac{1}{v} \log \frac{1}{v} dq_j$$

$$= kN \log v. \qquad (3.12.26)$$

For a perfect gas of N atoms, the internal energy $U = 3NkT/2$, as may be concluded from the equipartition theorem, Section 3.11, or by computation of its partition function and application of Eq. (3.9.3). Therefore, by use of Eq. (1.6.11),

$$p = -\frac{\partial F}{\partial v} = T\frac{\partial S}{\partial v} = T\frac{\partial S_q}{\partial v} = \frac{NkT}{v}, \qquad (3.12.27)$$

the equation of state of a perfect gas.

We see from Eq. (3.12.26) that the configurational entropy of a perfect gas increases upon expansion. From the present viewpoint, this is a consequence of the resulting increase in uncertainty of the location of the atoms of the gas.

CHAPTER FOUR

Crystal Elasticity

4.1 INTRODUCTION

We considered the basic principles of equilibrium statistical mechanics in Chapters 2 and 3. These were developed in a general form and are applicable to broad classes of physical systems. In this chapter we apply them to the study of the thermoelasticity of single crystals. We will, therefore, be examining from an atomistic viewpoint the phenomena considered earlier in Sections 1.6–1.9 from the continuum viewpoint.

The salient characteristic of a crystalline substance is the geometric regularity of the atomic positions. This is described in Section 4.2 in terms of the concepts of simple Bravais lattices and composite lattices.

Our discussion of the general principles of statistical mechanics spoke of generalized strains $\mathscr{A}_\alpha$ and generalized stresses $\mathscr{F}_\alpha$; in the discussion of thermoelasticity these are replaced by strain components E_{LM} or deformation matrix elements a_{iL} and by stress components T_{LM} or T_{iL}. The details of this transcription are given in Section 4.3 for the case of a strain ensemble.

If the temperature level is not too high, it is possible to regard the atoms of the crystal as executing small vibrations in the neighborhood of the perfect crystal lattice sites. These vibrations may be treated on the basis of the harmonic or quasi-harmonic approximations as discussed in Section 4.4, where the difference in the thermoelastic relations obtained on the basis of these two approximations is emphasized.

One question concerning the relation between macroscopic behavior and atomistic models which goes back almost to the beginning of the subject of elasticity involves the so-called Cauchy relations among the elastic moduli. These are discussed in Section 4.6 where sufficient conditions on atomistic models for their validity are derived.

In Chapter 3 we considered the general principles of both strain and stress ensembles. Historically, the former plays a much larger role in the discussion of crystal thermoelasticity and accordingly we have emphasized it in this chapter. In Section 4.7 we turn for the first time to the use of a stress ensemble and show how this concept may be employed for an alternative treatment of the thermoelasticity of crystals. In order to illustrate some of the general ideas discussed in this chapter, we consider in Section 4.8 the simple model of the linear chain of atoms with nearest neighbor interactions. The thermoelastic stress–strain relations for this model are derived in this section in three different ways: (a) by means of the thermodynamic relations based on a strain ensemble, (b) by a direct method that bypasses the concepts of macroscopic thermodynamics, and (c) by use of a stress ensemble.

Finally, in Section 4.9, we present a brief discussion of the viewpoint and aims of the discipline of lattice dynamics and its relationship to the subject of crystal elasticity.

Interatomic potentials

We defer a detailed consideration of the nature of interatomic interactions until Chapter 9, when this question can be discussed on a quantum mechanical basis. That discussion shows that for a collection of N atoms at positions $\mathbf{r}_1, \ldots, \mathbf{r}_N$ it is possible to demonstrate, under broadly satisfied conditions, the existence of a potential energy of interaction $V(\mathbf{r}_1, \ldots, \mathbf{r}_N)$ which depends on the positions of all of the atoms as arguments. This is termed a general, many-body interatomic potential. The force $\mathbf{f}_l$ acting on the lth atom due to all of the other atoms is[1]

$$\mathbf{f}_l = -\frac{\partial V}{\partial \mathbf{r}_l}(\mathbf{r}_1, \ldots, \mathbf{r}_N). \tag{4.1.1}$$

The character of the interatomic potential for different types of atoms and interatomic bonding is discussed in Section 9.6. In particular, in some cases it is permissible to write V as a sum of two-body potentials,

$$V(\mathbf{r}_1, \ldots, \mathbf{r}_N) = \sum_{\substack{l, l' = 1 \\ l < l'}}^{N} \phi_{ll'}(\mathbf{r}_l, \mathbf{r}_{l'}). \tag{4.1.2}$$

Only in this case is it possible to speak of the force exerted by one atom on another.

---

[1]In component form, Eq. (4.1.1) takes the form

$$f_{li} = -\frac{\partial V}{\partial r_{li}}(\mathbf{r}_1, \ldots, \mathbf{r}_N), \qquad i = 1, 2, 3.$$

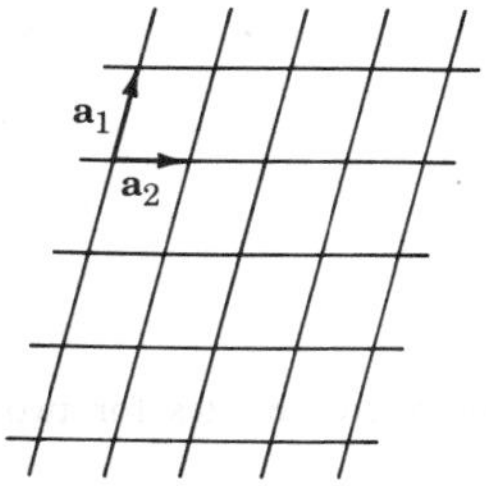

Figure 4.1 Simple Bravais lattice. (For simplicity, only a single plane of the lattice is shown.)

4.2 BRAVAIS LATTICES

The concept of a Bravais lattice is a purely geometric one that serves to describe a regularly distributed array of sites or points in space. To define first a simple Bravais lattice, we start with three noncoplanar vectors, $\mathbf{a}_i$, $i = 1, 2, 3$. A simple Bravais lattice (Figure 4.1) is the set of all points of the form $\mathbf{x}(l) = l^i \mathbf{a}_i$, summed over $i = 1, 2, 3$, with the $l^i = 0, \pm 1, \pm 2, \ldots$. The symbol l for the triple (l^1, l^2, l^3) is employed as argument for compactness[2]. It is clear (Figure 4.1) that given a particular simple Bravais lattice, that is a particular array of points in space, it is possible to choose the basis vectors $\mathbf{a}_i$ which generate them in an infinite number of ways. Generally, it is most convenient to choose the set that most nearly consists of mutually orthogonal vectors. The basis vectors form the edges of a parallelepiped, referred to as a lattice cell, and the lack of uniqueness of the basis vectors is reflected in a corresponding arbitrariness in the designation of a lattice cell. The simple Bravais lattice may be thought of as formed by the translation of this parallelepiped throughout space by integral multiples of $\mathbf{a}_i$, $i = 1, 2, 3$.

Thus far, we have been speaking only of lattice sites in space. A real crystal[3] is said to correspond to a simple Bravais lattice if it contains only one type of atom and the reference position of each atom is the site or point of a simple Bravais lattice. In this way, one atom is assigned to each lattice cell.

Composite Lattice

For all crystals composed of several types of atoms, and for some consisting of only one type of atom, it is necessary to use a set of reference sites forming what is known as a composite lattice. The terms general lattice or lattice with a basis are also used. The starting point is again that of a simple Bravais lattice, but now each lattice cell contains sites for s atoms, labeled $k = 1, \ldots, s$ (Figure 4.2). Then the reference position of the $\binom{l}{k}$ atom (the atom of type k in the

---

[2] Many different notations have been divised for discussing lattice geometry and lattice dynamics; we are here following, with slight modifications, the notation of Born and Huang (1954).

[3] Hereafter, we use the term "crystal" as denoting a collection of atoms, as distinguished from a lattice, which describes a regular array of points in space.

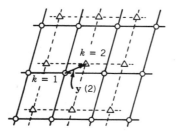

Figure 4.2 Composite lattice of reference sites for two types of atoms.

lattice cell corresponding to $l = (l^1, l^2, l^3))$ may be written as[4]

$$\mathbf{x}\begin{pmatrix} l \\ k \end{pmatrix} = \mathbf{x}(l) + \mathbf{y}(k) \tag{4.2.1}$$

where $\mathbf{x}(l) = l^i \mathbf{a}_i$, $\mathbf{y}(k) = \lambda^i(k)\mathbf{a}_i$, $0 \leqslant \lambda^i(k) < 1$.

There are two alternate ways of regarding a crystal corresponding to a composite lattice: (1) we may start with a simple Bravais lattice and place a molecule (sometimes referred to as a basis) consisting of s atoms, in a configuration described by the vectors $\mathbf{y}(k)$, at each lattice site, or (2) we may start with s identical simple Bravais lattices, displaced relative to each other by the vectors $\mathbf{y}(k)$, and place an atom of the appropriate type at the sites of each lattice.

Many detailed accounts of the symmetry properties of different types of crystal structures may be found in the literature[5] and we do not repeat these discussions here. We mention only three of the simplest structures, which we will use as examples in future discussions.

Simple Cubic Lattice

For this simple Bravais lattice, the base vectors $\mathbf{a}_i$ may be taken as three orthogonal vectors of equal magnitude a. The distance a between neighboring lattice sites is termed the lattice parameter; the lattice cell is a cube of edge a. There are no natural monatomic crystals corresponding to this lattice.

Body-Centered Cubic Lattice

This simple Bravais lattice may be obtained from the simple cubic by placing an additional lattice site at the center of each lattice cell. The body-centered

---

[4] The reader accustomed to the indicial notation of tensor analysis will no doubt find his first encounter with the Born and Huang lattice notation confusing and perhaps irritating. In tensor analysis all letters or symbols from the same typeface have the same character and range. Here the letter l is always used for the lattice cell and denotes the triple (l^1, l^2, l^3) and $k = 1, \ldots, s$ denotes the particular site within the cell. If it is necessary to refer to more than one site in a composite lattice, the notation $\begin{pmatrix} l \\ k \end{pmatrix}$, $\begin{pmatrix} l' \\ k' \end{pmatrix}$, $\begin{pmatrix} l'' \\ k'' \end{pmatrix}$, etc., is employed.

[5] See, for example, Smith (1961, Chapter 5) or Weinreich (1965, Chapter 1).

cubic lattice may also be regarded as two simple cubic lattices displaced relative to each other by the vector $\mathbf{y} = \frac{1}{2}(\mathbf{a}_1 + \mathbf{a}_2 + \mathbf{a}_3)$. There exist both monatomic and diatomic crystals corresponding to this lattice. A representative of the latter is CsCl and the diatomic body-centered cubic structure is frequently called the cesium chloride structure.

Face-Centered Cubic Lattice

This simple Bravais lattice may be obtained from the simple cubic by placing an additional lattice site at the center of each face of each lattice cell. An important diatomic structure, called the sodium chloride structure, is obtained by starting from a simple cubic lattice and placing atoms of types A and B at alternate lattice sites in the directions $\mathbf{a}_1$, $\mathbf{a}_2$, and $\mathbf{a}_3$.

A crystal structure is said to possess an n-fold rotation axis if a rotation about this axis through an angle of $2\pi/n$ leaves the structure unchanged. The cubic structures have two fourfold axes perpendicular to each other;[6] the resulting symmetry is called cubic symmetry.

4.3 THE ATOMISTIC CONCEPT OF STRESS IN A PERFECT CRYSTAL

In our discussion of the general principles of statistical mechanics, we considered a system described by a Hamiltonian $H(q, p; \mathscr{A}_1, \ldots, \mathscr{A}_\nu)$, where $\mathscr{A}_1, \ldots, \mathscr{A}_\nu$ represent controllable kinematical parameters, and derived the phase functions $\mathscr{F}_\alpha^m(q, p; \mathscr{A})$ for the corresponding generalized forces $\mathscr{F}_\alpha$, $\alpha = 1, \ldots, \nu$, by means of the relations

$$\mathscr{F}_\alpha^m = \frac{\partial H}{\partial \mathscr{A}_\alpha}, \qquad \alpha = 1, \ldots, \nu. \tag{4.3.1}$$

For an elastic solid we may take the six independent material strain components $E_{LM}(= E_{ML})$ as the controllable kinematical parameters. From the expression for the rate of doing work on an elastic solid [Eq. (1.3.16)]

$$\dot{W} = \mathscr{V} T_{LM} \dot{E}_{LM} \tag{4.3.2}$$

it is seen that the corresponding generalized forces are $\mathscr{V} T_{LM}$ and Eq. (4.3.1) takes the form[7]

$$\mathscr{V} T_{LM}^m = \frac{\partial H}{\partial E_{LM}}(q, p; E_{RS}). \tag{4.3.3}$$

---

[6] These are all that are required for the definition of the cubic systems; other symmetries follow from these. See, for example, Weinreich (1965, pp. 13–18).

[7] For the purpose of the partial derivative notation only, the nine components E_{RS} are regarded as independent variables in Eq. (4.3.3); see the discussion following Eq. (1.6.1).

Since, Eq. (1.2.27),

$$E_{LM} = \tfrac{1}{2}(a_{iL}a_{iM} - \delta_{LM}) \qquad (4.3.4)$$

where a_{iL} are the elements of the deformation matrix [Eq. (1.2.25)], we may alternatively regard H as a function of the quantities a_{iL} as controllable parameters. In this case [Eq. (1.3.14)], the corresponding generalized forces are $\mathscr{V} T_{iL}$ and Eq. (4.3.1) takes the form

$$\mathscr{V} T_{iL}^m = \frac{\partial H}{\partial a_{iL}}(q, p; a_{jK}). \qquad (4.3.5)$$

In this section we consider the class of elastic solids corresponding to single perfect crystals. We wish to examine (a) the physical mechanism which causes the kinematic parameters E_{LM} or a_{iL} to enter the Hamiltonian and (b) the physical significance of Eqs. (4.3.3) and (4.3.5).

Simple Bravais Lattice

We begin the discussion of these questions for a hypothetical crystal that corresponds in its reference configuration[8] to a simple cubic lattice with the basis vectors $\mathbf{a}_i$, $i = 1, 2, 3$ a set of orthogonal vectors of equal magnitude. In order to avoid surface effects, we focus attention on a central, interior portion of the crystal and assume that the lattice corresponding to this interior portion undergoes a homogeneous deformation corresponding to the deformation matrix a_{iL} and material strain tensor E_{LM} (Figure 4.3).

In what follows we will speak, for brevity, of the interior crystal and refer to its atoms as interior atoms and of the remainder as the exterior crystal and exterior atoms. From the viewpoint of statistical mechanics, the system we are treating explicitly is the interior crystal, while the exterior crystal together with the surrounding ambient constitutes the heat bath.

This device of focusing attention on an interior uniformly deformed, portion of the crystal also permits us to ignore the details of the mechanism, generally involving other bodies, which deforms the crystal.[9] From the present viewpoint, it is the forces exerted by the atoms of the exterior crystal which deform the interior crystal.

Let $\mathbf{X}(l)$, with rectangular Cartesian components $X_L(l)$, be the position of the lth site of the undeformed reference lattice of the interior crystal and $\mathbf{x}(l)$,

---

[8] The choice of the reference configuration will be discussed further in Section 4.5.

[9] For an alternate treatment of this question which does not make use of this device and considers the distortion of the crystal at the surface separating it from other bodies, see Grindlay (1963). This device of focusing on the interior crystal also clarifies the question of the role of external surface forces in the statistical mechanics of solids which has been the subject of some discussion; see Luban and Novogrodsky (1972), Shalitin and Imry (1975), and Luban (1975).

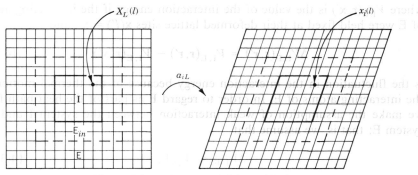

Figure 4.3   Reference and deformed lattices.

with components $x_i(l)$, be the position of the corresponding site in the deformed lattice (Figure 4.3). Here $l = (l^1, l^2, l^3)$ is a site label which ranges over the set I corresponding to all sites of the interior lattice. For the exterior lattice, a site label l', ranging over the set E corresponding to all sites of the exterior lattice, is used. For the interior lattice,

$$x_i(l) = a_{iL} X_L(l), \qquad l \in \text{I}. \qquad (4.3.6)$$

We assume that Eq. (4.3.6) applies as well to sites of E close to I; it need not apply to all of E because of surface effects.

As part of the idealization of the elastic behavior of a perfect crystal, it is assumed that an atom initially in the vicinity of a site l (or l') remains in the vicinity[10] of that site at later times, even if the crystal (and the lattice) is subjected to a deformation. The label l (or l') may be used, therefore, to designate a particular atom as well as a particular lattice site. At a given instant of time, let the positions of the interior atoms be $\mathbf{r}(l, t)$, $l \in \text{I}$, and those of exterior atoms, $\mathbf{r}(l', t)$, $l' \in \text{E}$. For brevity, we will sometimes refer to these positions collectively as $\mathbf{r}$ and $\mathbf{r}'$, respectively. We restrict attention to short-range interatomic forces (Section 9.6) and assume that the otherwise general, many-body interatomic potential $V_{\text{I}+\text{E}}(\mathbf{r}, \mathbf{r}')$ of all the atoms of the crystal can be written

$$V_{\text{I}+\text{E}}(\mathbf{r}, \mathbf{r}') = V_{\text{I}}(\mathbf{r}) + V_{\text{E}}(\mathbf{r}') + V_{\text{I},\text{E}}(\mathbf{r}, \mathbf{r}') \qquad (4.3.7)$$

where $V_{\text{I},\text{E}}(\mathbf{r}, \mathbf{r}')$ describes the short-range interaction between the atoms of I and E which lie near the surface separating the two regions. We further decompose this interaction energy as follows:

$$V_{\text{I},\text{E}}(\mathbf{r}, \mathbf{r}') = V_{\text{I},\text{E}}(\mathbf{r}, \mathbf{x}') + \Delta V_{\text{I},\text{E}}(\mathbf{r}, \mathbf{r}') \qquad (4.3.8)$$

[10] That is, we are excluding such phenomena as atom diffusion; the latter is discussed in Chapter 7.

where $V_{\mathrm{I,E}}(\mathbf{r}, \mathbf{x}')$ is the value of the interaction energy if the interacting atoms of E were held fixed at their deformed lattice sites $\mathbf{x}(l') = \mathbf{x}'$, and

$$\Delta V_{\mathrm{I,E}}(\mathbf{r}, \mathbf{r}') = V_{\mathrm{I,E}}(\mathbf{r}, \mathbf{r}') - V_{\mathrm{I,E}}(\mathbf{r}, \mathbf{x}') \qquad (4.3.9)$$

is the fluctuation in the interaction energy because of the thermal motion of the interacting atoms of E. In order to regard E as part of the heat bath for I we make the assumption of weak interaction between the system I and the system E; that is, we assume that

$$\Delta V_{\mathrm{I,E}} \ll V_{\mathrm{I}}, V_{\mathrm{E}} \qquad (4.3.10)$$

and neglect $\Delta V_{\mathrm{I,E}}$ in what follows. Then the total potential energy $V(\mathbf{r}; \mathbf{x}')$, to be employed in the Hamiltonian of I is[11]

$$V(\mathbf{r}; \mathbf{x}') = V_{\mathrm{I}}(\mathbf{r}) + V_{\mathrm{I,E}}(\mathbf{r}, \mathbf{x}'). \qquad (4.3.11)$$

We recall now that the uniform deformation described by Eq. (4.3.6) applies as well to those sites of E close to I. We introduce the terminology E_{in} for those atoms of E which are in a thin layer about I and interact with the atoms of I, Figure 4.3. Therefore, the Hamiltonian of I may be written[12]

$$H(r, p; a_{iL}) = \frac{1}{2} \sum_{l \in \mathrm{I}} \frac{|\mathbf{p}(l, t)|^2}{m(l)} + V(\mathbf{r}; a_{iL}) \qquad (4.3.12)$$

where

$$V(\mathbf{r}; a_{iL}) = V_{\mathrm{I}}(\mathbf{r}) + V_{\mathrm{I,E}}(\mathbf{r}; a_{iL} X_L') \qquad (4.3.13)$$

and the notation

$$a_{iL} X_L' = a_{iL} X_L(l'), \qquad l' \in \mathrm{E}_{in} \qquad (4.3.14)$$

denotes collectively the positions of the deformed lattice sites of the atoms in E_{in}.

---

[11] The device of regarding those atoms of E which interact with I as fixed at the deformed lattice sites may appear artificial at first sight, but it is essential in order to arrive at a Hamiltonian for I which depends only on the coordinates and momenta of the atoms of I and on the controllable kinematic parameters. If we replace $\mathbf{x}'$ in Eq. (4.3.11) by $\mathbf{r}' = \mathbf{r}(l', t)$, then we must know all the forces that govern the motion of these atoms, that is, we must include another layer of atoms, etc., *ad infinitum*. Note that this use of the concept of weak interaction is in accord with the general discussion of Section 2.6; it was stressed there that it is only that portion of the interaction energy which depends on the thermal motion of the heat bath atoms which must be small enough to be negligible.

[12] We are using, as convenient, several different notations for the arguments describing positions and momenta of atoms in I and E in the following equations: $(r, p), \mathbf{r}, a_{iL} X_L = x_i$, etc. The context should make the usage clear.

This completes the demonstration of the manner in which the kinematic parameters a_{iL} enter the Hamiltonian of the inner crystal. The requirement of invariance of H with respect to a rigid rotation of the deformed crystal implies that the parameters a_{iL} appear in combinations that are correspondingly invariant, such as the material strain components E_{LM} [Eq. (4.3.4)], and alternatively we may regard $H = H(r, p; E_{LM})$.

Specification of Reference Configuration

In our discussion of thermoelastic stress–strain relations from the continuum viewpoint (Section 1.6), we emphasized the dependence of thermodynamic functions such as the Helmholtz free energy upon the reference configuration $\mathscr{R}$ and included the latter among its arguments, writing $F = F(E_{LM}, T; \mathscr{R})$; the thermoelastic stress–strain relation derived from this free energy function then has like arguments, $T_{LM} = T_{LM}(E_{NK}, T; \mathscr{R})$.

There is, as can be seen from the discussion of this section, a corresponding dependence on $\mathscr{R}$ of the Hamiltonian describing a particular atomistic model of a crystal and this dependence carries through to all quantities derived from it. A completely parallel notation would require that we write $H = H(q, p; E_{LM}; \mathscr{R})$, but we omit the argument $\mathscr{R}$ and take it as understood.

We see, also, that there is a distinction in the manner in which $\mathscr{R}$ is specified in continuum and in atomistic discussions. In the former, the specification of $\mathscr{R}$ corresponds to setting conditions on the thermoelastic relation: the stress is T_{LM}^0 when the system is in $\mathscr{R}$, that is, when $E_{LM} = 0$, and at reference temperature T_0. In the latter the specification of $\mathscr{R}$ is, for crystalline materials, made by the designation of the reference lattice $\mathbf{X}(l)$.

Phase Function for the Stress Tensor

We turn next to the clarification of the physical significance of Eq. (4.3.5) for the phase function $T_{iL}^m(r, p; a_{jM})$. By use of Eqs. (4.3.12)–(4.3.14), Eq. (4.3.5) takes the form

$$T_{iL}^m = \frac{1}{\mathscr{V}} \frac{\partial V}{\partial a_{iL}} = \frac{1}{\mathscr{V}} \sum_{l' \in \mathrm{E}_{in}} \frac{\partial V}{\partial x_j(l')} \frac{\partial x_j(l')}{\partial a_{iL}}$$

$$= \frac{1}{\mathscr{V}} \sum_{l' \in \mathrm{E}_{in}} \frac{\partial V_{\mathrm{I, E}}}{\partial x_i(l')} X_L(l'),$$

or

$$T_{iL}^m = -\frac{1}{\mathscr{V}} \sum_{l' \in \mathrm{E}_{in}} f_i(l') X_L(l'), \qquad (4.3.15)$$

where

$$f_i(l') = -\frac{\partial V_{\mathrm{I,E}}}{\partial x_i(l')}(\mathbf{r}; \mathbf{x}'), \qquad l' \in \mathrm{E}_{in}. \qquad (4.3.16)$$

are the components of the force exerted on the l' atom in E_{in} by the atoms of I at $\mathbf{r}(l, t)$, $l \in \mathrm{I}$. The situation is shown schematically in Figure 4.4 in which the reference and deformed configurations of the inner crystal I, together with the thin interacting layer E_{in}, is shown.

To establish the relation between the phase function T_{iL}^m defined in Eq. (4.3.15) and the macroscopic Piola–Kirchhoff stress tensor, consider first the case in which all of the atoms of I are at the deformed lattice sites. For I of macroscopic size and short-range interactions, except for a negligible fraction of the atoms of E_{in} near the edges and corners of I, the forces $f_i(l')$ will be uniform over each face. Since I is in equilibrium, these forces will be equal and opposite on opposing faces of I. Consider a typical component of T_{iL}^m, say T_{i1}^m,

$$T_{i1}^m = \frac{-1}{\mathcal{V}} \sum_{l' \in \mathrm{E}_{in}} f_i(l') X_1(l'). \qquad (4.3.17)$$

Then, as may be seen from Figure 4.4b, all the contributions to the sum in Eq. (4.3.17) from the atoms of E_{in} near the opposing faces originally perpendicular to X_2 will cancel in pairs for atoms that had (in the undeformed configuration) the same coordinates X_1 and similarly there is cancellation of the terms corresponding to the opposing faces originally perpendicular to the X_3 direction. However, only the contribution from the front face survives for the pair

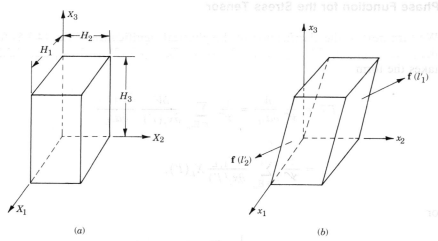

(a)   (b)

Figure 4.4 (a) Reference configuration of $I + E_{in}$. (b) Forces acting on atoms l_1' and l_2' of E_{in} in deformed configuration.

of faces originally perpendicular to X_1 since $X_1(l') \cong 0$ for atoms near the rear face.[13] Since $X_1(l') \cong H_1$ for the atoms of E which interact with the atoms of I near the face $X_1 = H_1$ [denoted by $(E_{in})_1$ in Eq. (4.3.18)], Eq. (4.3.17) takes the form

$$T_{i1}^m = -\frac{1}{A_1} \sum_{l' \in (E_{in})_1} f_i(l')$$

(4.3.18)

where $A_1 = H_2 H_3$ is the original area of the face in question. Therefore T_{i1}^m has precisely the physical significance required of the corresponding Piola–Kirchhoff stress tensor (Section 1.3): it is the negative of the ith component of the force exerted by the interior crystal on the exterior crystal, across a face originally perpendicular to the X_1-axis, per unit of original area of that face.

We have gone through this discussion for the case in which all atoms of I are at their lattice sites $\mathbf{x}(l)$. For a general point in phase space at which $\mathbf{r}(l) \neq \mathbf{x}(l)$ for all $l \in$ I, the exact cancellation in pairs of forces such as $\mathbf{f}(l_1)$, and $\mathbf{f}(l_2)$ (Figure 4.4) will not occur. Nevertheless, in taking the phase average of T_{iL}^m to arrive at the macroscopic stress tensor T_{iL}, we may expect this cancellation to occur on average providing the interior crystal is large enough to be regarded as macroscopic.

It is now easy to verify Eq. (4.3.3) for T_{LM}^m. From Eq. (4.3.4),

$$\frac{\partial H}{\partial a_{iL}} = \frac{\partial H}{\partial E_{LR}} a_{iR}$$

(4.3.19)

so that

$$\frac{\partial H}{\partial E_{LM}} = \frac{\partial H}{\partial a_{iL}} A_{Mi}$$

(4.3.20)

where A_{Mi} is the matrix inverse to a_{iR}, $A_{Mi} a_{iR} = \delta_{MR}$. From the preceding discussion,

$$T_{iL} = \int_\Gamma T_{iL}^m \rho \, dq \, dp = \frac{1}{\mathscr{V}} \int_\Gamma \frac{\partial H}{\partial a_{iL}} \rho \, dq \, dp.$$

(4.3.21)

Therefore, by use of Eqs. (1.3.10) and (1.2.26),

$$T_{LM} = A_{Li} T_{iM} = \frac{1}{\mathscr{V}} \int_\Gamma A_{Li} \frac{\partial H}{\partial a_{iM}} \rho \, dq \, dp = \frac{1}{\mathscr{V}} \int_\Gamma \frac{\partial H}{\partial E_{LM}} \rho \, dq \, dp,$$

(4.3.22)

which verifies Eq. (4.3.3).

---

[13] The use of the approximately equal ($\cong$) sign indicates equality with deviations of the order of the interatomic spacing. The dimensions H_1, H_2, H_3, on the other hand, are of macroscopic size.

We have gone through this discussion for a hypothetical crystal corresponding to a simple cubic lattice in the interests of geometric simplicity. The argument may be adapted to the case of a crystal corresponding to an arbitrary simple Bravais lattice by regarding its nonorthogonal basis vectors $\mathbf{a}_L$, $L = 1, 2, 3$ as the covariant base vectors (Section 6.2) for a nonrectangular Cartesian coordinate system X^L used to denote the reference lattice site positions.

Composite Lattice

We consider next how these ideas are generalized to a crystal corresponding to a composite lattice. As discussed in Section 4.2, a composite lattice can be considered as a set of simple Bravais lattices, all of the same type, which are translated relative to each other. For geometric simplicity, we again take each component lattice to be simple cubic in its reference state.

Let $\mathbf{X}\binom{l}{k}$ [with rectangular Cartesian components $X_L\binom{l}{k}$] be the position of the kth site ($k = 1, \ldots, s$) in the lth cell and $\mathbf{x}\binom{l}{k}$ (with components $x_i\binom{l}{k}$) be the position of the same site after deformation. We subdivide the crystal, as in Figure 4.3, into an interior crystal I and an exterior crystal E with E_{in} denoting the thin[14] layer of E which interacts with I. The total potential energy to be employed in the Hamiltonian of I is $V(\mathbf{r}; \mathbf{x}')$, as in Eq. (4.3.11), where $\mathbf{r}$ now denotes the set of variables $\mathbf{r}(l, k, t)$, $l \in I$, the positions of the atoms of I moving in the vicinity of the lattice sites at $\mathbf{x}\binom{l}{k}$, while $\mathbf{x}'$ denotes the set of the positions of the atoms of E_{in} which are fixed at their lattice sites at $\mathbf{x}\binom{l'}{k}$, $l' \in E_{in}$.

The extension of the macroscopic concept of a uniform deformation described by the deformation matrix a_{iL} to the atomistic level is straightforward for a crystal corresponding to a simple Bravais lattice but requires closer examination for those corresponding to a composite lattice. In the latter case, each of the component lattices is subjected to the same affine transformation, but an additional relative displacement[15] between lattices is necessary if every atom of I is to be in equilibrium under the action of V when all of the atoms of $I + E_{in}$ are placed at their lattice sites. That is, we require that

$$x_i\binom{l}{k} = a_{iL} X_L\binom{l}{k} + b_i(k).\qquad (4.3.23)$$

[14]We continue to restrict attention to short-range interatomic forces.
[15]Since this relative displacement is of the same scale as interatomic distances, it has no macroscopic kinematic manifestation; that is, it cannot be detected by the use of strain gauges or by the observation through an optical microscope of the deformation of a grid scribed on the crystal. Nevertheless, the displacement produces macroscopic energy changes in the crystal and changes its macroscopic behavior as is discussed in Section 4.6.

Since we are not concerned with the translation of the crystal as a whole, we may set $\mathbf{b}(1) = 0$ and determine only the relative displacements $\mathbf{b}(k)$, $k = 2, \ldots, s$, by the equilibrium requirement. When all of the atoms of $I + E_{in}$ are at their lattice sites, each atom of I is surrounded by the same configuration of interacting atoms; therefore, it is only necessary to impose equilibrium on the atoms of a typical cell, say $l = 0$, in I. That is, we require[16]

$$\frac{\partial V}{\partial x_i \binom{0}{k}} (\mathbf{x}, \mathbf{x}') = 0 \qquad \text{for } k = 2, \ldots, s \qquad (4.3.24)$$

when the arguments of V are given by Eq. (4.3.23) for $l \in I + E_{in}$. This provides $3(s - 1)$ implicit equations for the necessary relative displacements $b_i(k) = b_i(k; a_{jM})$. In the interatomic potential $V(\mathbf{r}; \mathbf{x}')$ we now regard the atoms of E_{in} to be fixed at the lattice sites thus determined; that is

$$x_i \binom{l'}{k} = a_{iL} X_L \binom{l'}{k} + b_i(k; a_{jM}), \qquad l' \in E_{in}$$

$$k = 1, \ldots, s \qquad (4.3.25)$$

while the atoms of I are free to undergo thermal motion in the vicinity of their lattice sites. Therefore, for a composite lattice, the deformation matrix a_{iL} enters the Hamiltonian of I through the fixing of the atoms of E_{in} at lattice sites which are obtained by the deformation of each component lattice by a_{iL} and their displacement relative to each other by vectors that depend on a_{iL}.

We consider next for this case the physical significance of Eq. (4.3.5) for the phase function $T_{iL}^m(r, p; a_{jM})$. By use of Eq. (4.3.25), Eq. (4.3.5) takes the form

$$T_{iL}^m = \frac{1}{\mathscr{V}} \sum_{k=1}^{s} \sum_{l' \in E_{in}} \frac{\partial V_{\mathrm{I,E}}}{\partial x_j \binom{l'}{k}} \left[\delta_{ij} X_L \binom{l'}{k} + \frac{\partial b_j}{\partial a_{iL}} (k; a_{rS}) \right]$$

$$= -\frac{1}{\mathscr{V}} \sum_{k=1}^{s} \sum_{l' \in E_{in}} f_i \binom{l'}{k} X_L \binom{l'}{k} - \frac{1}{\mathscr{V}} \sum_{k=1}^{s} \sum_{l' \in E_{in}} f_j \binom{l'}{k} \frac{\partial b_j}{\partial a_{iL}} (k; a_{rS})$$

$$(4.3.26)$$

where $f_i \binom{l'}{k}$ are components of the force exerted on the k atom in the l' cell in E_{in} by the atoms of I at $\mathbf{r}(l, k, t)$. Consider first the special case of the latter atoms all at their lattice sites. Then, as discussed for the simple Bravais lattice,

---

[16] Note that it is not necessary to impose this requirement in the case of a simple Bravais lattice; in this case it follows directly by a symmetry argument that all of the atoms of I are in equilibrium when all the atoms of $I + E_{in}$ are at the lattice sites.

$\mathbf{f}\begin{pmatrix} l' \\ k \end{pmatrix} = -\mathbf{f}\begin{pmatrix} l'' \\ k \end{pmatrix}$ for atoms in E_{in} in symmetric positions on opposite forces. Therefore, the second sum in Eq. (4.3.26) vanishes and

$$T_{iL}^m = -\frac{1}{\mathscr{V}} \sum_{k=1}^{s} \sum_{l' \in E_{in}} f_i\begin{pmatrix} l' \\ k \end{pmatrix} X_L\begin{pmatrix} l' \\ k \end{pmatrix} \qquad (4.3.27)$$

in close analogy to Eq. (4.3.17). By the same reasoning as followed that equation, we see that T_{iL}^m has the physical significance of the Piola–Kirchhoff stress tensor.

4.4   HARMONIC AND QUASI-HARMONIC APPROXIMATIONS

As seen in the previous section, the Hamiltonian of a uniformly deformed perfect crystal can be written [Eq. 4.3.12)] in the form[17]

$$H(r, p^*; E_{LM}) = \frac{1}{2} \sum_{l \in I} \frac{|\mathbf{p}^*(l, t)|^2}{m(l)} + V(\mathbf{r}; E_{LM}) \qquad (4.4.1)$$

where we have used the material strain components, E_{LM}, to describe the deformation of the lattice from its unstressed reference state. Let

$$\mathbf{r}(l, t) = \mathbf{x}(l) + \mathbf{q}^*(l, t), \qquad l \in I. \qquad (4.4.2)$$

Since the deformed lattice site positions $\mathbf{x}(l)$ are determined (up to a rigid motion) by the parameters E_{LM}, we may rewrite the Hamiltonian as

$$H(q^*, p^*; E_{LM}) = \frac{1}{2} \sum_{l \in I} \frac{|\mathbf{p}^*(l, t)|^2}{m(l)} + V(\mathbf{q}^*; E_{LM})$$

$$= \frac{1}{2} \sum_{i=1}^{n} \frac{(p_i^*)^2}{m_i} + V(q_1^*, \dots, q_n^*; E_{LM}) \qquad (4.4.3)$$

where we have reverted to the serial notation of Section 2.2 (with $n = 3N$ for N atoms in I). That is q_1^*, q_2^*, q_3^* are the rectangular Cartesian components of $\mathbf{q}^*(1, t)$ for atom 1 with mass $m_1 = m_2 = m_3, q_4^*, q_5^*, q_6^*$ are the components of $\mathbf{q}^*$ for atom 2 with mass $m_4 = m_5 = m_6$, etc. Mass reduced coordinates and

---

[17]For simplicity of notation we denote lattice sites by the single index l as in a simple Bravais lattice; the discussion applies equally well to crystals corresponding to a composite lattice in which case the index l is replaced by $\begin{pmatrix} l \\ k \end{pmatrix}$. The use at the beginning of this section of the starred notation, $\mathbf{p}^*(l, t)$ for the momenta and $\mathbf{q}^*(l, t)$ in Eq. (4.4.2) for the coordinates of the atoms of I, is motivated by the desire to retain the simpler (q, p) notation for mass-reduced coordinates [Eq. (4.4.4)].

momenta are introduced by the definitions

$$q_i = \sqrt{m_i}\, q_i^*,$$

$$p_i = p_i^* / \sqrt{m_i}\,, \qquad \text{(no sum on } i\text{)}, \qquad (4.4.4)$$

so that in terms of these variables

$$H(q, p; E_{LM}) = \frac{1}{2} \sum_{i=1}^{n} p_i^2 + V(q_1, \ldots, q_n; E_{LM}). \qquad (4.4.5)$$

The displacements q_i describe the thermal motion of the atoms in the vicinity of the deformed lattice sites. If the crystal temperature is not too high, we expect these displacements to be small (in a sense to be made more precise below) and the theory of small vibrations to apply. We briefly review, therefore, the aspects of this theory which we will need.

Theory of Small Vibrations

Expand the potential energy function $V(q_1, \ldots, q_n; E_{LM}) = V(q; E_{LM})$ in a Taylor series expansion about $q_i = 0$, $i = 1, \ldots, n$ (in abbreviated notation, about $q = 0$).

$$V(q; E_{LM}) = V(0; E_{LM}) + \sum_{i=1}^{n} \frac{\partial V}{\partial q_i}\Big|_{q=0} q_i + \frac{1}{2} \sum_{i,j=1}^{n} \frac{\partial^2 V}{\partial q_i \partial q_j}\Big|_{q=0} q_i q_j + \cdots.$$

$$(4.4.6)$$

The displacements $q = 0$ correspond to atom positions $\mathbf{r}(l, t) = \mathbf{x}(l)$. These are the equilibrium positions of the interior atoms under the action of $V = V_I + V_{I,E}$ [Eq. (4.3.13)]. Therefore,

$$\frac{\partial V}{\partial q_i}\Big|_{q=0} = 0, \qquad i = 1, \ldots, n. \qquad (4.4.7)$$

The harmonic approximation to the potential $V(q; E_{LM})$ is based on the assumption that the displacements q_i are sufficiently small so that the Taylor series of Eq. (4.4.6) may be truncated at the quadratic terms. Therefore, in the harmonic approximation, denoted in the following by subscript h,

$$V_h(q; E_{LM}) = V_0 + \frac{1}{2} V_{ij} q_i q_j, \qquad (4.4.8)$$

where here, and in what follows, the summation convention, $i, j = 1, \ldots, n$ is employed and

$$V_0(E_{LM}) = V(0; E_{LM}), \qquad (4.4.9)$$

$$V_{ij}(E_{LM}) = \left.\frac{\partial^2 V}{\partial q_i \partial q_j}\right|_{q=0}. \qquad (4.4.10)$$

$V_{ij}(E_{LM})$ is referred to as the potential energy matrix of the system (with respect to mass-reduced coordinates).

In the theory of lattice dynamics,[18] two types of harmonic approximations are distinguished: (a) the strict harmonic approximation, in which it is assumed further that the elements V_{ij} of the potential energy matrix are independent of the strain components E_{LM} and so are strict constants; (b) the quasi-harmonic approximation in which $V_{ij} = V_{ij}(E_{LM})$ as in Eq. (4.4.10). The theory of small vibrations, as outlined below, is based on Eq. (4.4.8) and takes the same form for both cases.

The equations of motion corresponding to the Hamiltonian of Eq. (4.4.5), with the harmonic approximation of Eq. (4.4.8), are

$$\ddot{q}_i = -V_{ij}q_j. \qquad (4.4.11)$$

Consider a particular solution of the form

$$q_i = \alpha_i \cos \omega t. \qquad (4.4.12)$$

A solution of this form is called a normal mode of the system with mode shape α_i and circular frequency ω. By substitution in Eq. (4.4.11) it is seen that Eq. (4.4.12) will define a solution if and only if

$$V_{ij}\alpha_j = \omega^2 \alpha_i. \qquad (4.4.13)$$

That is, the n-dimensional vector with components α_j is an eigenvector of the potential energy matrix V_{ij} corresponding to the eigenvalue ω^2. By its definition V_{ij} is a real, symmetric matrix so that there exist n eigenvalues ω_r^2 with corresponding eigenvectors α_{rj}, $r = 1, \ldots, n$ which satisfy the equations

$$V_{ij}\alpha_{rj} = \omega_r^2 \alpha_{ri} \quad \text{(no summation over } r\text{)}. \qquad (4.4.14)$$

As is well known, the eigenvectors may be taken[19] as orthonormal

$$\alpha_{ri}\alpha_{si} = \delta_{rs}, \qquad (4.4.15)$$

[18]See for example, Born and Huang (1954), Maradudin, Montroll, and Weiss (1963), Leibfried and Ludwig (1961), and Barron, Collins, and White (1980). The term quasi-harmonic is also used to describe theories, which we do not treat, in which $V_{ij} = V_{ij}(E_{LM}, T)$; cf. Cowley (1963).

[19]See Section 1.10 for the discussion of degenerate eigenvalues.

and they satisfy the completeness relation

$$a_{ri}a_{rj} = \delta_{ij}. \qquad (4.4.16)$$

Normal coordinates Q_r and corresponding momenta P_r are introduced by the relations

$$Q_r = a_{ri}q_i, \qquad P_r = a_{ri}p_i \qquad (4.4.17)$$

with the inverse relations [obtained by use of Eq. (4.4.16)]

$$q_i = a_{ri}Q_r, \qquad p_i = a_{ri}P_r. \qquad (4.4.18)$$

The Hamiltonian $H(q, p; E_{LM})$ of Eq. (4.4.5) with the harmonic approximation of Eq. (4.4.8) then takes the form

$$H_h(Q, P; E_{LM}) = V_0(E_{LM}) + \frac{1}{2}\sum_{r=1}^{n}\left(P_r^2 + \omega_r^2 Q_r^2\right) \qquad (4.4.19)$$

as may be verified by direct substitution of Eqs. (4.4.18) into Eqs. (4.4.5) and (4.4.8) and use of Eqs. (4.4.14) and (4.4.15). As before, the subscript h indicates that the Hamiltonian is based on the harmonic approximation. Note that $\omega_r = \omega_r(E_{LM})$ in the quasi-harmonic approximation and are strict constants in the strict harmonic approximation. The full Hamiltonian of Eq. (4.4.5) may be written in terms of normal coordinates as

$$H(Q, P; E_{LM}) = H_h(Q, P; E_{LM}) + A(Q; E_{LM}) \qquad (4.4.20)$$

where $A(Q; E_{LM})$ represent the anharmonic terms; a Taylor series expansion of A in the variables Q_r will begin with third-order terms.

For the elastic behavior presently under discussion it is assumed that the equilibrium configuration corresponding to $q = 0$ is stable. It then follows that the potential energy matrix V_{ij} is nonnegative and therefore all the eigenvalues ω_r^2 are nonnegative.

4.5   THERMOELASTIC STRESS – STRAIN RELATIONS BASED ON THE HARMONIC APPROXIMATION

In order to determine the thermoelastic stress–strain relations for an elastic solid by means of equilibrium statistical mechanics it is necessary to first compute $Z(E_{LM}, T)$, the partition function of the system, by means of Eq. (3.6.18):

$$Z(E_{LM}, T) = \int_{\Gamma} e^{-\beta H(q, p; E_{LM})} dq\, dp$$

$$= Z_p(T)Z_q(E_{LM}, T) \qquad (4.5.1)$$

where $\beta = (kT)^{-1}$ and

$$Z_p(T) = \int_{\Gamma_p} e^{-\frac{\beta}{2} \sum_{i=1}^{n} p_i^2} dp, \qquad (4.5.2)$$

$$Z_q(E_{LM}, T) = \int_{\Gamma_q} e^{-\beta V(q; \, E_{LM})} dq. \qquad (4.5.3)$$

Z_p is referred to as the momentum partition function and Z_q is the configuration partition function. Clearly, there is no difficulty in the computation of $Z_p(T)$, and the computation of $Z_q(E_{LM}, T)$ would be nearly as straightforward if $V(q; E_{LM})$ in Eq. (4.5.3) could be replaced by its harmonic approximation $V_h(q; E_{LM})$ as defined in Eq. (4.4.8). That this is permissible for sufficiently low temperature levels (and consequent small amplitude of thermal motion) may be seen from the following heuristic argument. Since $q = 0$ corresponds to a stable equilibrium configuration we expect $\Delta V(\xi)$, where $\Delta V = V - V_0(E_{LM})$, to appear as in Figure 4.5a where ξ is the coordinate along a straight line in configuration space passing through $q = 0$ in an arbitrary direction. In the interval $\delta_1 < \xi < \delta_2$, V_h is a good approximation to V while outside that interval the anharmonic portion of V becomes appreciable. Next we consider, in Figure 4.5b, the appearance of $e^{-\beta \Delta V}$ for two values of β, $\beta_1 > \beta_2$ corresponding to temperature levels $T_1 < T_2$. For the values of T_2 shown schematically in Figure 4.5b, $e^{-\beta_2 \Delta V}$ still has a substantial value outside the region in which the harmonic approximation is valid, but at the lower temperature T_1, $e^{-\beta_1 \Delta V}$ is negligible there. If this is true for all the directions along which ξ is measured it may be expected[20] that the harmonic approximation can be used for the computation of Z for $T \leqslant T_1$. This is the assumption that we make in what follows.

We turn, therefore, to the computation of $Z_h(E_{LM}, T)$, the partition function based on the harmonic Hamiltonian $H_h(q, p; E_{LM})$, by the relation

$$Z_h(E_{LM}, T) = \int_{\Gamma} e^{-\beta H_h(q, \, p; \, E_{LM})} dq \, dp. \qquad (4.5.4)$$

We next change the variables of integration from the mass-reduced rectangular Cartesian coordinates and momenta (q, p) to the normal coordinates and momenta (Q, P) by means of Eq. (4.4.18). Since, from Eqs. (4.4.15) and (4.4.16), the matrix a_{ri} is orthogonal, the Jacobian of this transformation is

---

[20] This argument could be made more rigorous by considering the asymptotic expansion of Z for large β by a generalization to multiple integrals of Laplace's expansion procedure. For one-dimensional integrals, this procedure is discussed, for example, by Sirovich (1971, pp. 80–86).

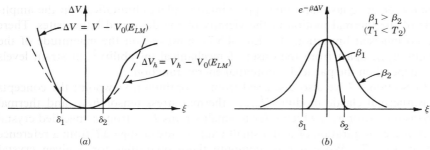

Figure 4.5 Low-temperature approximation to configuration partition function.

unity and

$$Z_h(E_{LM}, T) = \int_\Gamma e^{-\beta H_h(Q, P; E_{LM})} dQ \, dP$$

$$= e^{-\beta V_0(E_{LM})} \prod_{r=1}^n \int_{-\infty}^\infty e^{-\frac{\beta}{2} P_r^2} \int_{-\infty}^\infty e^{-\frac{\beta}{2} \omega_r^2 Q_r^2} dQ_r$$

$$= \left(\frac{2\pi}{\beta}\right)^n e^{-\beta V_0(E_{LM})} \prod_{r=1}^n \omega_r^{-1} \qquad (4.5.5)$$

where Eq. (4.4.19) for H_h has been employed. From the relation between the free energy and the partition function, Eq. (3.6.17),

$$F_h(E_{LM}, T) = -kT \log Z_h(E_{LM}, T)$$

$$= V_0(E_{LM}) - nkT \log(2\pi kT) + kT \sum_{r=1}^n \log \omega_r. \qquad (4.5.6)$$

Eq. (4.5.6) gives the expression for the free energy when the harmonic approximation in either of its two forms is employed. When the strict harmonic approximation is employed, the ω_r are strict constants and the strains E_{LM} enter only as arguments for V_0, the potential energy of the system when all the atoms are at their equilibrium positions under the imposed deformation E_{LM}. In the quasi-harmonic approximation, $\omega_r = \omega_r(E_{LM})$ as well; in this case we write F_{qh} for the free energy function of Eq. (4.5.6).

The thermoelastic stress–strain relation on the basis of the quasi-harmonic approximation follows from the use of Eq. (1.6.3):

$$T_{LM}(E_{RS}, T) = \frac{1}{\mathcal{V}} \frac{\partial F_{qh}}{\partial E_{LM}}\bigg|_T$$

$$= \frac{1}{\mathcal{V}} \left[\frac{\partial V_0}{\partial E_{LM}} + kT \sum_{r=1}^n \frac{\partial \log \omega_r}{\partial E_{LM}} \right]. \qquad (4.5.7)$$

The use of the quasi-harmonic approximation places limitations on the amplitude of the thermal motion in the vicinity of the deformed lattice sites. There are no inherent limitations for Eq. (4.5.7), however, on the magnitude of the strains E_{LM}, apart from the onset of mechanical instability[21] at strain levels that depend on the particular potential energy function.

In Section 1.7 we also discussed from a continuum viewpoint the concepts of isothermal elastic moduli C^T_{LMNK}, thermal stress tensor b_{LM}, and thermal expansion tensor α_{LM} which refer to small strains E_{LM} from a specified crystal reference configuration $\mathscr{R}$ and a small temperature change ΔT from a reference temperature T_0. We can now compute these quantities for a given crystal model by use of the equations of macroscopic thermodynamics, Eqs. (1.7.5), (1.7.7) and (1.7.15), applied to the free energy function of Eq. (4.5.6) based on the quasi-harmonic approximation:

$$C^T_{LMNK} = \frac{1}{\mathscr{V}}\left[\left.\frac{\partial^2 V_0}{\partial E_{LM}\partial E_{NK}}\right|_0 + kT_0 \sum_{r=1}^{n} \left.\frac{\partial^2 \log \omega_r}{\partial E_{LM}\partial E_{NK}}\right|_0\right], \qquad (4.5.8)$$

$$b_{LM} = \frac{k}{\mathscr{V}} \sum_{r=1}^{n} \left.\frac{\partial \log \omega_r}{\partial E_{LM}}\right|_0, \qquad (4.5.9)$$

$$\alpha_{LM} = \frac{-kS^T_{LMNK}}{\mathscr{V}} \sum_{r=1}^{n} \left.\frac{\partial \log \omega_r}{\partial E_{NK}}\right|_0, \qquad (4.5.10)$$

where the partial derivatives are evaluated at $E_{LM} = 0$, that is, the specified crystal reference configuration; S^T_{LMNK} are the isothermal elastic compliances, the tensor inverse [Eq. (1.7.13)] to the moduli C^T_{LMNK} obtained in Eq. (4.5.8).

In order to complete the determination of the linear thermoelastic relation for small strains E_{LM} from a specified reference configuration and small temperature changes ΔT from a reference temperature T_0, we see from Eq. (1.7.3) that it is necessary to calculate the initial stress T^0_{LM} in the reference state. This is obtained from Eq. (4.5.7):

$$T^0_{LM} = T_{LM}(0, T_0) = \frac{1}{\mathscr{V}}\left[\left.\frac{\partial V_0}{\partial E_{LM}}\right|_0 + kT_0 \sum_{r=1}^{n} \left.\frac{\partial \log \omega_r}{\partial E_{LM}}\right|_0\right] \quad (4.5.11)$$

where the derivatives are evaluated at $E_{RS} = 0$, that is, at the reference configuration $\mathscr{R}$.

---

[21] The theory of the stability of perfect crystals at finite strain is treated in Hill (1975) and Milstein and Hill (1979); a review is contained in Milstein (1980).

We may now summarize the procedure for computing the linear thermoelastic relation for a given crystal model, where the term model comprises a short-range interatomic potential V and an assumed crystal structure.

1   Choose size of inner portion I and corresponding interacting layer E_{in}.
2   Fix reference configuration, that is, fix size of reference lattice parameters.
3   Compute $V_0(E_{LM})$, the energy of all atoms in I + E_{in} when atoms are at deformed lattice sites, and $\omega_r(E_{LM})$, the normal mode frequencies for small vibrations in the vicinity of these sites.
4   Compute $F_{qh}(E_{LM}, T)$ from Eq. (4.5.6).
5   Compute T_{LM}^0, the stress in the reference configuration at the reference temperature from Eq. (4.5.11).
6   Compute C_{LMNK}^T and b_{LM} from Eq.s (4.5.8) and (4.5.9) where the derivatives are evaluated at the reference configuration.

An example for a one-dimensional idealized model is given in Section 4.8.

Temperature Dependence of Elastic Constants

The elastic constants C_{LMNK}^T computed in Eq. (4.5.8) depend on the reference configuration $\mathscr{R}$ and on the reference temperature T_0, so that we can write $C_{LMNK}^T = C_{LMNK}^T(T_0; \mathscr{R}) = C_{LMNK}^T(T_0; \mathbf{a}_0)$, where $\mathbf{a}_0$ denotes the set of basis vectors describing the reference configuration. If we wish to discuss the temperature dependence of these moduli, two different possibilities should be considered.

(1) The reference configuration $\mathbf{a}_0$ is kept fixed while the reference temperature T_0 is varied. Then, it follows from Eq. (4.5.8) that the classical quasi-harmonic approximation predicts a strict linear dependence of C_{LMNK}^T on T_0. Note from Eq. (4.5.11) that if the reference configuration is kept fixed while T_0 is varied, T_{LM}^0 will be a linear function of T_0; that is, it is necessary to impose a variable initial stress in order to keep the reference configuration constant as T_0 varies.

As seen from Eq. (4.5.9), the theory predicts that the thermal stress tensor b_{LM} is temperature independent for fixed reference configuration and the same is true for C_e, the specified heat at constant strain as will be derived in Eq. (4.5.15). It follows from Eq. (1.8.18), which relates the adiabatic and isothermal elastic moduli, that the classical quasi-harmonic prediction of a linear temperature dependence of C_{LMNK}^T applies as well to C_{LMNK}^S.

(2) The initial stress T_{LM}^0 is held fixed, say $T_{LM}^0 = 0$. Then it is clear from Eq. (4.5.11) that the reference configuration must vary with T_0; that is, $\mathbf{a}_0 = \mathbf{a}_0(T_0)$. The temperature dependence of the moduli which is predicted by the classical quasi-harmonic approximation is therefore not as clear-cut in this case as in the case of fixed reference configuration. If one assumes a thermal

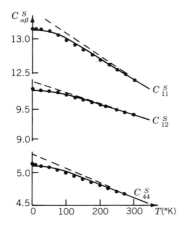

Figure 4.6 Adiabatic elastic constants of silver. Units are $10''$ dynes/cm². Experimental values (●) from Neighbors and Alers (1958). Theoretical curves, computed by Leibfried and Ludwig (1961) based on Debye model (Section 10.3); dashed lines show linear extrapolation. (After Leibfried and Ludwig, 1961, with permission.)

expansion that is small and linear in T_0, an expansion of Eq. (4.5.8) about a fixed reference configuration suggests[22] that the term giving the linear dependence on T_0 remains the predominant mode of variation.

Much of the available experimental data on the temperature dependence of elastic moduli is obtained by ultrasonic techniques which give results for zero initial stress adiabatic moduli. Numerous graphs of such results will be found in Leibfried and Ludwig (1961); these graphs show a linear temperature dependence over a broad temperature range with the moduli generally decreasing with temperature, although this is not always the case. As an example, some data for the experimentally observed elastic moduli of silver are shown in Figure 4.6. The departure from linearity at low temperature levels is to be expected on the basis of quantum statistical mechanics and will be discussed further in Section 10.3.

Strict Harmonic Approximation

In the strict harmonic approximation, the frequencies ω_r are strict constants; in this approximation, the elastic moduli are temperature independent and the thermal stress and thermal expansion tensors vanish. We may say, therefore, that the phenomena of thermal expansion and of the temperature dependence of the elastic moduli are anharmonic effects.

The elastic moduli $\tilde{C}_{LMNK}$ computed on the basis of the strict harmonic approximation are, from Eq. (4.5.6),

$$\tilde{C}_{LMNK} = \frac{1}{\mathscr{V}} \left. \frac{\partial^2 V_0}{\partial E_{LM} \partial E_{NK}} \right|_0 \tag{4.5.12}$$

[22]Ludwig (1967, p. 98). See also the discussion in Wallace (1972, p. 369), who presents an approximate procedure using higher-order elastic moduli to convert constant initial stress moduli to constant configuration moduli.

and are referred to as the harmonic elastic moduli. Note that it may be seen from Eq. (1.8.18) that the isothermal and adiabatic moduli are equal when computed on the basis of the strict harmonic approximation since, in this case, $b_{LM} = 0$.

U_h, S_h, and C_ε

It is a straightforward matter to compute other thermodynamic functions of the interior crystal I from the harmonic partition function $Z_h(E_{LM}, T)$ of Eq. (4.5.5). For example, by use of Eqs. (3.9.3) and (3.9.5) we can compute $U_h(E_{LM}, T)$ and $S_h(E_{LM}, T)$, the internal energy and entropy based on the harmonic approximation, and by use of Eq. (1.8.1) we can compute C_ε, the specific heat at constant deformation. The results are

$$U_h(E_{LM}, T) = 3NkT + V_0(E_{LM}), \qquad (4.5.13)$$

$$S_h(E_{LM}, T) = 3Nk(1 + \log(2\pi kT)) - k \sum_{r=1}^{3N} \log \omega_r(E_{LM}), \quad (4.5.14)$$

$$C_\varepsilon = 3Nk, \qquad (4.5.15)$$

where we recall that N is the number of atoms in I. The term $3NkT$ in U_h is seen to be a direct consequence of the equipartition theorem (Section 3.11) since the harmonic Hamiltonian, Eq. (4.4.19), represents a collection of N harmonic oscillators.

The information theoretical interpretation (Section 3.12) of the entropy is useful in understanding the two terms in Eq. (4.5.14): As the temperature increases the amplitude of atomic vibrations increases, thus increasing the uncertainty in their positions. Similarly, the decrease of a frequency ω_r with increasing strain E_{LM} implies a more shallow potential and a greater amplitude of vibration at a given temperature.

It is also of interest to note that the classical harmonic theory predicts that the specific heat C_ε is a constant proportional to the number of atoms N and is independent of the particular crystalline material. At sufficiently high temperature levels this prediction is in reasonably good agreement with experiment and is referred to as the law of Dulong and Petit. However, there remains at high temperature levels a small increasing component, approximately linear in T, which requires consideration of further anharmonic terms[23] in the potential for its prediction. At low temperature levels the classical prediction is drastically modified by quantum statistical effects; these will be discussed in Section 10.3.

---

[23] See, for example, Wallace (1972).

4.6 CAUCHY RELATIONS

As we discussed in Section 1.7, it follows from general considerations that the elastic constants C_{LMNK} (either isothermal or adiabatic) possess complete Voigt symmetry. That is, they are invariant under the pair interchange

   (i) $(LM) \leftrightarrow (ML)$

   (ii) $(NK) \leftrightarrow (KN)$

   (iii) $(LM) \leftrightarrow (NK)$

and there are, therefore, only 21 independent components.

The only remaining symmetry for the tensor C_{LMNK} which is not implied by properties (i) to (iii) is

   (iv) $(MN) \leftrightarrow (NM)$.

With the addition of this property, the tensor C_{LMNK} has complete symmetry; the interchange of any pair of indices leaves the value of the component unchanged. Property (iv) is nontrivial only if the indices M and N take on different values. It, therefore, corresponds to six additional relations, known as the Cauchy relations, and reduces by that number the number of components that can be assigned values independently; that is, properties (i) to (iv), or complete symmetry, imply 15 independent elastic moduli.

The six Cauchy relations may be written explicitly as follows:

$$C_{1122} = C_{1212}, \qquad C_{1133} = C_{1313}, \qquad C_{2233} = C_{2323},$$
$$C_{1213} = C_{1123}, \qquad C_{2213} = C_{2123}, \qquad C_{3312} = C_{3132}. \tag{4.6.1}$$

In Voigt notation, Eq. (1.3.21), the Cauchy relations take the form

$$C_{14} = C_{56}, \qquad C_{12} = C_{66}, \qquad C_{13} = C_{55},$$
$$C_{36} = C_{45}, \qquad C_{23} = C_{44}, \qquad C_{25} = C_{46}. \tag{4.6.2}$$

The transcription provides a good example of a transparent relationship rendered obscure by a suitable change of notation.

The terminology, Cauchy relations for Eq. (4.6.1), is due to Love (1927) who also gives an interesting historical account. The origin of the subject may be traced to the work by Cauchy in the early part of the nineteenth century on the foundations of the theory of elasticity. As part of this effort, Cauchy presented an atomistic model for elastic behavior[24] which predicted complete symmetry for the elastic moduli. There was much experimental effort expended in the

[24]See Love (1927, Note B, pp. 616–617).

nineteenth century to determine whether the elastic moduli of real materials satisfied Cauchy's relations.[25] Accumulating experimental evidence that Cauchy's relations were not satisfied by the moduli for most materials prompted theoretical investigations to determine the characteristics of Cauchy's atomistic model which were responsible for these relations, and for ways in which the model could be altered so that they did not follow as a necessary result.

Work has continued on this question to the present. The results that have emerged are that properties of the atomistic model which are important in this connection are (1) the nature of the interatomic force law, in particular whether it is many-body or two-body in character, and (2) the geometric nature of the crystal, whether it corresponds to a simple or to a composite Bravais lattice.

One of the difficulties confronting early experimenters in this field was the lack of an adequate theoretical model of the process; this left unclear the type of experimental data to collect and examine. From the quasi-harmonic analysis of Section 4.5, it is now clear that if we seek properties of the elastic moduli which can be ascribed to the nature of the interatomic potential and which are not obscured by additional thermal effects, it is necessary to look at the values of the moduli as functions of temperature in the linear temperature dependence regime and their linear extrapolations back to $T = 0°$. It is these extrapolated values of experimentally measured moduli which should be compared to the theoretical harmonic moduli $\tilde{C}_{LMNK}$, defined in Eq. (4.5.12) in terms of the potential energy of atomic interaction. Consider, for example, the experimental data for silver shown in Figure 4.6. In its reference state silver corresponds to a cubic crystal. Cubic symmetry implies[26] only three independent elastic moduli as shown in the array

$$(C_{\alpha\beta}) = \begin{pmatrix} C_{11} & C_{12} & C_{12} & 0 & 0 & 0 \\ C_{12} & C_{11} & C_{12} & 0 & 0 & 0 \\ C_{12} & C_{12} & C_{11} & 0 & 0 & 0 \\ 0 & 0 & 0 & C_{44} & 0 & 0 \\ 0 & 0 & 0 & 0 & C_{44} & 0 \\ 0 & 0 & 0 & 0 & 0 & C_{44} \end{pmatrix}. \quad (4.6.3)$$

Therefore, the only Cauchy relation of Eqs. (4.6.2) which is not trivially

---

[25]As noted in Section 1.7, material symmetries further reduce the number of independent elastic moduli. For an isotropic substance, complete Voigt symmetry implies the existence of two independent moduli, frequently chosen as E and ν, Young's modulus and Poisson's ratio. The addition of Cauchy's relations further reduces the number of independent constants to one, assigning the universal value of $\nu = \frac{1}{4}$ to Poisson's ratio. Much of the early experimental effort was directed at this prediction but interpretation was not clear because of the difficulty of verifying the isotropy of the tested materials. The experiments of Voigt in the latter part of the nineteenth century on single crystals were more clear-cut and revealed that Cauchy's relations were violated in many substances.

[26]See, for example, Mason (1958, p. 389).

satisfied is $C_{12} = C_{66}$, which, in this case, becomes $C_{12} = C_{44}$. It is clear from Figure 4.6 that the experimental data show that the harmonic moduli $\tilde{C}_{12} \neq \tilde{C}_{44}$ for silver.

Theory

We present next an analysis due to Stakgold (1950) which provides sufficient conditions on the nature of the interatomic potential and the crystal structure under which the harmonic moduli $\tilde{C}_{LMNK}$ will satisfy Cauchy's relations.[27]

Returning to the formulation and the notation of Section 4.3, we consider first a crystal of like atoms corresponding to a simple Bravais lattice. As before, we focus on an interior region I together with E_{in} the thin layer of surrounding atoms which interact with the atoms of I (see Figure 4.3). The positions of the lattice sites of $I + E_{in}$ in the reference configuration are denoted by $X_L(l)$, and the corresponding sites in the deformed configuration are $x_i(l)$. The two are related by the affine transformation

$$x_i(l) = a_{iL} X_L(l), \qquad l \in I + E_{in}. \tag{4.6.4}$$

Since we are dealing with a crystal consisting of all like atoms and corresponding to a simple Bravais lattice, the atoms of I will be in equilibrium when they are all located at their lattice sites. This follows immediately from symmetry considerations, since each atom of I is at a center of symmetry with respect to all of the atoms with which they interact, that is, those of $I + E_{in}$. (Recall that, as part of the formalism of Section 4.3, we impose the requirement that the atoms of E_{in} are fixed at the sites $x_i(l)$ of the deformed lattice; these are geometric constraints and it is not necessary that these atoms satisfy equilibrium conditions.)

If we assume that the atoms of the crystal interact with a general, many-body interatomic potential,[28] then the potential energy of $I + E_{in}$, with all the atoms at the sites of the deformed lattice, is $V_0(x(l), x(l'), \dots)$ where the arguments $x(l), x(l'), \dots$ cover all the sites in $I + E_{in}$. The subscript 0 on the potential energy V is in conformity with the notation of Section 4.5; it refers to the potential energy in the absence of thermal motion.

The function V_0 is invariant with respect to a rigid rotation of the entire configuration of $I + E_{in}$. Therefore it is possible to rewrite V_0 as a function of a new set of variables, functions of $x(l), x(l'), \dots$, which have the properties that the specification of the set of new variables completely defines the relative positions of the collection of atoms, but the values of the new variables are invariant with respect to a rigid motion of the configuration. Such a set of new

---

[27]See also Hill (1975) for a further discussion. As Hill remarks, the work of Stakgold (1950) does not appear to be widely known.

[28]The concept of a many-body interatomic potential is discussed briefly in Section 4.1 and at greater length in Section 9.6.

variables which is convenient for our purposes is the distance squared, $r(ll')$, between pairs of atoms of a set of pairs of $I + E_{in}$ which is sufficient to fix all of their relative positions:

$$r(ll') = \Delta x_i(ll')\Delta x_i(ll') \tag{4.6.5}$$

where

$$\Delta x_i(ll') = x_i(l) - x_i(l'). \tag{4.6.6}$$

The distance squared $R(ll')$ between the same pair of atoms in the reference state is

$$R(ll') = \Delta X_L(ll')\Delta X_L(ll') \tag{4.6.7}$$

where

$$\Delta X_L(ll') = X_L(l) - X_L(l'). \tag{4.6.8}$$

If $E_{LM} = \frac{1}{2}(a_{iL}a_{iM} - \delta_{LM})$ is the material strain tensor corresponding to the affine transformation a_{iL} then, as developed in Section 1.2,

$$r(ll') - R(ll') = 2E_{LM}\Delta X_L(ll')\Delta X_M(ll'). \tag{4.6.9}$$

We now regard V_0 as a function of distance squared between pairs of atoms, $V_0 = V_0(r(ll'), r(ll''), \ldots)$, where the index pairs (ll') range over a set B sufficient to fix the relative positions of all the lattice sites of $I + E_{in}$. Then, from Eq. (4.6.9),

$$\frac{\partial V_0}{\partial E_{LM}} = 2 \sum_{(ll') \in B} \frac{\partial V_0}{\partial r(ll')} \Delta X_L(ll')\Delta X_M(ll'), \tag{4.6.10}$$

and, from Eq. (4.5.12),

$$\tilde{C}_{LMNK} = \frac{1}{\mathscr{V}} \left. \frac{\partial^2 V_0}{\partial E_{LM}\partial E_{NK}} \right|_0$$

$$= \frac{4}{\mathscr{V}} \sum_{\substack{(ll') \in B \\ (l''l''') \in B}} \left. \frac{\partial^2 V_0}{\partial r(ll')\partial r(l''l''')} \right|_0$$

$$\times \Delta X_L(ll')\Delta X_M(ll')\Delta X_N(l''l''')\Delta X_K(l''l'''). \tag{4.6.11}$$

It is seen from Eq. (4.6.11) that for a general many-body potential, the harmonic moduli $\tilde{C}_{LMNK}$ have complete Voigt symmetry, but do not automatically satisfy Cauchy's relations since the indices M and N correspond to different summation indices in the double sum.

Consider next the case in which the interatomic potential is two-body in character, that is[29]

$$V_0 = \sum_{(ll') \in B} \varphi_{ll'}(r(ll')).$$ (4.6.12)

Then

$$\frac{\partial^2 V_0}{\partial r(ll')\partial r(l''l''')} = \frac{\partial^2 \varphi_{ll'}(r(ll'))}{\partial r(ll')^2} \quad \text{for } (ll') = (l''l''')$$

$$= 0 \quad \text{for } (ll') \neq (l''l'''),$$ (4.6.13)

and Eq. (4.6.11) becomes

$$\tilde{C}_{LMNK} = \frac{4}{\mathscr{V}} \sum_{(ll') \in B} \frac{\partial^2 \varphi_{ll'}(r(ll'))}{\partial r(ll')^2}\bigg|_0 \Delta X_L(ll')\Delta X_M(ll')\Delta X_N(ll')\Delta X_K(ll').$$

(4.6.14)

Therefore, under these conditions, the harmonic moduli $\tilde{C}_{LMNK}$ satisfy Cauchy's relations and are completely symmetric.

We have gone through this analysis for a crystal of like atoms corresponding to a simple Bravais lattice. We show next, however, that the analysis applies as well to a crystal with more than one kind of atom subject to a two-body potential as in Eq. (4.6.12) and corresponding to a composite lattice, providing that in the undeformed reference configuration at equilibrium each atom occupies a site which is a center of symmetry (Figure 4.7a). Such crystals are termed centrosymmetric; the cesium chloride and sodium chloride structures (Section 4.2) are examples. If we now transform all of the lattice sites $X_L(l)$ by the same affine transformation a_{iL}, as in Eq. (4.6.4), then each atom will again occupy a center of symmetry in the deformed crystal (Figure 4.7b) and will therefore be in equilibrium. The basic assumption, therefore, that the equilibrium positions of all of the atoms of I in the deformed configuration are obtained from those in the reference configuration by the same affine transformation applies and the previous analysis goes through.

Note that this would not be the case if we had a composite lattice in which each atom did not occupy a center of symmetry when at equilibrium in the

---

[29] The notation $\varphi_{ll'}(r(ll'))$ includes the possibility that different pairs of atoms (ll') are subject to different interatomic potential functions $\varphi_{ll'}$. This is not the case of crystals with all like atoms, as are being presently considered, but is required when treating crystals with more than one type of atom.

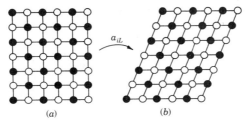

a_{iL}

(a)   (b)

Figure 4.7 Centro-symmetric crystals remain centro-symmetric under an affine deformation.

reference configuration. In general, as discussed in Section 4.3, additional displacements between the sublattices of the compound lattices are required to achieve an equilibrium configuration and the preceding analysis therefore breaks down.

To summarize: what has been shown is that Cauchy's relations will be satisfied for the harmonic moduli of a crystal which is centrosymmetric and whose atoms interact with a two-body potential. If either of these conditions is violated, Cauchy's relations need not be satisfied.

It is important to recognize that the conditions just derived are sufficient but not necessary.[30] Another sufficient condition for the Cauchy relations, based on the Hellmann–Feynman theorem of quantum mechanics, will be derived in Section 9.5.

Computation of Elastic Moduli

Equations (4.6.11) and (4.6.14), which have been developed here for the discussion of the Cauchy relations, are also useful for the computation of elastic moduli from empirical interatomic potentials. Consider, for example, a centrosymmetric crystal with a two-body interatomic potential. Let N be the number of primitive cells in I and let l_i, $i = 1, \ldots, N$ be the index for a corresponding atom in each cell. Then, Eq. (4.6.14) can be rewritten in the form

$$\tilde{C}_{LMNK} = \frac{4}{\mathcal{V}} \sum_{i=1}^{N} \sum_{(l_i l')} \frac{\partial^2 \varphi_{ll'}\big(r(l_i l')\big)}{\partial r(l_i l')^2}\bigg|_0$$

$$\times \Delta X_L(l_i l') \Delta X_M(l_i l') \Delta X_N(l_i l') \Delta X_K(l_i l') \qquad (4.6.15)$$

where the second sum ranges over all atoms l' in I + E_{in} which interact with

---

[30] See, for example, the experimental data for NaI shown on p. 408 of Leibfried and Ludwig (1961) which indicates $\tilde{C}_{12} = \tilde{C}_{44}$. In this case, however, the nature of the temperature dependence of the moduli led these authors to the conclusion that a many-body potential is needed for their description.

atom l_i. Since the atoms l' are in the same relative configuration with respect to l_i for all i, the second sum is independent of i and Eq. (4.6.15) can be written

$$\tilde{C}_{LMNK} = \frac{4}{\mathcal{V}_0} \sum_{l'} \left. \frac{\partial^2 \varphi_{0l'}(r(0l'))}{\partial r(0l')^2} \right|_0 \Delta X_L(0l') \Delta X_M(0l') \Delta X_N(0l') \Delta X_K(0l')$$

$$(4.6.16)$$

where $\mathcal{V}_0$ is the volume of a single primitive cell and the sum is over all atoms l' which interact with a particular atom, here denoted by the index 0.

For centrosymmetric crystals with many-body interatomic potentials, Eq. (4.6.11) may be used as starting point. We have used the variables $r(ll')$ to describe the interatomic configuration in the general discussion leading to that equation. For particular empirical potentials, other choices of variables that are also invariant to rigid body motions, for example, the angle between two pairs of atoms, may be more convenient.

For the computation of the harmonic elastic moduli for noncentrosymmetric crystals, it is necessary to include the shifts between component lattices as described by Eq. (4.3.25); see, for example, Guttman and Rothstein (1979).

4.7   STRESS ENSEMBLE

In the previous sections of this chapter, we dealt with the statistical mechanics of crystal elasticity based on a canonical strain ensemble in which a_{iL}, the components of the deformation matrix, or E_{LM}, the components of the material strain tensor, were the controlled parameters. In the terminology of Section 3.7, the Hamiltonian on which the canonical ensemble was based was of the type $H_{\mathscr{A}}(q, p; \mathscr{A})$, one with controlled kinematical parameters. We also considered in Section 3.7 canonical stress ensembles that were based on a Hamiltonian $H_{\mathscr{F}}(q, p; \mathscr{F})$, that is, with controlled mechanical variables. In this section, we focus on the latter and indicate how some of the results obtained previously in this chapter on the basis of the strain ensemble may be rederived on the basis of the stress ensemble.

For the purpose of this discussion, we denote the Hamiltonian of Eq. (4.3.12) of the strain ensemble for the inner crystal I (Figure 4.3) by $H_{\mathscr{A}}(r, p; a_{iL})$. To avoid indeterminacies introduced by rigid rotations, we confine attention in this section to the set of deformation matrices a_{iL} of the form $a_{iL} = \delta_{iK} S_{KL}$, $S_{KL} = S_{LK}$. That is, the rotation matrix R_{iK} which is associated with a_{iL} by the polar decomposition theorem (Section 1.10) is required to be the identity matrix. In order to obtain the Hamiltonian $H_{\mathscr{F}}(r, p; T_{iL})$ for the corresponding stress ensemble, we follow the Legendre transform procedure as given by Eqs. (3.7.1)–(3.7.5). We recall that in these equations we regard (r, p), the coordinates and momenta of the system, as fixed at arbitrary values. It is not necessary, therefore, in the writing of these equations to distinguish between controlled parameters, whose values are independent of the microstates (r, p), and phase functions, which do depend on these quantities. Equations (3.7.1)–(3.7.5) transcribed to the present circumstances take the form

$$\mathcal{V} T_{iL} = \frac{\partial H_{\mathcal{A}}}{\partial a_{iL}}(r, p; a_{jK}) \tag{4.7.1}$$

which provides the functional relationship

$$T_{iL} = T_{iL}(r, p; a_{jK}) \tag{4.7.2}$$

with inverse relation

$$a_{jK} = a_{jK}(r, p; T_{iL}). \tag{4.7.3}$$

Then, $H_{\mathcal{F}}(r, p; T_{iL})$, the Legendre transform of $H_{\mathcal{A}}$, is defined as

$$H_{\mathcal{F}}(r, p; T_{iL}) = H_{\mathcal{A}}(r, p; a_{jK}) - \mathcal{V} T_{iL} a_{iL} \tag{4.7.4}$$

where, in this last equation $a_{jK} = a_{jK}(r, p; T_{iL})$, as given in Eq. (4.7.3). It then follows, as shown in Section 3.7, that an explicit form of this relation for a_{jK} in terms of $H_{\mathcal{F}}$ is [see Eq. (3.7.5)]

$$a_{jK} = -\frac{1}{\mathcal{V}} \frac{\partial H_{\mathcal{F}}}{\partial T_{jK}}(r, p; T_{iL}). \tag{4.7.5}$$

Furthermore, if we now regard the microstate (r, p) as variable, as it will be with the atoms of the inner crystal I in thermal motion, then Eq. (4.7.5) provides the correct form for the phase function $a_{jK}^m(r, p; T_{iL})$, that is,

$$a_{jK}^m(r, p; T_{iL}) = -\frac{1}{\mathcal{V}} \frac{\partial H_{\mathcal{F}}}{\partial T_{jK}}(r, p; T_{iL}). \tag{4.7.6}$$

We have gone through this discussion in terms of the full Hamiltonians $H_{\mathcal{A}}$ and $H_{\mathcal{F}}$ in order to stress the parallel with the general discussion of Section 3.7. However, when rectangular Cartesian coordinates are employed, as in our discussion of crystalline elasticity, the expression for the kinetic energy is independent of either a_{jK} or T_{iL}, and we can write

$$H_{\mathcal{A}}(r, p; a_{jK}) = K(p) + V_{\mathcal{A}}(r; a_{jK}) \tag{4.7.7}$$

and

$$H_{\mathscr{F}}(r, p; T_{iL}) = K(p) + V_{\mathscr{F}}(r; T_{iL}) \qquad (4.7.8)$$

where

$$K(p) = \frac{1}{2} \sum_{l \in I} \frac{|\mathbf{p}(l, t)|^2}{m(l)} \qquad (4.7.9)$$

is the kinetic energy of the atoms of I. Furthermore, $V_{\mathscr{A}}(r; a_{jK})$ is their potential energy when the components of the deformation matrix a_{jK} are the controlled parameters and $V_{\mathscr{F}}(r; T_{iL})$ is their potential energy when the stress components T_{iL} are the controlled parameters. It is clear, therefore, that the kinetic energy and the momenta p in this case play no role in Eqs. (4.7.1)–(4.7.6) and that they may be rewritten, as follows, in terms of $V_{\mathscr{A}}$ and $V_{\mathscr{F}}$ with the p dependence omitted throughout. The potential $V_{\mathscr{A}}$ is given by Eq. (4.3.13), namely,

$$V_{\mathscr{A}}(r; a_{jK}) = V_{\mathrm{I}}(r) + V_{\mathrm{I,E}}(r; a_{jk} X'_K) \qquad (4.7.10)$$

in the notation of Section 4.3. Then, Eqs. (4.7.1)–(4.7.6) take the form

$$\mathscr{V} T_{iL} = \frac{\partial V_{\mathscr{A}}}{\partial a_{iL}}(r; a_{jK}) \qquad (4.7.1')$$

or

$$T_{iL} = T_{iL}(r; a_{jK}) \qquad (4.7.2')$$

with inverse relations

$$a_{jK} = a_{jK}(r; T_{iL}). \qquad (4.7.3')$$

Then, $V_{\mathscr{F}}(r; T_{iL})$, the Legendre transform of $V_{\mathscr{A}}$, is

$$V_{\mathscr{F}}(r; T_{iL}) = V_{\mathscr{A}}(r; a_{jK}) - \mathscr{V} T_{iL} a_{iL} \qquad (4.7.4')$$

where $a_{jK} = a_{jK}(r; T_{iL})$ as in Eq. (4.7.3'). Then,

$$a_{jK} = -\frac{1}{\mathscr{V}} \frac{\partial V_{\mathscr{F}}}{\partial T_{jK}}(r; T_{iL}), \qquad (4.7.5')$$

and if now we regard the configuration (r) of I as variable, Eq. (4.7.5') provides the definition of the phase function a^m_{jK}, that is,

$$a^m_{jK}(r; T_{iL}) = -\frac{1}{\mathscr{V}} \frac{\partial V_{\mathscr{F}}}{\partial T_{jK}}(r; T_{iL}). \qquad (4.7.6')$$

It is of interest to contrast the physical pictures presented by the strain and stress ensembles. As noted in Eq. (4.7.10), the potential energy of the interior crystal I includes the interaction of its atoms with those of E_{in}, the thin layer of atoms surrounding I (Figure 4.3). Furthermore, the atoms of E_{in} are regarded as located at the lattice sites $x(l')$, which are obtained from the reference lattice sites $X(l')$ by the affine transformation

$$x_i(l') = a_{iL}X_L(l'), \qquad l' \in E_{in}. \qquad (4.7.11)$$

In the strain ensemble, the elements a_{iL} are the controlled parameters and the lattice sites $x(l')$ given by Eq. (4.7.11) are time independent, that is, the atoms of E_{in} are fixed. Since the atoms of I are in thermal motion, the forces exerted by them on the atoms of E_{in} are fluctuating. That is, the stress is a fluctuating quantity whose average is obtained from the phase average of the phase function $T_{iL}^m(r; a_{jK})$ given by Eq. (4.3.5) or, in the notation of this section, by

$$\mathscr{V} T_{iL}^m = \frac{\partial V_{\mathscr{A}}}{\partial a_{iL}}(r; a_{jK}). \qquad (4.7.12)$$

In the stress ensemble, on the other hand, the controlled parameters are the stress components T_{iL} and the affine components $a_{jK}(r; T_{iL})$, given by Eq. (4.7.6), are fluctuating quantities because of the thermal motion of the atoms of I. We can interpret this situation physically by use of Eq. (4.7.11) as one in which the atoms of E_{in} now fluctuate, that is,

$$x_i(l', t) = a_{iL}(r(t); T_{iL})X_L(l'), \qquad l' \in E_{in} \qquad (4.7.13)$$

remaining, however, always at the sites of a perfect, time-dependent lattice. The fluctuation of this lattice for E_{in} is such that the stress T_{iL} remains constant[31] in spite of the thermal motion of the atoms of I.

The distinction between the strain and stress ensembles for a crystal is analogous to that between volume and pressure ensembles for a gas in a cylinder with sliding piston. If the position of the piston is controlled, that is, fixed, then the pressure which the gas exerts on it fluctuates. Similarly, if the pressure is fixed, the position of the cylinder fluctuates. In both cases, the detailed dynamical effects of the thermal motion of the atoms of the piston on the gas atoms are neglected. In the crystal, the atoms of the interior crystal I correspond to the gas and the atoms of the layer E_{in} play the role of the piston. Of course, neither the strain nor the stress ensemble corresponds directly to a

---

[31]Recall that the affine deformation of Eq. (4.7.13) leaves the lattice site corresponding to $X_L = 0$ fixed and that the function T_{iL} of Eq. (4.7.1) describes, as discussed in Section 4.3, the tractions across the three faces of I corresponding to $X_L = H_L$, $L = 1, 2, 3$ (Figure 4.4). It is therefore these tractions which are maintained constant in a stress ensemble. This point is illustrated in the treatment of a stress ensemble for the linear chain in Section 4.8.

physically realizable situation. However, either procedure may be used for computational purposes and should lead to the same macroscopic constitutive relations for sufficiently large crystals, just as the volume and pressure ensembles for a gas lead to the same macroscopic relations only for macroscopic portions of the gas. We will see (Sections 4.8, 6.9) that for some idealized crystal or polymer models the stress ensemble leads to simpler calculations than does the strain ensemble.

4.8   LINEAR CHAIN WITH NEAREST NEIGHBOR INTERACTIONS

As a simple example of some of the principles of the statistical mechanics of crystal elasticity which we have discussed in this chapter, we consider a linear chain of atoms with nearest neighbor interactions. In order to relate its one-dimensional geometry to some of the concepts of the three-dimensional theory previously presented, we start by considering it as part of a three-dimensional crystal model. However, the required idealizations are so drastic, that the resulting one-dimensional model cannot be considered as an approximation to the three-dimensional crystal but must be considered in its own right as an instructive model.

Consider, therefore, a hypothetical simple cubic crystal with short-ranged interatomic interaction and with lattice parameter b_0 in its reference state (Figure 4.8a). Shown also in this figure is I, the interior portion of crystal considered explicitly in the statistical mechanics treatment of Section 4.3 and E_{in}, the collection of atoms interacting with I.

We assume that, from a macroscopic viewpoint, the crystal is subjected to a uniform elongation in the x_1 direction corresponding to values a_{1I} and T_{1I} for the significant components[32] of deformation matrix a_{iL} and stress tensor T_{iL} (Figure 4.8b).

Under the imposed uni-axial deformation, we take the important interatomic interaction as those between the atoms in the x_1 direction (which we hereafter denote simply by x). As additional idealizations, we focus attention on a linear chain of atoms excised from I + E_{in} and permit the motion of these atoms only in the x direction. We assume further that the interactions between the atoms of this chain occur only between nearest neighbors so that only one atom from E_{in} appears at either end (Figure 4.9).

In a simplified version of the general notation of Section 4.3, the x coordinates of the lattice sites in the reference configuration (Figure 4.9a) are denoted by $X_j = jb_0$ and in the deformed configuration (Figure 4.9b) they are denoted by $x_j, j = 0, \ldots, N + 1$, where $j = 0$ and $N + 1$ are the sites for E_{in}, with the former regarded as fixed[33] at the origin. For the linear chain model,

---

[32] For present purposes we are ignoring other aspects of the deformation apart from the elongation in the x_1 direction.

[33] See footnote 31 p. 159.

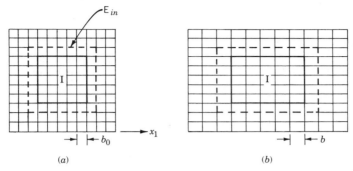

Figure 4.8 Crystal model subjected to simple elongation in x_1 direction.

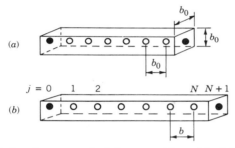

Figure 4.9 Linear chain of atoms excised from crystal model of Figure 4.8 in reference configuration (a) and deformed configuration (b). ○, Atoms of I; ●, atoms of E_{in}.

we may also express the state of deformation and stress by the quantities ℓ, the present chain length and f, the applied axial force. They are related to the quantities a_{1I} and T_{1I} as follows:

$$\ell = \ell_0 a_{1I} \tag{4.8.1}$$

$$f = b_0^2 T_{1I} \tag{4.8.2}$$

where

$$\ell_0 = X_{N+1} - X_0 = X_{N+1} = (N + 1)b_0 \tag{4.8.3}$$

is the length of the chain (including the atoms of E_{in}) in the reference state.

We will treat the thermoelastic properties of this model using three different formulations: The first will make use of a strain ensemble and the thermoelastic stress–strain relation will be computed on the basis of the quasi-harmonic free energy. The second will also make use of a strain ensemble and the quasi-harmonic approximation but will bypass the thermodynamic concept of free energy. Finally, the model will be treated on the basis of a stress ensemble.

Strain Ensemble and Quasi-Harmonic Free Energy

(a) Potential Energy

In the strain ensemble the deformation parameters, a_{11} or ℓ, are regarded as controlled and fixed and the stress, T_{11} or f, are fluctuating quantities. The deformed lattice sites are therefore fixed and located at

$$x_j = jb, \qquad j = 0,\ldots, N+1, \tag{4.8.4}$$

where

$$b = a_{11}b_0 \tag{4.8.5}$$

is the deformed lattice parameter.

The thermal displacements of the atoms of I from the deformed reference sites are denoted by $q_j(t)$ so that the positions $r_j(t)$ of these atoms is

$$r_j(t) = x_j + q_j(t) = jb + q_j(t), \qquad j = 1,\ldots, N. \tag{4.8.6}$$

Since the atoms of E_{in} are fixed at their reference sites, $q_0 \equiv q_{N+1} \equiv 0$, and

$$r_0 \equiv x_0 \equiv 0, \qquad r_{N+1} \equiv x_{N+1} \equiv (N+1)b = \ell. \tag{4.8.7}$$

The total potential energy V to be employed in the Hamiltonian of I is, as a specific example of Eq. (4.3.11),

$$V(r_1,\ldots, r_N; x_0, x_{N+1}) = V(r_1,\ldots, r_N; \ell) = \sum_{j=1}^{N+1} \varphi(r_j - r_{j-1})$$

$$= V_{\mathrm{I}} + V_{\mathrm{I,E}} \tag{4.8.8}$$

where

$$V_{\mathrm{I}}(r_1,\ldots, r_N) = \sum_{j=2}^{N} \varphi(r_j - r_{j-1}) \tag{4.8.9}$$

and

$$V_{\mathrm{I,E}}(r_1,\ldots, r_N; x_0, x_{N+1}) = \varphi(r_1 - x_0) + \varphi(x_{N+1} - r_N). \tag{4.8.10}$$

The function $\varphi(\xi)$, representing the potential energy of a pair of atoms at distance ξ, has the general form shown in Figure 4.10, where the short range of interaction is emphasized.

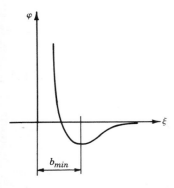

b_{min}

Figure 4.10   Interatomic potential.

(b)   Normal Modes

Consider next the harmonic vibrations of the atoms of the chain in the neighborhood of the deformed lattice sites at $x_j = jb$. From Eq. (4.8.8)

$$\frac{\partial V}{\partial r_j} = -\varphi'(r_{j+1} - r_j) + \varphi'(r_j - r_{j-1}) \qquad (4.8.11)$$

$$\frac{\partial^2 V}{\partial r_j^2} = \varphi''(r_{j+1} - r_j) + \varphi''(r_j - r_{j-1}) \qquad (4.8.12)$$

$$\frac{\partial^2 V}{\partial r_{j+1} \partial r_j} = -\varphi''(r_{j+1} - r_j) \qquad (4.8.13)$$

$$\frac{\partial^2 V}{\partial r_{j+k} \partial r_j} = 0, \qquad k > 1 \qquad (4.8.14)$$

where

$$\varphi'(\xi) = \frac{d\varphi}{d\xi}(\xi), \qquad \varphi''(\xi) = \frac{d^2\varphi}{d\xi^2}(\xi). \qquad (4.8.15)$$

Therefore, for $r_j = x_j = jb$, $\partial V/\partial r_j \equiv 0$ and the harmonic approximation to V takes the form

$$V_h = V_0(b) + \tfrac{1}{2} V_{ij} q_i q_j \qquad (4.8.16)$$

where

$$V_0(b) = (N + 1)\varphi(b) \qquad (4.8.17)$$

and where the potential energy matrix is tridiagonal,

$$V_{ii} = 2\varphi''(b), \qquad i = 1,\ldots, N$$

$$V_{i,i+1} = -\varphi''(b), \qquad i = 1,\ldots, N-1 \qquad (4.8.18)$$

$$V_{i-1,i} = -\varphi''(b), \qquad i = 2,\ldots, N, \text{ (no sum)}$$

with all other elements zero.

In Eq. (4.8.16), and in what follows, the range of summation is $i = 1,\ldots, N$, that is, over the degrees of freedom of the vibrating atoms. When summation over a different range is required, it is indicated explicitly. The eigenvectors and eigenvalues of V_{ij} are given by [see Section 4.4 and Eq. (4.4.13)][34]

$$V_{ij}a_j = m\omega^2 a_i. \qquad (4.8.19)$$

By use of Eq. (4.8.18), this eigenvalue equation takes the form

$$-\varphi''(b)[a_2 - 2a_1] = m\omega^2 a_1$$

$$-\varphi''(b)[a_{j+1} - 2a_j + a_{j-1}] = m\omega^2 a_j, \qquad j = 2,\ldots, N-1$$

$$(4.8.20)$$

$$-\varphi''(b)[-2a_N + a_{N-1}] = m\omega^2 a_N.$$

These may be rewritten more compactly as[35]

$$-\varphi''(b)[a_{j+1} - 2a_j + a_{j-1}] = m\omega^2 a_j, \qquad j = 1,\ldots, N \quad (4.8.21)$$

with the boundary conditions

$$a_0 = a_{N+1} = 0. \qquad (4.8.22)$$

A solution to this difference equation may be sought in the form $a_j = B\cos kj + C\sin kj$ with k, B, and C constants. Substitution into Eq. (4.8.21) and use of trigonometric identities indicates that it is a solution providing k and ω^2 satisfy the relation

$$\omega^2 = \frac{2\phi''(b)}{m}(1 - \cos k) = \frac{4\phi''(b)}{m}\sin^2\left(\frac{k}{2}\right). \qquad (4.8.23)$$

---

[34]Since we are treating a system of like atoms, we are not using mass-reduced coordinates in this discussion as we did in Section 4.4. This introduces the atom mass m into the eigenvalue equation, Eq. (4.8.19).

[35]We are following the general procedure of Section 4.4 for illustrative purposes. For this simple example, it is easier to derive Eq. (4.8.21) directly from the equations of motion.

The boundary condition $a_0 = 0$ requires that $B = 0$ and the boundary condition $a_{N+1} = 0$ requires that

$$\sin k(N + 1) = 0 \tag{4.8.24}$$

or

$$k = k_r = \pm \frac{r\pi}{N + 1}, \qquad r = 1, \ldots, N. \tag{4.8.25}$$

(It is seen that $r = N + 1$ leads to $a_j \equiv 0$, and that $r = N + 2$ leads to the same eigenvector as does $r = 1$, etc.) Therefore, the eigenvectors or normal modes are

$$a_{rj} = C_r \sin\left(\frac{r\pi j}{N + 1}\right), \qquad r = 1, \ldots, N, \tag{4.8.26}$$

with corresponding normal mode frequencies

$$\omega_r = 2\left(\frac{\varphi''(b)}{m}\right)^{1/2} \sin\left(\frac{r\pi}{2(N + 1)}\right). \tag{4.8.27}$$

The orthogonality of the eigenvectors is demonstrated by use of the trigonometric identity

$$\sum_{j=1}^{N} \sin\left(\frac{r\pi j}{N + 1}\right) \sin\left(\frac{s\pi j}{N + 1}\right) = \left(\frac{N + 1}{2}\right)\delta_{rs}, \tag{4.8.28}$$

which also indicates that normalization requires

$$C_r = \left(\frac{2}{N + 1}\right)^{1/2}. \tag{4.8.29}$$

(c) Quasi-Harmonic Free Energy

The quasi-harmonic free energy of the chain $F_{qh}(b, T)$ is, from Eq. (4.5.6),

$$F_{qh}(b, T) = V_0(b) - NkT\log(2\pi kT) + kT \sum_{r=1}^{N} \log \omega_r \tag{4.8.30}$$

with $V_0(b)$ given by Eq. (4.8.17) and ω_r by Eq. (4.8.27).
From Eq. (1.6.10), the value of T_{11} is obtained from Eq. (4.8.30) as

$$T_{11} = \frac{1}{\mathcal{V}} \frac{\partial F_{qh}}{\partial a_{11}} = \frac{1}{(N + 1)b_0^3}\left[\frac{\partial V_0}{\partial a_{11}} + kT\frac{\partial \log \omega_r}{\partial a_{11}}\right] \tag{4.8.31}$$

where

$$\mathcal{V} = (N + 1)b_0^3 \tag{4.8.32}$$

is the original volume of $I + E_{in}$.

By use of Eqs. (4.8.27), (4.8.31), and (4.8.5), we find

$$T_{II}(b) = \frac{1}{b_0^2}\left[\varphi'(b) + \frac{NkT}{2(N + 1)}\frac{\varphi'''(b)}{\varphi''(b)}\right] \tag{4.8.33}$$

which, for large N, assumes the even simpler form,[36]

$$T_{II}(b) = \frac{1}{b_0^2}\left[\varphi'(b) + \frac{\varphi'''(b)kT}{2\varphi''(b)}\right]. \tag{4.8.34}$$

The stress–strain–temperature relation of Eq. (4.8.33) or (4.8.34) applies for this model for arbitrary lattice parameter b, that is, for arbitrarily large deformations from the reference lattice parameter b_0. Its validity is restricted, however, to sufficiently low temperature levels so that the amplitude of thermal motion is small enough to justify the quasi-harmonic approximations.

We can also compute the linear thermoelastic stress strain relation which will be valid for small deformations from the reference configuration characterized by the lattice parameter b_0 and small changes in temperature from a reference temperature T_0. For this one-dimensional model this relation, given in general terms in Eq. (1.7.3), takes the form

$$T_{II}(E_{II}, T) = T_{II}^0 + C_{IIII}^T E_{II} + b_{II}(T - T_0), \tag{4.8.35}$$

and we can compute the various quantities appearing in it based on the quasi-harmonic free energy of Eq. (4.8.30). For the homogeneous deformation in which the lattice parameter b_0 goes to b, $a_{II} = b/b_0$ and

$$E_{II} = \tfrac{1}{2}(a_{II}^2 - 1) = \tfrac{1}{2}\left[\left(\frac{b}{b_0}\right)^2 - 1\right]. \tag{4.8.36}$$

It follows that

$$T_{II}^0 = \frac{1}{\mathcal{V}}\frac{\partial F}{\partial E_{II}}\bigg|_0 = \frac{1}{\mathcal{V}}\left(\frac{b_0^2}{b}\frac{\partial F}{\partial b}\right)_0$$

$$= \frac{1}{(N + 1)b_0^2}\frac{\partial F}{\partial b}\bigg|_0 \tag{4.8.37}$$

---

[36]Equation (4.8.33) provides a simple example of the size dependence of the equation of state of a finite system as derived by statistical mechanics, as discussed in Section 3.8, and Eq. (4.8.34) represents the thermodynamic limit. (The definition of the original volume of $I + E_{in}$ is arbitrary to some degree ($\pm b_0$); however the size dependence of Eq. (4.8.33) cannot be removed by its redefinition.)

where the subscript 0 denotes evaluation at the reference state (b_0, T_0). Therefore

$$T_{II}^0 = \frac{1}{b_0^2}\left[\varphi_0' + \frac{NkT_0}{2(N+1)}\frac{\varphi_0'''}{\varphi_0''}\right] \tag{4.3.38}$$

where $\varphi_0' = d\varphi/db$ evaluated at b_0, etc. Note that, as seen from Eqs. (4.8.33) and (4.8.38), $T_{II}^0 = T_{II}^0$. As discussed in Section 1.9, this is a consequence of the fact that the initial stress acts in the reference configuration and therefore the distinction between the three forms of the stress tensor vanishes. Similarly,

$$C_{IIII}^T = \frac{1}{\mathcal{V}}\left.\frac{\partial^2 F}{\partial E_{II}^2}\right|_0 = \frac{1}{(N+1)b_0^3}\left[\left(\frac{b_0^4}{b^2}\frac{\partial^2 F}{\partial b^2}\right)_0 - \left(\frac{b_0^4}{b^3}\frac{\partial F}{\partial b}\right)_0\right]$$

$$= \frac{1}{(N+1)b_0}\left[\left.\frac{\partial^2 F}{\partial b^2}\right|_0 - \frac{1}{b_0}\left.\frac{\partial F}{\partial b}\right|_0\right]. \tag{4.8.39}$$

By use of Eq. (4.8.30),

$$C_{IIII}^T = \frac{1}{b_0}\left[\left(\varphi_0'' - \frac{1}{b_0}\varphi_0'\right) + \frac{NkT_0}{2(N+1)}\left(\frac{\varphi_0^{IV}}{\varphi_0''} - \left(\frac{\varphi_0'''}{\varphi_0''}\right)^2 - \frac{1}{b_0}\frac{\varphi_0'''}{\varphi_0''}\right)\right]$$

$$\tag{4.8.40}$$

and

$$b_{II} = \frac{1}{\mathcal{V}}\left.\frac{\partial^2 F}{\partial E_{II}\partial T}\right|_0 = \frac{1}{\mathcal{V}}\left(\frac{b_0^2}{b}\frac{\partial^2 F}{\partial b\partial T}\right)_0$$

$$= \frac{1}{b_0^2}\frac{Nk}{2(N+1)}\frac{\varphi_0'''}{\varphi_0''}. \tag{4.8.41}$$

This model calculation illustrates two points previously discussed.

1 The choice of the reference state (b_0, T_0) may be made arbitrarily[37] if the presence of an initial stress, given by Eq. (4.8.38), is acceptable. Or, if we wish, we may use Eq. (4.8.38) to determine the reference temperature T_0, which leads to zero initial stress for a given choice of b_0. Note that if the potential is anharmonic ($\varphi_0''' \neq 0$) the choice of $b_0 = b_{min}$ corresponding to the potential

---

[37]Within the limits of stability requirements, the quasi-harmonic approximation, and the requirement that it lead to a reasonable initial stress.

minimum (so that $\varphi_0' = 0$) leads to $T_{11} = 0$ only for $T_0 = 0$.[38] Since, for potentials of the form shown in Figure 4.10, $\varphi_0'' > 0$, $\varphi_0''' < 0$, we see that $T_{11}^0 = 0$ requires $b_0 > b_{min}$ for $T_0 > 0$, a result that reflects the phenomenon of thermal expansion.

  2   The calculation leads to the modulus $C^T (= C_{1111}^T)$ as a function of the reference state, $C^T = C^T(b_0, T_0)$. If the reference configuration, b_0, is kept fixed as T_0 varies (by the variation of T_{11}^0), then Eq. (4.8.40) predicts a linear dependence of C^T on the reference temperature T_0. If, on the other hand, the initial stress is held fixed, for example, $T_{11}^0 = 0$, then $b_0 = b_0(T_0)$ and the temperature dependence of C^T predicted by Eqs. (4.8.38) and (4.8.40) is more complicated.

We may also compute the displacement gradient modulus $\mathscr{S}_{1111}^T$ (Section 1.9) for this model. The displacement gradient for this case is

$$u_{11} = a_{11} - 1 = \frac{b}{b_0} - 1. \tag{4.8.42}$$

By application of Eqs. (1.9.9) and (4.8.33),

$$\mathscr{S}_{1111}^T = \left. \frac{\partial T_{11}}{\partial u_{11}} \right|_0 = b_0 \left. \frac{\partial T_{11}}{\partial b} \right|_0$$

$$= \frac{1}{b_0} \left[\varphi_0'' + \frac{NkT_0}{2(N+1)} \left(\frac{\varphi_0^{IV}}{\varphi_0''} - \left(\frac{\varphi_0'''}{\varphi_0''} \right)^2 \right) \right]. \tag{4.8.43}$$

It is readily verified, by use of Eqs. (4.8.38), (4.8.40), and (4.8.43), that $\mathscr{S}_{1111}^T$ and $C_{1111}^T (= C_{1111}^T)$ are related as required by Eq. (1.9.12).

Alternate computation of thermoelastic relation

We continue to employ the strain ensemble and the quasi-harmonic approximation. However, we bypass completely the macroscopic thermodynamic concept of free energy and present a more direct computation of T_{11}, one that is based on the phase average of forces exerted on the atoms of the chain. Let

$$f_j(t) = \varphi'(r_j - r_{j-1}). \tag{4.8.44}$$

It is seen that $f_{j+1}(t)$ is the force exerted on the j atom by the $j + 1$ atom and that $-f_j(t)$ is the force exerted on the j atom by the $j - 1$ atom. The resultant

---

[38] This statement is correct only from the classical viewpoint. The choice of $b_0 = b_{min}$ does not lead to $T_{11} = 0$ at $T_0 = 0$ when quantum mechanics is employed. See Section 10.3.

force $F_j(t)$ on the j atom is therefore

$$F_j(t) = f_{j+1}(t) - f_j(t), \qquad j = 1, \ldots, N. \qquad (4.8.45)$$

Since the j atom is executing oscillatory motion in the vicinity of x_j, it follows that the time average $\hat{F}_j = 0$ and, by the ergodic hypothesis, the phase average $\overline{F}_j = 0, j = 1, \ldots, N$. Therefore, from Eq. (4.8.45), $\overline{f}_j = \overline{f}, j = 1, \ldots, N + 1$, and $\overline{f}$ may be computed from the relation

$$\overline{f} = \frac{1}{N + 1} \sum_{j=1}^{N+1} \overline{f}_j. \qquad (4.8.46)$$

From Eqs. (4.8.6) and (4.8.44)

$$f_j = \varphi'(b + q_j - q_{j-1})$$

$$= \varphi'(b) + \varphi''(b)(q_j - q_{j-1}) + \tfrac{1}{2}\varphi'''(b)(q_j - q_{j-1})^2, \qquad (4.8.47)$$

where we have carried out an expansion of f_j through quadratic terms in $(q_j - q_{j-1})$. Recall that in this calculation we are continuing to make the harmonic approximation and to use the canonical ensemble based on the harmonic Hamiltonian, Eq. (4.4.19), in computing phase averages. By use of this distribution function, we may readily calculate the phase average $\overline{Q}_r = 0$. From the expression of q_j in terms of normal coordinates, $q_j = a_{rj}Q_r$, it follows, since the computation of phase averages is a linear operation, that $\overline{q}_j = a_{rj}\overline{Q}_r = 0$. Therefore,[39]

$$\overline{f}_j = \varphi'(b) + \tfrac{1}{2}\varphi'''(b)\left(\overline{q_j^2} - 2\overline{q_j q_{j-1}} + \overline{q_{j-1}^2}\right). \qquad (4.8.48)$$

From Eq. (4.8.46),

$$\overline{f} = \varphi'(b) + \frac{\varphi'''(b)}{2(N+1)} \sum_{j=1}^{N+1}\left(\overline{q_j^2} - 2\overline{q_j q_{j-1}} + \overline{q_{j-1}^2}\right). \qquad (4.8.49)$$

Consider next

$$\varphi''(b) \sum_{j=1}^{N+1}\left(q_j^2 - 2q_j q_{j-1} + q_{j-1}^2\right) = V_{ij} q_i q_j \qquad (4.8.50)$$

---

[39] This simple example helps clarify the absence of thermal effects on the stress in a purely harmonic potential. Although the thermal motion contributes to the force in Eq. (4.8.47) with a linear term multiplying $\varphi''(b)$, the time or phase average of this term is zero.

where the equality follows by use of Eq. (4.8.18). However,

$$\tfrac{1}{2}\overline{V_{ij}q_iq_i} = \frac{1}{2}\sum_{r=1}^{N}\omega_r^2\overline{Q_r^2} = \tfrac{1}{2}NkT \qquad (4.8.51)$$

by the equipartition theorem, Section 3.11. Substitution of Eqs. (4.8.50) and (4.8.51) into (4.8.49) leads to the result

$$\bar{f} = \varphi'(b) + \frac{NkT}{2(N+1)}\frac{\varphi'''(b)}{\varphi''(b)}. \qquad (4.8.52)$$

Since $T_{11} = f/b_0^2$, we are thus led to the same result as given in Eq. (4.8.33) which was based on the quasi-harmonic free energy.

Stress ensemble

We next consider the linear chain model on the basis of a stress ensemble in which the stress T_{11} is fixed and the deformation a_{11} is permitted to fluctuate. Because of the relations of Eqs. (4.8.1) and (4.8.2), we can equivalently regard the linear force f as fixed and the length ℓ as fluctuating and we will find it simpler to use the latter conjugate pair of variables.

Let $V_{\mathcal{A}}(r_1,\ldots,r_N;\ell)$ denote the potential energy of I employed in the strain ensemble; it is defined in Eq. (4.8.8) (where the subscript $\mathcal{A}$ is omitted). Then, by the general theory of Section 4.7, the potential energy $V_{\mathcal{F}}(r_1,\ldots,r_N;f)$ of I to be employed in the stress ensemble is

$$V_{\mathcal{F}}(r_1,\ldots,r_N;f) = V_{\mathcal{A}}(r_1,\ldots,r_N;\ell) - f\ell \qquad (4.8.53)$$

where now $\ell = \ell(r_1,\ldots,r_N;f)$ is, since $\ell = x_{N+1}$, the required position of the $N+1$ atom (in E_{in}) so that the force exerted on it by the atoms in I remains constant at the controlled value $-f$. For the case of the linear chain with nearest neighbor interactions, $\ell = \ell(r_N;f)$, and the expression for $V_{\mathcal{F}}$ may be simplified. If the force exerted on the $N+1$ atom by the N atom remains constant at $-f$, the force exerted by the $N+1$ atom on the N atom remains constant at f. Therefore ℓ, the position of the $N+1$ atom, may be eliminated from $V_{\mathcal{F}}$ and it can be written as[40]

$$V_{\mathcal{F}}(r_1,\ldots,r_N;f) = \sum_{j=1}^{N}\varphi(r_j - r_{j-1}) - fr_N. \qquad (4.8.54)$$

[40]Alternatively, we could have replaced ℓ by ℓ' (a fluctuating quantity) in Eq. (4.8.53) and regarded it as the defining equation for an augmented stress ensemble (Section 3.7). The two procedures are equivalent in this case.

We compute next the partition function $Z_{\mathscr{F}}$ for I for the stress ensemble:

$$Z_{\mathscr{F}}(f, T) = \int_{\Gamma} e^{-\beta H_{\mathscr{F}}(r, p; f)} dr \, dp$$

$$= \int_{\Gamma_p} e^{-\beta K(p)} dp \int_{\Gamma_r} e^{-\beta V_{\mathscr{F}}(r, f)} dr \qquad (4.8.55)$$

$$= C \int_{\Gamma_r} \exp -\beta \left[\sum_{j=1}^{N} \phi(r_j - r_{j-1}) - f r_N \right] dr_1, \ldots, dr_N,$$

where $\beta = (kT)^{-1}$. We have denoted the integral over momentum space by C; since it is independent of f it plays no role in these computations. It is readily verified by direct computation that, in accordance with Eq. (3.7.29),

$$\frac{1}{\beta} \frac{\partial}{\partial f} \log Z_{\mathscr{F}}(f, T) = Z_{\mathscr{F}}^{-1} \int_{\Gamma} r_N e^{-\beta H_{\mathscr{F}}} dr \, dp = \overline{r_N}. \qquad (4.8.56)$$

The multiple integral over configuration space in Eq. (4.8.55) may be reduced to a product of one-dimensional integrals. For this purpose let[41]

$$\xi_j = r_j - r_{j-1}, \qquad j = 1, \ldots, N. \qquad (4.8.57)$$

Then

$$V_{\mathscr{F}}(r, f) = \sum_{j=1}^{N} \varphi(\xi_j) - f r_N = \sum_{j=1}^{N} \left[\varphi(\xi_j) - f \xi_j \right] \qquad (4.8.58)$$

since

$$\sum_{j=1}^{N} \xi_j = r_N. \qquad (4.8.59)$$

We can use the variables ξ_j in place of r_j, $j = 1, \ldots, N$, to evaluate the configuration integral in $Z_{\mathscr{F}}$ and write [42]

$$Z_{\mathscr{F}}(f, T) = C \int_0^{\infty} \cdots \int_0^{\infty} \exp -\beta \sum_{j=1}^{N} \left[\varphi(\xi_j) - f \xi_j \right] d\xi_1 \cdots d\xi_N$$

$$= C \left[Z_1(f, T) \right]^N \qquad (4.8.60)$$

---

[41] This approach to the treatment of the linear chain with nearest neighbor interactions is due to Takahasi (1942). See also Gürsey (1950) and Mazur and Rubin (1963).

[42] Note that Eq. (4.8.57) defines an orthogonal transformation. The range of integration is restricted to $\xi_j \geq 0$, $j = 1, \ldots, N$ because of the nature of $\varphi(\xi)$ (see Figure 4.10).

where

$$Z_1(f, T) = \int_0^\infty \exp - \beta[\varphi(\xi) - f\xi] \, d\xi. \tag{4.8.61}$$

It follows from Eqs. (4.8.56), (4.8.60), and (4.8.61) that

$$\bar{r}_N(f, T) = N\bar{\xi}(f, T) \tag{4.8.62}$$

where

$$\bar{\xi}(f, T) = \beta^{-1} \frac{\partial}{\partial f} \log Z_1 = Z_1^{-1} \int_0^\infty \xi \exp - \beta[\varphi(\xi) - f\xi] \, d\xi$$

$$\tag{4.8.63}$$

is simply the phase average distance between any pair of atoms in the chain, a distance that is, of course, a direct measure of the strain in the chain. The use of a stress ensemble for a linear chain with nearest-neighbor interactions leads therefore to a strain–stress relation, Eq. (4.8.63), which is size independent.

The strain–stress–temperature relation of Eq. (4.8.63) is valid for arbitrary values of f and T and is easily evaluated numerically for a given interatomic potential $\varphi(\xi)$ since it involves only a single integral. In contrast, the strain ensemble formulation involved multiple integrals, which could be evaluated conveniently only on the basis of the quasi-harmonic approximation that is valid only for sufficiently low temperature levels. In order to compare the two formulations, we next consider an approximate evaluation of $Z_1(f, T)$ valid for sufficiently low temperature levels. It corresponds to the first term in its asymptotic expansion for large β by Laplace's method.[43] Let

$$\Phi(\xi) = \varphi(\xi) - f\xi \tag{4.8.64}$$

and let b_f be the solution to

$$\Phi'(b_f) = 0 \tag{4.8.65}$$

or equivalently, to

$$\varphi'(b_f) = f; \tag{4.8.66}$$

that is, b_f is the interatomic spacing under the applied force f in the absence of thermal motion. Then, the harmonic approximation to $\Phi(\xi)$ in the neighbor-

[43] See, for example, Sirovich (1971, pp. 80–86).

hood of $\xi = b_f$ is

$$\Phi(\xi) = \Phi(b_f) + \tfrac{1}{2}\Phi''(b_f)(\xi - b_f)^2 \qquad (4.8.67)$$

and, for sufficiently low temperature levels,

$$Z_1(f, T) \cong e^{-\beta\Phi(b_f)} \int_{-\infty}^{\infty} \exp\left[\frac{-\beta}{2}\Phi''(b_f)(\xi - b_f)^2\right] d\xi$$

$$= e^{-\beta\Phi(b_f)} \sqrt{\frac{2\pi}{\beta\Phi''(b_f)}} \cdot \qquad (4.8.68)$$

Therefore, from Eq. (4.8.63),

$$\bar{\xi} = -\frac{d}{df}\Phi(b_f) - \frac{kT}{2}\left[\frac{d}{df}\Phi''(b_f)\right]\bigg/\Phi''(b_f). \qquad (4.8.69)$$

But

$$\frac{d}{df}\Phi(b_f) = -b_f \qquad (4.8.70)$$

and

$$\frac{d}{df}\Phi''(b_f) = \varphi'''(b_f)\frac{db_f}{df} = \frac{\varphi'''(b_f)}{\varphi''(b_f)} \qquad (4.8.71)$$

by use of Eq. (4.8.64). Therefore,

$$\bar{\xi} = b_f - \frac{kT}{2}\frac{\varphi'''(b_f)}{(\varphi''(b_f))^2}, \qquad (4.8.72)$$

and the mean interatomic spacing $\bar{\xi}$ is seen to be the sum of b_f, that due to the applied force alone, and the thermal expansion term proportional to T.

The size-independent strain–stress–temperature relation of Eq. (4.8.72) may be compared with the thermodynamic limit of the stress–strain–temperature relation

$$\bar{f} = \varphi'(b) + \frac{kT}{2}\frac{\varphi'''(b)}{\varphi''(b)} \qquad (4.8.73)$$

based on the strain ensemble and given by Eq. (4.8.52) for finite N. In making the comparison we must remember that both relations are low-temperature approximations, which are correct only to first-order in T, and agreement to this order only can be expected. Consider, therefore, $\varphi'(\bar{\xi})$ with $\bar{\xi}$ as computed from Eq. (4.8.72) and its expansion about b_f to first order in T:

$$\varphi'(\bar{\xi}) = \varphi'\left(b_f - \frac{kT}{2} \frac{\varphi'''(b_f)}{\left(\varphi''(b_f)\right)^2} \right)$$

$$\cong \varphi'(b_f) - \frac{kT}{2} \frac{\varphi'''(b_f)}{\varphi''(b_f)} \qquad (4.8.74)$$

$$= f - \frac{kT}{2} \frac{\varphi'''(b_f)}{\varphi''(b_f)}$$

where Eq. (4.8.66) has been employed. If we now identify[44] $f = \bar{f}$ and $b = \bar{\xi}$, then it is seen that Eq. (4.8.73) agrees with Eq. (4.8.74) to first-order in T, since $\bar{\xi} - b_f = 0(T)$.

4.9   LATTICE DYNAMICS AND CRYSTAL ELASTICITY

We have already treated some aspects of lattice dynamics in Section 4.4, which contained a general discussion of the normal modes of vibration of a collection of atoms in a crystal, and in Section 4.8 where the normal modes of a linear chain were computed. More frequently, in the subject of lattice dynamics, it is customary to give primary emphasis to traveling waves rather than to normal modes. The methods of lattice dynamics have had a strong influence on the mathematical formulations employed for the study of crystal elasticity. We discuss the relationship between these subjects in this section. For that purpose we present first a brief discussion of traveling waves in the monatomic linear chain

Traveling Waves in the Linear Chain

In order to see the subject in the simplest setting, we consider a linear chain of identical atoms as discussed in Section 4.8; the equilibrium spacing is b and q_l is the displacement of atom l from its equilibrium site. The harmonic potential

---

[44] Recall that in macroscopic equations of state no distinction is made between controlled parameters and phase averages of phase functions.

V_h can be written,[45] as in Eq. (4.8.16),

$$V_h = V_0(b) + \tfrac{1}{2}V_{ll'}q_lq_{l'} \qquad (4.9.1)$$

but we do not restrict attention to nearest-neighbor interactions as in Eqs. (4.8.11)–(4.8.15). The equation of motion for atom l is

$$m\ddot{q}_l = -\frac{\partial V_h}{\partial q_l} = -V_{ll'}q_{l'}. \qquad (4.9.2)$$

In Section 4.8 we considered a finite chain, $l = 0,\ldots, N + 1$ with $q_0 = q_{N+1}$ = 0 and discussed normal modes, that is, solutions of the form $q_l(t) = a_l \cos \omega t$. We now wish, instead, to consider traveling waves. For this purpose, we consider an infinite chain, $-\infty < l, \; l' < \infty$ and rewrite the equations of motion, making the summation explicit, as[46]

$$m\ddot{q}_l = -\sum_{l'=-\infty}^{\infty} V_{ll'}q_{l'}, \qquad (4.9.3)$$

and seek solutions of the form

$$q_l(t) = C\cos(\omega t - flb). \qquad (4.9.4)$$

It is convenient to use complex exponentials, writing

$$q_l(t) = Ce^{i(\omega t - flb)}, \qquad (4.9.5)$$

with the physical wave corresponding to the real part. We may regard the lattice wave of Eq. (4.9.5) as derived from a continuous wave

$$q(x, t) = Ce^{i(\omega t - fx)} \qquad (4.9.6)$$

with the understanding that only the values of the continuous wave at the points $x = lb$, l an integer, have physical significance; namely $q(lb, t) = q_l(t)$ is the displacement at time t of the atom which in equilibrium is at $x = lb$.

As seen from Eq. (4.9.6), $2\pi/f$ is the wavelength so that $f/2\pi$ is the number of waves per unit distance; f is therefore referred to as the wave number. The wave speed or phase velocity is ω/f as seen from Eq. (4.9.6).

[45] We are using l, l' in place of i, j as atom indices since we will be using $i = \sqrt{-1}$ in this section. Our treatment of the linear chain follows, in part, Peierls (1955, pp. 11–14).
[46] We assume interatomic forces of sufficiently short range so that all infinite sums in this discussion converge.

We substitute $q_l(t)$ as given by Eq. (4.9.5) into the equations of motion, Eq. (4.9.3). The exponential $e^{i\omega t}$ cancels from both sides leading to

$$m\omega^2 = \sum_{l'=-\infty}^{\infty} V_{ll'} e^{if(l-l')b}. \tag{4.9.7}$$

It is not yet clear from this result whether a traveling wave is a solution to the equations of motion since the left-hand side of Eq. (4.9.7) is a constant and the right-hand side apparently depends on l. In fact, single traveling waves of the form of Eq. (4.9.5) will not be possible solutions to the equations of motion unless we are dealing with an infinite, uniform chain consisting of like atoms with equal equilibrium spacing and it is therefore necessary to make use of this property of the chain in order to demonstrate that the right-hand side of Eq. (4.9.7) is independent of l. This property may be described formally by the statements that the chain in equilibrium is translationally invariant with respect to translations of $\pm lb$, in the x-direction, l an integer, and it is rotationally invariant with respect to a rotation through an angle π about an axis perpendicular to the chain through any atom. These invariance properties lead to the conclusions that

$$V_{ll'} = V(l - l') = V(l' - l), \tag{4.9.8}$$

that is, the potential energy matrix elements depend only on absolute values of the differences between the indices l and l'. By use of Eq. (4.9.8), Eq. (4.9.7) takes the form

$$m\omega^2 = \sum_{s=-\infty}^{\infty} V(s) e^{ifsb} = \sum_{s=-\infty}^{\infty} V(s) \cos fsb, \tag{4.9.9}$$

where $s = l - l'$, and where we have used the relation $V(s) = V(-s)$, from Eq. (4.9.8), in order to conclude that $\sum_{s=-\infty}^{\infty} V(s) \sin fsb = 0$. We may now conclude that traveling wave solutions of the form of Eq. (4.9.4) or (4.9.5) are possible, providing the frequency ω and wave number f satisfy Eq. (4.9.9).

The functional relationship $\omega = \omega(f)$ given by Eq. (4.9.9) is referred to as the dispersion relation[47] of the chain. The origin of this term is as follows: an initial disturbance $q(x,0)$ in the chain may be expressed, by the Fourier integral theorem, as a superposition of traveling waves of the form of Eq. (4.9.6) with wave number $-\infty < f < \infty$. If all of these waves move with the same wave speed, that is, if ω/f is a constant for all traveling waves, then the disturbance will move along the chain without change of shape or without dispersion. Therefore, the functional relationship $\omega = \omega(f)$ of Eq. (4.9.9) describes the dispersion characteristics of the chain.

[47]Also referred to as the phonon dispersion relation (see Section 8.9).

We wish next to examine some general properties of the dispersion relation. Toward this end, we first derive a further property of the quantities $V(s)$ from the behavior of the chain under translation. From Eq. (4.9.3), we see that the force F_l on atom l corresponding to a set of atom displacements $q_{l'}$ is

$$F_l = - \sum_{l'=-\infty}^{\infty} V_{ll'} q_{l'}. \tag{4.9.10}$$

This force must be unchanged by a rigid displacement of the chain as a whole through an arbitrary distance a; that is,

$$F_l = - \sum_{l'=-\infty}^{\infty} V_{ll'} q_{l'} = - \sum_{l'=-\infty}^{\infty} V_{ll'} (q_{l'} + a).$$

Therefore,

$$\sum_{l'=-\infty}^{\infty} V_{ll'} = \sum_{s=-\infty}^{\infty} V(s) = 0. \tag{4.9.11}$$

Use of Eq. (4.9.11) and the relation $V(s) = V(-s)$ permits recasting of Eq. (4.9.9) in the form

$$m\omega^2 = 2 \sum_{s=1}^{\infty} V(s)(\cos fsb - 1) \tag{4.9.12}$$

so that for sufficiently small f (or for sufficiently long wavelengths)

$$m\omega^2 \cong -f^2 b^2 \sum_{s=1}^{\infty} s^2 V(s). \tag{4.9.13}$$

It follows that stability of the chain requires that the potential satisfy the condition

$$\sum_{s=1}^{\infty} s^2 V(s) < 0 \tag{4.9.14}$$

and, from Eq. (4.9.13), that $\omega(f)$ is linear for small f. From Eq. (4.9.9) it is seen that the dispersion relation is periodic in f with period $2\pi/b$. This fact, together with the linearity of $\omega(f)$ for small f, implies that the general appearance of this function is as shown in Figure 4.11.

The periodicity of the dispersion relation is a consequence of the discrete character of the mechanical system as may be seen from the following considerations: Replacement of f by $f + 2\pi n/b$, n an integer, certainly changes the shape of the continuous wave defined in Eq. (4.9.6); however, this

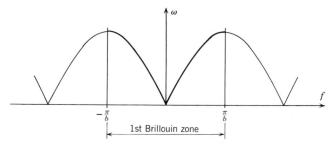

Figure 4.11 Dispersion relation for linear chain.

replacement leaves unchanged the displacements $q_i(t)$ as seen from Eq. (4.9.5), and it is only these displacements that affect the equations of motion and ω. Since a periodic function cannot be linear, we conclude that there is an inherent dispersion for wave propagation in a crystal which arises from its discrete character; only for wavelengths long with respect to interatomic distances is the function $\omega(f)$ linear and dispersion absent.

Because of the periodicity of the dispersion relation, it is necessary to define it only for the values of f that lie in an interval of length $2\pi/b$. This interval is generally chosen to be $-\pi/b \leqslant f < \pi/b$, referred to as the first Brillouin zone; this choice leads to equivalent continuous waves, Eq. (4.9.6), of the shortest wavelengths.

(a) Chain with Nearest-Neighbor Interactions

We now specialize the discussion to the case of the chain with nearest-neighbor interactions treated in Section 4.8. From Eq. (4.8.18) we see that, in the notation of Eq. (4.9.8), $V(0) = 2\varphi''(b)$, $V(1) = V(-1) = -\varphi''(b)$, and $V(s) = 0$ for $|s| > 1$. Then Eq. (4.9.12) becomes

$$\omega^2 = \frac{2\varphi''(b)}{m}(1 - \cos fb) = \frac{4\varphi''(b)}{m}\sin^2 \frac{fb}{2} \qquad (4.9.15)$$

in agreement with Eq. (4.8.23) with $k = fb$. As seen from this equation or, equivalently, from Eq. (4.9.13), for small f or for long wavelengths

$$\omega \cong \left(\frac{\varphi''(b)}{m} \right)^{1/2} fb = \left(\frac{\varphi''(b)}{b\rho} \right)^{1/2} f \qquad (4.9.16)$$

where $\rho = m/b^3$ is the mass density of the equivalent three-dimensional crystal (see Figure 4.9(b)). Therefore the wave speed, c, in the long wavelength, dispersion-free regime is

$$c = \left(\frac{\varphi''(b)}{b\rho} \right)^{1/2}. \qquad (4.9.17)$$

Assume next, in the notation of Section 4.8, that the reference temperature $T_0 = 0$, and $b = b_0 = b_{min}$, so that $T_{II}^0 = 0$. Then, as seen from Eq. (4.8.40) or (4.8.43), $\tilde{C}_{IIII} = \mathscr{S}_{IIII} = \varphi_0''/b_0$,[48] a result that is readily derived by elementary means. Under these conditions, the wave speed becomes

$$c_0 = \left(\frac{\tilde{C}_{IIII}}{\rho}\right)^{1/2} \tag{4.9.18}$$

as would be obtained on the basis of continuum linear elasticity; that is, when the wavelength of the disturbance is long compared to the interatomic spacing, the discrete crystal behaves like a continuum.

(b) Traveling Waves and Normal Modes

We see from Figure 4.11 that corresponding to a given frequency ω in the proper range there are two traveling waves corresponding to $+f$ and $-f$, both lying in the first Brillouin zone. These correspond to traveling waves moving to the right and to the left, respectively. The superposition of this pair of traveling waves leads to a normal mode, since (taking the real part)

$$q_l(t) = \text{Re}\left(e^{(i\omega t - flb)} + e^{i(\omega t + flb)}\right)$$

$$= \text{Re}\left(2e^{i\omega t}\cos flb\right), \tag{4.9.19}$$

$$= 2\cos flb \cos \omega t,$$

which corresponds to a normal mode solution with the mode shape $a_l = 2\cos flb$. Similarly, the difference of these two traveling waves leads to a normal mode with mode shape $a_l = 2\sin flb$.

To complete the comparison between traveling wave and normal mode solutions we wish to restrict attention to a chain with a finite number of degrees of freedom and verify that the superposition of traveling waves leads to the correct number of normal modes. For this purpose, we impose the restriction

$$q_l(t) = q_{l+N}(t) \tag{4.9.20}$$

on the permitted motion of the atoms of the chain. Under this condition, only N atoms of the chain, say $l = 1,\ldots, N$, may have arbitrary displacements; the motion of all the other atoms of the chain then have their motion determined by Eq. (4.9.20). (We can visualize this requirement as connecting all pairs of atoms that are at a distance Nb apart when in equilibrium by rigid rods of this length.) The chain now has N degrees of freedom.

[48] The superposed tilde indicates, in accord with Eq. (4.5.12), that these are the harmonic elastic moduli, and we recall that at $T = 0$, isothermal and adiabatic moduli are equal.

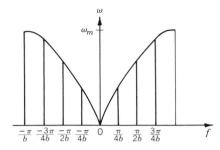

Figure 4.12 Allowed wave vectors, Eq. (4.9.21), with $N = 8$.

Among the traveling wave solutions of Eq. (4.9.5), only those for which $fNb = 2\pi\alpha$, α an integer, will satisfy the required periodic boundary condition, as Eq. (4.9.20) is generally termed, that is, the allowed values of f are

$$f_\alpha = \frac{2\pi\alpha}{Nb}. \qquad (4.9.21)$$

Since an increase of α by N increases f by $2\pi/b$, we see that there are N allowed wave numbers in any interval of f of length $2\pi/b$, for example, in the first Brillouin zone. Consider the example of $N = 8$ for which the allowed wave numbers and corresponding frequencies are shown in Figure 4.12. Two of the allowed traveling waves are also in normal mode form: (i) $f = 0$ corresponds to $\omega = 0$ so that $\text{Re}(e^{i(\omega t - flb)}) = 1$. This is the translational mode in which all atoms have equal displacements. There is, therefore, no restoring force and $\omega = 0$. (ii) $f = -\pi/b$, $\omega = \omega_m$, so that $\text{Re}(e^{i(\omega t - flb)}) = \cos l\pi \cos \omega_m t$. Therefore, this traveling wave, which corresponds to the edge of the Brillouin zone, can be regarded also as a normal mode in which neighboring atoms vibrate out of phase by π. The other six allowed traveling waves must be combined in pairs with wave numbers $\pm f$ in each pair; each pair yields two normal modes by addition and subtraction. Therefore, the resulting number of normal modes is equal to the number of degrees of freedom of the system.

(c)   Density of Allowed Wave Numbers

It is seen from Eq. (4.9.21), in which α takes on integer values, that the allowed wave numbers are separated by the constant interval $2\pi/Nb$. Equivalently, the density of allowed wave numbers along a wave number axis f (Figure 4.12) is $Nb/2\pi = L/2\pi$, where $L = Nb$ is the length of the chain to which the periodic boundary condition, Eq. (4.9.20), has been applied.

Although this result has been derived on the basis of periodic boundary conditions, it may be shown[49] that, for large N or L, it applies as well for other boundary conditions.

[49]See, for example, the discussion in Weinreich (1965, pp. 44–47).

(d) Coupling Parameters

As a consequence of Eq. (4.9.11), it is possible to rewrite Eq. (4.9.10) for the force on the l atom as

$$F_l = \sum_{l'=-\infty}^{\infty} V_{ll'}(q_l - q_{l'}).$$ (4.9.22)

This expression leads to the simple interpretation of $V_{ll'}$ as the spring constant of a linear spring connecting the l and l' atoms. For this reason, these second-order derivatives of the potential energy V evaluated at the equilibrium sites of the atoms are frequently referred to as force constants or as second-order coupling parameters, with a similar terminology for derivatives of other order.

Relation to Crystal Elasticity Formulations

We have gone through the discussion of traveling waves for the example of a linear chain of identical atoms in order to introduce some of the principal concepts and terminology of lattice dynamics. The subject is one that is highly developed and well covered in an extensive literature[50] where these simple ideas are generalized to apply to realistic, three-dimensional, crystal models. An important development, beginning in the 1950s, that gave additional impetus to the subject was the exploitation of an experimental technique using inelastic neutron scattering, which leads to measured values for the dispersion relation for real crystals.[51]

We may now characterize the relationship between the subjects of lattice dynamics and crystal elasticity: Both deal with experimentally observed phenomena, the lattice wave dispersion relations, on the one hand, and the elastic moduli, on the other. Both of these phenomena can be described theoretically by models whose critical element is the interatomic potential used for the particular crystal being studied. Clearly, it is desirable to be able to demonstrate that a given choice of interatomic potential leads to agreement with experiment for both the lattice wave dispersion relations and the elastic moduli. As a result, many formulations of the theory of crystal elasticity have been based on the type of models best suited to lattice wave calculations. In these formulations, an infinite lattice is postulated and the interatomic potential is expressed directly in terms of coupling parameters, exemplified by the quantities $V_{ll'}$ in the linear chain example but extended to three-dimensional models, as well as by coupling parameters of higher order in order to treat anharmonic effects. These coupling parameters must satisfy conditions, analo-

[50] Two of the standard works are Born and Huang (1954) and Maradudin, Montroll, and Weiss (1963). A clear introductory treatment is given by Smith (1961, Chapters 3 and 6) and by Cochran (1973). A very brief account of the nature of the generalizations to three-dimensional crystals is given at the end of this section.

[51] An introductory description of this technique is given, for example, by Cochran (1973).

gous to those of Eq. (4.9.8), to satisfy requirements of translational and rotational invariance of the infinite crystal.

Two types of formulations have been proposed for the computation of harmonic elastic moduli on the basis of coupling parameter models (see Born and Huang, 1954). The first, referred to as the method of homogeneous deformation, is purely static. The second, referred to as the method of long waves, deduces the values of the harmonic moduli by the calculation of the wave speeds in the long wavelength limit as in the simple example leading to Eq. (4.9.18). It has since been recognized that the two methods are equivalent.[52] The formulations are complicated by the need for incorporation of the relations between the coupling parameters required for invariance under rigid motions. Furthermore, since the formulations involve displacements, they lead to the calculation of the displacement gradient moduli, $\mathscr{S}_{iLjM}$, rather than to the elastic constants C_{LMNK}. For this reason, the Born–Huang relations (Section 1.9) play an important role in these formulations. Detailed discussions of the calculation of harmonic elastic moduli on the basis of force-constant or coupling-parameter formulations may be found in numerous references[53] and we do not repeat these derivations here.

The viewpoint we have adopted in this chapter is that for the purpose of the discussion of crystal elasticity, a more natural and convenient starting point is to express the interatomic potential as a function of arguments that are themselves invariant with respect to rigid motions, for example, $V(R(ll'), R(ll''), \ldots)$, with $R(ll')$ the square of interatomic distances, as described in Section 4.6. If one wishes to compute both elastic moduli and lattice wave dispersion relations based on the same potential, then the coupling parameters $V_{ll'}$, etc., can be computed from the potential $V(R(ll'), \ldots)$; these coupling parameters will automatically satisfy the necessary invariance requirements.[54]

Three-Dimensional Generalizations

We briefly indicate here the manner in which some of the preceding concepts of lattice dynamics are generalized to three dimensions. These concepts will be needed in Section 10.3 for the discussion of the Debye model and the low-temperature behavior of crystals.

We begin with a monatomic crystal that corresponds to a simple Bravais lattice. The one-dimensional traveling waves of Eq. (4.9.6) take, in three

[52] Wallace (1972, p. 137).

[53] See, for example, Born and Huang (1954), Hedin (1960), Leibfried and Ludwig (1961), and Wallace (1972).

[54] Kaplan (1962). The relative merits of the two types of formulations have a familiar analog in continuum mechanics. In that field it has been recognized for some time that while the use of particle displacements is necessary for discussing dynamic problems, their use tends to complicate general treatments of static problems involving finite deformations.

dimensions, the form

$$\mathbf{u}_l(t) = \mathbf{v}\, \exp\, i(\omega t - \mathbf{f} \cdot \mathbf{x}_l) \qquad (4.9.23)$$

where $\mathbf{u}_l(t)$ is the displacement of atom l from its equilibrium position $\mathbf{x}_l$. The wave travels in the direction of the vector $\mathbf{f}$ with $|\mathbf{f}|/2\pi$ waves per unit distance in that direction; $\mathbf{f}$ is therefore known as the wave number vector. The vector $\mathbf{v}$, known as the polarization vector, describes the traveling displacement disturbance.

Substitution of Eq. (4.9.23) into the equations of motion describing the given crystal model then shows that, for a given $\mathbf{f}$, a traveling wave solution will be possible for three values of $\omega = \omega(\mathbf{f}, j), j = 1, 2, 3$ with corresponding polarization vectors $\mathbf{v}(\mathbf{f}, j)$. The functions $\omega = \omega(\mathbf{f}, j), j = 1, 2, 3$, are the three branches of the dispersion relation for the crystal. Several properties of the dispersion relation in the one-dimensional example carry over to the functions $\omega(\mathbf{f}, j)$ with $\mathbf{f}$ restricted to a fixed direction $\hat{\mathbf{f}} = \mathbf{f}/|\mathbf{f}|$. (a) $\lim_{|\mathbf{f}| \to 0} \omega(\mathbf{f}, j) = 0$ with $\omega(\mathbf{f}, j)$ linear in $\mathbf{f}$ in the $|\mathbf{f}| \cong 0$ long wavelength region. (b) The speed $c_j(\hat{\mathbf{f}})$ of the long waves can be computed on the basis of macroscopic linear anisotropic elasticity. (c) The function $\omega(\mathbf{f}, j)$ is periodic in $\mathbf{f}$, with the period dependent on $\hat{\mathbf{f}}$.

This periodicity implies that $\omega(\mathbf{f}, j)$ need be defined only inside the first Brillouin zone. In three dimensions this zone is a polyhedron in wave–vector space, the three-dimensional space spanned by the components of $\mathbf{f}$. The shape of the polyhedron is determined by the crystal geometry. In the one-dimensional model, it was seen that the imposition of boundary conditions on a chain of length L led to a uniform density of allowed wave numbers in the first Brillouin zone of $L/2\pi$. Similar reasoning in the three-dimensional case shows that the imposition of boundary conditions on a crystal of volume V leads to a uniform density of allowed wave number vectors in the first Brillouin zone of $V/(2\pi)^3$.

As in the one-dimensional example, the superposition of two traveling waves corresponding to $\mathbf{f}$ and to $-\mathbf{f}$ leads, upon taking the real part, to normal modes of the form

$$\mathbf{u}_l(t) = \mathbf{v}\cos\,(\mathbf{f} \cdot \mathbf{x}_l)\cos \omega t. \qquad (4.9.24)$$

Let $\mathbf{x}_0 = 0$ be the equilibrium position of the atom $l = 0$. Its motion in the normal mode of Eq. (4.9.24) is $\mathbf{u}_0(t) = \mathbf{v}\cos \omega t$. For a given value of $\mathbf{f}$, every other atom has a displacement with a fixed ratio, $\cos(\mathbf{f} \cdot \mathbf{x}_l)$ for atom l, of $\mathbf{u}_0(t)$. It is as though all atoms were connected to atom 0 with some linkage in order to relate their motion in this fashion. We may then think of Eq. (4.9.24) as describing the motion of a single particle with three degrees of freedom moving in a harmonic potential. From this viewpoint it is clear that for a given $\mathbf{f}$ there will be three frequencies $\omega(\mathbf{f}, j)$ and three corresponding polarization vectors $\mathbf{v}(\mathbf{f}, j)$. It is also clear that $\lim_{|\mathbf{f}| \to 0} \omega(\mathbf{f}, j) = 0$, since for $\mathbf{f} = 0$ there is no relative displacement between the atoms and therefore no restoring force.

We turn next to a composite lattice with s atoms per unit cell and consider traveling waves of the form

$$\mathbf{u}'_k(t) = \mathbf{v}_k \exp i\left(\omega t - \mathbf{f} \cdot \mathbf{x}'_k\right), \tag{4.9.25}$$

where $\mathbf{u}'_k$ is the displacement of atom k, $k = 1,\ldots, s$, in cell l from its equilibrium position $\mathbf{x}'_k$. To understand the nature of the dispersion relations in this case, it is again helpful to consider the normal modes,

$$\mathbf{u}'_k(t) = \mathbf{v}_k \cos\left(\mathbf{f} \cdot \mathbf{x}'_k\right) \cos \omega t, \tag{4.9.26}$$

obtained by the superposition of two traveling waves corresponding to $\mathbf{f}$ and $-\mathbf{f}$. As noted in Section 4.2, we may think of the composite lattice as made up of s simple Bravais lattices. If $\mathbf{f}$ is fixed, then the displacements of all of the atoms in the k component lattice are determined by that of one of its atoms, for example, the atom k in the cell $l = 0$. However, the displacements of the atoms in cell 0, $\mathbf{v}_k \cos(\mathbf{f} \cdot \mathbf{x}^0_k)$, remain free. We may then think of Eq. (4.9.26) as describing the motion of s particles, each with three degrees of freedom, subject to harmonic restoring forces. Therefore, for a given $\mathbf{f}$, there will be $3s$ frequencies $\omega(\mathbf{f}, j)$ with corresponding polarization vectors $\mathbf{v}_k(\mathbf{f}, j), j = 1,\ldots,$ $3s$. In the traveling wave terminology, there will be $3s$ branches of the dispersion relation. For three of these, indexed $j = 1, 2, 3, \lim_{|\mathbf{f}| \to 0} \omega(\mathbf{f}, j) = 0$, and these are termed the acoustic branches. They correspond to the case in which the polarization vectors $\mathbf{v}_k(0, j), j = 1, 2, 3$, are independent of k. In that case, for $\mathbf{f} = 0$, there are no relative displacements between the component lattices as well as no relative displacements between the atoms of each lattice. For the other branches of the dispersion relation, $j = 4,\ldots, 3s$, termed the optical branches, the vectors $\mathbf{v}_k(0, j)$ differ with k; the resulting relative motion between lattices produces restoring forces and $\omega(0; j) \neq 0$ for $j = 4,\ldots, 3s$. Traveling waves corresponding to the optical branches cannot be computed on the basis of macroscopic linear elasticity even for small values of $|\mathbf{f}|$ because the relative motion between the lattices is not accessible to that theory.[55] However, the speed $c_j(\hat{\mathbf{f}})$, $j = 1, 2, 3$, of long waves in the acoustic branches can be computed on the basis of macroscopic linear anisotropic elasticity.

As we have seen, the changes in the theory which are necessitated by the passage to composite crystals occur for a given value of $\mathbf{f}$. The theory which relates to the periodicity of $\omega(\mathbf{f}, j)$ in $\mathbf{f}$, and the density of allowed wave number vectors in the first Brillouin zone remains unchanged.

---

[55] For the construction of continuum theories which permit the calculation of the long wavelength limits of the optical as well as the acoustical branches, see Mindlin (1972).

CHAPTER FIVE

Rubber Elasticity, I

5.1 INTRODUCTION

The previous chapter dealt with the mechanical behavior of crystalline solids. We turn next to the study of the elastic behavior of a different class of materials, amorphous polymeric solids. Rubber is the earliest representative of this class, and frequently the type of behavior exhibited by its members, provided the temperature level is not too low,[1] is referred to collectively as rubber elasticity. The term elastomer is also used to describe such materials. Important characteristics that distinguish rubber elasticity from crystalline elasticity are the following:

1. Rubber exhibits large extensibility (500–1000%) in the elastic range whereas the maximum elastic strain for crystalline solids is less than 1%.
2. Rubber has a very low modulus of elasticity, of the order of 10^{-5} times the modulus of steel, for example.
3. Stretched rubber contracts upon heating.
4. Rubber gives off heat upon stretching.

The latter two thermal phenomena are referred to as the Gough–Joule effect.[2]

[1] Below a critical temperature, called the glass transition temperature, which is characteristic of a particular amorphous polymeric solid, its mechanical behavior ceases to be like that of rubber but becomes glasslike in nature; cf. Treloar (1975, pp. 13–16). We are confining attention to the regime of rubber elasticity.

[2] The early experimental work of Gough in 1805 first revealed these phenomena. They were subsequently restudied in greater detail by Joule in 1859. An interesting discussion of the history of these investigations is given by Flory (1953, pp. 434–440).

A basic question posed by these observations is the atomistic nature of rubber and rubberlike materials which accounts for the striking differences between their macroscopic behavior and that of crystalline solids. From a historical viewpoint, it is fair to say that the atomistic nature of the mechanical behavior of crystalline solids, at least in its essential characteristics, was already understood by Cauchy, as shown by his early work of the period 1820–1830. By contrast, the essential ideas of the atomistic basis of rubber elasticity were not put forward until 100 years later by Meyer, von Susich, and Valko (1932), Karrer (1932), and Guth and Mark (1934). One of the barriers that caused the long delay was the difficulty in the recognition, by available chemical techniques, of the existence of long-chain molecules. As late as 1920, certainly, their existence was still the subject of intense debate.[3] A second reason for the long period that elapsed between the understanding on an atomistic level of the mechanical behavior of crystalline and of polymeric solids lies, perhaps, in the fact that changes in energy play a leading role for the first whereas for the second it is the change in entropy which is important; the latter is a more subtle concept, one that appeals less directly to physical intuition.

Since its inception approximately 50 years ago, the subject of rubber elasticity has become, and continues to be, an extremely active one with a very extensive literature.[4] This chapter presents an introductory account of some of its basic aspects. In the next chapter, we treat some questions in the subject of a statistical mechanical nature in greater detail.

5.2 RELATIVE ROLES OF INTERNAL ENERGY AND ENTROPY

The relative importance of internal energy and entropy in the elastic behavior of materials may be evaluated by the use of continuum thermodynamics. The starting point is Eq. (1.6.3), which we rewrite here, setting $\mathscr{V} = 1$ (so that all extensive quantities are expressed per unit original volume).

$$T_{LM} = \left.\frac{\partial F}{\partial E_{LM}}\right|_T ; \qquad S = -\left.\frac{\partial F}{\partial T}\right|_{E_{LM}} . \qquad (5.2.1)$$

Since $F = U - TS$,

$$T_{LM} = \left.\frac{\partial U}{\partial E_{LM}}\right|_T - T\left.\frac{\partial S}{\partial E_{LM}}\right|_T , \qquad (5.2.2)$$

[3]A historical account is given by Flory (1953, pp. 3–25).
[4]Standard works in the field include Flory (1953, 1969), Volkenstein (1963), Birshtein and Ptitsyn (1966) and Treloar (1975); see also the review article of Saito et al. (1963) and the summary paper of Guth (1966).

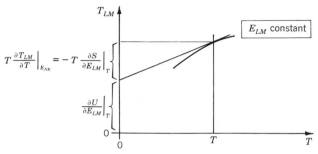

Figure 5.1   Graphical interpretation of Eq. (5.2.4).

and, from Eq. (5.2.1),

$$\left.\frac{\partial S}{\partial E_{LM}}\right|_T = -\frac{\partial^2 F}{\partial E_{LM} \partial T} = -\left.\frac{\partial T_{LM}}{\partial T}\right|_{E_{NK}}. \qquad (5.2.3)$$

Therefore,

$$\left.\frac{\partial U}{\partial E_{LM}}\right|_T = T_{LM} - T \left.\frac{\partial T_{LM}}{\partial T}\right|_{E_{NK}}. \qquad (5.2.4)$$

Equation (5.2.4) has a simple graphical interpretation (Figure 5.1),[5] which permits the determination of the relative importance of energy and entropy in the deformation of a material, by considering the stress–temperature relation at fixed strain. It is clear from Figure 5.1, as well as from Eq. (5.2.3) directly, that the requirement of increasing stress with increasing temperature to maintain a given strain implies that entropy decreases with strain. As a specific example, consider the early experimental results for rubber of Meyer and Ferri (1935) shown schematically in Figure 5.2. These results indicate that above[6] $T \sim 210°K$ there is little internal energy change with strain in this material and that the principal origin of stress is the fact that the entropy at constant temperature decreases with strain. This behaviour is in close analogy to that of a perfect gas, for which the internal energy is independent of the volume and, as previously discussed in Section 3.12,

$$p = -\frac{\partial F}{\partial v} = T\frac{\partial S}{\partial v} = nkTv. \qquad (5.2.5)$$

Therefore, the pressure–temperature relation at constant volume is also a straight line through the origin. Note, however, that because of the difference

[5]Treloar (1975, p. 31).
[6]The temperature $T \sim 210°$ K represents the glass transition temperature for this material.

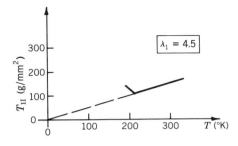

Figure 5.2 Temperature dependence of stress T_{11} for rubber in simple tension at fixed principal stretch $\lambda_1 = 4.5$. Dashed line shows linear extrapolation to $T = 0$. (After Meyer and Ferri, 1935, with permission.)

in sign between the definition of pressure and stress, entropy increases with volume for a gas, while it decreases with strain for a polymeric solid.

We have given, in Section 3.12, an atomistic interpretation of the increase in entropy with increase in volume of a gas. In the next section, we will give an atomistic interpretation for the contrasting behavior of a polymeric solid.

5.3 ATOMIC STRUCTURE OF LONG-CHAIN MOLECULES AND NETWORKS

Since carbon is the principal constituent of most long-chain molecules, we begin with a brief discussion of the tetrahedral bonds formed by a carbon atom with four neighboring atoms. These are covalent bonds (Section 9.6) and therefore are strong and highly directional. Their directions may be described by putting the carbon atom at the center of a cube and the neighbors at alternate vertices, as shown in Figure 5.3, so that the bonded atoms lie at the vertices of a regular tetrahedron. It is seen that the angle ψ between successive bonds, referred to as the bond angle, has the value $\psi = 2 \text{ arc sin } \sqrt{2/3} = 109.47°$.

Consider next polyethylene, one of the simplest long-chain molecules. Its structure is shown in Figure 5.4, where the covalent bonds are shown as solid lines. If we focus on a particular carbon atom in the interior of the chain, we see that it is bonded to four atoms; one carbon to either side along the chain and to two hydrogen atoms. The terminal carbon atoms are each bonded to three hydrogen atoms. The chemical formula of polyethylene is therefore,

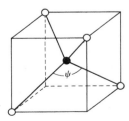

Figure 5.3 Covalent bonds formed by a carbon atom with four neighboring atoms.

● = Carbon atom
○ = Hydrogen atom

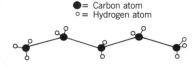

Figure 5.4 Schematic drawing of polyethylene molecule.

$CH_3(CH_2)_nCH_3$, where n denotes the number of CH_2 units (referred to as monomers) in the chain. The value of n depends on the conditions during chain formation and $n + 2$ (the total number of units in the chain) is referred to as the degree of polymerization; it is typically in the range 10^2 to 10^4. The chain of carbon atoms is referred to as the backbone and the hydrogen atoms form what are called the side groups. Many long-chain molecules have the same carbon-atom backbone and differ only in the nature of the sidegroups.[7] Other types of backbones occur; for example in polypeptides (proteins) the sequence is $[-N-C-C]_n$.

We next turn to an important topological characteristic of long-chain molecules: the great variety of atomic configurations compatible with their covalent bonding interactions. Consider four particular carbon atoms of the backbone as shown in Figure 5.5. As we noted, the covalent C—C bonds are both strong and directional. In terms of the potential energy of interaction of these atoms, this means that a large increase in energy would accompany a small change from the minimum-energy distance between a pair of neighboring carbon atoms or a change from the minimum-energy bond angle between a pair of neighboring bond directions. However, many different relative configurations of these four carbon atoms are possible while maintaining the bond lengths and bond angles constant. These different configurations are obtained by rotating atom 4 about the bond between atoms 2 and 3 through an angle φ (Figure 5.5b), where we have set $\varphi = 0$ in the planar configuration shown in Figure 5.5a. The angle φ is referred to as a dihedral angle. The planar configuration shown in Figure 5.5a is called the *trans* configuration (atoms 1 and 4 on opposite sides of the 2–3 bond) while that shown in Figure 5.5c corresponding to $\varphi = \pi$ is called *cis* (atoms 1 and 4 on the same side). The potential energy of interaction of the four carbon atoms alone is independent of φ but this is not the case for the interaction between the side groups. In the case of polyethylene, for example, although the principal interaction of the hydrogen atoms is through covalent bonding with their neighboring carbon atom, there still remains a weak interaction between neighboring side groups.[8] For the portion of a polyethylene chain shown in Figure 5.6a, this gives rise to

---

[7]See, for example, the table in Flory (1953, pp. 52–53). Some additional chemical terminology which may confuse the uninitiated: polyethylene is also referred to as polymethylene and either term is reserved for long chains; if n is small, less than about 100, the molecule $CH_3(CH_2)_nCH_3$ would be described as an n-alkane, with the n denoting normal, that is, unbranched, not degree of polymerization; the case of $n = 2$ is called n-butane.

[8]The fundamental quantum mechanical basis of the side-group interaction remains a subject for research (see Flory, 1969, p. 54).

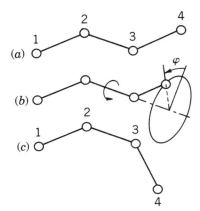

Figure 5.5 Rotation of backbone atoms about bond 2–3 from *trans* configuration (*a*) to *cis* configuration (*c*).

a potential energy variation with the dihedral angle φ whose general nature is shown in Figure 5.6*b*. The local maxima and minima are readily understood in terms of the relative positions of the sidegroups attached to carbon atoms 2 and 3 at various values of φ as shown in Figure 5.6*c*. The local minima at $\varphi = \pm 120°$ refer to what are termed *gauche* configurations.

Since it impedes free rotation about the bond, the function $V(\varphi)$ is referred to as a rotational energy barrier. In a longer chain, rotation about various bonds may bring nonneighboring sidegroups into close proximity, so that a more accurate description of the side-group interaction energy would describe it as a function $V(\varphi_1, \ldots, \varphi_n)$ of all of the dihedral angles. However, to keep the analysis reasonably simple, many treatments restrict attention to the interaction of neighboring side groups only.

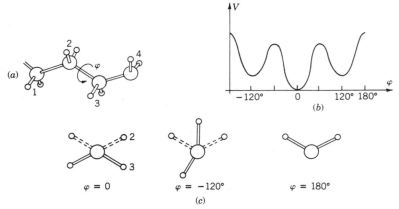

Figure 5.6 Side group interaction. (*a*) Hydrogen atoms bonded to carbon atom 3 rotate with respect to those bonded to atom 2 when rotation about bond 2–3 through dihedral angle φ occurs. (*b*) Variation of energy of interaction $V(\varphi)$ between side groups 2 and 3. (*c*) Relative positions of sidegroup 3 (solid) and side group 2 (dashed) as viewed along 2–3 bond.

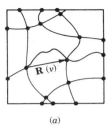
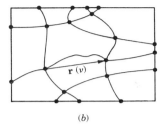

(a)   (b)

Figure 5.7 Amorphous cross-linked network before (a) and after (b) deformation.

The height, E_b, of rotational energy barriers is relatively low, typically of the order of [9] 3–5 kcal/mole. The torsional oscillation frequency in the potential well in the neighborhood of $\varphi = 0$ is of the order of $\nu = 10^{12}$ sec^{-1}. Since, as we will discuss in greater detail in Chapter 7, the rate f at which such barriers are overcome is given in first approximation by an Arrhenius relation of the form

$$f = \nu e^{-E_b/kT}, \qquad (5.3.1)$$

we see that f is of the order of 10^9 sec^{-1} at $T = 300°$K. Therefore, the changes of configuration of a long-chain molecule occur very rapidly on the usual macroscopic time scale.

Thus far, we have been speaking of a single long-chain molecule. In dealing with rubberlike elasticity, we will be concerned with amorphous networks of such molecules as shown schematically[10] in Figure 5.7. The molecules of the network are cross-linked at various random points along their lengths by a chemical process that replaces the side groups there by a molecular structure that ties the two chains together. An amorphous network of this type is sometimes referred to as a gel. The chains between cross-links are typically 100 to 1000 units in length and are in thermal motion, rapidly changing their configurations by rotations over energy barriers as just described, although interference from neighboring chains may impede this process somewhat. If the amorphous solid is deformed, the average end-to-end length of a chain between cross-linking points is correspondingly changed, as shown schematically in Figure 5.7b.

The mechanical behavior of such an amorphous network will be considered in greater detail in Sections 5.6 and 6.10. Here, we wish to discuss qualitatively the change in configurational entropy of a long-chain molecule as a function of its end-to-end length. When the end-to-end length is much less than its fully

[9]See Section 7.3 for a discussion of the energy units employed for the discussion of barrier heights.
[10]The highly idealized nature of our description of amorphous networks must be emphasized. Real networks presumably contain many defects, such as loose ends, closed loops and interlooping of chains (cf. Treloar, 1975, pp. 74–77). They may also contain regions of crystallinity (cf. Treloar, 1975, pp. 16–20).

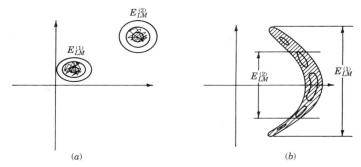

$$E_{LM}^{(2)}$$

$$E_{LM}^{(1)}$$

$$E_{LM}^{(2)}$$ $$E_{LM}^{(1)}$$

(a)   (b)

Figure 5.8 Schematic representation of constant energy contours and motion of system in configuration space at two levels of strain for crystals (*a*) and amorphous polymers (*b*).

extended length, there are many configurations accessible to it which are all compatible with fixed bond lengths and bond angles. As the end-to-end length is increased, the number of compatible configurations decreases until when it is fully extended there is only a single configuration possible. Since thermal motion causes the chain to move rapidly among the compatible configurations, the uncertainty in chain configuration decreases with increase in end-to-end length. From the uncertainty interpretation of entropy (Section 3.12) it follows that the configurational entropy decreases with increasing end-to-end length, that is, with increasing strain. This provides the basic atomistic interpretation of the macroscopic behavior described in Section 5.2.

Crystalline and Polymeric Solids

The contrast in the relative roles of energy and entropy in the deformation of crystalline and amorphous polymeric solids (above the glass transition temperature) can therefore be traced to the nature of the potential energy function $V(\mathbf{r}_1, \ldots, \mathbf{r}_N; E_{LM})$ describing the interaction energy among the atoms of the system under a prescribed deformation E_{LM}. This is shown schematically in configuration space in Figure 5.8 where constant energy contours are shown.

For a crystalline solid (Figure 5.8*a*), the interaction energy between atoms is such as to produce large energy changes for atom displacements in any direction. The effect of increasing strain is to shift to a higher energy region. The thermal vibrations in the vicinity of the two equilibrium configurations are substantially the same;[11] therefore, the uncertainty and the entropy changes little.

For a polymeric solid, by contrast, the potential energy changes are highly directional in configuration space (Figure 5.8*b*), being very large for atomic displacements that would change bond lengths or bond angles and very small

[11]The small change in amplitude of thermal vibrations comes about because of changes in curvature of V, that is, due to anharmonic effects (Section 4.5).

for rotations about backbone bonds. Furthermore, the effect of increasing strain from $E_{LM}^{(1)}$ to $E_{LM}^{(2)}$ is primarily to decrease the region of configuration space accessible to the system and therefore to decrease its entropy without any significant change in energy.

5.4   ONE-DIMENSIONAL POLYMER MODEL

To make the qualitative discussion of the entropy dependence on end-to-end length of the previous section more quantitative, we consider here a highly idealized model.[12] It consists of a chain of n rigid links each of length a connected by hinges that can only be either fully open or fully closed; the chain, therefore, is always constrained to lie along a straight line (Figure 5.9). The hinges are indexed $j = 1, \ldots, n$ and a configuration of the chain may be specified in terms of the generalized coordinates q_j, $j = 1, \ldots, n$, where

$q_j = +1$,   if the link originally[13] to the right of the hinge
               is directed to the right.

$q_j = -1$,   if the link originally to the right of the hinge
               is directed to the left.

We regard the end-to-end displacement of the chain as fixed at a value ℓ, where ℓ is an integral multiple of $2a$. The potential energy of the system can then be written as

$$V(q_1, \ldots, q_n; \ell) = 0 \qquad \text{if } (q_1, \ldots, q_n) \text{ is compatible with } \ell, \text{ or } q_{comp\,\ell}.$$

$$\quad = \infty \qquad \text{if } (q_1, \ldots, q_n) \text{ is incompatible with } \ell, \text{ or } q_{incomp\,\ell}. \qquad (5.4.1)$$

Note that fixing the end-to-end length ℓ is analogous to the prescription of the strain E_{LM} for a crystalline solid (see Section 4.8) or to the fixing of the volume v for a gas. However, the manner in which the controlled parameter ℓ appears in the potential function V is much closer to the case of a perfect gas [see Eq. (2.7.1)] than of a crystalline solid.

Since the coordinates $q = (q_1, \ldots, q_n)$ can assume only discrete values, we use sums instead of integrals in our statistical mechanics formulation. The configuration portion[14] of the canonical distribution takes the form

$$\rho_q(q; \ell, T) = Ce^{-V/kT} \qquad (5.4.2)$$

[12] This model has been discussed by James and Guth (1943, pp. 467–470); see also Kubo (1965).
[13] That is, in the fully extended configuration.
[14] We are assuming that the momentum portion of the canonical distribution is independent of ℓ and ignore it in what follows in this chapter. We return to its consideration in the next chapter.

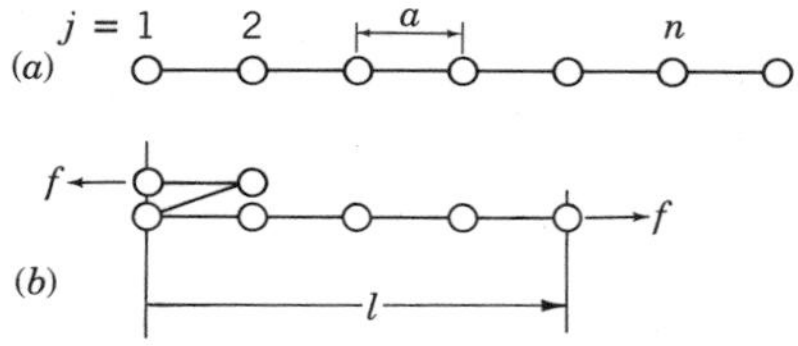

Figure 5.9 One-dimensional polymer model: (*a*) fully extended and (*b*) partially retracted.

where the normalization constant C is determined from the requirement

$$\sum_q \rho_q(q; \ell, T) = 1, \qquad (5.4.3)$$

where the summation is carried out over all n-tuples $q = (q_1, \ldots, q_n)$ with $q_j = \pm 1$. From Eqs. (5.4.1) and (5.4.2),

$$\rho_q(q; \ell, T) = C \qquad \text{for } q_{comp \, \ell}$$

$$= 0 \qquad \text{for } q_{incomp \, \ell}. \qquad (5.4.4)$$

Therefore,

$$C = \frac{1}{W(\ell)}, \qquad (5.4.5)$$

where $W(\ell)$ is the number of configurations which are compatible with ℓ.

The integral expression for the configurational entropy, Eq. (3.12.22), in this case becomes a sum

$$S_q(\ell) = -k \sum_q \rho_q \log \rho_q$$

$$= -k \sum_{q_{comp. \, \ell}} \frac{1}{W(\ell)} \log \frac{1}{W(\ell)} \qquad (5.4.6)$$

$$= k \log W(\ell).$$

Calculation of $W(\ell)$

Let $(q_1, \ldots, q_n)$ be compatible with the displacement ℓ, and let n_+ be the number of $q_j = +1$ and n_- be the number of $q_j = -1$. Then compatibility with ℓ requires

$$\ell = (n_+ - n_-)a$$

or

$$n_+ - n_- = \frac{\ell}{a}$$

and

$$n_+ + n_- = n$$

from which we find

$$n_+ = \tfrac{1}{2}\left(n + \frac{\ell}{a}\right)$$

$$n_- = \tfrac{1}{2}\left(n - \frac{\ell}{a}\right). \qquad (5.4.7)$$

Conversely, all $(q_1, \ldots, q_n)$ with n_+ and n_- given by Eq. (5.4.7) will be compatible with ℓ. Therefore, $W(\ell)$ is the number of ways n objects can be divided into two groups of n_+ and n_-, each without regard to order, that is,

$$W(\ell) = \frac{n!}{n_+! n_-!}. \qquad (5.4.8)$$

For n, n_+, and n_- all large (i.e., for a long chain far from fully extended), Stirling's approximation[15]

$$\log n! \sim \left(n + \tfrac{1}{2}\right)\log n - n + \tfrac{1}{2}\log(2\pi) \qquad (5.4.9)$$

may be used to obtain

$$\log W(\ell) = \left(n + \tfrac{1}{2}\right)\log n - \tfrac{1}{2}\left(n + \frac{\ell}{a} + 1\right)\log \tfrac{1}{2}\left(n + \frac{\ell}{a}\right)$$

$$- \tfrac{1}{2}\left(n - \frac{\ell}{a} + 1\right)\log \tfrac{1}{2}\left(n - \frac{\ell}{a}\right) - \tfrac{1}{2}\log(2\pi). \qquad (5.4.10)$$

Stress – Strain Relation

The internal energy of this model is independent of ℓ. Therefore its Helmholtz free energy

$$F(\ell, T) = -TS_q(\ell) = -kT \log W(\ell)$$

and, by application of Eq. (1.6.12), the force f required to maintain the length ℓ

[15]See, for example, Feller (1950, pp. 41–43).

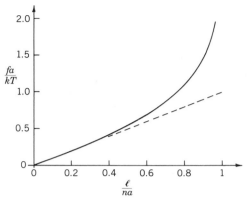

Figure 5.10   Force–length relation, Eq. (5.4.12), for one-dimensional polymer model of Figure 5.9; dashed line shows slope of linear relation valid for $\ell/na \ll 1$.

is

$$f = \frac{\partial F}{\partial \ell} = -kT \frac{d}{d\ell} \log W(\ell)$$

$$= \frac{kT}{2a} \left[\log \frac{\left(1 + \dfrac{\ell}{na}\right)}{\left(1 - \dfrac{\ell}{na}\right)} + \frac{\left(1 + \dfrac{\ell}{na} + \dfrac{1}{n}\right)}{\left(1 + \dfrac{\ell}{na}\right)} - \frac{\left(1 - \dfrac{\ell}{na} + \dfrac{1}{n}\right)}{\left(1 - \dfrac{\ell}{na}\right)} \right]$$

which, for large n, takes the form

$$f = \frac{kT}{2a} \log \frac{\left(1 + \dfrac{\ell}{na}\right)}{\left(1 - \dfrac{\ell}{na}\right)}$$

$$\cong \frac{kT}{na^2} \ell \quad \text{for } \frac{\ell}{na} \ll 1. \tag{5.4.12}$$

A graph of the stress–strain relation of Eq. (5.4.12) is shown in Figure 5.10. Note also, from that equation, that the stress required to maintain a given strain increases with temperature and therefore a rise in temperature at fixed stress would result in a contraction in length.

Random Walk Interpretation

An alternate and widely used framework for the discussion of long-chain model configurations is provided by the concept of a random walk. For the present model, we consider a one-dimensional random walk in which we start at $x = 0$ and take steps of length a in either the $+x$ or $-x$ direction, both directions having equal probability. What is then desired is the probability of arriving at position $x = \ell$ after n steps.

For fixed n, the possible final values of x differ from each other by multiples of $2a$ since changing the sign of a single step changes the final value by that amount. Nevertheless it is convenient to define the desired probability in terms of a probability density $p(\ell; n)$ (probability per unit distance) so that $2ap(\ell; n)$ is the probability of arriving at the position ℓ after n steps (or, equivalently, $2ap(\ell; n)$ is the probability of arriving in the interval $\ell \leqslant x < \ell + 2a$ after n steps). We will also write $p(\ell; n) = p(\ell)$ with n understood.

The relation between $p(\ell)$ and $W(\ell)$ is

$$2ap(\ell) = W(\ell)(\tfrac{1}{2})^n \qquad (5.4.13)$$

since any particular set $(q_1, \ldots, q_n)$ with $q_j = \pm 1$ (regarded now as defining a particular sequence of positive and negative steps in a random walk) has probability $(\tfrac{1}{2})^n$ and there are $W(\ell)$ such sets that lead to ℓ as the final point. Since $p(\ell)$ and $W(\ell)$ differ only by a multiplicative factor which is independent of ℓ, we can also compute the configurational entropy $S_q(\ell)$ of a chain with length ℓ from the relation

$$S_q(\ell) = k \log p(\ell). \qquad (5.4.14)$$

We turn next to the computation of $p(\ell; n)$ for $n \gg 1$ and $\ell/(na) \ll 1$. Then,

$$\log \tfrac{1}{2}\left(n \pm \frac{\ell}{a}\right) \cong \pm \frac{\ell}{na} - \frac{\ell^2}{2n^2 a^2} + \log\frac{n}{2},$$

and if we use this approximation in Eq. (5.4.10) for $\log W(\ell)$ together with Eq. (5.4.13) relating $p(\ell)$ and $W(\ell)$ we find that

$$p(\ell; n) = \frac{1}{(2\pi na^2)^{\frac{1}{2}}} e^{-\ell^2/(2na^2)}. \qquad (5.4.15)$$

That is, for $n \gg 1$ and $\ell/(na) \ll 1$, the probability distribution $p(\ell; n)$ is normal or Gaussian with mean $\langle \ell \rangle = 0$ and variance $\langle \ell^2 \rangle = \sigma_\ell^2 = na^2$.

Central Limit Theorem

This limiting probability distribution for a one-dimensional random walk is an example of the central limit theorem of probability.[16] Under very broad

[16] For the case in which all of the component random variables are governed by the same probability distribution, the proof follows directly from the Fourier transform relation given in Eq. (5.5.4); see Dym and McKean (1972, p. 114). For the general case see Khinchin (1949, Appendix).

conditions, this theorem states that the sum of n independent random variables, $X_n = \sum_{i=1}^{n} x_i$, has a probability distribution $p(X_n)$ that, with increasing n, approaches a normal or Gaussian distribution with mean $\langle X_n \rangle = \sum_{i=1}^{n} \langle x_i \rangle$ and variance $(\Delta X_n)^2 = \sum_{i=1}^{n} (\Delta x_i)^2$, where $(\Delta x_i)^2 = \langle x_i^2 \rangle - \langle x_i \rangle^2, (\Delta X_n)^2 = \langle X_n^2 \rangle - \langle X_n \rangle^2$.

In the case of the random walk just considered, $x_i = \pm a$ with equal probability so that $\langle x_i \rangle = 0$ and $(\Delta x_i)^2 = \langle x_i^2 \rangle = a^2$ and the random variable $X_n = \ell$. The central limit theorem, therefore, leads directly to Eq. (5.4.15).

5.5   THREE-DIMENSIONAL POLYMER MODELS

As preparation for the study of three-dimensional polymer models, we begin by outlining the use of the Fourier transform in random walk calculations.

Consider two independent continuous random variables x_1 and x_2 with probability distribution functions $p_1(x_1)$ and $p_2(x_2)$, where the range of x_1 and x_2 are $-\infty < x_1, x_2 < \infty$. Let y be a new random variable defined by the equation $y = x_1 + x_2$ for which we desire the probability distribution function $p(y)$.

We may regard y as the displacement from the origin along the x-axis which is reached after first taking a step of x_1 and then following it by a step of x_2. The probability $p(y)\,dy$ of arriving in this way in the interval y to $y + dy$ is the sum of the probabilities of all of the various two-step walks that arrive there, namely, walks in which the first step arrives in the interval x_1 to $x_1 + dx_1$, $-\infty < x_1 < \infty$, followed by a second displacement whose size is $y - x_1$ to $y + dy - x_1$. That is,

$$p(y)\,dy = \left(\int_{-\infty}^{\infty} p_1(x_1) p_2(y - x_1)\,dx_1 \right) dy$$

or

$$p(y) = \int_{-\infty}^{\infty} p_1(x_1) p_2(y - x_1)\,dx_1. \tag{5.5.1}$$

This convolution relationship points to the utility of the Fourier transform. Let

$$P(\eta) = \int_{-\infty}^{\infty} e^{-i\eta y} p(y)\,dy \tag{5.5.2}$$

be the Fourier transform of $p(y)$, with inverse

$$p(y) = \frac{1}{2\pi} \int_{-\infty}^{\infty} e^{i\eta y} P(\eta)\,d\eta,$$

and similarly let $P_1(\eta)$, $P_2(\eta)$ be the Fourier transforms of $p_1(x)$, $p_2(x)$. Then, it follows from Eq. (5.5.1) that

$$P(\eta) = P_1(\eta)P_2(\eta). \tag{5.5.3}$$

This result may be extended to the case $y = x_1 + \cdots + x_n$, where $x_1, \ldots, x_n$ are n independent random variables with probability distribution functions $p_j(x_j)$, $j = 1, \ldots, n$. In this case

$$P(\eta) = \prod_{j=1}^{n} P_j(\eta) \tag{5.5.4}$$

where $P_j(\eta)$ is the Fourier transform of $p_j(x_j)$. If the probability distribution function is identical for each step, that is, if $p_j(x_j) = p_1(x_j)$, $j = 1, \ldots, n$, then

$$P(\eta) = [P_1(\eta)]^n. \tag{5.5.5}$$

This procedure may also be extended to random walks in three dimensions. Let $\mathbf{r}_1, \ldots, \mathbf{r}_n$ be the individual independent steps or displacements, all subject to the same probability distribution function $p_1(\mathbf{r}_j)$, $j = 1, \ldots, n$. Let

$$\mathbf{R} = \mathbf{r}_1 + \mathbf{r}_2 + \cdots + \mathbf{r}_n \tag{5.5.6}$$

be the resulting displacement after n steps with probability distribution $p(\mathbf{R})$. We now use the three-dimensional Fourier transform

$$P(\boldsymbol{\rho}) = \int_{\mathbb{R}_3} e^{-i\boldsymbol{\rho} \cdot \mathbf{R}} p(\mathbf{R}) \, d\mathbf{R} \tag{5.5.7}$$

with inverse

$$p(\mathbf{r}) = \frac{1}{(2\pi)^3} \int_{\mathbb{R}_3} e^{i\boldsymbol{\rho} \cdot \mathbf{R}} P(\boldsymbol{\rho}) \, d\boldsymbol{\rho}. \tag{5.5.8}$$

Then, by a procedure analogous to the derivation of Eq. (5.5.5),

$$P(\boldsymbol{\rho}) = [P_1(\boldsymbol{\rho})]^n. \tag{5.5.9}$$

Freely Jointed Chain

We can now treat the three-dimensional version of the simple polymer model discussed in the previous section. It consists of a freely jointed chain of n links, each of length a. We seek the probability distribution function $p(\mathbf{R})$ for its end-to-end vector $\mathbf{R}$.

The problem is equivalent to a three-dimensional random walk of n steps where each step is of length a and the direction of each step is randomly distributed in space. That is, the terminus of each step is uniformly distributed on a sphere of radius a with center at its starting point. Therefore,

$$p_1(\mathbf{r}) = \frac{1}{4\pi a^2} \delta(r - a) \tag{5.5.10}$$

where $r = |\mathbf{r}|$ and $\delta(x)$ is the one-dimensional Dirac delta function. Note that, by use of spherical coordinates,

$$\int_{\mathbb{R}_3} p_1(\mathbf{r}) \, d\mathbf{r} = \frac{1}{4\pi a^2} \int_0^\pi \sin\theta \, d\theta \int_0^{2\pi} d\varphi \int_0^\infty \delta(r - a) r^2 \, dr = 1 \tag{5.5.11}$$

so that $p_1(r)$ is properly normalized.

The Fourier transform of $p_1(\mathbf{r})$ is

$$P_1(\boldsymbol{\rho}) = \frac{1}{4\pi a^2} \int_{\mathbb{R}_3} e^{-i\boldsymbol{\rho}\cdot\mathbf{r}} \delta(r - a) \, d\mathbf{r}. \tag{5.5.12}$$

The integral may be evaluated by the use of spherical coordinates with $\boldsymbol{\rho}$ taken as the direction of the polar axis so that θ is the angle between $\boldsymbol{\rho}$ and $\mathbf{r}$. Then,

$$P_1(\boldsymbol{\rho}) = \frac{1}{4\pi a^2} \int_0^{2\pi} d\varphi \int_0^\infty dr \int_0^\pi d\theta \, e^{-i\rho r\cos\theta} \delta(r - a) r^2 \sin\theta$$

where $p = |\boldsymbol{\rho}|$. The integration with respect to θ is performed first followed by that with respect to r, with the result that

$$P_1(\boldsymbol{\rho}) = \frac{\sin\rho a}{\rho a} \tag{5.5.13}$$

and, from Eq. (5.5.9),

$$P(\boldsymbol{\rho}) = \left(\frac{\sin\rho a}{\rho a} \right)^n. \tag{5.5.14}$$

The desired probability distribution function $p(\mathbf{R})$ is obtained by use of the inverse Fourier transform,

$$p(\mathbf{R}) = \frac{1}{(2\pi)^3} \int_{\mathbb{R}_3} e^{i\boldsymbol{\rho}\cdot\mathbf{R}} \left(\frac{\sin\rho a}{\rho a} \right)^n d\boldsymbol{\rho}. \tag{5.5.15}$$

The integral may be reduced to an integral over ρ by again introducing spherical coordinates, with $\mathbf{R}$ now serving as polar axis. The result, due to Rayleigh, is

$$p(\mathbf{R}) = \frac{1}{2\pi^2 R} \int_0^\infty \sin\rho R \left(\frac{\sin\rho a}{\rho a} \right)^n \rho \, d\rho. \tag{5.5.16}$$

We see that $p(\mathbf{R})$, the probability per unit volume of an end-to-end displacement $\mathbf{R}$ after n steps, depends only on $R = |\mathbf{R}|$; that is, the probability distribution is spherically symmetric, as would be expected on the basis of physical intuition. For small n it is convenient to evaluate the integral by the use of trigonometric identities (see Flory, 1969, pp. 399 and 400); for future reference, we list the results for $n = 2$, 3, and 4

$$n = 2: p(\mathbf{R}) = (8\pi a^2 R)^{-1}, \qquad 0 \leqslant R/a < 2 \qquad (5.5.17)$$

$$n = 3: p(\mathbf{R}) = (8\pi a^3)^{-1}, \qquad 0 \leqslant R/a \leqslant 1$$

$$= (16\pi a^2 R)^{-1}(3 - R/a), \qquad 1 \leqslant R/a < 3 \quad (5.5.18)$$

$$n = 4: p(\mathbf{R}) = (64\pi a^3)^{-1}(8 - 3R/a), \qquad 0 \leqslant R/a \leqslant 2$$

$$= (64\pi a^2 R)^{-1}(4 - R/a), \qquad 2 \leqslant R/a < 4 \quad (5.5.19)$$

with $p(\mathbf{R}) = 0$ for $R > na$.

The asymptotic behavior of $p(\mathbf{R})$ for large n may be obtained as follows. By the change of variable $\rho = yn^{-1/2}/a$,

$$p(\mathbf{R}) = \frac{1}{2\pi^2 Rna^2} \int_0^\infty \sin(yRn^{-1/2}/a)\left(\frac{\sin yn^{-1/2}}{yn^{-1/2}}\right)^n y\, dy. \quad (5.5.20)$$

But

$$\left(\frac{\sin yn^{-1/2}}{yn^{-1/2}}\right)^n = \left(1 - \frac{y^2}{3!n}[1 + o(1)]\right)^n \sim e^{-y^2/6} \text{ for large } n,$$

where $o(1)$ indicates an error that approaches 0 as $n \to \infty$. Substitution of this asymptotic expression, $e^{-y^2/6}$, into the integral of Eq. (5.5.20) and integration by parts leads to the asymptotic form of $p(\mathbf{R})$ for large n:

$$p(\mathbf{R}) = \left(\frac{3}{2\pi na^2}\right)^{3/2} \exp\left[-3R^2/(2na^2)\right]. \qquad (5.5.21)$$

That is, the probability distribution for the freely jointed chain in three dimensions approaches, for large n, a three-dimensional normal or Gaussian distribution. This result can also be regarded as an example of the central limit theorem, extended to vector-valued random variables. Note that for this distribution

$$\langle R^2 \rangle = \int_{\mathbf{R}_3} R^2 p(\mathbf{R})\, d\mathbf{R} = 4\pi \int_0^\infty R^4 p(\mathbf{R})\, dR = na^2 \qquad (5.5.22)$$

as in the one-dimensional random walk.[17] We can, therefore, also write

$$p(\mathbf{R}) = \left(\frac{3}{2\pi\langle R^2\rangle}\right)^{3/2} e^{-3R^2/2\langle R^2\rangle}. \qquad (5.5.23)$$

The Gaussian distribution, Eq. (5.5.21), yields a value of $p(\mathbf{R}) > 0$ for $R \geqslant na$. Since the correct probability must be zero for this range, it is clear that the Gaussian distribution of Eq. (5.5.21) is applicable only to long chains that are far from fully extended.

Further Polymer Models

The freely jointed chain is the simplest possible three-dimensional polymer model. There are a sequence of steps that can be taken toward greater realism and they lead to the following models.

1 Freely rotating chain The fixed bond angle between successive links is included in the model, but rotational energy barriers are assumed absent.

2 Chain with hindered rotation In addition to fixed bond angles, the effect of rotational energy barriers is included. Most frequently it is assumed that the sidegroup interaction energy $V(\varphi_1, \ldots, \varphi_n) = \sum_{i=1}^{n} V_1(\varphi_i)$, that is, that the energy barrier opposing the rotation about a given bond depends only on the dihedral angle associated with that bond. This assumption facilitates the analysis but is a drastic simplification as may be seen most readily by the examination of a molecular model that permits rotations about backbone bonds.[18]

Persistence Length

The freely jointed chain corresponds, as we have seen, to a random walk in which each step has a probability distribution uniform on a sphere of radius a, independent of the previous steps taken. For a freely rotating chain, on the other hand, the requirement of a fixed bond angle restricts a given step to lie on the intersection of this sphere with a cone which has the previous link as axis. The presence of rotational energy barriers will make the probability distribution on this circle of intersection nonuniform.

The persistence length is a useful concept for the study of the effect of these additional restrictions. Let $\mathbf{a}_i$, $i = 1, \ldots, n$ be vectors of magnitude a directed

---

[17] The notation $\langle R^2\rangle_0 = na^2$ is sometimes employed to emphasize that this is the mean-square length in the absence of an applied stress; see Section 6.9.

[18] See discussion in Flory (1969, p. 19).

along the links of the chain. Then, the end-to-end vector $\mathbf{R} = \sum_{i=1}^{n} \mathbf{a}_i$ and

$$R^2 = \mathbf{R} \cdot \mathbf{R} = \sum_{i,\,j=1}^{n} \mathbf{a}_i \cdot \mathbf{a}_j = na^2 + 2 \sum_{i=1}^{n} \sum_{j=i+1}^{n} \mathbf{a}_i \cdot \mathbf{a}_j. \qquad (5.5.24)$$

Therefore,

$$\langle R^2 \rangle = na^2 + 2 \sum_{i=1}^{n} \sum_{j=i+1}^{n} \langle \mathbf{a}_i \cdot \mathbf{a}_j \rangle. \qquad (5.5.25)$$

For the freely jointed chain, $\langle \mathbf{a}_i \cdot \mathbf{a}_j \rangle = 0$ for $j \neq i$ since there is no correlation between successive steps. Therefore, in that case, $\langle R^2 \rangle = na^2$, as noted previously in Eq. (5.5.22) for the long freely jointed chain, and as may be verified for Eqs. (5.5.17)–(5.5.19) describing short freely jointed chains. In the presence of valence angle restrictions and hindered rotation, $\langle \mathbf{a}_i \cdot \mathbf{a}_j \rangle \neq 0$ for $j \neq i$, but we may expect these quantities to be decreasing in magnitude with $|j - i|$ so that, for chains that are arbitrarily long, the infinite series $\sum_{j=i+1}^{\infty} \langle \mathbf{a}_i \cdot \mathbf{a}_j \rangle$ is convergent and independent of i. The persistence length h is then defined as

$$h = a^{-1} \sum_{j=1}^{\infty} \langle \mathbf{a}_0 \cdot \mathbf{a}_j \rangle, \qquad (5.5.26)$$

and represents the average projection on the direction of an arbitrary link $\mathbf{a}_0$ of the remainder of the chain to one side of it. This length is a convenient measure of the stiffness of the chain.

Kuhn Statistical Segments

We have seen that for sufficiently long freely jointed chains, the distribution $p(\mathbf{R})$ is Gaussian. The arguments used do not apply to chains with fixed bond angle or with hindered rotation since the steps in the random walks corresponding to the latter models are not independent. Nevertheless, the Gaussian distribution applies as well to sufficiently long model chains which incorporate these features. This can be seen by the following heuristic argument[19] due to Kuhn. Consider a chain of n links of length a. We regard the chain as composed of N segments with n/N links in each segment, and let $\mathbf{r}_\nu$, $\nu = 1, \ldots,$ N, be the end-to-end vector of the segment. If na/N is sufficiently large relative to h, the persistence length for the chain, then it is reasonable to regard the vectors $\mathbf{r}_\nu$ as independent displacements. It then follows from the central limit theorem that, for sufficiently large N, the end-to-end vector of the chain $\mathbf{R} = \sum_{\nu=1}^{N} \mathbf{r}_\nu$ will have a Gaussian distribution with

$$\langle R^2 \rangle = \sum_{\nu=1}^{N} \langle r_\nu^2 \rangle \triangleq nb^2 \qquad (5.5.27)$$

[19]For a more rigorous discussion see Flory (1969, pp. 309–313).

where

$$b \triangleq \left(\frac{1}{n} \langle R^2 \rangle \right)^{1/2} \tag{5.5.28}$$

is defined as the effective link length of the chain. The ratio $b/a = C_\infty$ is known as the limiting (for arbitrarily long chains) characteristic ratio of the chain. For a freely jointed chain we see that $C_\infty = 1$.

There exist experimental techniques[20] for the measurement of $\langle R^2 \rangle$ for macromolecules in solution and for the determination of the degree of polymerization. Therefore, the characteristic ratio for real chains can be estimated. In this way it is found[21] that $C_\infty \cong 6.7$ for polyethylene and it is clear that a freely jointed chain, for which $C_\infty = 1$, is far from a quantitative model for this molecule. For a freely rotating model, with bond angle corresponding to polyethylene, it is found that $C_\infty \cong 2$. With hindered rotation and an energy barrier that depends only on a single dihedral angle $C_\infty \cong 3$. It is necessary to consider rotational energies that are functions of two adjacent dihedral angles in order to arrive at a model for which $C_\infty \cong 7$.

Gaussian Chains

The preceding discussion has indicated that a succession of increasingly realistic models for long-chain molecules have probability distributions $p(\mathbf{R})$ for the end-to-end vector $\mathbf{R}$ which are Gaussian for sufficiently long chains,

$$p(\mathbf{R}) = \left(\frac{3}{2\pi nb^2} \right)^{3/2} \exp\left[-3R^2/(2nb^2) \right] \tag{5.5.29}$$

for a chain of n links, with b an effective link length, which is related to the actual link length in a manner that depends on the model characteristics. This type of model is referred to as a Gaussian chain. If we adopt a generalization of Eq. (5.4.14) to three-dimensional chains we can write its configurational entropy $S_q(\mathbf{R})$ as

$$S_q(\mathbf{R}) = k \log p(\mathbf{R}) = -\frac{3R^2 k}{2nb^2} \tag{5.5.30}$$

where we have made use of Eq. (5.5.29) and neglected a constant independent of $\mathbf{R}$. We shall consider the basis for the relation $S_q(\mathbf{R}) = k \log p(\mathbf{R})$ in greater detail in Section 6.7.

---

[20] See, for example, Flory (1953, Chapter VII).
[21] This discussion follows Richards (1980, pp. 78 et seq.). Further details will be found in Flory (1969, pp. 144–147).

Excluded Volume Effects

Thus far in our discussion of the interactions between portions of the chain, we have considered only those between neighboring side groups or between next-nearest neighbors. Because of the great length and flexibility of these molecules, however, there is the possibility that the chain will double back on itself and bring into close proximity portions of the chain which are far apart when the chain is fully extended. This possibility introduces additional complexities into the problem that are referred to as excluded volume or steric hindrance effects: two portions of the chain cannot occupy the same volume. In other terminology it leads to the class of problems called self-avoiding random walks. Inclusion of this effect into the analysis of polymer chains is difficult, leading to a non-Gaussian probability distribution, and is an active area of current research.[22]

5.6 NETWORK THEORY OF RUBBER ELASTICITY

The network theory of rubber elasticity had its beginnings in the 1930s with such work as that of Meyer, von Susich, and Valko (1932), Guth and Mark (1943), and Kuhn (1934). By about 1950, the theory had developed to a point where "it appeared to be capable of providing a quantitative explanation—at least to a first approximation—of the principal mechanical and other physical properties of rubber."[23] Although there were some systematic deviations between theory and experiment, it must have seemed at that time that minor refinements of the theory would serve to remove them. This has not proved to be the case. In spite of a great deal of effort in numerous directions, these discrepancies have not yet been resolved in a manner that is regarded as generally satisfactory and has achieved general acceptance.

We will confine ourselves here to presenting only the basic elementary theory of rubber elasticity. It may be regarded as the starting point for refinements in various directions.

Network description

We start with an amorphous network of cross-linked long-chain molecules (Figure 5.7). In the undeformed state the network is assumed to occupy a unit cube. It consists of N chains, $\nu = 1, \ldots, N$, each with n_ν links, and each link has effective length b (Section 5.5).

A number of simplifying assumptions of varying degrees of plausibility are made. The principal assumptions will be listed at the appropriate point in the

[22]See Barber and Ninham (1970) and de Gennes (1979) for a discussion of methods used in this research and the results obtained.
[23]Treloar (1976).

discussion. To begin with,

1 Assume that all chains are sufficiently long and far from full extension, both in the undeformed and in the deformed state, to be treated as Gaussian.[24]

2 Assume that the points of cross-linking between different chains, which we will refer to as nodes, do not participate in the thermal motion but only in the imposed deformation. The links of the chain between nodes, however, are in thermal motion.

Let $\mathbf{R}(\nu)$ be the end-to-end vector of the νth chain before deformation and let $\mathbf{r}(\nu)$ be the same vector after deformation (Figure 5.7). From Eq. (5.5.30) the entropy of the chain before and after deformation is (neglecting a constant which does not change with deformation)

$$S_\nu(\mathbf{R}(\nu)) = k \log p(\mathbf{R}(\nu)) = -\frac{3k}{2} \frac{R^2(\nu)}{n_\nu b^2}$$

$$S_\nu(\mathbf{r}(\nu)) = -\frac{3k}{2} \frac{r^2(\nu)}{n_\nu b^2} \tag{5.6.1}$$

so that its change in entropy is

$$\Delta S_\nu = -\frac{3k}{2n_\nu b^2}\left(r^2(\nu) - R^2(\nu)\right). \tag{5.6.2}$$

We next make the affine assumption, namely,

3 It is assumed that all of the nodes, those in the interior of the cube as well as those on its boundary, undergo the same affine transformation [see Eq. (1.2.25)] in going from the undeformed to the deformed state.

Let E_{LM} be the material strain tensor [Eq. (1.2.27)] corresponding to this affine transformation. Then, from Eq. (1.2.9),

$$r^2(\nu) - R^2(\nu) = 2E_{LM}R_L(\nu)R_M(\nu) \tag{5.6.3}$$

where $R_L(\nu)$ are the components of $\mathbf{R}(\nu)$. The total entropy of the network, $S(E_{LM})$, measured with respect to that of the undeformed network as reference, is

$$S(E_{NK}) = -\frac{3kE_{LM}}{b^2} \sum_{\nu=1}^{N} n_\nu^{-1} R_L(\nu) R_M(\nu)$$

$$= -kE_{LM}K_{LM}, \tag{5.6.4}$$

[24] Excluded-volume effects in each chain are neglected.

where

$$K_{LM} = \frac{3}{b^2} \sum_{\nu=1}^{N} n_\nu^{-1} R_L(\nu) R_M(\nu). \qquad (5.6.5)$$

The tensor K_{LM} is a property of the undeformed network.

4 It is assumed that the undeformed network is, from the macroscopic viewpoint, homogeneous and isotropic.

It follows that K_{LM} must be an isotropic tensor,[25] that is,

$$K_{LM} = K\delta_{LM} \qquad (5.6.6)$$

so that $K = \frac{1}{3}K_{LL}$ or

$$K = \frac{1}{b^2} \sum_{\nu=1}^{N} n_\nu^{-1} R_L(\nu) R_L(\nu)$$

$$= \frac{1}{b^2} \sum_{\nu=1}^{N} n_\nu^{-1} R^2(\nu) \qquad (5.6.7)$$

and

$$S(E_{NK}) = -kKE_{LL}. \qquad (5.6.8)$$

Evaluation of K

Since the constant K describes the original undeformed network, its value will depend on the details of the cross-linking process. We consider next an idealized picture, which leads to a simple calculation of K. Begin with a set of non-cross-linked long-chain molecules in thermal motion in proximity to each other. For example, they may all be in solution in some suitable solvent.

5 It is assumed that all of the cross-links occur simultaneously between a set of points on different chains which are adjacent at the cross-linking instant.

We consider the points on the individual chains at which cross-linking occurs to be identifiable prior to cross-linking, at least conceptually, and in this way we can speak of the N chains prior to the cross-linking instant as well as after it. We now assume that this collection of N chains may be subdivided

---

[25] See, for example, Jeffreys (1931).

into m groups, each group containing c_α chains of n_α links, $\alpha = 1, \ldots, m$ and with end-to-end distance $R(p, \alpha)$, $p = 1, \ldots, c_\alpha$. Then,

$$K = \frac{1}{b^2} \sum_{\alpha=1}^{m} n_\alpha^{-1} \sum_{p=1}^{c_\alpha} R^2(p, \alpha).$$ (5.6.9)

Prior to cross-linking, $R^2(p, \alpha)$ is a fluctuating quantity. If the cross-linking occurs simultaneously at a random instant, then the values of $R^2(p, \alpha)$, $p = 1, \ldots, c_\alpha$, will be drawn from a Gaussian distribution with variance $n_\alpha b^2$ and we may expect that

$$\sum_{p=1}^{c_\alpha} R^2(p, \alpha) = c_\alpha n_\alpha b^2$$ (5.6.10)

and therefore[26]

$$K = N.$$ (5.6.11)

Under these assumptions, Eq. (5.6.8) becomes

$$S(E_{NK}) = -kNE_{LL}.$$ (5.6.12)

It will also be convenient to express the entropy per unit original volume in terms of the principal stretches λ_L, $L = 1, 2, 3$, by use of Eq. (1.10.15),

$$S(\lambda_1, \lambda_2, \lambda_3) = -\frac{kN}{2} \sum_{L=1}^{3} \left(\lambda_L^2 - 1 \right).$$ (5.6.13)

Internal Energy

Thus far, we have not included in our model any interactions between the chains of the network. Empirically, we know that rubber and rubberlike solids are nearly incompressible and presumably this is a consequence of chain–chain interactions. In some treatments of the network theory, incompressibility is introduced as an *a priori* geometric constraint. A somewhat clearer approach[27]

[26] This method of evaluating K is due to James and Guth (1947); this paper also presents a critique of the assumption of simultaneous cross-link formation and considers the effect of successive bond formation. Flory (1976) has presented a treatment in which assumption 5 is replaced by a quantitative characterization of the topology of the network using concepts of graph theory. This analysis replaces Eq. (5.6.11) by $K = CN$, where C is a constant determined by the topology and has a value of order unity. See also Graessley (1975) and Pearson and Graessley (1978) for more detailed treatments of network topology.
[27] James and Guth (1949). See also Boggs (1952) and Eichinger (1981) for other treatments of chain–chain interactions.

is to make the following assumption:

6 In addition to the entropy change upon deformation, there is a change in internal energy, $U(v, T)$, which depends only on the resulting volume change. Therefore, the change in free energy per unit volume is

$$F(\lambda_1, \lambda_2, \lambda_3, T) = U(v, T) + \frac{NkT}{2} \sum_{L=1}^{3} (\lambda_L^2 - 1) \quad (5.6.14)$$

where

$$v = \lambda_1 \lambda_2 \lambda_3 \quad (5.6.15)$$

is the volume after deformation of the original unit cube (Eq. 1.10.12).

Stress – Strain Relations

By application of Eq. (1.10.24),

$$T_L = \frac{\partial F}{\partial \lambda_L} \quad (5.6.16)$$

where T_L are the normal components of the Piola–Kirchhoff stress tensor T_{iL} as discussed in Section 1.10. That is, T_L is the normal force per unit original area acting on the face normal to X_L, a principal direction of the deformation. Furthermore, as a consequence of the fact that the network is initially isotropic, T_L are the only nonzero components of T_{iL}. Therefore,

$$T_1 = \frac{\partial U}{\partial v} \lambda_2 \lambda_3 + G\lambda_1 \quad (5.6.17)$$

$$T_2 = \frac{\partial U}{\partial v} \lambda_3 \lambda_1 + G\lambda_2 \quad (5.6.18)$$

$$T_3 = \frac{\partial U}{\partial v} \lambda_1 \lambda_2 + G\lambda_3 \quad (5.6.19)$$

where

$$G = NkT. \quad (5.6.20)$$

Uniaxial Tension

Consider a state of uniaxial tension in the X_3 direction:

$$T_1 = T_2 = 0, \quad \lambda_1 = \lambda_2.$$

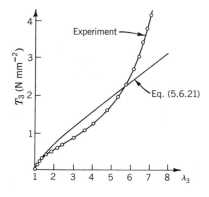

Figure 5.11 Comparison of theory, Eq. (5.6.21), and experiment for uniaxial tension of rubber at room temperature. The value of G in Eq. (5.6.21), $G = 0.39$ N mm^{-2} has been chosen to produce agreement with experiment for small extensions. (After Treloar, 1975, with permission.)

From Eqs. (5.6.17) and (5.6.15), the condition that $T_1 = 0$ implies that in this case,

$$\frac{\partial U}{\partial v} = \frac{-G\lambda_1}{\lambda_2\lambda_3} = \frac{-G}{\lambda_3} = \frac{-Gv}{\lambda_1\lambda_2\lambda_3^2}$$

and Eq. (5.6.19) becomes

$$T_3 = G\left(\lambda_3 - \frac{v}{\lambda_3^2}\right) \cong G\left(\lambda_3 - \frac{1}{\lambda_3^2}\right), \qquad (5.6.21)$$

where as a further approximation, we have set $v = 1$ based on empirical observation.

The stress–strain behavior of Eq. (5.6.21) is compared with experiment in Figure 5.11. The divergence between theory and experiment at large strain is not unexpected, although there is still disagreement as to its cause. Treloar (1976) traces the discrepancy to the Gaussian chain assumption, which is expected to lose accuracy as the chains approach full extension. Flory (1976), on the other hand, believes that before this happens, strain-induced crystallization will occur and it is this process that causes the observed stress to rise.

A more puzzling discrepancy between theory and experiment is that occurring in the range $2 < \lambda_3 < 5$, a region in which the Gaussian chain assumption should be accurate.[28] A great deal of effort has been expended to explain this discrepancy and to develop theories that agree better with experiment, but thus far there are no definitive and broadly accepted results. For further discussions of comparisons between theory and experiment and of more recent theoretical developments we refer to Treloar (1975, 1976) and Flory (1976, 1977b).

---

[28] This discrepancy is sometimes called the Mooney effect.

CHAPTER SIX

Rubber Elasticity, II

6.1 INTRODUCTION

In the previous chapter we presented an elementary account of the theory of rubber elasticity. We return in the present chapter to a deeper consideration of some aspects of the subject. The questions we will be concerned with include the statistical mechanical basis for the use of the relation $S = k \log p$ for stretched polymers, a relation that played a key role in Chapter 5, and a reexamination of some of the assumptions made in the discussion of the network theory of rubber elasticity in Section 5.6.

In order to treat these questions, it is necessary to describe polymer chain models in terms of appropriate curvilinear coordinate systems. The formulation of the laws of mechanics of a system of particles in terms of curvilinear coordinates is developed in general terms in Sections 6.2–6.4, while in Section 6.5 we introduce specific coordinate systems useful for the study of polymer chains. An important aspect of these molecules, as we have seen in Chapter 5, is the strong covalent bonds that require large energy changes to vary bond lengths and bond angles. There are two distinct ways of mathematically describing these bonds: In the first, referred to as rigid models, fixed bond lengths are imposed as geometric constraints in the Hamiltonian of the model. In the second, referred to as flexible models, these bond lengths are kept nearly constant by means of stiff linear springs with a spring constant that is allowed to become arbitrarily large after the partition function is computed. Bond angles may be treated similarly. The distinction between the two classes of models is discussed in Section 6.6. We can then turn, in Section 6.7, to the question of the use of the relation $S = k \log p$ for deriving the force–length relation for a stretched polymer and demonstrate that it is valid only when flexible models are employed.

As examples of these general principles, we consider the force–length relation for short freely jointed chains on the basis of a strain ensemble in Section 6.8 and, for chains of arbitrary length, on the basis of a stress ensemble in Section 6.9. We shall see, in Section 6.8, that although rigid and flexible models appear very similar on the basis of physical intuition, they can lead to strikingly different force–length relations.

Finally, in Section 6.10 we consider the statistical mechanics of a flexible model of a phantom network,[1] that is, a network in which excluded volume effects are neglected and there is no interaction between the atoms of different chains so that, in effect, chains may pass through each other.

6.2   CURVILINEAR COORDINATES[2]

Consider a system of N particles free of any geometric constraints. Denote the position of the first by its coordinates y^1, y^2, y^3 with respect to a rectangular Cartesian coordinate system, the position of the second with respect to the same coordinate system by y^4, y^5, y^6, etc. Similarly, the mass of the first particle is denoted by $m_1 = m_2 = m_3$, the mass of the second by $m_4 = m_5 = m_6$, etc. Then, the kinetic energy K of the system is

$$K = \frac{1}{2} \sum_{i=1}^{n} m_i (\dot{y}^i)^2, \tag{6.2.1}$$

where $n = 3N$. Introduce mass-reduced coordinates

$$x^i = (m_i)^{1/2} y^i \text{ (no sum)}. \tag{6.2.2}$$

The kinetic energy may now be written as

$$K = \tfrac{1}{2} \delta_{ij} \dot{x}^i \dot{x}^j \tag{6.2.3}$$

where the summation convention $i, j = 1, \ldots, n$ over pairs (one upper and one lower) of repeated indices is employed.

Let $\mathbf{e}_i$ be a set of constant orthonormal vectors tangent to the coordinate lines x^i. In terms of them, we may denote the position of the system in configuration space by the n-dimensional vector $\mathbf{r} = x^i \mathbf{e}_i$. We will also use the notation $\mathbf{e}^i = \mathbf{e}_i$ for these base vectors.

We next introduce into configuration space a curvilinear coordinate system q^i defined by

$$q^i = q^i (x^1, \ldots, x^n) \tag{6.2.4}$$

---

[1] The term is due to Flory (1976).
[2] The reader to whom this material is unfamiliar may find it helpful to follow the simple example of Section 6.4 concurrently with Sections 6.2 and 6.3. For additional background reading see Green and Zerna (1954, Chapter 1) and Lichnerowicz (1962, Chapter 6).

with single-valued inverse functions

$$x^i = x^i(q^1, \ldots, q^n). \qquad (6.2.5)$$

Define the vector fields $\mathbf{g}_r(q), \mathbf{g}^r(q), q = (q^1, \ldots, q^n)$, as

$$\mathbf{g}_r = \frac{\partial x^i}{\partial q^r} \mathbf{e}_i, \qquad \mathbf{g}^r = \frac{\partial q^r}{\partial x^i} \mathbf{e}^i. \qquad (6.2.6)$$

They are referred to, respectively, as the covariant and contravariant base vectors of the q^i coordinate system. This system of nomenclature is followed consistently: quantities with all lower indices are termed covariant, quantities with all upper indices are termed contravariant. The base vectors for the rectangular coordinate system $x^i, \mathbf{e}_i = \mathbf{e}^i$, form a constant orthonormal set. In contrast to these, the set of covariant base vectors $\mathbf{g}_r(q)$ for a curvilinear coordinate system will, in general, vary with position and be neither unit vectors nor mutually orthogonal. Similar comments apply to the set of contravariant base vectors $\mathbf{g}^s(q)$. As a mnemonic device for Eqs. (6.2.6), note that pairs of free indices (e.g., r) refer to the same coordinate system and one member of each pair appears on the same level (i.e., either as upper or lower) on both sides of the equation; similarly, pairs of bound indices (one upper and one lower, e.g., i) appear on the same side of the equation and refer to the same coordinate system. This practice is followed throughout.

The equation of the q^r coordinate line through the point with coordinates $q = (q^1, \ldots, q^n)$ is obtained from Eq. (6.2.5) by regarding q^r as a variable parameter with all of the other q^i fixed at their values at q. It then follows from the first of Eqs. (6.2.6) that $\mathbf{g}_r(q)$ is tangent to the q^r line through q (Figure 6.1).

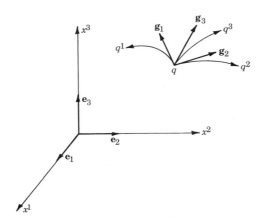

Figure 6.1 Curvilinear coordinate system.

It also follows from Eq. (6.2.6) that

$$\mathbf{g}^s \cdot \mathbf{g}_r = \frac{\partial q^s}{\partial x^i} \frac{\partial x^j}{\partial q^r} \mathbf{e}^i \cdot \mathbf{e}_j = \frac{\partial q^s}{\partial x^i} \frac{\partial x^j}{\partial q^r} \delta^i_j = \frac{\partial q^s}{\partial x^i} \frac{\partial x^i}{\partial q^r} = \frac{\partial q^s}{\partial q^r} = \delta^s_r. \quad (6.2.7)$$

Therefore, the contravariant base vector $\mathbf{g}^s(q)$ is orthogonal to all the covariant base vectors $\mathbf{g}_r(q)$ for which $r \neq s$. (Note that it cannot be concluded from Eq. (6.2.7) that $\mathbf{g}^s(q)$ is parallel to $\mathbf{g}_r(q)$ for $r = s$ since these are not unit vectors and, in general, these vectors are not parallel.)

Metric Tensor

The distance ds corresponding to a displacement dx^i is

$$(ds)^2 = \delta_{ij} dx^i dx^j. \quad (6.2.8)$$

The same displacement may be expressed in terms of the q^i coordinate system by use of Eq. (6.2.5) as $dx^i = (\partial x^i / \partial q^r) dq^r$ so that

$$(ds)^2 = \delta_{ij} \frac{\partial x^i}{\partial q^r} \frac{\partial x^j}{\partial q^s} dq^r dq^s = g_{rs} dq^r dq^s \quad (6.2.9)$$

where

$$g_{rs} = \delta_{ij} \frac{\partial x^i}{\partial q^r} \frac{\partial x^j}{\partial q^s} \quad (6.2.10)$$

is the covariant metric tensor for the q^i coordinate system. Similarly,

$$g^{rs} = \delta^{ij} \frac{\partial q^r}{\partial x^i} \frac{\partial q^s}{\partial x^j} \quad (6.2.11)$$

is termed the contravariant metric tensor. It follows from Eqs. (6.2.10) and (6.2.11) that

$$g^{rs} g_{st} = \delta^r_t, \quad (6.2.12)$$

and, from Eq. (6.2.6), that

$$g_{rs} = \mathbf{g}_r \cdot \mathbf{g}_s, \qquad g^{rs} = \mathbf{g}^r \cdot \mathbf{g}^s. \quad (6.2.13)$$

Volume Elements

Consider a set of n linearly independent vectors $\mathbf{f}_r$, which, in terms of the rectangular Cartesian base vectors $\mathbf{e}_i$, may be written $\mathbf{f}_r = f^i_r \mathbf{e}_i$. The n-dimensional volume, v, of the parallelepiped with these vectors as edges is defined as the determinant,

$$v = |f_r^i|, \tag{6.2.14}$$

with the understanding here, and in what follows, that the ordering of the vectors is chosen to make this determinant positive. Clearly this definition is consistent with the concepts of length (in which case the determinant is interpreted as absolute value), area, and volume for spaces of dimension $n = 1$, 2, and 3, respectively.

It follows from the rules for the multiplication of determinants that

$$|\mathbf{f}_r \cdot \mathbf{f}_s| = |\delta_{ij} f_r^i f_s^j| = |f_r^i|^2, \tag{6.2.15}$$

so that

$$v = |\mathbf{f}_r \cdot \mathbf{f}_s|^{1/2}. \tag{6.2.16}$$

Replacement of the vectors $\mathbf{f}_r$ by $a_r \mathbf{f}_r$ (no sum) with $a_r > 0$, results, as seen from Eq. (6.2.14), in a parallelepiped of volume v',

$$v' = v a_1 \cdots a_n. \tag{6.2.17}$$

Therefore, the volume element dv corresponding to the n differential displacements $dq^r \mathbf{g}_r$ (no sum), is

$$dv = |\mathbf{g}_r \cdot \mathbf{g}_s|^{1/2} dq^1 \cdots dq^n = |g_{rs}|^{1/2} dq^1 \cdots dq^n, \tag{6.2.18}$$

where Eq. (6.2.13) has been employed. Since, from Eq. (6.2.12),

$$|g_{rs}| = |g^{rs}|^{-1}, \tag{6.2.19}$$

we may also write

$$dv = |g^{rs}|^{-1/2} dq^1 \cdots dq^n. \tag{6.2.20}$$

Note that it follows from Eq. (6.2.10) that

$$|g_{rs}| = \left| \frac{\partial x^i}{\partial q^r} \right|^2, \tag{6.2.21}$$

so that Eq. (6.2.18) also may be put in the form

$$dv = \left| \frac{\partial x^j}{\partial q^r} \right| dq^1 \cdots dq^n \tag{6.2.22}$$

in accord with the usual Jacobian procedure.

Generalized Momenta

Given an (n-dimensional) vector $\mathbf{F}$. It may be expressed in terms of the base vectors $\mathbf{g}_r(q)$ or $\mathbf{g}^r(q)$ at a given point q as

$$\mathbf{F} = F^r\mathbf{g}_r = F_s\mathbf{g}^s; \qquad (6.2.23)$$

that is, the same vector $\mathbf{F}$ can be expressed in terms of either its contravariant components F^r or covariant components F_s. From Eqs. (6.2.7), and (6.2.13),

$$F_r = g_{rs}F^s, \qquad F^r = g^{rs}F_s, \qquad (6.2.24)$$

a process referred to as lowering and raising indices by means of the metric tensor.

Consider next the motion of the system in configuration space described by the equations $x^i(t)$ in terms of the rectangular cartesian coordinate system x^i or by the equations $q^i(t)$ in terms of the curvilinear coordinate system q^i. Then, from Eq. (6.2.5),

$$\dot{x}^i = \frac{\partial x^i}{\partial q^r}\dot{q}^r \qquad (6.2.25)$$

and the kinetic energy K of Eq. (6.2.3) takes the form

$$K = \tfrac{1}{2}g_{rs}\dot{q}^r\dot{q}^s \qquad (6.2.26)$$

in the q^r system, where we have used Eq. (6.2.10).

The generalized momentum p_r associated with the coordinate q^r is defined as

$$p_r = \frac{\partial K}{\partial \dot{q}^r} = g_{rs}\dot{q}^s \qquad (6.2.27)$$

and, by use of Eq. (6.2.12), it follows that

$$\dot{q}^r = g^{rs}p_s. \qquad (6.2.28)$$

Therefore, from the differential geometry viewpoint, $\dot{q}^r$ and p_r are the contravariant and covariant components of the same vector $\mathbf{v}$, the system velocity; that is,

$$\mathbf{v} = \dot{q}^s\mathbf{g}_s = p_r\mathbf{g}^r = \mathbf{p} \qquad (6.2.29)$$

where, in the final form of the equation, we have noted that with mass-reduced coordinates the system velocity $\mathbf{v}$ is equal to the system momentum $\mathbf{p}$. By use of Eqs. (6.2.26), (6.2.28) and (6.2.12) the kinetic energy can be expressed in terms of the momenta as

$$K = \tfrac{1}{2}g^{rs}p_rp_s. \qquad (6.2.30)$$

6.3   GEOMETRIC CONSTRAINTS

In the preceding section we treated a system of N particles moving in a configuration space of $n = 3N$ dimensions. Since there were no geometric constraints, we could describe its motion equally well in terms of rectangular Cartesian coordinates x^i or curvilinear coordinates q^i.

We now consider the imposition of time-independent geometric constraints, which confine the system to an f-dimensional subspace, $f < n$. For this purpose we choose an appropriate curvilinear coordinate system q^i, $i = 1, \ldots, n$, for the full n-dimensional space so that the degrees of freedom of the system are described by q^α, $\alpha = 1, \ldots, f$, and the geometric constraints are described by the equations[3]

$$q^A = q^A(x^1, \ldots, x^n) = 0, \qquad A = f + 1, \ldots, N. \qquad (6.3.1)$$

In the following discussion the range of indices of the three types just introduced will consistently have the indicated range, that is

$$i, j, \ldots = 1, \ldots, n$$

$$\alpha, \beta, \ldots = 1, \ldots, f$$

$$A, B, \ldots = f + 1, \ldots, N$$

and repeated indices will imply summation over the appropriate range, for example,

$$g^{i\alpha}g_{\alpha j} = \sum_{\alpha=1}^{f} g^{i\alpha}g_{\alpha j}, \qquad g^{iA}g_{Aj} = \sum_{A=f+1}^{N} g^{iA}g_{Aj}.$$

Consider the f-dimensional subspace consisting of points $q' = (q^1, \ldots, q^f, 0, \ldots, 0)$; for brevity we will refer to this subspace as the α-space and the full space as the i-space. By considering a differential displacement dq^α in the α-space and paralleling the derivation of Eqs. (6.2.8)–(6.2.10), we see that the covariant metric tensor $g_{\alpha\beta}$ for the α-space is

$$g_{\alpha\beta} = \delta_{ij}\frac{\partial x^i}{\partial q^\alpha}\frac{\partial x^j}{\partial q^\beta} \qquad (6.3.2)$$

with the partial derivatives evaluated at $q' = (q^1, \ldots, q^f, 0, \ldots, 0)$. That is, the covariant metric tensor $g_{\alpha\beta}$ for the α-space is obtained from the covariant metric tensor g_{rs} for the i-space, Eq. (6.2.10), simply by restricting the range of the indices and evaluating the remaining components for $q^A \equiv 0$.

---

[3]Constraints expressible in the form of Eq. (6.3.1) are described as holonomic. We are employing the notation for the different coordinate classes used by Rallison (1979) in his study of the treatment of constraints in polymer models.

However, the definition of the contravariant metric tensor for the α-space which is appropriate for the description of the dynamics of the constrained system requires more care. The system velocity $\mathbf{v}(q')$ of the constrained system at q' takes the form

$$\mathbf{v}(q') = \dot{q}^{\alpha}\mathbf{g}_{\alpha}(q'),\qquad (6.3.3)$$

that is, $\mathbf{v}(q')$ lies in the f-dimensional vector space spanned by the covariant base vectors $\mathbf{g}_{\alpha}(q')$. The contravariant base vectors $\mathbf{g}^{\alpha}(q')$ will also span an f-dimensional vector space, but one which differs, in general,[4] from that spanned by the vectors $\mathbf{g}_{\alpha}(q')$; a simple example is shown in Figure 6.2. Therefore, it is not possible to express the system velocity $\mathbf{v}$ solely as a linear combination of the $\mathbf{g}^{\alpha}(q')$, but the other contravariant vectors $\mathbf{g}^{A}(q')$ must be used as well. As seen in Section 6.2, the covariant components of $\mathbf{v}$ are the system's generalized momenta; therefore, if we wish a Hamiltonian formulation expressed solely in terms of the α-space, it is necessary to introduce a new set of contravariant base vectors, $\bar{\mathbf{g}}^{\alpha}$, which span the same vector space as do the covariant base vectors $\mathbf{g}_{\alpha}$ at the same point q'. That is, we define the $\bar{\mathbf{g}}^{\alpha}$ to be linear combinations of the $\mathbf{g}_{\alpha}$,

$$\bar{\mathbf{g}}^{\alpha} = \bar{g}^{\alpha\beta}\mathbf{g}_{\beta}\qquad (6.3.4)$$

which satisfy the orthogonality condition required of contravariant base vectors, namely

$$\bar{\mathbf{g}}^{\alpha} \cdot \mathbf{g}_{\beta} = \delta_{\beta}^{\alpha}.\qquad (6.3.5)$$

It follows from these equations and Eq. (6.2.13) that at any q'

$$\bar{g}^{\alpha\beta}g_{\beta\gamma} = \delta_{\gamma}^{\alpha}.\qquad (6.3.6)$$

Therefore, $\bar{g}^{\alpha\beta}$, which we will refer to as the intrinsic[5] contravariant metric tensor for the α-space, bears the same inverse relation to the covariant metric tensor $g_{\alpha\beta}$ as does g^{ij} to g_{ij}, Eq. (6.2.12). Note, however, that it follows from the latter equation that

$$g^{\alpha\beta}g_{\beta\gamma} = \delta_{\gamma}^{\alpha} - g^{\alpha A}g_{A\gamma}\qquad (6.3.7)$$

so that, in general, $g^{\alpha\beta} \neq \bar{g}^{\alpha\beta}$.

---

[4] The exception occurs for orthogonal curvilinear coordinate systems.

[5] In the usual discussion of the intrinsic geometry of the α-space which is made without reference to the i-space in which it is embedded, the intrinsic contravariant metric tensor is introduced *ab initio* by means of Eq. (6.3.6), and the superposed bar is omitted. We retain the bar here, and in subsequent discussions where the distinction is needed.

The kinetic energy of the constrained system is

$$K = \tfrac{1}{2} g_{\alpha\beta} \dot{q}^{\alpha} \dot{q}^{\beta}. \tag{6.3.8}$$

This follows directly from Eq. (6.2.26) since $\dot{q}^{A} \equiv 0$ for the constrained system. The corresponding momenta p_{α} are

$$p_{\alpha} = \frac{\partial K}{\partial \dot{q}^{\alpha}} = g_{\alpha\beta} \dot{q}^{\beta} \tag{6.3.9}$$

and, by use of Eq. (6.3.6),

$$\dot{q}^{\alpha} = \bar{g}^{\alpha\beta} p_{\beta}. \tag{6.3.10}$$

Therefore, the kinetic energy of the constrained system may be written in terms of the momenta p_{α} as

$$K = \tfrac{1}{2} \bar{g}^{\alpha\beta} p_{\alpha} p_{\beta} \tag{6.3.11}$$

and the Hamiltonian $H(q^{\alpha}, p_{\beta})$ for a system constrained to move in α-space can be written

$$H(q^{\alpha}, p_{\beta}) = \tfrac{1}{2} \bar{g}^{\alpha\beta} p_{\alpha} p_{\beta} + V(q^{1}, \ldots, q^{f}). \tag{6.3.12}$$

Note that generalized momenta p_{i} for the constrained system could also have been derived from Eq. (6.2.26) (with $\dot{q}^{A} \equiv 0$) as

$$p_{i} = \frac{\partial K}{\partial \dot{q}^{i}} = g_{i\beta} \dot{q}^{\beta} \tag{6.3.13}$$

and that $p_{i} = p_{\alpha}$, as given in Eq. (6.3.9), for $i = \alpha = 1, \ldots, f$. However, it follows from Eq. (6.3.13) that p_{i} ($i = 1, \ldots, n$) are the covariant components of $\mathbf{v}$ with respect to the $\mathbf{g}^{i}$ base vectors, whereas p_{α} ($\alpha = 1, \ldots, f$) are the covariant components with respect to the $\bar{\mathbf{g}}^{\alpha}$ base vectors. That is

$$\mathbf{v} = p_{i} \mathbf{g}^{i} = p_{\alpha} \bar{\mathbf{g}}^{\alpha} \tag{6.3.14}$$

but $\mathbf{v} \neq p_{\alpha} \mathbf{g}^{\alpha}$. This point is illustrated in the simple example of Section 6.4. We may say, therefore, that the momenta p_{A} corresponding to the constrained coordinates q^{A} must be included[6] in a description of the motion of the constrained system only if this description is made in terms of the geometry of the full i-space, that is, in terms of the contravariant base vectors $\mathbf{g}^{i}$ and the contravariant metric tensor g^{ij}. The momenta p_{A} may be ignored if the

---

[6] For related discussions of this question see Brillouin (1964, p. 231), Fixman (1974), and Helfand (1979).

description of the motion of the constrained system is made in terms of the intrinsic geometry of the α-space, that is, in terms of the contravariant base vectors $\bar{\mathbf{g}}^\alpha$ and the intrinsic contravariant metric tensor $\bar{g}^{\alpha\beta}$.

Fixman's Relation[7]

A useful relation between the determinants of various restrictions of the metric tensors g_{ij} and g^{ij} may be derived as follows. Equation (6.2.12), namely,

$$g^{rs}g_{st} = \delta_t^r,$$

implies the following two equations:

$$g_{\alpha k}g^{kA} = g_{\alpha\beta}g^{\beta A} + g_{\alpha C}g^{CA} = 0 \qquad (6.3.15)$$

and

$$g_{Ai}g^{iB} = g_{A\alpha}g^{\alpha B} + g_{AC}g^{CB} = \delta_A^B. \qquad (6.3.16)$$

These equations, in turn, lead to the following matrix equation:

$$\begin{pmatrix} g_{\alpha\beta} & \vline & g_{\alpha B} \\ \hline g_{A\beta} & \vline & g_{AB} \end{pmatrix} \begin{pmatrix} \delta^{\alpha\beta} & \vline & g^{\alpha B} \\ \hline 0^{A\beta} & \vline & g^{AB} \end{pmatrix} = \begin{pmatrix} g_{\alpha\beta} & \vline & 0_\alpha^A \\ \hline g_{A\beta} & \vline & \delta_A^B \end{pmatrix} \qquad (6.3.17)$$

where the dimensions of the blocks of the partitioned matrices are indicated by the types of indices and where $0^{A\beta}$ indicates a $c \times f$ matrix ($c = n - f$) with all zero entries, etc. It then follows by taking the determinants of both sides of Eq. (6.3.17) that

$$|g_{ij}||g^{AB}| = |g_{\alpha\beta}|. \qquad (6.3.18)$$

Volume Elements

The volume element $(dv)_\alpha$ for α-space is the volume of the parallelepiped based on the vectors $dq^\alpha \mathbf{g}_\alpha$ (no sum). By the same analysis that led to Eq. (6.2.18),

$$(dv)_\alpha = |\mathbf{g}_\alpha \cdot \mathbf{g}_\beta|^{1/2}dq^1 \cdots dq^f = |g_{\alpha\beta}|^{1/2}dq^1 \cdots dq^f. \qquad (6.3.19)$$

Similarly $(dv)_A$, the volume element for A space is

$$(dv)_A = |g_{AB}|^{1/2}dq^{f+1} \cdots dq^n. \qquad (6.3.20)$$

---

[7]Fixman (1974).

Note that since in general $|g_{AB}| \neq |g^{AB}|^{-1}$, it follows from Fixman's relation, Eq. (6.3.18), that

$$|g_{ij}| \neq |g_{\alpha\beta}||g_{AB}| \tag{6.3.21}$$

and

$$dv \neq (dv)_\alpha (dv)_A \tag{6.3.22}$$

where dv is the volume element of the full i-space as given in Eq. (6.2.18). This inequality is a consequence of the fact that at a given point q' the sets of vectors $\mathbf{g}_\alpha$ and $\mathbf{g}_A$ span vector spaces which are not mutually orthogonal.

6.4 AN EXAMPLE

We present here a simple example to illustrate some of the concepts of the previous two sections. It is based on a two-dimensional configuration space ($n = 2$) with rectangular Cartesian reduced-mass coordinates x^i. We introduce a new coordinate system[8] q^i

$$q^1 = x^1$$

$$q^2 = x^1 + x^2 \tag{6.2.4'}$$

with inverse

$$x^1 = q^1$$

$$x^2 = q^2 - q^1. \tag{6.2.5'}$$

Then, the covariant base vectors are

$$\mathbf{g}_1 = \frac{\partial x^r}{\partial q^1} \mathbf{e}_r = \mathbf{e}_1 - \mathbf{e}_2$$

$$\mathbf{g}_2 = \frac{\partial x^r}{\partial q^2} \mathbf{e}_r = \mathbf{e}_2 \tag{6.2.6'}$$

and the contravariant base vectors are

$$\mathbf{g}^1 = \frac{\partial q^1}{\partial x^r} \mathbf{e}^r = \mathbf{e}^1$$

$$\mathbf{g}^2 = \frac{\partial q^2}{\partial x^r} \mathbf{e}^r = \mathbf{e}^1 + \mathbf{e}^2. \tag{6.2.6'}$$

---

[8] This particular q^i system remains Cartesian with constant base vectors. However, it is nonorthogonal and serves to illustrate this important aspect of general curvilinear coordinate systems. The notation for equation numbers such as (6.2.4') indicates the general equation to which the example refers.

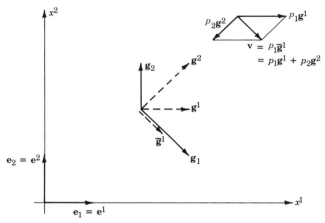

Figure 6.2   Example of system subjected to a geometric constraint.

The various base vectors are shown in Figure 6.2. The metric tensors are

$$(g_{ij}) = \begin{pmatrix} 2 & -1 \\ -1 & 1 \end{pmatrix}; \qquad (g^{ij}) = \begin{pmatrix} 1 & 1 \\ 1 & 2 \end{pmatrix} \qquad (6.2.13')$$

and it is readily verified that they satisfy Eq. (6.2.12).

We next assume that the system is subject to the constraint $q^2 = 0$. That is, in the notation of Section 6.3, $\alpha = 1$ and $A = 2$ and both α-space and A-space are one-dimensional. From Eq. (6.2.13')

$$g_{\alpha\beta} = g_{11} = 2$$

and therefore

$$\bar{g}^{\alpha\beta} = \bar{g}^{11} = \tfrac{1}{2} \qquad (6.3.5')$$

and

$$\bar{g}^{\alpha} = \bar{g}^1 = \tfrac{1}{2}g_1. \qquad (6.3.4')$$

The system velocity in α-space is of the form

$$\mathbf{v} = \dot{q}^{\alpha}\mathbf{g}_{\alpha} = \dot{q}^1\mathbf{g}_1.$$

The system momenta are

$$p_{\alpha} = p_1 = g_{11}\dot{q}^1 = 2\dot{q}^1 \qquad (6.3.9')$$

and

$$p_A = p_2 = g_{21}\dot{q}^1 = -\dot{q}^1. \qquad (6.3.13')$$

Therefore, the system velocity **v** can be written alternatively as

$$\mathbf{v} = p_i \mathbf{g}^i = 2\dot{q}^1 \mathbf{g}^1 - \dot{q}^1 \mathbf{g}^2 \qquad (6.3.14')$$

or

$$\mathbf{v} = p_\alpha \bar{\mathbf{g}}^\alpha = 2\dot{q}^1 \bar{\mathbf{g}}^1.$$

The two vector sums leading to **v** are illustrated in Figure 6.2.

We consider finally the relations among the metric determinants for this example. From Eq. (6.2.13'),

$$|g_{ij}| = 1, |g_{\alpha\beta}| = |g_{11}| = 2, |g^{AB}| = |g^{22}| = 2$$

so that Fixman's relation, Eq. (6.3.18), is satisfied. Note also that

$$|g_{AB}| = |g_{22}| = 1 \neq |g^{22}|^{-1} = |g^{AB}|^{-1} = 1/2.$$

6.5 CURVILINEAR COORDINATES FOR STRESSED POLYMER CHAINS

We consider next curvilinear coordinate systems that are convenient for the analysis of stressed polymer chains, that is, either chains with imposed end-to-end vector (strain ensemble) or chains with imposed forces on their end atoms (stress ensemble).

In our discussion of the strain ensemble, we will consider a chain of atoms $l = 0, 1, \ldots, N, N + 1$. Let $\mathbf{x}_l$ denote the position of the lth atom with respect to a fixed reference frame with $\mathbf{x}_0 = 0$ and $\mathbf{x}_{N+1} = \mathbf{r}$, where $\mathbf{r}$ is the prescribed end-to-end vector. In our discussion of the stress ensemble, we will consider a chain of atoms $l = 0, 1, \ldots, N$ with $\mathbf{x}_0 = 0$ and with the Nth atom subjected to a prescribed force $\mathbf{f}$ while its position $\mathbf{x}_N$ can fluctuate.[9]

Therefore, in both cases, we have N atoms subject to thermal motion which, in the absence of constraints, requires an $n = 3N$-dimensional configuration space for its description. The curvilinear coordinates to be introduced into this space must contain, as a subset, those that correspond to the desired constraints. Therefore, different curvilinear coordinate systems will be required for the analysis of a chain with only one fixed end, and for the analysis of a chain with both ends fixed.

---

[9]Looking ahead, the distinction we are making here between coordinate systems which are convenient for the strain and stress ensembles, respectively, applies only to rigid models, in the terminology of Section 6.6. As we shall see, in our analysis of the strain ensemble for flexible models, we shall frequently make use, in intermediate stages of the analysis, of the coordinate system developed here for the case of only one end of the chain fixed.

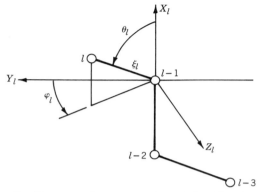

Figure 6.3   Curvilinear coordinate system for a chain with only one end fixed.

Curvilinear Coordinates for a Chain with One Fixed End[10]

For simplicity, we assume that all atoms have the same mass[11] and refer the position of the lth atom, $l = 1, \ldots, N$, to a local, mass-reduced, rectangular Cartesian coordinate system X_l, Y_l, Z_l, which is defined as follows (Figure 6.3) for $l = 3, \ldots, N$:

1   Atom $l - 1$ is at the origin.
2   The vector $\mathbf{x}_{l-1} - \mathbf{x}_{l-2}$ defines the X_l direction.
3   Atoms $l - 1, l - 2, l - 3$ define the X_l, Y_l plane.

We then introduce spherical coordinates ξ_l, θ_l, and φ_l in place of the rectangular Cartesian coordinates X_l, Y_l, Z_l, where ξ_l is the radial distance, θ_l is the polar angle and φ_l is the dihedral angle (Figure 6.3). The angles θ_l are also referred to as valence angles; they are the supplements of the bond angles. The dihedral angle φ_l is measured from the $+Y_l$ axis in the direction from $+Y_l$ to $+Z_l$ with $\varphi_l = 0$ corresponding to the *trans* configuration. This requirement fixes the direction of the $+Y_l$ axis in terms of the positions of atoms $l - 1$, $l - 2$ and $l - 3$ as shown in Figure 6.3.

The coordinate system X_1, Y_1, Z_1 coincides with the fixed reference frame and the X_2, Y_2, Z_2 coordinate system is defined by properties (**1**) and (**2**) and with the $X_2 Y_2$ plane taken to coincide with the $X_1 X_2$ plane. Therefore, angles θ_1, φ_1 orient $\mathbf{x}_1 - \mathbf{x}_0$ with respect to the reference frame and angle φ_2 orients the plane of atoms 0, 1, and 2 with respect to this reference. Dihedral angles $\varphi_3, \ldots, \varphi_N$ are referred to as internal dihedral angles since they relate the orientations of portions of the chain with respect to each other.

---

[10] We follow, in part, the notation of Gō and Scheraga (1976).
[11] Mass-reduced coordinates are inconvenient for polymer chains if the atoms have different mass since then interatomic distances are distorted. They are easily bypassed at the expense of a slightly lengthier notation (see Gō and Scheraga, 1976).

The $3N$-dimensional volume element dv corresponding to differential displacements $d\xi_l, d\theta_l, d\varphi_l, l = 1,\ldots, N$ may be seen to be a product of the usual three-dimensional volume elements for spherical coordinates,[12]

$$dv = \prod_{l=1}^{N} \xi_l^2 \sin \theta_l \, d\xi_l \, d\theta_l \, d\varphi_l. \tag{6.5.1}$$

To relate this coordinate system to the general notation of the preceding sections, we set $q^1 = \xi_1, q^2 = \theta_1, q^3 = \varphi_1, q^4 = \xi_2,\ldots, q^n = \varphi_N$, with $n = 3N$ as before. It then follows directly from Eqs. (6.2.18) and (6.5.1) that for this coordinate system

$$|g_{ij}^{(1)}|^{1/2} = \prod_{l=1}^{N} \xi_l^2 \sin \theta_l, \tag{6.5.2}$$

where the superscript (1) indicates that this curvilinear coordinate system is appropriate for a chain with one fixed end.

Curvilinear Coordinates for a Chain with Two Fixed Ends

In order to provide an indication of the principles involved, we treat the cases of $N = 1$ and 2. The general case is discussed in Perchak and Weiner (1982).

N = 1

We are considering a chain of three atoms, $l = 0, 1, 2$ with $\mathbf{x}_0 = 0, \mathbf{x}_2 = \mathbf{r}$, where $\mathbf{r}$ is the prescribed end-to-end vector, and only atom 1 is free to move. We use the notation $\mathbf{x}_1 = \mathbf{x}$ and let x^1, x^2, x^3 be the coordinates of atom 1 with respect to a fixed rectangular Cartesian coordinate system (Figure 6.4). Introduce curvilinear coordinates q^1, q^2, q^3 by means of the relations

$$q^1 = \arctan \frac{x^3}{x^2}, \tag{6.5.3}$$

$$q^2 = |\mathbf{x}| - a \tag{6.5.4}$$

$$q^3 = |\mathbf{x} - \mathbf{r}| - a, \tag{6.5.5}$$

where a is the prescribed bond length.

Since the bond angle for this chain is determined by the imposed end-to-end vector $\mathbf{r}$, this model is appropriate only for the case in which bond lengths are the sole constraints. Therefore, $f = 1$, $c = 2$, and $q^\alpha = q^1, q^A = q^2, q^3$.

For future use we compute $|g_{ij}^{(2)}|^{1/2}$ and $|g_{\alpha\beta}^{(2)}|^{1/2}$ for this coordinate system where the superscript (2) indicates that this coordinate system is appropriate for a chain with two fixed ends. For the former we compute first the volume element dv corresponding to increments $dq^1 \, dq^2 \, dq^3$. As seen in Figure 6.5, dv corresponds to the indicated parallelogram, which has area $\csc\chi \, dq^2 \, dq^3$,

[12]A formal derivation is given by Gō and Scheraga (1976).

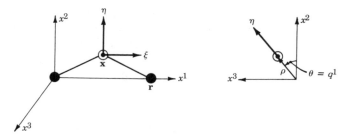

Figure 6.4 Chain of three atoms with both ends fixed. Local ξ, η rectangular Cartesian coordinate system in plane of the three atoms is used in analysis of flexible model.

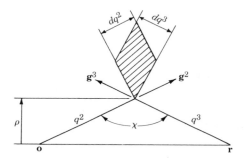

Figure 6.5 Volume element computation for chain of three atoms with both ends fixed. Figure is drawn in plane of three atoms.

rotated through an angle dq^1 so that the parallelogram is displaced by a distance $\rho\, dq^1$, with χ and ρ defined in the figure. Therefore,

$$dv = \rho \csc \chi\, dq^1\, dq^2\, dq^3.$$

It follows that

$$|g_{ij}^{(2)}|^{1/2} = \rho \csc \chi. \tag{6.5.6}$$

By application of Eq. (6.2.6) we find that $\mathbf{g}^2$ and $\mathbf{g}^3$ are unit vectors in the two bond directions (Figure 6.5) so that $\mathbf{g}^2 \cdot \mathbf{g}^3 = \cos \chi$. It then follows that

$$|g^{AB}| = |\mathbf{g}^A \cdot \mathbf{g}^B| = \begin{vmatrix} 1 & \cos \chi \\ \cos \chi & 1 \end{vmatrix} = \sin^2\chi. \tag{6.5.7}$$

We can now compute $|g_{\alpha\beta}^{(2)}|$ by use of Fixman's relation, Eq. (6.3.18),

$$|g_{\alpha\beta}^{(2)}| = |g_{ij}^{(2)}||g^{AB}| = \rho^2, \tag{6.5.8}$$

a result that also can be obtained directly by the computation of $\mathbf{g}_\alpha = \mathbf{g}_1$.

N = 2

The chain of four atoms, $l = 0, 1, 2, 3$ is shown in Figure 6.6 and has two atoms, $l = 1, 2$, free to undergo thermal motion. Let $x_1 = x$, $x_2 = y$ and introduce curvilinear coordinates q^i, $i = 1,\ldots, 6$, for the motion of these

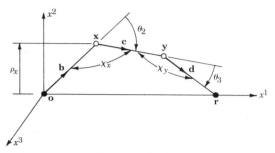

Figure 6.6   Chain of four atoms with both ends fixed. ρ_x is radial distance of $\mathbf{x}$ from x^1 axis.

atoms as follows:

$$q^1 = \arctan\frac{x^3}{x^2}, \qquad q^2 = |\mathbf{x} - \mathbf{r}|, \qquad q^3 = |\mathbf{y}|,$$

$$q^4 = |\mathbf{x}| - a, \qquad q^5 = |\mathbf{x} - \mathbf{y}| - a, \qquad q^6 = |\mathbf{y} - \mathbf{r}| - a. \qquad (6.5.9)$$

The six-dimensional volume element is $dv = \prod_{j=1}^{3} dx^j \, dy^j$. As in the case of $N = 1$, we see that

$$dx^1 \, dx^2 \, dx^3 = \rho_x \csc \chi_x \, dq^1 \, dq^2 \, dq^4 \qquad (6.5.10)$$

where ρ_x, χ_x are defined in Figure 6.6. By similar reasoning it is found that

$$dy^1 \, dy^2 \, dy^3 = \csc \chi_y \sec \eta \, dq^3 \, dq^5 \, dq^6, \qquad (6.5.11)$$

where χ_y is defined in Figure 6.6 and η is the angle between $\mathbf{x} - \mathbf{y}$ and the normal to the plane containing atoms 0, 2, and 3. Therefore,

$$dv = \rho_x \csc \chi_x \csc \chi_y \sec \eta \prod_{i=1}^{6} dq^i \qquad (6.5.12)$$

and

$$|g_{ij}^{(2)}|^{1/2} = \rho_x \csc \chi_x \csc \chi_y \sec \eta. \qquad (6.5.13)$$

In order to compute g^{AB}, we first note that

$$\frac{\partial q^4}{\partial \mathbf{x}} = \mathbf{b}, \qquad \frac{\partial q^4}{\partial \mathbf{y}} = 0; \qquad \frac{\partial q^5}{\partial \mathbf{x}} = -\mathbf{c},$$

$$\frac{\partial q^5}{\partial \mathbf{y}} = \mathbf{c}; \qquad \frac{\partial q^6}{\partial \mathbf{x}} = 0, \qquad \frac{\partial q^6}{\partial \mathbf{y}} = -\mathbf{d}, \qquad (6.5.14)$$

where $\mathbf{b}$, $\mathbf{c}$, and $\mathbf{d}$ are unit three-dimensional vectors directed along the bonds as shown in Figure 6.6. Therefore, the relation

$$g^{AB} = \mathbf{g}^A \cdot \mathbf{g}^B = \frac{\partial q^A}{\partial x} \cdot \frac{\partial q^B}{\partial x} + \frac{\partial q^A}{\partial y} \cdot \frac{\partial q^B}{\partial y} \qquad (6.5.15)$$

leads to

$$|g^{AB}| = \begin{vmatrix} 1 & \cos \theta_2 & 0 \\ \cos \theta_2 & 2 & -\cos \theta_3 \\ 0 & -\cos \theta_3 & 1 \end{vmatrix} = \sin^2\theta_2 + \sin^2\theta_3, \qquad (6.5.16)$$

where θ_2, θ_3 are the indicated valence angles, and, by the use of Eq. (6.3.18),

$$|g_{\alpha\beta}^{(2)}|^{1/2} = \rho_x \csc \chi_x \csc \chi_y \sec \eta \left(\sin^2\theta_2 + \sin^2\theta_3\right)^{1/2}. \qquad (6.5.17)$$

6.6   RIGID AND FLEXIBLE POLYMER MODELS

As discussed in Section 5.3, the backbone atoms of a polymer chain interact with covalent bonds, which are strong and highly directional. Nevertheless, when these molecules are in thermal motion, they change shape constantly by means of rotations about the backbone bonds, rotations that are opposed only by the weak interaction between the side groups attached to the backbone atoms.

It is natural, therefore, to model such molecules as having constant bond lengths and, depending on the degree of realism desired, constant bond angles as well. Such models were discussed in a preliminary fashion in Section 5.5. We now reexamine the statistical mechanical basis of these models, making use of the concepts introduced in Sections 6.3–6.5. Accordingly, using the notation of these sections, we first reorder and subdivide the curvilinear coordinates q^i, $i = 1, \ldots, n$ of Section 6.5 into two classes: the soft variables, q^α, $\alpha = 1, \ldots, f$ and the hard variables, q^A, $A = f + 1, \ldots, n$. For a chain with one free end, for example, the q^α include the dihedral angles φ_l and the q^A include the bond lengths ξ_l, while the valence angles θ_l are included with the q^α for freely jointed models or with the q^A for fixed valence angle models. It is convenient, by the subtraction of appropriate constants, to define the q^A so that their constrained values are equal to zero.

We consider next the computation of the partition function

$$Z(T) = \int_\Gamma e^{-H(q, p)/kT} dq dp \qquad (6.6.1)$$

for these models. We are omitting reference here to kinematical or mechanical parameters such as fixed length or fixed applied force (strain or stress ensembles) since the discussion of this section applies to both.

There are two distinct paths for arriving at this partition function:

Rigid Models

The desired constraints may be imposed directly as geometric constraints in the Hamiltonian, which then takes the form given in Eq. (6.3.12), namely,

$$H_R(q^\alpha, p_\beta) = \tfrac{1}{2}\bar{g}^{\alpha\beta}p_\alpha p_\beta + V(q^\alpha), \qquad (6.6.2)$$

where $\bar{g}^{\alpha\beta}$ is the intrinsic contravariant metric tensor for α-space as discussed in Section 6.3 and $V(q^\alpha)$ represents the rotational potential discussed in Section 5.3. The partition function $Z_R(T)$ is computed as in Eq. (6.6.1) based on the Hamiltonian $H_R(q^\alpha, p_\beta)$ using a $2f$-dimensional phase space, Γ_α. That is,

$$Z_R(T) = \int_{\Gamma_\alpha} e^{-H_R(q^\alpha, p_\beta)/kT} \prod_{\alpha=1}^{f} dq^\alpha\, dp_\alpha. \qquad (6.6.3)$$

This procedure is referred to as imposing rigid constraints[13] and the resulting model is called a rigid model although, of course, it still possesses a high degree of mobility corresponding to the unconstrained coordinates q^α.

The integration in Eq. (6.6.3) over the momentum portion of phase space may be carried out with the result

$$Z_R(T) = (2\pi kT)^{f/2} \int_{\Gamma_{q^\alpha}} |\bar{g}^{\alpha\beta}|^{-1/2} e^{-V(q^\alpha)/kT} \prod_{\alpha=1}^{f} dq^\alpha, \qquad (6.6.4)$$

or, since by use of Eq. (6.3.6), $|\bar{g}^{\alpha\beta}| = |g_{\alpha\beta}|_0^{-1}$,

$$Z_R(T) = (2\pi kT)^{f/2} \int_{\Gamma_{q^\alpha}} |g_{\alpha\beta}|_0^{1/2} e^{-V(q^\alpha)/kT} \prod_{\alpha=1}^{f} dq^\alpha, \qquad (6.6.5)$$

where the subscript 0 emphasizes that $|g_{\alpha\beta}|$ is evaluated for $q^A \equiv 0$.

Flexible Models

We may, instead, begin with a Hamiltonian for a model with $n = 3N$ degrees of freedom of the form

$$H_F(q^i, p_i) = \tfrac{1}{2}g^{ij}p_i p_j + \tfrac{1}{2}\kappa a_{AB}q^A q^B + V(q^\alpha) \qquad (6.6.6)$$

---

[13] See, for example, Saito et al. (1963), Gō and Scheraga (1976), Rallison (1979), Helfand (1979), and Pechukas (1980).

with a_{AB} a constant, positive-definite matrix and $\kappa > 0$. In the model corresponding to this Hamiltonian, therefore, the coordinates q^A are permitted to vary but are maintained close to their assigned zero values by a harmonic potential whose strength depends on the parameter κ. As κ is permitted to become arbitrarily large the system, with prescribed finite energy, will become confined to α-space.

In this approach, the partition function, $Z_F(T; \kappa)$, is first computed for finite κ based on $H_F(q^i, p_i)$, using a $2n$-dimensional phase space Γ_i. The limiting form assumed by $Z_F(T; \kappa)$ for arbitrarily large κ then leads to $Z_F(T)$.

This procedure is referred to as imposing flexible constraints and the result is called a flexible model.

To carry out these computations explicitly, we first note that for arbitrary values of κ,

$$Z_F(T; \kappa) = \int_{\Gamma_i} e^{-H_F(q^i, p_i)/kT} \prod_{i=1}^{n} dq^i \, dp_i$$

$$= (2\pi kT)^{n/2} \int_{\Gamma_{q^i}} |g_{ij}|^{1/2} e^{-(\frac{\kappa}{2}a_{AB}q^A q^B + V(q^\alpha))/kT} \prod_{i=1}^{n} dq^i \quad (6.6.7)$$

where we have carried out the integration over momentum space in a manner analogous to the method of deriving Eq. (6.6.5). For sufficiently large κ the integrand is negligible except in the neighborhood of $q^A = 0$. We may, therefore, set $q^A = 0$ in $|g_{ij}|$ and carry out the integration with respect to the q^A variables in the exponential, with the result

$$Z_F(T) = (2\pi kT)^{(n+c)/2} \kappa^{-c/2} |a_{AB}|^{-1/2} \int_{\Gamma_{q^\alpha}} |g_{ij}|_0^{1/2} e^{-V(q^\alpha)/kT} \prod_{\alpha=1}^{f} dq^\alpha,$$

$$(6.6.8)$$

where $c = n - f$ is the number of constraints and $|g_{ij}|_0$ denotes the determinant $|g_{ij}|$ evaluated at $q^A = 0$.

We are focusing on the derivation of mechanical properties of the models; their calculation involves the differentiation of $\log Z$ with respect to the conjugate mechanical property. Therefore, the factors multiplying the integrals in these expressions are not of direct concern to us.[14] In particular, the presence of κ and $|a_{AB}|$ in the prefactor of Z_F plays no role in the mechanical behavior; this behavior will be the same independently of the magnitude of κ as long as it is large enough to justify the procedure used for reducing the integral of Eq. (6.6.7) to that of Eq. (6.6.8) and, under this condition, it also

---

[14] The difference in the factor $(2\pi kT)^{f/2}$ and $(2\pi kT)^{(n+c)/2}$ in Z_R and Z_F, respectively, does point to the difference in specific heat of these two models.

will be independent of the matrix a_{AB} describing the harmonic potential used to impose the constraints.

The principal difference between Z_R and Z_F, therefore, is the presence of $|g_{\alpha\beta}|_0$ in the former and $|g_{ij}|_0$ in the latter. This difference has large consequences in some calculations, a result that is quite surprising since physical intuition would lead one to expect that the two models behave similarly if not identically.

We will demonstrate the possible large contrast in behavior between rigid and flexible models in Section 6.8. Granted this difference, the natural question which arises is: Which type of model is a closer approximation to physical reality? This question has been considered by Gō and Scheraga (1976) on the basis of quantum statistical mechanics (see Section 10.4). They came to the conclusion that although both Z_R and Z_F involve some error with respect to the quantum analysis, Z_F is generally the more accurate of the two. The calculations we present in Section 10.4 are in accord with this conclusion. Although the results are not yet definitive (see Rallison, 1979), it is clear that Z_F is the easier quantity to compute. For example, if a model with one free end and with fixed bond length a and fixed valence angle θ_0 is employed then from Eq. (6.5.2)

$$|g_{ij}^{(1)}|_0 = \left(a^2 \sin\theta_0\right)^N, \qquad (6.6.9)$$

a constant that may be brought outside the integral in Eq. (6.6.8), whereas $|g_{\alpha\beta}^{(1)}|_0$ is a complicated function of the q^α (the dihedral angles φ_l) which is difficult to compute.

Distribution Functions $\rho_R(q^\alpha)$ and $\rho_F(q^\alpha)$

In addition to the partition functions, it is of interest to compute $\rho(q^\alpha)$, the probability distribution function in the configuration space Γ_{q^α}, for the two models.

For the rigid model, this is computed simply from the canonical distribution function over the $2f$-dimensional phase space

$$\rho_R(q^\alpha, p_\alpha) = Z_R^{-1}(T)e^{-H_R(q^\alpha, p_\alpha)/kT} \qquad (6.6.10)$$

by integrating over momentum space. The result is

$$\rho_R(q^\alpha) = C_R|g_{\alpha\beta}|_0^{1/2}e^{-V(q^\alpha)/kT} \qquad (6.6.11)$$

where C_R is a normalization constant or the reciprocal of the configuration partition function, that is,

$$C_R^{-1} = \int_{\Gamma_{q^\alpha}} |g_{\alpha\beta}|_0^{1/2}e^{-V(q^\alpha)/kT}\prod_{\alpha=1}^{f} dq^\alpha. \qquad (6.6.12)$$

For the flexible model, we begin with the canonical distribution function $\rho_F(q^i, p_i; \kappa)$ over phase space Γ_i for arbitrary κ,

$$\rho_F(q^i, p_i; \kappa) = Z_F^{-1}(T; \kappa)\exp\left(\frac{-H_F(q^i, p_i; \kappa)}{kT}\right), \qquad (6.6.13)$$

integrate first over all momenta p_i, and then integrate over the variables q^A under the assumption of arbitrarily large κ. The result is

$$\rho_F(q^\alpha) = C_F|g_{ij}|_0^{1/2}\exp\left(\frac{-V(q^\alpha)}{kT}\right), \qquad (6.6.14)$$

where C_F is a normalization constant.

Consider the special case of a model with $V(q^\alpha) \equiv 0$. Then, the fraction of time which the rigid model spends in the differential interval $\prod_{\alpha=1}^{f}dq^\alpha$ is

$$\rho_R(q^\alpha)\prod_{\alpha=1}^{f}dq^\alpha = C_R|g_{\alpha\beta}|_0^{1/2}\prod_{\alpha=1}^{f}dq^\alpha = C_R(dv)_\alpha \qquad (6.6.15)$$

by Eq. (6.3.19); that is, the fraction of time which a rigid model with $V(q^\alpha) \equiv 0$ spends in a differential interval $\prod_{\alpha=1}^{f}dq^\alpha$ is proportional to the f-dimensional volume element to which this interval corresponds.

On the other hand, the fraction of time which the corresponding flexible model spends in the same interval is

$$\rho_F(q^\alpha)\prod_{\alpha=1}^{f}dq^\alpha = C_F|g_{ij}|_0^{1/2}\prod_{\alpha=1}^{f}dq^\alpha. \qquad (6.6.16)$$

This may be given the following geometric interpretation: the fraction of time which a flexible model with $V(q^\alpha) \equiv 0$ spends in a differential interval $\prod_{\alpha=1}^{f}dq^\alpha$ is proportional to the n-dimensional volume of the parallelepiped with edges dq^α, $\alpha = 1,\ldots,f$ and $\Delta q^A = 1$, $A = f + 1,\ldots,N$.

If we consider a model with one free end, no applied force, no rotational potential, and with both bond lengths and bond angles constrained, then it follows from Eqs. (6.6.9) and (6.6.16) that a flexible model will spend an equal fraction of time in all equal dihedral angle intervals, whereas a rigid model will spend a nonuniform fraction of time in these intervals because of the dihedral angle dependence of the metric determinant $|g_{\alpha\beta}^{(1)}|_0$. Computer simulation results for a chain with $N = 3$ which demonstrate this effect will be found in Pear and Weiner (1979). Computer simulation results which demonstrate the difference between flexible and rigid models for the case $N = 2$ (with unconstrained bond angle) are given by Gottlieb and Bird (1976).

Partition Functions as Areas

Consider the case of a strain ensemble with prescribed end-to-end vector **r**. Since the q^α represent angle variables, we may speak of the configuration space

Γ_{q^α} as an f-dimensional torus whose metric tensor depends on $\mathbf{r}$, that is $g^{(2)}_{\alpha\beta} = g^{(2)}_{\alpha\beta}(\mathbf{r})$. In the special case in which there are no rotational potentials, the partition function for the rigid model, Eq. (6.6.5), assumes the form

$$Z_R(\mathbf{r}, T) = (2\pi kT)^{f/2} D_R(\mathbf{r}) \qquad (6.6.17)$$

where

$$D_R(\mathbf{r}) = \int_{\Gamma_{q^\alpha}} |g^{(2)}_{\alpha\beta}(\mathbf{r})|_0^{1/2} \prod_{\alpha=1}^{f} dq^\alpha \qquad (6.6.18)$$

is the surface area of the f-dimensional torus on which the chain is constrained to move. The close analogy to the partition function $Z(v, T) = (2\pi mkT)^{3N/2} v^N$ for a perfect gas of N atoms of mass m confined to a volume v may be noted.

The partition function for the flexible model with no rotational potentials, Eq. (6.6.8), may also be interpreted as proportional to a surface area of the f-dimensional torus on which the chain moves, but an area computed on the basis of the metric $(g^{(2)}_{ij}(\mathbf{r}))_0$ rather than the true metric $g_{\alpha\beta}(\mathbf{r})$. That is, we can write

$$Z_F(\mathbf{r}, T) = (2\pi kT)^{(n+c)/2} \kappa^{-(c/2)} |a_{AB}|^{-1/2} D_F(\mathbf{r}) \qquad (6.6.19)$$

where

$$D_F(\mathbf{r}) = \int_{\Gamma_{q^\alpha}} |g^{(2)}_{ij}(\mathbf{r})|_0^{1/2} \prod_{\alpha=1}^{f} dq^\alpha. \qquad (6.6.20)$$

$D_F(\mathbf{r})$ may be also visualized as the n-dimensional volume of a shell whose inner surface is the f-dimensional torus Γ_{q^α}. The "thickness" of the shell is a c-dimensional volume where c is the number of constraints. This shell thickness[15] is variable with q^α and is a reflection of the variable amplitude of the thermal vibrations which the flexible constraints permit in the q^A directions. Although the amplitude of these vibrations becomes arbitrarily small as the constraint spring constant parameter becomes arbitrarily large, the mode of variation of this amplitude with q^α remains and leaves its effect on $Z_F(\mathbf{r}, T)$ and the resulting force–length relation.

A case for which this shell may be represented in three-dimensional space and therefore easily visualized is that of the two-bonded chain (see Section 6.8 and Figure 6.5).

---

[15] We can conclude from Eq. (6.3.18) that the shell thickness equals $|g^{AB}|_0^{-1}$.

6.7 USE OF $S = k \log p$ FOR STRETCHED POLYMERS[16]

In Section 5.5, $S(\mathbf{r})$, the entropy of a long-chain molecule with prescribed end-to-end vector $\mathbf{r}$ was computed on the basis of the formula

$$S(\mathbf{r}) = k \log p(\mathbf{r}) \tag{6.7.1}$$

where $p(\mathbf{r})$ is the probability density of the end-to-end vector $\mathbf{r}$; that is, $p(\mathbf{r})\, d\mathbf{r}$ is the probability of finding this vector in the differential volume $d\mathbf{r}$ about $\mathbf{r}$. This probability density was computed for several models on the basis of suitable random walks in Section 5.5 and it was seen there that for these models $p(\mathbf{r}) = p(r)$, where $r = |\mathbf{r}|$. If it is assumed further that the internal energy U of the chain is independent of $\mathbf{r}$, then, for the purpose of computing the applied force $\mathbf{f}$ necessary to maintain the end-to-end vector $\mathbf{r}$, we may set $U = 0$ and write the free energy $F(r, T) = -TS(r) = -kT \log p(r)$. It then follows that the required force is colinear with the vector $\mathbf{r}$ and has magnitude

$$f = \frac{\partial F}{\partial r} = -kT \frac{\partial}{\partial r} \log p(r). \tag{6.7.2}$$

In this section, we relate this procedure to the more basic computation of the force $\mathbf{f}$ which uses the partition function $Z(\mathbf{r}, T)$ for a strain ensemble of chains in which the end-to-end vector is fixed.

For the class of models we are considering here,[17] it is readily verified that $Z(\mathbf{r}, T) = Z(r, T)$, so that the required force is again seen to be colinear with $\mathbf{r}$ and

$$f = -kT \frac{\partial}{\partial r} \log Z(r, T). \tag{6.7.3}$$

It is clear, therefore, that the probability approach of Eq. (6.7.2) will be justified if we can give a probabilistic interpretation to the partition function so that $Z(r, T) = p(r, T)$ to within a multiplicative function independent of r. We show next that this can be done if flexible polymer models (in the sense of the previous section) are employed.

Consider, therefore, a flexible model of a long-chain molecule consisting of atoms $l = 0, 1, \ldots, N, N + 1$, all of mass m. Although we will be ultimately using a strain ensemble, to begin with we regard only the zeroth atom as fixed, with all of the others free to engage in thermal motion. These atoms, therefore, require a $3(N + 1)$-dimensional configuration space. In terms of the curvilinear coordinate system introduced in Section 6.5 for chains with one free end, its Hamiltonian can be written, as in Eq. (6.6.6),

$$H_F\left(q^i, p_i; \kappa\right) = \tfrac{1}{2} g^{ij} p_i p_j + \tfrac{1}{2} \kappa a_{AB} q^A q^B + V(q^\alpha) \tag{6.7.4}$$

---

[16] Weiner (1982).
[17] For brevity, we refer to chains with spherically symmetric $p(r)$ and $Z(r, T)$ as isotropic.

where $i, j = 1, \ldots, 3(N + 1)$ and the coordinates q^α, q^A have the significance described in Section 6.6. Since we will be using a flexible model throughout the remainder of this section, we omit the subscript F in the subsequent discussion.

Since the model is flexible we can, for finite values of κ, also write its Hamiltonian in terms of mass-reduced rectangular Cartesian coordinates as

$$H(\mathbf{x}_1, \ldots, \mathbf{x}_{N+1}, \mathbf{p}_1, \ldots, \mathbf{p}_{N+1}; \kappa) = \frac{1}{2} \sum_{i=1}^{N+1} |\mathbf{p}_i|^2 + \overline{V}(\mathbf{x}_1, \ldots, \mathbf{x}_{N+1}; \kappa)$$

$$(6.7.5)$$

where $\overline{V}$ is the sum of the harmonic constraining potential, $\frac{1}{2}\kappa a_{AB} q^A q^B$, and the rotational potentials $V(q^\alpha)$, both expressed in terms of $\mathbf{x}_1, \ldots, \mathbf{x}_{N+1}$.

The canonical distribution function $\rho(\mathbf{x}_1, \ldots, \mathbf{x}_{N+1}, \mathbf{p}_1, \ldots, \mathbf{p}_{N+1}, T; \kappa)$ for this model with the $N + 1$'st atom free is

$$\rho(\mathbf{x}_1, \ldots, \mathbf{x}_{N+1}, \mathbf{p}_1, \ldots, \mathbf{p}_{N+1}, T; \kappa) = Z^{-1} e^{-H/kT} \qquad (6.7.6)$$

with H given by Eq. (6.7.5) and

$$Z(T) = \int_\Gamma e^{-H/kT} \prod_{l=1}^{N+1} d\mathbf{x}_l \, d\mathbf{p}_l. \qquad (6.7.7)$$

The probability density $p(\mathbf{r}, T; \kappa)$ of finding the $N + 1$'st atom at $\mathbf{r}$ is obtained from ρ by integration over the remaining atomic positions and over all of the momenta:

$$p(\mathbf{r}, T; \kappa) = \int \rho(\mathbf{x}_1, \ldots, \mathbf{x}_N, \mathbf{r}, \mathbf{p}_1, \ldots, \mathbf{p}_{N+1}, T; \kappa) \prod_{l=1}^{N} d\mathbf{x}_l \prod_{l'=1}^{N+1} d\mathbf{p}_{l'},$$

$$= Z^{-1}(T)(2\pi kT)^{3(N+1)/2}$$

$$\times \int \exp\left[-\overline{V}(\mathbf{x}_1, \ldots, \mathbf{x}_N, \mathbf{r}; \kappa)/kT\right] \prod_{l=1}^{N} d\mathbf{x}_l. \qquad (6.7.8)$$

On the other hand, the Hamiltonian for the model with $\mathbf{r}$ as imposed end-to-end vector is obtained from that of Eq. (6.7.5) by setting $\mathbf{x}_{N+1} = \mathbf{r}$ and $\mathbf{p}_{N+1} = 0$. The corresponding partition function is

$$Z(\mathbf{r}, T; \kappa) = \int \exp\left[-H(\mathbf{x}_1, \ldots, \mathbf{x}_N, \mathbf{r}, \mathbf{p}_1, \ldots, \mathbf{p}_N, 0; \kappa)/kT\right] \prod_{l=1}^{N} d\mathbf{x}_l \, d\mathbf{p}_l$$

$$= (2\pi kT)^{3N/2} \int \exp\left[-\overline{V}(\mathbf{x}_1, \ldots, \mathbf{x}_N, \mathbf{r}; \kappa)/kT\right] \prod_{l=1}^{N} d\mathbf{x}_l.$$

$$(6.7.9)$$

By comparison of Eqs. (6.7.8) and (6.7.9), we see that, except for a multiplicative function independent of $\mathbf{r}$, the partition function $Z(\mathbf{r}, T; \kappa)$ for the chain with fixed end-to-end vector $\mathbf{r}$ is equal to the probability density $p(\mathbf{r}, T; \kappa)$ of finding the $N + 1$'st atom at $\mathbf{r}$ when this atom is free to undergo thermal motion.[18]

We next wish to show that, for sufficiently large κ, this probability density can be given a random walk interpretation. For this purpose we first introduce the three-dimensional Dirac delta function $\delta(\mathbf{x})$ by the operational property that

$$\int_{\mathbb{R}_3} g(\mathbf{x})\delta(\mathbf{x} - \mathbf{r})\, d\mathbf{x} = g(\mathbf{r}) \tag{6.7.10}$$

for an arbitrary function $g(\mathbf{x})$ and, by use of this function, rewrite Eq. (6.7.8) as

$$p(\mathbf{r}, T; \kappa) = C(T)\int e^{-\bar{V}(\mathbf{x}_1,\ldots,\mathbf{x}_{N+1};\kappa)/kT}\delta(\mathbf{x}_{N+1} - \mathbf{r})\prod_{l=1}^{N+1} d\mathbf{x}_l, \tag{6.7.11}$$

where $C(T)$ is independent of $\mathbf{r}$. We now rewrite the integral in terms of the curvilinear coordinate system $q^i = (q^\alpha, q^A)$ defined in Section 6.5 as appropriate for the chain of atoms $l = 0, 1, \ldots, N + 1$ with only atom 0 fixed. Then,

$$p(\mathbf{r}, T; \kappa) = C(T)$$

$$\times \int e^{-(\frac{\kappa}{2}a_{AB}q^A q^B + V(q^\alpha))/kT}\delta\left(\mathbf{x}_{N+1}(q^\alpha, q^A) - \mathbf{r}\right)|g_{ij}^{(1)}|^{1/2}$$

$$\times \prod_{\alpha=1}^{f} dq^\alpha \prod_{A=f+1}^{3(N+1)} dq^A, \tag{6.7.12}$$

where $|g_{ij}^{(1)}|^{1/2}$ is defined as in Eq. (6.5.2) with N replaced by $N + 1$, and $\mathbf{x}_{N+1}(q^\alpha, q^A)$ is the position of the $N + 1$'st atom expressed as a function of the curvilinear coordinates (q^α, q^A). By the usual argument, the limiting form of $p(\mathbf{r}, T; \kappa)$ for arbitrarily large κ may be obtained by carrying out the integration with respect to the q^A variables in the exponential while evaluating the remainder of the integrand at $q^A = 0$. The result is

$$p(\mathbf{r}, T) = C(T)\left(\frac{2\pi kT}{\kappa}\right)^{c/2}|a_{AB}|^{-1/2}$$

$$\times \int_{\Gamma_{q^\alpha}} e^{-V(q^\alpha)/kT}\delta\left(\mathbf{x}_{N+1}^0(q^\alpha) - \mathbf{r}\right)|g_{ij}^{(1)}|_0^{1/2}\prod_{\alpha=1}^{f} dq^\alpha \tag{6.7.13}$$

where $\mathbf{x}_{N+1}^0(q^\alpha)$ and $|g_{ij}^{(1)}|_0$ are the functions $\mathbf{x}_{N+1}(q^\alpha, q^A), |g_{ij}^{(1)}|(q^\alpha, q^A)$

[18]An equivalent result has been obtained by Volkenstein (1963, p. 454) who did not, however, distinguish between rigid and flexible models.

evaluated at $q^A = 0$ and $c = 3(N + 1) - f$. It is seen that the integral defining $p(\mathbf{r}, T)$ in Eq. (6.7.13) lends itself directly to a random walk interpretation. If, for example, both bond lengths and bond angles are constrained variables set equal to a and θ_0, respectively, and there are no rotational potentials, $V(q^\alpha) = 0$, then the q^α correspond to the dihedral angles φ_l, $l = 1, \ldots, N + 1$. In this case, $|g_{ij}^{(1)}|_0 = (a^2 \sin \theta_0)^{N+1}$ and the integral yields the probability density $p(\mathbf{r})$ of arriving at $\mathbf{r}$ by means of a random walk in which each dihedral angle has a uniform probability distribution on $0 < \varphi_l \leqslant 2\pi$. For a freely jointed chain, the valence angles θ_l join the dihedral angles φ_l in the set of unconstrained variables q^α and

$$|g_{ij}^{(1)}|_0^{1/2} = a^{2(N+1)} \prod_{l=1}^{N+1} \sin \theta_l;$$

the integral in Eq. (6.7.13) then corresponds to a random walk in which each step is uniformly distributed over a sphere of radius a.

The random walk interpretation of the integral remains possible in the presence of functions $V(q^\alpha)$, which can be written as the sum of rotational potentials $V(\varphi)$, each depending on a single dihedral angle. However, in this case the probability associated with each step is temperature dependent, as is the probability density $p(\mathbf{r}, T)$.

This demonstration of the possible probability interpretation of the partition function $Z(\mathbf{r}, T)$ depended on the possibility of using rectangular Cartesian coordinates $\mathbf{x}_1, \ldots, \mathbf{x}_{N+1}$, as in Eq. (6.7.8) and is, therefore, restricted to flexible models. We are therefore led to the rather paradoxical result that the procedure based on Eq. (6.7.1) with $p(\mathbf{r})$ computed as the result of a random walk executed on the basis of what appears to be a rigid model leads to correct results only for flexible models.

It should be emphasized that the result that $p(r, T) = Z(r, T)$ to within a multiplicative function independent of r applies to flexible models of arbitrary length. This justifies the use of the relation

$$f = -kT \frac{\partial}{\partial r} \log p(r, T) \tag{6.7.14}$$

without the need of the introduction of macroscopic thermodynamic functions as in Eqs. (6.7.1) and (6.7.2). Examples of its application to very short chains will be presented in the next section.

6.8   STRAIN ENSEMBLE FOR SHORT FREELY JOINTED CHAINS

As an extreme example of the possible difference in mechanical behavior of rigid and flexible models, we first consider a freely jointed chain with only two bonds with fixed end-to-end vector $\mathbf{r}$ (Figure 6.4, p. 226). The chain, therefore, consists of three atoms, $l = 0, 1, 2$ with $x_0 = 0$ and $x_2 = r$; only atom $l = 1$ is free to undergo thermal motion. There are no rotational potentials.

We first treat the rigid and flexible models for this case directly, using an *ad hoc* notation and approach. We will then relate the results to the curvilinear coordinate formalism of the previous sections.

Rigid Model

Noting the analogy of the model shown in Figure 6.4 to a centrifugal governor, Frenkel (1946) has used it to provide an explanation of what he termed the kinetic origin of the force required to maintain a given extension of a polymer molecule.[19] An elementary derivation of this force may be given as follows:[20]

Because of the fixed bond length a, the free central atom is constrained to move on a circle of radius ρ, where

$$\rho = \left(a^2 - r^2/4\right)^{1/2}. \tag{6.8.1}$$

If the atom of mass m moves about this circle with speed v, then the force F_1 directed toward the center of the circle required to produce the centripetal acceleration is

$$F_1 = \frac{mv^2}{\rho}. \tag{6.8.2}$$

The required forces F_2 in the two connecting bonds are

$$F_2 = \frac{aF_1}{2\rho} \tag{6.8.3}$$

and the required applied force f, in the direction of $\mathbf{r}$, is

$$f = \frac{F_2 r}{2a} = \frac{F_1 r}{4\rho} = \frac{mv^2 r}{4\rho^2}. \tag{6.8.4}$$

Since the atom velocity v is a fluctuating quantity, so is the required force f. We next take time averages and, under the assumption that the molecule is in thermal equilibrium with a heat bath at T, use the equipartition relation $\widehat{\tfrac{1}{2}mv^2} = \tfrac{1}{2}kT$, leading to the result that

$$\hat{f} = \frac{r}{4\rho^2}kT = \frac{rkT}{4a^2 - r^2}. \tag{6.8.5}$$

[19]See also James and Guth (1943, p. 459), for a qualitative discussion of the kinetic origin of the force on an extended polymer molecule.
[20]Frenkel (1946, p. 475) or Kubo (1965, pp. 131 and 141).

We next rederive this result by use of the partition function Z_R. A natural generalized coordinate to use for this rigid model is the angle coordinate θ shown in Figure 6.4b. The kinetic energy is

$$K = \tfrac{1}{2} m \rho^2 \dot{\theta}^2 \tag{6.8.6}$$

and therefore the corresponding momentum is

$$p_\theta = \frac{\partial K}{\partial \dot{\theta}} = m \rho^2 \dot{\theta}. \tag{6.8.7}$$

Since there are no rotational potentials, the Hamiltonian is simply

$$H_R(\theta, p_\theta; r) = \frac{1}{2} \frac{p_\theta^2}{m \rho^2}, \tag{6.8.8}$$

with ρ defined in Eq. (6.8.1). The corresponding partition function is, with $\beta = (kT)^{-1}$,

$$Z_R(r, T) = \int_0^{2\pi} d\theta \int_{-\infty}^{\infty} e^{-\beta p_\theta^2 /(2m\rho^2)} \, dp_\theta \tag{6.8.9}$$

$$= 2\pi (2\pi m k T)^{1/2} \rho$$

$$= 2\pi (2\pi m k T)^{1/2} (a^2 - r^2/4)^{1/2}. \tag{6.8.10}$$

Therefore, f_R, the force required for the rigid model is

$$f_R = -\frac{\partial}{\partial r} kT \log Z_R(r, T) = \frac{rkT}{4a^2 - r^2} \tag{6.8.11}$$

in agreement with the result derived by time averages.

Flexible Model

The Hamiltonian for the corresponding flexible model may be described in terms of a rectangular Cartesian coordinate system (Figure 6.4), with $\mathbf{x}$ the position and $\mathbf{p}$ the momentum of the moving atom, as

$$H_F(\mathbf{x}, \mathbf{p}) = \frac{1}{2m} |\mathbf{p}|^2 + V(\mathbf{x}) \tag{6.8.12}$$

where

$$V(\mathbf{x}) = \tfrac{1}{2}\kappa\left[(|\mathbf{x}| - a)^2 + (|\mathbf{x} - \mathbf{r}| - a)^2)\right].$$ (6.8.13)

The corresponding partition function is

$$Z_F(r, T; \kappa) = \int_{\Gamma_p} e^{-\beta|\mathbf{p}|^2/2m}\, d\mathbf{p} \int_{\Gamma_x} e^{-\beta V(\mathbf{x})}\, d\mathbf{x}$$

$$= (2\pi mkT)^{3/2} \int_{\Gamma_x} e^{-\beta V(\mathbf{x})}\, d\mathbf{x},$$ (6.8.14)

where the integration over momentum space Γ_p has been performed. To determine the limiting form of $Z_F(r, T; \kappa)$ for arbitrarily large κ, we use the fact that for large κ, $V(\mathbf{x})$ is large except when $\mathbf{x}$ is in the neighborhood of a point on the circle of radius $\rho = (a^2 - r^2/4)^{1/2}$ at an arbitrary angle θ as in Figure 6.4b. We introduce local rectangular Cartesian coordinates ξ, η with origin on this circle in the plane of the three atoms as shown in Figure 6.4. A Taylor series expansion of $V(\mathbf{x})$ up to quadratic terms of ξ and η leads to the result

$$V(\mathbf{x}) \cong V(\xi, \eta) = \frac{\kappa}{a^2}\left(\frac{r^2\xi^2}{4} + \rho^2\eta^2\right),$$ (6.8.15)

so that for arbitrarily large κ,

$$Z_F(r, T) = (2\pi mkT)^{3/2} \int_0^{2\pi} \rho\, d\theta \int_{-\infty}^{\infty} d\xi \int_{-\infty}^{\infty} d\eta \exp\left[-\frac{\beta\kappa}{a^2}\left(\frac{r^2}{4}\xi^2 + \rho^2\eta^2\right)\right]$$

$$= (2\pi mkT)^{3/2} \frac{4\pi^2 kT}{\kappa} \frac{a^2}{r}.$$ (6.8.16)

Therefore, f_F, the force required for the flexible model is

$$f_F = -\frac{\partial}{\partial r} kT \log Z_F = \frac{kT}{r}.$$ (6.8.17)

The results for the rigid and flexible models are compared in Figure 6.7. Remarkably, their behavior is totally different. Moreover, the dependence of f_F on r is not at all like that of an entropic spring.

The behavior of the flexible model as predicted by Eq. (6.8.17) is so counterintuitive that a computer simulation of the model in order to confirm these results was performed by the method of Brownian dynamics.[21] The results are shown in Figure 6.7 and are seen to agree quite well with the theoretical predictions except in a small region near that corresponding to full extension where the approximations made in the evaluation of Z_F break down.

[21]Weiner and Perchak (1981).

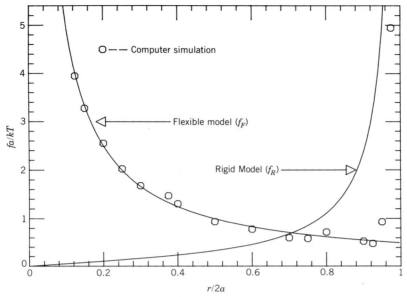

Figure 6.7 Force–length relation for flexible and rigid models of two-bond chain with pre-scribed end-to-end vector **r**. (Reprinted with permission from Weiner and Perchak 1981. Copyright 1981 American Chemical Society.)

Curvilinear Coordinate Analysis

It is instructive to relate this simple model to the general curvilinear coordinate formalism of the previous sections.

In this model only a single atom is subject to thermal motion, so that $N = 1$, $n = 3$. There are two constraints corresponding to the two bond lengths so that $f = 1$. Both ends of the chain are fixed at a distance r apart. The appropriate curvilinear coordinate system has been treated in Section 6.5 where we see that $q^\alpha = q^1$ corresponds to the angle θ used in the previous discussion. The metric determinant $|g^{(2)}_{\alpha\beta}|_0 = \rho^2$, as derived in Eq. (6.5.8), and therefore we can compute $Z_R(r, T)$ for this case directly from Eq. (6.6.5) by noting that $V(q^\alpha) = 0$ and $\Gamma_{q^\alpha} = \{q^1 : 0 \leqslant q^1 \leqslant 2\pi\}$; the result is in agreement[22] with Eq. (6.8.10).

The metric determinant $|g^{(2)}_{ij}|$ for this coordinate system is given in Eq. (6.5.6); from it we see, by simple geometry, that

$$|g^{(2)}_{ij}|_0^{1/2} = (\rho \csc \chi)_0 = a^2/r \qquad (6.8.18)$$

---

[22] Note that the use of reduced-mass coordinates in the general discussion corresponds to setting $m = 1$ in the particular calculations of this section.

where, we recall, the subscript 0 refers to the functions evaluated for $q^A = 0$ or, in this case, for the bond lengths set equal to a. Furthermore, the potential $V(\mathbf{x})$ of Eq. (6.8.13) used in the definition of the flexible model corresponds to $a_{AB} = \delta_{AB}$, where a_{AB} is the matrix introduced in the general formulation in Eq. (6.6.6). Therefore, $Z_F(r, T)$ can be computed directly from the general Eq. (6.6.8) leading to the same result as Eq. (6.8.16).

Area Interpretation of Partition Functions

This model provides a simple example of the interpretation of the partition function $Z(\mathbf{r}, T)$ as proportional to the appropriately defined area of the f-dimensional torus to which the chain is confined when its end-to-end vector is fixed at $\mathbf{r}$ [Eqs. (6.6.17)–(6.6.20)]. In this case, $f = 1$ and the torus is simply the circle of radius $\rho = (a^2 - r^2/4)^{1/2}$. Therefore, the area $D_R(\mathbf{r})$ appropriate for the rigid model is the circumference of this circle, $D_R(\mathbf{r}) = 2\pi\rho$. On the other hand, for the flexible model, $D_F(\mathbf{r})$ is computed on the basis of $|g_{ij}^{(2)}|_0$. As seen from the discussion following Eq. (6.6.16), $D_F(\mathbf{r})$ may be interpreted as the three-dimensional volume of the region obtained by rotating the parallelogram shown in Figure 6.5 about the end-to-end vector. The manner in which this area varies with r gives rise to the large difference in behavior between the flexible and rigid models for this case.

Use of $p(r)$

We turn next to the relationship discussed in the previous section between $Z_F(r, T)$ and $p(r)$, the probability density of finding the end-to-end vector at $\mathbf{r}$. For the freely jointed chain with two bonds, we see from Eq. (5.5.17) that $p(r) = C/r$, that is, the same r dependence as found for $Z_F(r, T)$ in Eq. (6.8.16). Therefore, the force f_F required to maintain the length r computed on the basis of $p(r)$ by Eq. (6.7.2) gives the same result as that computed on the basis of $Z_F(r, T)$ by Eq. (6.8.17).

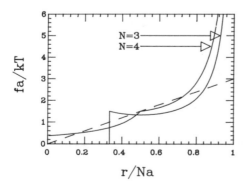

Figure 6.8 Force–length relation for strain ensemble of flexible model with $N = 3$ and 4 bonds. Dashed line is relation for Gaussian chain.

Results for Chains with Three and Four Bonds

The force–length relation of the strain ensemble for the flexible model of a freely jointed chain with three and four bonds are readily obtained by the force–probability relation, Eq. (6.7.2), applied to the probability distributions as given in Eqs. (5.5.18) and (5.5.19). The results are shown in Figure 6.8. We

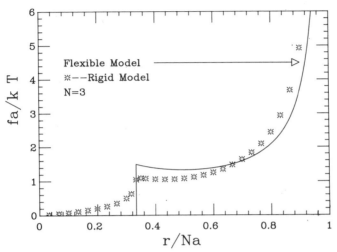

Figure 6.9   Comparison of force-length relation, strain ensemble, for flexible and rigid models with $N = 3$ bonds. (Reprinted with permission from Perchak and Weiner 1982. Copyright 1982 American Chemical Society.)

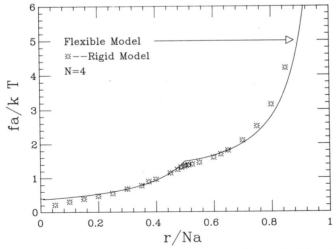

Figure 6.10   Comparison of force-length relation, strain ensemble, for flexible and rigid models with $N = 4$ bonds. (Reprinted with permission from Perchak and Weiner 1982. Copyright 1982 American Chemical Society.)

see, that although the results are still somewhat counter to physical intuition, they assume more of the character to be expected of an entropic spring as the number of bonds, N, increases. In this sense, the case of $N = 2$ is an anomaly in the sequence. We defer consideration of the cases $N = 5$ and 6 until the next section, where they will be compared with the results of a stress ensemble.

The contrast in behavior between rigid[23] and flexible models also decreases with increasing N, as seen in Figures 6.9 and 6.10.

6.9 STRESS ENSEMBLE FOR CHAIN MOLECULES

Consider a flexible model for a chain molecule, denoting the positions of its atoms with respect to a fixed rectangular Cartesian coordinate system by $x_0, x_1, \ldots, x_N$ with $x_0 = 0$.

As in Section 6.7, let $\bar{V}(x_0, x_1, \ldots, x_N)$ denote the sum of the harmonic constraining potential $\frac{1}{2}\kappa a_{AB}q^A q^B$ and the rotational potentials $V(q^\alpha)$, both expressed in terms of the rectangular Cartesian components of $x_0, \ldots, x_N$. We take the augmented stress ensemble viewpoint (Section 3.7) and consider that the Nth atom is subject to a constant force $\mathbf{f}$. Then the total potential for the system is $V = \bar{V} - \mathbf{f} \cdot x_N$. Since we are using rectangular Cartesian coordinates, the momentum portion of the partition function is deformation independent and we may confine attention to the configuration portion:

$$Z_{\mathscr{F}}(\mathbf{f}, T) = \int e^{-\beta(\bar{V} - \mathbf{f} \cdot x_N)} \prod_{l=1}^{N} dx_l \qquad (6.9.1)$$

where the subscript $\mathscr{F}$ denotes a stress ensemble, as in Section 3.7.

Consider next the strain ensemble for the same chain with $x_N = \mathbf{r}$. The configuration portion of the strain ensemble partition function is

$$Z_{\mathscr{A}}(\mathbf{r}, T) = \int e^{-\beta \bar{V}(x_0, x_1, \ldots, x_{N-1}, \mathbf{r})} \prod_{l=1}^{N-1} dx_l. \qquad (6.9.2)$$

Therefore,

$$Z_{\mathscr{F}}(\mathbf{f}, T) = \int_{\mathbb{R}_3} Z_{\mathscr{A}}(\mathbf{r}, T) e^{\beta \mathbf{f} \cdot \mathbf{r}} d\mathbf{r}, \qquad (6.9.3)$$

a result that is seen to be a special case of Eq. (3.7.27). Note that the present derivation depends on the use of a flexible model so that the position x_N is available as an independent variable.

As noted in Section 6.7,

$$Z_{\mathscr{A}}(\mathbf{r}, T) = Cp(\mathbf{r}, T), \qquad (6.9.4)$$

[23] Details of these calculations will be found in Perchak (1981) and in Perchak and Weiner (1982).

where $p(\mathbf{r}, T)$ is the probability density of finding atom N at $\mathbf{r}$, when atom N is free of any constraints or applied force and C is deformation independent; therefore, we may also write

$$Z_{\mathscr{F}}(\mathbf{f}, T) = C \int_{\mathbb{R}_3} p(\mathbf{r}, T) e^{\beta \mathbf{f} \cdot \mathbf{r}} \, d\mathbf{r}. \qquad (6.9.5)$$

By application of Eq. (3.8.37) to each component of $\mathbf{f}$, we find[24]

$$\langle \mathbf{r} \rangle = kT \frac{\partial}{\partial \mathbf{f}} \log Z_{\mathscr{F}}, \qquad (6.9.6)$$

or

$$\langle \mathbf{r} \rangle = \left[\int_{\mathbb{R}_3} p(\mathbf{r}, T) e^{\beta \mathbf{f} \cdot \mathbf{r}} \, d\mathbf{r} \right]^{-1} \int_{\mathbb{R}_3} \mathbf{r} p(\mathbf{r}, T) e^{\beta \mathbf{f} \cdot \mathbf{r}} \, d\mathbf{r}. \qquad (6.9.7)$$

Let

$$r_f = \mathbf{r} \cdot \mathbf{f}/f \qquad (6.9.8)$$

be the component of $\mathbf{r}$ in the direction of $\mathbf{f}$. Then, since $\langle r_f \rangle = \langle \mathbf{f} \cdot \mathbf{r} \rangle / f = \mathbf{f} \cdot \langle \mathbf{r} \rangle / f$,

$$\langle r_f \rangle = \left[\int_{\mathbb{R}_3} p(\mathbf{r}, T) e^{\beta f r_f} \, d\mathbf{r} \right]^{-1} \int_{\mathbb{R}_3} r_f p(\mathbf{r}, T) e^{\beta f r_f} \, d\mathbf{r}. \qquad (6.9.9)$$

We now restrict attention to isotropic chains, that is, $p(\mathbf{r}, T) = p(r, T)$, and study the behavior of the length–force relation for small f. For this purpose we expand Eq. (6.9.9) up to first order in f, obtaining

$$\langle r_f \rangle \cong \left[\int_{\mathbb{R}_3} (1 + \beta f r_f) p(\mathbf{r}, T) \, d\mathbf{r} \right]^{-1} \int_{\mathbb{R}_3} r_f (1 + \beta f r_f) p(\mathbf{r}, T) \, d\mathbf{r}$$

$$= \beta f \int_{\mathbb{R}_3} r_f^2 p(\mathbf{r}, T) \, d\mathbf{r} = \frac{\beta f}{3} \int_{\mathbb{R}_3} r^2 p(\mathbf{r}, T) \, d\mathbf{r} = \frac{\beta f}{3} \langle r^2 \rangle_0, \qquad (6.9.10)$$

where we have made use of the spherically symmetric character of $p(\mathbf{r}, T)$ and where we have written $\langle r^2 \rangle_0$ to emphasize that this mean is computed on the basis of $p(\mathbf{r}, T)$ and corresponds therefore to $\mathbf{f} = 0$.

The results obtained thus far apply to a flexible model of a chain of arbitrary length and character so long as it is isotropic.[25] For a sufficiently

---

[24] In component form, Eq. (6.9.6) takes the form $\langle r_i \rangle = kT(\partial/\partial f_i) \log Z_F$ where r_i, f_i are the rectangular Cartesian components of $\mathbf{r}$ and $\mathbf{f}$.

[25] It applies as well, therefore, in the presence of excluded volume effects (see Oono, Ohta, and Freed, 1981).

long chain, the distinction between stress and strain ensembles vanishes and we can rewrite Eq. (6.9.10) as

$$f \cong \frac{3kTr_f}{\langle r^2 \rangle_0} \tag{6.9.11}$$

with the result valid for either sufficiently small applied force f, or for sufficiently small applied end-to-end displacement r_f. For a Gaussian chain it is seen, from Eqs. (5.5.23) and (6.7.2), that Eq. (6.9.11) will be valid for arbitrary values of f and r_f.

Freely Jointed Chain

We consider next a flexible model for a freely jointed chain with N bonds of equilibrium length a. Let

$$\boldsymbol{\xi}_l = \mathbf{x}_l - \mathbf{x}_{l-1}, \qquad l = 1, \ldots, N \tag{6.9.12}$$

denote the bond vectors, so that

$$\mathbf{x}_N = \sum_{l=1}^{N} \boldsymbol{\xi}_l \tag{6.9.13}$$

since $\mathbf{x}_0 = 0$. Introduce a local spherical coordinate system for the position of atom $l, l = 1, \ldots, N$, with origin at atom $l - 1$ and with polar axis in the direction of $\mathbf{f}$. Then

$$Z_{\mathscr{F}}(\mathbf{f}, T; \kappa) = \int \exp\left\{ -\beta \sum_{l=1}^{N} \left[\kappa(\xi_l - a)^2 - f\xi_l \cos\theta_l \right] \right\} \prod_{l=1}^{N} \xi_l^2 \sin\theta_l \, d\xi_l \, d\theta_l \, d\varphi_l \tag{6.9.14}$$

which, for arbitrarily large κ, takes the form

$$Z_{\mathscr{F}}(f, T) = C \prod_{l=1}^{N} \int_0^{\pi} e^{\beta f a \cos\theta_l} \sin\theta_l \, d\theta_l$$

$$= C \left[\int_0^{\pi} e^{\beta f a \cos\theta} \sin\theta \, d\theta \right]^N = C \left[\frac{2}{\beta f a} \sinh\beta f a \right]^N. \tag{6.9.15}$$

Therefore

$$\langle r_f \rangle = kT \frac{\partial}{\partial f} \log Z_{\mathscr{F}} = Na \left[\coth\left(\frac{fa}{kT} \right) - \frac{kT}{fa} \right] = Na \mathscr{L}\left(\frac{fa}{kT} \right) \tag{6.9.16}$$

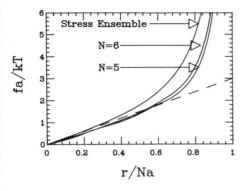

Figure 6.11 Comparison of force–length relation for flexible models: strain ensemble for $N = 5$ and 6, and stress ensemble for arbitrary N. Dashed line is relation for Gaussian chain. (Reprinted with permission from Perchak and Weiner 1982. Copyright 1982 American Chemical Society.)

where $\mathscr{L}(x) = \coth x - (1/x)$ is known as the Langevin function. For a freely jointed chain, $\langle r^2 \rangle_0 = Na^2$. It may be verified by direct computation that Eq. (6.9.16) satisfies Eq. (6.9.11) for sufficiently small f although, unlike the Gaussian chain, the length–force relation ceases to be linear for larger f.

As was the case for the linear chain crystalline model considered in Section 4.8, we see that the stress ensemble for the freely jointed chain leads to a relation for the strain measure, $\langle r_f \rangle / Na$, which is independent of N; it may be expected, therefore, from the discussion of Section 3.8, that Eq. (6.9.16) also describes the limiting behavior for large N for the strain ensemble. Figure 6.11 shows the result for the stress ensemble obtained by inversion of Eq. (6.9.16), and graphing fa/kT as function of r/Na; it is compared there with results for the strain ensemble, obtained by use of Eq. (6.7.2), for $N = 5$ and 6. The approach of the strain ensemble to its limiting behavior appears reasonably rapid.

6.10 STATISTICAL MECHANICS OF PHANTOM NETWORKS

The theory of rubber elasticity based on the model of a cross-linked network was considered from an elementary viewpoint in Section 5.6. We reexamine the subject in this section, attempting to tie the discussion more closely to the basic principles of statistical mechanics and to relate it, when possible, to the treatment of crystal elasticity in Chapter 4.

Consider a large cross-linked network, Figure 6.12. Choose a portion of the network which, in the reference state and at a given instant, t_0, occupies a rectangular parallelepiped $\mathscr{P}_0$. The atoms of the network in the interior of $\mathscr{P}_0$ at t_0, the interior atoms, comprise the system to be treated explicitly by statistical mechanics. The remaining atoms of the network, the exterior atoms, act as heat bath for the interior network and also act to impose either a specified deformation or stress on it. We will focus here on the first possibility, that is, we treat a strain ensemble. From the macroscopic viewpoint we regard the body as subjected to an affine deformation, which deforms the rectangular

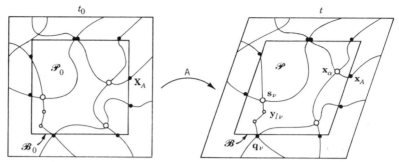

Figure 6.12   Schematic representation of deformed random network.

parallelepiped $\mathscr{P}_0$ and its boundary $\mathscr{B}_0$ into parallelpiped $\mathscr{P}$ and boundary $\mathscr{B}$. On the atomistic level, this deformation is imposed in the following manner:

Consider the chains which cross the boundary $\mathscr{B}_0$ at time t_0. On each such chain we select the exterior atom closest to $\mathscr{B}_0$ and designate it as a boundary node.[26] We assume that the position of each boundary node at time t is related to its position at time t_0 by the same affine deformation that takes $\mathscr{B}_0$ into $\mathscr{B}$. That is, we regard the boundary nodes as fixed in $\mathscr{B}_0$ and moving with it.

We see that the set of boundary node atoms corresponds to the interacting layer of atoms, E_{in}, in a crystal. They constitute only a single layer of atoms in the network since, as part of the model of chain molecules, each backbone atom interacts through covalent bonding only with its nearest neighbors along the chain. That their motion is controlled by the imposed affine deformation is consistent with the strain ensemble concept and the fact that they are part of the set of exterior atoms.[27]

We assume throughout this section the use of flexible models (Section 6.6) so that rectangular Cartesian coordinates may be employed. Let $\mathbf{x}_\alpha$, $\alpha = 1,\ldots,$ N_I be the positions at t of the interior nodes of the network, that is, the cross-linking atoms in the interior of $\mathscr{P}$, and let $\mathbf{x}_A, A = N_{I+1},\ldots, N$ be the positions of the boundary nodes at that time. As noted

$$\mathbf{x}_B = \mathbf{A}\mathbf{x}_B, \qquad B = N_{I+1},\ldots, N \qquad (6.10.1)$$

where $\mathbf{A}$ is the imposed affine deformation[28] and $\mathbf{X}_B$ is the position of boundary node B at time t_0. However, the set of interior nodes are in thermal motion and are not subjected to the imposed deformation.

The positions at time t of all of the nodes, interior and boundary, will be denoted by $\mathbf{x}_i$, $i = 1,\ldots, N$. In addition to this notation, it will be convenient

[26]A boundary node, therefore, may or may not be a node of the original cross-linked network.
[27]See also footnote 11, p. 134.
[28]This matrix notation has been introduced in Section 1.10. See Eq. (1.10.16).

to have, as well, an alternate notation for these positions which refers to the chains which run between them, writing $\mathbf{q}_\nu, \mathbf{s}_\nu$, for the positions of the terminal nodes of the ν'th chain, $\nu = 1, \ldots, N_C$. If the νth chain ends on the boundary, then $\mathbf{q}_\nu$ represents the boundary node; that is, $\mathbf{q}_\nu = \mathbf{x}_A$ for some A. If both ends of the chain are in the interior, then the choice of $\mathbf{q}_\nu, \mathbf{s}_\nu$ is immaterial.

Finally, let $\mathbf{y}_{l\nu}$, $l = 1, \ldots, N_\nu$, be the positions of the N_ν interior atoms of the νth chain. The notation is summarized in Figure 6.12.

Partition Function

Since we are using rectangular Cartesian coordinates, the momentum portion of the partition function is independent of deformation and therefore we consider, in what follows, only the configuration portion. Let V be the potential energy of interaction of all of the atoms of the network,

$$V = V(\mathbf{x}_I, \mathbf{x}_B, \mathbf{y})$$

where $\mathbf{x}_I = (\mathbf{x}_1, \ldots, \mathbf{x}_{N_I})$ denotes the positions of the interior nodes,

$\mathbf{x}_B = (\mathbf{x}_{N_I+1}, \ldots, \mathbf{x}_N)$ denotes the positions of the boundary nodes,

$\mathbf{y}$ denotes the positions of all of the chain atoms not at nodes.

Then, the configuration partition function of the network is

$$Z_{net}(\mathbf{x}_B, T) = \int e^{-\beta V} \prod_{\alpha=1}^{N_I} d\mathbf{x}_\alpha \prod_{\nu=1}^{N_C} \prod_{l=1}^{N_\nu} d\mathbf{y}_{l\nu} \qquad (6.10.2)$$

where the integration is carried out over all of the configuration space of the atoms which are in thermal motion.

It is now necessary to distinguish between intermolecular or interchain interactions between atoms belonging to different chains, and intramolecular or intrachain interactions between atoms belonging to the same chain. As we have discussed, the intrachain interactions, and in particular the covalent bonding between chain atoms, are primarily responsible for the characteristic features of rubber elasticity. Interchain interactions are certainly present. However, they are due primarily to steric effects (different atoms cannot occupy the same region of space), and their primary result appears to be to introduce a volume-dependent internal energy term whose effect is to make the material incompressible. It appears reasonable, therefore, to include the effect of interchain interactions phenomenologically, by means of an additional volume-dependent internal energy term, as in Section 5.6, and to consider on the basis of statistical mechanics a network in which interchain interactions are omitted.[29] We are also neglecting intrachain excluded volume effects so that, as

---

[29]Statistical mechanical treatments of interchain interactions, using approximations appropriate for the study of liquids, have been given by Boggs (1952) and Eichinger (1981). See also Flory (1977) for a discussion of the basis for the neglect of intermolecular interactions.

previously described, we are treating a phantom network. For such a network,

$$V(\mathbf{x}_I, \mathbf{x}_B, \mathbf{y}) = \sum_{\nu=1}^{N_\nu} V_\nu(\mathbf{q}_\nu, \mathbf{y}_{1\nu}, \ldots, \mathbf{y}_{N_\nu\nu}, \mathbf{s}_\nu) \tag{6.10.3}$$

where V_ν is the potential energy of the νth chain; it is of the form $\overline{V}$, introduced in Eq. (6.7.5), and is the sum of the harmonic constraining potential that simulates the covalent bonds and of any rotational potentials that are present. The remaining considerations of this section are confined to phantom networks, that is, to networks that satisfy Eq. (6.10.3).

By substitution of Eq. (6.10.3) into Eq. (6.10.2) it follows that

$$Z_{net}(\mathbf{x}_B, T) = \int \prod_{\nu=1}^{N_C} Z_\nu(\mathbf{q}_\nu, \mathbf{s}_\nu, T) \prod_{\alpha=1}^{N_I} d\mathbf{x}_\alpha \tag{6.10.4}$$

where

$$Z_\nu(\mathbf{q}_\nu, \mathbf{s}_\nu, T) = \int \exp\left[-\beta V_\nu(\mathbf{q}_\nu, \mathbf{y}_{1\nu}, \ldots, \mathbf{y}_{N_\nu\nu}, \mathbf{s}_\nu)\right] \prod_{l=1}^{N_\nu} d\mathbf{y}_{l\nu} \tag{6.10.5}$$

is the partition function for the νth chain when its ends are fixed at $\mathbf{q}_\nu, \mathbf{s}_\nu$.

From the basic interpretation of the canonical distribution function, we see that the probability density of finding the α node at $\mathbf{x}$ is

$$p_\alpha(\mathbf{x}; \mathbf{x}_B, T) = \frac{1}{Z_{net}} \int e^{-\beta V} \prod_{\alpha'}{}' d\mathbf{x}_{\alpha'} \prod_{\nu=1}^{N_C} \prod_{l=1}^{N_\nu} d\mathbf{y}_{l\nu}, \tag{6.10.6}$$

where $\prod'$ denotes the product over all internal nodes with $\alpha' = \alpha$ omitted. From Eqs. (6.10.3), (6.10.5), and (6.10.6),

$$p_\alpha(\mathbf{x}; \mathbf{x}_B, T) = \frac{1}{Z_{net}} \int \prod_{\nu=1}^{N_C} Z_\nu(\mathbf{q}_\nu, \mathbf{s}_\nu, T) \prod_{\alpha'}{}' d\mathbf{x}_{\alpha'}, \tag{6.10.7}$$

where, in Eqs. (6.10.6) and (6.10.7), the arguments $\mathbf{s}_\nu = \mathbf{x}$ for the values of ν which connect to the α node.

Force on Boundary Node

We turn next to $\mathbf{f}_A$, the time average of the force exerted on boundary node A. It is computed from the configuration space average[30]

$$\mathbf{f}_A = \frac{-1}{Z_{net}} \int \frac{\partial V}{\partial \mathbf{x}_A} e^{-\beta V} \prod_{\alpha=1}^{N_I} d\mathbf{x}_\alpha \prod_{\nu=1}^{N_C} \prod_{l=1}^{N_\nu} d\mathbf{y}_{l\nu} = +kT \frac{\partial}{\partial \mathbf{x}_A} \log Z_{net}$$

$$\tag{6.10.8}$$

---

[30] Recall that the distribution in momentum space is deformation independent.

or

$$\mathbf{f}_A = \frac{kT}{Z_{net}} \int \frac{\partial}{\partial \mathbf{x}_A} \prod_{\nu=1}^{N_C} Z_\nu(\mathbf{q}_\nu, \mathbf{s}_\nu, T) \prod_{\alpha=1}^{N_I} d\mathbf{x}_\alpha \qquad (6.10.9)$$

by use of Eq. (6.10.4). Let $\mathbf{q}_{\nu_A} = \mathbf{x}_A$ for $\nu_A = 1, \ldots, N_A$; that is, these are the N_A chains which end in the boundary node at $\mathbf{x}_A$. Then,

$$\frac{\partial}{\partial \mathbf{x}_A} \prod_{\nu=1}^{N_C} Z_\nu(\mathbf{q}_\nu, \mathbf{s}_\nu, T) = \sum_{\nu_A=1}^{N_A} \frac{\partial Z_{\nu_A}}{\partial \mathbf{x}_A} \prod_{\nu' \neq \nu_A}' Z_{\nu'}, \qquad (6.10.10)$$

where each product $\prod'$ is over all chains except ν_A. But

$$\mathbf{f}_{\nu_A}(\mathbf{s}, T) = kT \frac{\partial}{\partial \mathbf{x}_A} \log Z_{\nu_A}(\mathbf{x}_A, \mathbf{s}, T) = \frac{kT}{Z_{\nu_A}} \frac{\partial Z_{\nu_A}}{\partial \mathbf{x}_A} \qquad (6.10.11)$$

is the force[31] exerted on the boundary node at $\mathbf{x}_A$ through the ν_A chain if its interior node is fixed at $\mathbf{s}$. By substitution of Eqs. (6.10.10) and (6.10.11) into Eq. (6.10.9)

$$\mathbf{f}_A = \frac{1}{Z_{net}} \int \sum_{\nu_A=1}^{N_A} \mathbf{f}_{\nu_A} \prod_{\nu=1}^{N_C} Z_\nu \prod_{\alpha=1}^{N_I} d\mathbf{x}_\alpha. \qquad (6.10.12)$$

where, in each term of the sum over ν_A, the argument $\mathbf{s}_{\nu_A} = \mathbf{s}$. It then follows from Eq. (6.10.7) that

$$\mathbf{f}_A(\mathbf{x}_B, T) = \sum_{\nu_A=1}^{N_A} \int \mathbf{f}_{\nu_A}(\mathbf{s}, T) p_{\nu_A}(\mathbf{s}; \mathbf{x}_B, T) \, d\mathbf{s}, \qquad (6.10.13)$$

where p_{ν_A} is the probability density, defined in Eq. (6.10.7), for the position of the internal node of chain ν_A. This result, with a transparent physical interpretation, is due to James and Guth.[32]

With the availability of this interpretation of the force exerted on the boundary modes, we can also obtain a microscopic interpretation, for the network, of Eq. (1.6.10) which relates the Piola–Kirchhoff stress tensor and the affine deformation matrix. We rewrite Eq. (1.6.10) in matrix form as

$$\mathbf{T} = \frac{1}{\mathcal{V}} \frac{\partial F}{\partial \mathbf{A}} \qquad (6.10.14)$$

---

[31] For brevity, we are here using the term force in place of time average or phase average of the force.

[32] James and Guth (1943, p. 478).

where T is the Piola–Kirchhoff tensor, A is the deformation matrix, $\mathscr{V}$ is the original volume of the network and $F(A, T)$ is its Helmholtz free energy. Then,

$$T = \frac{-kT}{\mathscr{V}} \frac{\partial}{\partial A} \log Z_{net} = \frac{-kT}{\mathscr{V}} \sum_{A = N_I + 1}^{N} \left(\frac{\partial}{\partial x_A} \log Z_{net} \right) X_A$$

$$= -\frac{1}{\mathscr{V}} \sum_{A = N_I + 1}^{N} f_A X_A \tag{6.10.15}$$

by use of Eqs. (6.10.1) and (6.10.8). This is of the same form as Eq. (4.3.15) in our discussion of crystalline elasticity. By similar arguments to those used there,[33] we see that T has the physical significance of the Piola–Kirchhoff stress tensor. It treats only that part of the stress that corresponds to force transmitted through chains since interchain forces are not included in this discussion.[34] Note, that as in the discussion of crystal elasticity in Section 4.3, the natural atomistic interpretation of the stress tensor is in terms of the negative of the force f_A exerted by the interior atoms on the exterior atoms.

Gaussian Phantom Network[35]

We have seen in Section 6.7 that when flexible models are used, $Z_\nu(q_\nu, s_\nu, T) = Cp_\nu(q_\nu - s_\nu, T)$ where p_ν is the probability density for the end-to-end displacement vector of the νth chain and C is independent of this displacement.[36] Furthermore, for isotropic conditions,[37] $p_\nu = p_\nu(|q_\nu - s_\nu|, T)$. Therefore, for computations of mechanical behavior, we can replace Eq. (6.10.4) by

$$Z_{net}(x_B, T) = \int \prod_{\nu = 1}^{N_C} p_\nu(|q_\nu - s_\nu|, T) \prod_{\alpha = 1}^{N_I} dx_\alpha. \tag{6.10.16}$$

[33] For the perfect crystal the argument referred to the phase function for the stress tensor and it was possible to invoke symmetry considerations in the discussion. Here, it is necessary to restrict attention to the phase average of the stress tensor and to use the statistical homogeneity of the system.

[34] A discussion which treats the portion of the stress tensor due to interchain forces is given by Weiner and Stevens (1983).

[35] James and Guth (1943) and James (1947). See also the presentation of this theory given by Flory (1976) and by Kästner (1981).

[36] In the following discussion we use the notation C to represent any deformation independent quantity, not always the same one.

[37] For short chains, this requires that the initial link be uniformly distributed in direction, that is, the fixed node corresponds to a freely jointed connection. For sufficiently long chains, isotropy follows from chain flexibility independently of initial conditions.

We assume next that all the chains are Gaussian (Section 5.5) and write

$$p_\nu = \left(\frac{3}{2\pi N_\nu b^2}\right)^{3/2} \exp - \frac{3|\mathbf{q}_\nu - \mathbf{s}_\nu|^2}{2N_\nu b^2}$$

$$= C \exp - c_\nu |\underline{\mathbf{q}}_\nu - \underline{\mathbf{s}}_\nu|^2 \qquad (6.10.17)$$

where b is the effective link length and

$$c_\nu = 3(2N_\nu b^2)^{-1}. \qquad (6.10.18)$$

Therefore,

$$\prod_{\nu=1}^{N_C} p_\nu = C \exp - \sum_{\nu=1}^{N_C} c_\nu(\mathbf{q}_\nu \cdot \mathbf{q}_\nu - 2\mathbf{q}_\nu \cdot \mathbf{s}_\nu + \mathbf{s}_\nu \cdot \mathbf{s}_\nu) \qquad (6.10.19)$$

or

$$\prod_{\nu=1}^{N_C} p_\nu = C \exp - b_{ij}\mathbf{x}_i \cdot \mathbf{x}_j \qquad (6.10.20)$$

where we have gone from the notation $\mathbf{q}_\nu, \mathbf{s}_\nu, \nu = 1,\ldots, N_C$ for the nodal positions to the notation $\mathbf{x}_i, i = 1,\ldots, N$ for these same positions. The elements of the matrix b_{ij} are obtained by comparison of Eqs. (6.10.19) and (6.10.20):

$$\underline{b_{ii}} = \sum c_{\nu_{ii}} \qquad (6.10.21)$$

with the summation over all the chains ν_{ii} that join at node i;

$$b_{ij} = b_{ji} = -\sum c_{\nu_{ij}}, i \neq j, \qquad (6.10.22)$$

with the summation over all the chains ν_{ij} that join nodes i and j;

$$b_{ij} = 0 \qquad (6.10.23)$$

if nodes i and j are unconnected. It is seen that the network matrix b_{ij} depends only on the topology or the connectivity of the network and on the number of links in the chains connecting the various nodes; it is independent of the network configuration.[38]

---

[38]It is assumed that the matrix b_{ij} is nonsingular. This will be the case if every internal node is linked to a boundary node by at least one continuous path and one boundary node is fixed in space. Under these conditions, b_{ij} is positive definite as may be seen by considering the quadratic form $b_{ij}\mathbf{x}_i \cdot \mathbf{x}_j$ in the $\mathbf{q}_\nu, \mathbf{s}_\nu$ notation (see James, 1947; Flory, 1976).

Equation (6.10.20) describes a multivariate Gaussian distribution for $\mathbf{x}_\alpha$, the positions of the internal nodes, with $\mathbf{x}_A$, the positions of the boundary nodes, as parameters. Let

$$g(\mathbf{x}_\alpha, \mathbf{x}_A) = b_{ij}\mathbf{x}_i \cdot \mathbf{x}_j = b_{\alpha\beta}\mathbf{x}_\alpha \cdot \mathbf{x}_\beta + 2b_{\alpha A}\mathbf{x}_\alpha \cdot \mathbf{x}_A + b_{AB}\mathbf{x}_A \cdot \mathbf{x}_B.$$

(6.10.24)

For a Gaussian distribution, mean values and values of maximum probability coincide. Therefore, $\bar{\mathbf{x}}_\alpha$, the mean internal node positions, are obtained as solutions to the equations

$$\frac{\partial g}{\partial \mathbf{x}_\alpha} = 0 = 2(b_{\alpha\beta}\mathbf{x}_\beta + b_{\alpha A}\mathbf{x}_A)$$

(6.10.25)

or

$$\bar{\mathbf{x}}_\alpha = d_{\alpha A}\mathbf{x}_A$$

(6.10.26)

where

$$d_{\alpha A} = -b_{\alpha\beta}^{-1}b_{\beta A}$$

(6.10.27)

with $b_{\alpha\beta}^{-1}$ the matrix inverse to $b_{\alpha\beta}$. Since Eq. (6.10.26) is a linear relation, we have the following important result: If, in a Gaussian phantom network, the boundary nodes are subjected to an affine deformation from their reference configuration, as in Eq. (6.10.1), then the mean positions of the internal nodes in the reference and deformed configurations are related by the same affine deformation:

$$\bar{\mathbf{x}}_\alpha = A\bar{\mathbf{X}}_\alpha.$$

(6.10.28)

Let

$$\boldsymbol{\xi}_\alpha = \mathbf{x}_\alpha - \bar{\mathbf{x}}_\alpha$$

(6.10.29)

be the displacements of the internal nodes from their mean positions. By substituting $\mathbf{x}_\alpha = \boldsymbol{\xi}_\alpha + \bar{\mathbf{x}}_\alpha$ into Eq. (6.10.24) and using the fact that $\bar{\mathbf{x}}_\alpha$ satisfies Eq. (6.10.25), we find

$$g = b_{\alpha\beta}\boldsymbol{\xi}_\alpha \cdot \boldsymbol{\xi}_\beta + b_{ij}\bar{\mathbf{x}}_i \cdot \bar{\mathbf{x}}_j$$

(6.10.30)

where we have written $\bar{\mathbf{x}}_A = \mathbf{x}_A$ for the boundary node positions. It is now a straightforward matter to compute the network partition function Z_{net} by making a change in variable of integration in Eq. (6.10.16) from $\mathbf{x}_\alpha$ to $\boldsymbol{\xi}_\alpha$. The result is

$$Z_{net}(\mathbf{x}_B, T) = Ce^{-b_{ij}\bar{\mathbf{x}}_i \cdot \bar{\mathbf{x}}_j} \int e^{-b_{\alpha\beta}\boldsymbol{\xi}_\alpha \cdot \boldsymbol{\xi}_\beta} \prod_{\alpha=1}^{N_I} d\boldsymbol{\xi}_\alpha$$

$$= C\frac{(\pi)^{3N_I/2}}{|b_{\alpha\beta}|^{3/2}}e^{-b_{ij}\bar{\mathbf{x}}_i \cdot \bar{\mathbf{x}}_j}$$

(6.10.31)

or, since $b_{\alpha\beta}$ is deformation independent,

$$Z_{net}(\mathbf{x}_B, T) = C \exp - b_{ij} \bar{\mathbf{x}}_i \cdot \bar{\mathbf{x}}_j$$

$$= C \exp - \sum_{\nu=1}^{N_C} c_\nu |\bar{\mathbf{q}}_\nu - \bar{\mathbf{s}}_\nu|^2 = C \exp - \sum_{\nu=1}^{N_C} c_\nu \bar{r}_\nu^2 \quad (6.10.32)$$

where we have returned to the $\mathbf{q}_\nu, \mathbf{s}_\nu$ notation for the nodes, with

$$\bar{\mathbf{r}}_\nu = \bar{\mathbf{q}}_\nu - \bar{\mathbf{s}}_\nu \quad (6.10.33)$$

and $\bar{r}_\nu = |\bar{\mathbf{r}}_\nu|$.

The same analysis applies to the network in the reference configuration, so that

$$Z_{net}(\mathbf{X}_B, T) = C \exp - \sum_{\nu=1}^{N_C} c_\nu \overline{R}_\nu^2 \quad (6.10.34)$$

where

$$\overline{\mathbf{R}}_\nu = \overline{\mathbf{Q}}_\nu - \overline{\mathbf{S}}_\nu \quad (6.10.35)$$

are the mean end-to-end chain displacements in the reference configuration. Therefore, $F(\mathbf{A}, T)$, the Helmholtz free energy of the interior network in the deformed configuration, measured with respect to that in the reference configuration, is

$$F(\mathbf{A}, T) = -kT\left[\log Z_{net}(\mathbf{x}_B, T) - \log Z_{net}(\mathbf{X}_B, T)\right]$$

$$= kT \sum_{\nu=1}^{N_C} c_\nu\left(\bar{r}_\nu^2 - \overline{R}_\nu^2\right). \quad (6.10.36)$$

But, from Eqs. (6.10.1) and (6.10.28),

$$\bar{\mathbf{r}}_\nu = \mathbf{A}\overline{\mathbf{R}}_\nu, \qquad \nu = 1,\ldots, N_C, \quad (6.10.37)$$

so that $\bar{r}_\nu^2 - \overline{R}_\nu^2$ may be expressed in terms of the material strain tensor E_{LM} that corresponds to the affine deformation $\mathbf{A}$. Let $\overline{R}_L(\nu)$, $L = 1, 2, 3$, be the rectangular cartesian components of $\overline{\mathbf{R}}_\nu$; then,

$$\bar{r}_\nu^2 - \overline{R}_\nu^2 = 2E_{LM}\overline{R}_L(\nu)\overline{R}_M(\nu),$$

and

$$F(E_{LM}, T) = \frac{3kTE_{LM}}{b^2} \sum_{\nu=1}^{N_C} N_\nu^{-1} \overline{R}_L(\nu)\overline{R}_M(\nu), \quad (6.10.38)$$

where we have used Eq. (6.10.18). This result for the free energy of a phantom Gaussian network is of the same form as obtained in Section 5.6, Eq. (5.6.4); there are, however, the following differences in interpretation:

1 The end-to-end chain distances in the reference configuration, $R(\nu)$, were regarded as time-independent quantities after cross-linking in the discussion of Section 5.6. In the discussion of this section these distances are time-dependent fluctuating quantities and their means appear in Eq. (6.10.38).

2 The discussion of Section 5.6 was based on the $S = k \log p$ relation, and therefore Eq. (5.6.4) refers only to the entropy, while Eq. (6.10.38) refers to the free energy. The two are equivalent (Section 6.7) only if the model is one without rotational barriers so that $\overline{R_\nu^2}$ is temperature independent and the chain internal energy is deformation independent.

The remaining analysis of Section 5.6 can be applied directly to Eq. (6.10.38) in place of Eq. (5.6.4) and leads to the same stress–strain relations [Eqs. (5.6.17)–(5.6.20)].

Although, as noted in Eq. (6.10.28), the means of the internal node positions are transformed by the affine deformation, it follows from Eq. (6.10.30) that their fluctuations depend only on $b_{\alpha\beta}$ and are, therefore, independent of the deformation. The implications of this dichotomy for the behavior of real networks is discussed by Flory (1976, 1977a, b) and by Ronca and Allegra (1975). See also Dossin and Graessley (1979), Kästner (1981), and Gottlieb and Macosko (1982).

The model of Gaussian phantom chains treated in this section is, as we have noted, highly idealized. Inclusion of interchain interactions, and entanglement effects greatly complicate the analysis. See, for example, the statistical mechanics treatments of Deam and Edwards (1976) and Freed (1971).

CHAPTER SEVEN

Rate Theory in Solids

7.1 INTRODUCTION

In the previous chapters we were concerned with the principles of thermodynamics and statistical mechanics as applied to the elastic behavior of solids. In this chapter we present a brief discussion of the principles of the theory of rate processes in solids, a theory that finds important application in the study of some inelastic phenomena, such as the thermally activated creep of dislocations in crystals.

Although our primary concern in this book is with elastic behavior, we include this treatment of rate theory both because of its intrinsic interest and because it serves as a useful basis for clarifying and making more concrete some of the abstract principles of equilibrium statistical mechanics previously introduced.

In order to make the general nature of the theory of rate processes in solids clearer, we begin in Section 7.2 with a discussion of a specific application, the diffusion of impurity atoms in a crystal. A one-dimensional rate theory for this process is developed in Section 7.3. It is based on a large number of simplifying assumptions and represents the simplest theoretical formulation for this class of problems; the remainder of the chapter is concerned with refinements of this derivation in various directions.

One approximation made in the theory of Section 7.3 lies in the calculation of the normalization constant of the probability distribution function. New physical insight into the theory is obtained by an appropriate recasting of the exact calculation of this constant; details are presented in Section 7.4. The generalization of the one-dimensional theory to systems with many degrees of freedom is carried out in Section 7.5.

To this point in the chapter, the discussion of rate theory has been made on the basis of an important simplification, namely, the *transition-state* assumption. The nature of this assumption is discussed in Section 7.6. In order to go beyond this assumption, it is necessary to consider how the weak interactions between a small component and its heat bath affect the trajectory of the small component in its phase space (see Section 2.4 and Figure 2.4). One of the simplest ways of modeling this effect is in terms of the Langevin equation approach to the study of Brownian motion as discussed in Section 7.7. It is then shown in Section 7.8 how this approach can be used to derive Kramers rate formula, an important step in rate theory beyond the transition-state assumption.

7.2   IMPURITY ATOM DIFFUSION

Before beginning a detailed development of rate theory on the atomistic level, it will be helpful to consider a process whose macroscopic manifestations are clear and can be measured unambiguously. This is the process of impurity atom diffusion in crystals. Consider the following schematic experiment.

At time $t = 0$, we deposit a uniform surface layer of interstitial impurity atoms on a crystal with cubic symmetry, on a plane perpendicular to one of its principal axes, say the x direction. If we confine attention to early times, before the effects of other boundaries become significant, the process is equivalent by symmetry to one-dimensional diffusion in an infinite medium with an initially prescribed uniform concentration on the plane $x = 0$.

The macroscopic formulation of this diffusion problem is derived as follows. Consider the portion of the crystal shown in Figure 7.1. Let $c(x, t)$ be the impurity atom concentration, that is the number of impurity atoms per unit volume of the crystal. By Ficks' law, the flux J of impurity atoms (number of impurity atoms per unit time and area) crossing the plane at x in the $+x$

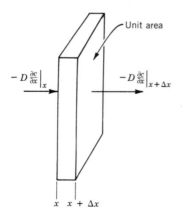

Figure 7.1   Diffusion from the macroscopic viewpoint.

direction is

$$J(x, t) = -D\frac{\partial c}{\partial x}(x, t) \tag{7.2.1}$$

where the proportionality constant D is called the diffusion constant. Then, by conservation of the number of impurity atoms, it is seen that

$$D\left(\left.\frac{\partial c}{\partial x}\right|_{x+\Delta x} - \left.\frac{\partial c}{\partial x}\right|_{x}\right) = \frac{\partial c}{\partial t} \cdot \Delta x \tag{7.2.2}$$

or, taking the limit as $\Delta x \to 0$,

$$D\frac{\partial^2 c}{\partial x^2} = \frac{\partial c}{\partial t}, \quad -\infty < x < \infty. \tag{7.2.3}$$

This partial differential equation is subject to the initial condition

$$c(x, 0) = c_0\delta(x), \tag{7.2.4}$$

where c_0 is the initial concentration expressed as the number of atoms per unit area, and $\delta(x)$ is the one-dimensional Dirac delta function. The solution to this standard problem is well known, namely,

$$c(x, t) = \frac{c_0}{(4\pi Dt)^{1/2}} e^{-x^2/(4Dt)}. \tag{7.2.5}$$

Experiments of this type are frequently performed. Concentration profiles at various times are obtained, for example, by sectioning the crystal into thin layers and determining the impurity atom concentration in each layer. By comparison of the experimentally determined concentration profile with the theoretical result of Eq. (7.2.5), the diffusion constant D for the process at the imposed temperature level is determined. For details see, for example, Shewmon (1963). Typical results of experiments conducted at different temperature levels are shown in Figure 7.2. They reveal that the diffusion coefficient has a temperature dependence of the form[1]

$$D = Ae^{-B/kT}. \tag{7.2.6}$$

A temperature dependence of this type is referred to as an Arrhenius relation and the semilog plot of Figure 7.2 is called an Arrhenius plot.[1]

We next consider the same process on an atomistic level. Initially there is one atom per area c_0^{-1} on the plane $x = 0$. We assume that the concentration is

[1]Figure 7.2 is illustrative only of typical results. Departures from Arrhenius behavior are frequently observed. Such departures present a further challenge for explanation on the atomic level.

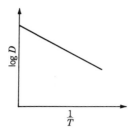

Figure 7.2   Arrhenius relation.

sufficiently dilute that impurity atoms do not interfere or interact with each other and we focus attention on a typical atom. We assume that it executes a random walk (Section 5.4), moving from one interstitial site to a neighboring interstitial site at an average rate of F jumps (or changes in sites) per unit time. Because of the cubic symmetry, the jump rate will be the same in the x, y, z directions, so that the jump rate f in the x direction is $F/3$ and, under the present conditions, which are macroscopically one-dimensional, it is only the distance that the atom travels in the x direction which affects the development of the concentration profile $c(x, t)$. In the time t, the impurity atom has executed a random walk in the x direction, having taken $n = ft$ steps of length a, where a is the lattice parameter of the crystal. Therefore, the probability distribution $p(x, t)$, describing the probability per unit distance of finding the atom at position x after time t is, as derived for a one-dimensional walk in Section 5.4,

$$p(x, t) = \frac{1}{(2\pi na^2)^{1/2}} \exp\left[-x^2/(2na^2)\right] = \frac{1}{(2\pi fa^2 t)^{1/2}} \exp\left[-x^2/(2fa^2 t)\right].$$

$$(7.2.7)$$

Since there are initially c_0 atoms per unit area in the plane $x = 0$, the expected concentration at (x, t) is $c(x, t) = c_0 p(x, t)$ or

$$c(x, t) = \frac{c_0}{(2\pi fa^2 t)^{1/2}} \exp\left[-x^2/(2fa^2 t)\right]. \qquad (7.2.8)$$

Comparison of Eqs. (7.2.5) and (7.2.8) shows that they are of the same form and that

$$D = \tfrac{1}{2}fa^2 = \tfrac{1}{6}Fa^2. \qquad (7.2.9)$$

This analysis has served, therefore, to relate the macroscopically observable diffusion coefficient D to the atomistic jump rate f. It follows that f also obeys an Arrhenius relation if the diffusion constant D does. It is the goal of rate theory to proceed further in the understanding of this process on the atomistic level and to relate the parameters of the observed Arrhenius relation to detailed aspects of an atomistic model of the process.

7.3 A SIMPLE ONE-DIMENSIONAL RATE THEORY

We begin with a simple one-dimensional rate theory, which serves to introduce many of the basic ideas. As the underlying physical process for the discussion, we continue to use the diffusion of impurity atoms in a crystal, although many other examples can serve as a basis for the same simple theory.

We may represent the basic step of the impurity diffusion process schematically, as in Figure 7.3. The host atoms are shown in the vicinity of their regular lattice sites; the impurity atom, of mass m, is shown in an interstitial position at S. Because of thermal motion it may move to the equivalent interstitial position at S'. In order to reduce the problem to one spatial dimension we concentrate on the motion of the impurity atom in the x direction and ignore the motion of the other atoms. Then we may regard the force exerted on the impurity atom as derived from a potential function $V(x)$, which represents the total interaction of all the host atoms with the impurity atom. Since both S and S' are stable equilibrium positions for the impurity, this potential is periodic, taking the form shown schematically in Figure 7.3.

Thus far, our discussion has centered on a single impurity atom. In a real crystal we have a large number of impurity atoms, all of the same type, near equivalent positions and in thermal motion (Figure 7.4a). In order to describe the dynamical state of a given impurity atom at a given instant of time it is, from the viewpoint of classical mechanics, necessary and sufficient to determine its position and momentum then. That is, its instantaneous state

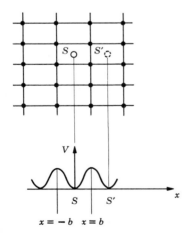

Figure 7.3 Basic step of impurity diffusion.

corresponds to a point (x, p) in a phase space with those coordinates (Figure 7.4b). In this description the distance x for each impurity atom is measured from its nearest stable equilibrium position so that $-b < x < b$ (Figure 7.3). To describe the instantaneous state of the entire collection of impurity atoms, we use a distribution function $\rho(x, p)$. This function is defined so that the value of the integral

$$\int_D \rho(x, p)\, dx\, dp \qquad\qquad (7.3.1)$$

equals the fraction of all the impurity atoms in an arbitrary region D of phase space. Therefore $\rho(x, p)$ must satisfy the normalization condition

$$\int_{-b}^{b} dx \int_{-\infty}^{\infty} dp\, \rho(x, p) = 1. \qquad\qquad (7.3.2)$$

A tacit assumption has been made in this description which should be made explicit. The distribution function $\rho(x, p)$ has been assumed not to depend explicitly on time so that the distribution of impurity atoms corresponds to steady-state conditions; although there is continual motion of the impurity atoms throughout phase space, the fraction of the total in a given region of phase space remains constant.

With the aid of the distribution function, $\rho(x, p)$, we can readily derive an expression for the average rate at which impurity atoms leave one stable equilibrium configuration and move to an adjacent one. Those impurity atoms that will cross the line $x = b$ in a time interval dt and with momentum in the range p to $p + dp$ must be contained in the region of phase space shown in Figure 7.5. By the definition of the distribution function, Eq. (7.3.1), these impurity atoms represent the fraction

$$\frac{1}{m}\rho(b, p)(p\, dt)(dp)$$

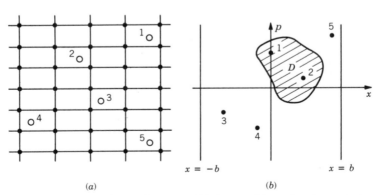

(a) (b)

Figure 7.4 (a) Collection of impurity atoms (b) States of impurity atoms at given instant displayed in phase space. (After Weiner 1970.)

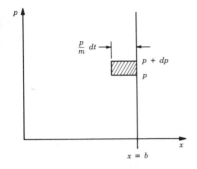

Figure 7.5   Calculation of rate of barrier crossing.

of the total number of impurity atoms in the collection. Division by the time interval dt and integration over all positive velocities, therefore, yields the desired average fractional rate,[2] f, with which impurity atoms cross the potential barrier at $x = b$;

$$f = \frac{1}{m} \int_0^{\infty} p\rho(b, p) \, dp. \tag{7.3.3}$$

In order to proceed further, it is necessary to fix the explicit form of $\rho(x, p)$. If we assume that we have a dilute collection of impurity atoms which do not interact with each other, and that they are in thermal equilibrium with the rest of the crystal at some common temperature T, then we may take the collection of impurity atoms as a physical representation of the concept of a canonical ensemble of replicas of a single impurity atom. Therefore,

$$\rho(x, p) = C \exp - \left[\frac{H(x, p)}{kT} \right] \tag{7.3.4}$$

where

$$H(x, p) = \frac{p^2}{2m} + V(x) \tag{7.3.5}$$

and where C is a normalization constant to be determined from Eq. (7.3.2). As it stands, the spatial portion of the normalization integral is difficult to evaluate because of the form of $V(x)$ and the finite range of integration. However, for low temperature levels the major contribution to the integral with respect to x comes from the neighborhood of $x = 0$ in which $V(x)$ may be approximated

$$V(x) = \tfrac{1}{2}\kappa_w x^2. \tag{7.3.6}$$

---

[2] That is, if there are N impurity atoms in the crystal, fN will cross per unit time. The discussion of this section follows, in part, Weiner (1970).

Since in the region where this approximation is poor the contribution to the integral is negligible in any case,[3] the range of integration may be extended to $-\infty < x < \infty$. The normalization constant C may then be evaluated readily as

$$C = \frac{\nu_0}{kT} \tag{7.3.7}$$

where $\nu_0 = \frac{1}{2\pi}\sqrt{\kappa_w/m}$ is the natural frequency of oscillation in the harmonic region of the well. The physical significance of this mathematical approximation is important. Consider a thought experiment for the determination of all the dynamical states (x, p) at a given instant of time and hence for the determination of $\rho(x, p)$. Then, this approximation for the normalization constant C implies that almost all impurity atoms will be observed near the bottom of the well with only a few observed up on slopes of the barrier. The latter are neglected in the normalization of the distribution in phase space of the ensemble.

With $\rho(x, p)$ thus made explicit, the integration in Eq. (7.3.3) for the rate f may be performed, leading to the result

$$f = \nu_0 e^{-V(b)/kT} = \nu_0 e^{-E_b/kT}. \tag{7.3.8}$$

We are thus led to a rate expression of the general Arrhenius type Eq. (7.2.6). The one-dimensional analysis has served to provide an atomistic interpretation of the parameters that appear in an Arrhenius relation. The preexponential multiplying factor A is here given the interpretation of ν_0, the frequency of oscillation of the particle in the harmonic well. The quantity B in the exponent is here seen as $V(b) = E_b$, the height of the energy barrier; it is referred to as the activation energy of the process.

This simple analysis, therefore, permits us to take experimental data for the diffusion coefficient D, as exemplified by Eq. (7.2.6), relate it to the jump frequency, f, by a relation such as[4] Eq. (7.2.9), and then to extract information, ν_0 and E_b, about the impurity atom–host lattice interaction by use of Eq. (7.3.8). Of course, the reliability of this information depends on the degree to which the idealized model represents the real situation. In the following sections of this chapter we consider various directions in which the model can be made more realistic.

Energy Units

Another convention widely used for presenting an experimentally determined Arrhenius relation is to write it in the form

$$f = \nu_0 e^{-E_b/RT} \tag{7.3.9}$$

---

[3] This is the same argument as used in Section 4.5 in the discussion of the harmonic approximation.
[4] Equation (7.2.9) applies only to interstitial diffusion in simple cubic crystals (cf. Shewmon, 1963). Equations of similar nature are available for other cases.

where

$$R = N_{Av}k = 8.314 \times 10^7 \text{ erg deg}^{-1} \text{ mole}^{-1} \qquad (7.3.10)$$

is the gas constant and

$$N_{Av} = 6.023 \times 10^{23} \text{ mole}^{-1} \qquad (7.3.11)$$

is Avogadro's number. When Eq. (7.3.8) is used, the activation energy E_b is expressed in units of energy, for example, $E_b = 0.5$ eV, while if Eq. (7.3.9) is used, E_b is expressed in units of energy/mole, for example, 3 kcal/mole. The following energy equivalents may be noted:

1 kilocalorie (kcal) = 4.184×10^{10} erg
1 kilojoule (kJ) = 1×10^{10} erg
1 electron volt (eV) = 1.602×10^{-12} erg

and we recall that Boltzmann's constant $k = 1.380 \times 10^{-16}$ erg deg^{-1}. With the aid of these values, we can compute the temperatures listed in the following table at which either E_b/kT or E_b/RT, as appropriate, is unity when $E_b = 1$ in the given system of units.

E_b	1 eV	1 kcal mole^{-1}	1 kJ mole^{-1}
T, °K	1.161×10^4	5.032×10^2	1.203×10^2

7.4   EXACT NORMALIZATION

We return to the question of the calculation of the normalization constant C in Eq. (7.3.4), which, by use of Eq. (7.3.2), is given by

$$C^{-1} = \int_{-\infty}^{\infty} dp \int_{-b}^{b} \exp\left[-\left(\frac{p^2}{2m} + V(x) \right) / kT \right] dx. \qquad (7.4.1)$$

In the previous section this integral was evaluated approximately, in a manner valid for low temperature levels, with the result given in Eq. (7.3.7). Here we consider its exact evaluation in a form (Weiner, 1978) that makes clear its general physical significance.

For this purpose, consider the trajectory in phase space, Figure 7.6, corresponding to constant energy $H(x, p) = E$, for the Hamiltonian of the impurity particle, Eq. (7.3.5). Let $t(E, x)$ be the time required for the particle to travel from position 1 to the position x along this trajectory. As noted in Figure 7.6, for $E > V(b)$, position 1 corresponds to $x = b$ while for $E < V(b)$ it corresponds to the maximum positive excursion of the particle, both on trajectories with $p < 0$; furthermore, for $E > E_b$ we set $t_a = t_{a'}$ (Figure 7.6) so that t varies continuously in going from 1 to a to a' to 2. We wish to use the curvilinear coordinates E, t in place of coordinates p, x (note that these are like oriented in this order) for the evaluation of the integral in Eq. (7.4.1), and for this purpose it is necessary to compute the Jacobian

$$\frac{\partial(E, t)}{\partial(p, x)} = \begin{vmatrix} E_p & E_x \\ t_p & t_x \end{vmatrix}, \tag{7.4.2}$$

where

$$E_p = \frac{\partial E}{\partial p}(p, x), \qquad t_p = \frac{\partial t}{\partial p}(p, x), \qquad \text{etc.}$$

While E is conveniently expressed as function of p, x,

$$E(p, x) = \frac{p^2}{2m} + V(x), \tag{7.4.3}$$

t is more conveniently obtained as function of E, x:

$$t(E, x) = m \int_1^x \frac{dx'}{p(E, x')} = \left(\frac{m}{2}\right)^{1/2} \int_1^x (E - V(x'))^{-1/2} \, dx' \tag{7.4.4}$$

and we must use the relations

$$t_p = \frac{\partial t}{\partial E}(E, x)E_P, \qquad t_x = \frac{\partial t}{\partial x}(E, x) + \frac{\partial t}{\partial E}(E, x)E_x. \tag{7.4.5}$$

From Eqs. (7.4.2)–(7.4.5) we find

$$\frac{\partial(E, t)}{\partial(p, x)} = E_p \frac{\partial t}{\partial x}(E, x) = \frac{p}{m} \cdot \frac{m}{p} = 1. \tag{7.4.6}$$

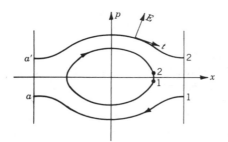

Figure 7.6 Energy–time coordinate system.

Therefore, Eq. (7.4.1) can be rewritten as

$$C^{-1} = \int_0^\infty e^{-E/kT} \int_{t_1(E)}^{t_2(E)} dt \, dE$$

$$= \int_0^\infty t(E) e^{-E/kT} dE, \tag{7.4.7}$$

where $t(E)$ is the time spent[5] by the particle in the region $-b < x < b$ when it has energy E. Therefore, we may write

$$C = \frac{\nu(T)}{kT}, \tag{7.4.8}$$

where

$$\nu(T) = \left[\frac{1}{kT} \int_0^\infty t(E) e^{-E/kT} dE \right]^{-1} \tag{7.4.9}$$

is the thermally averaged frequency of oscillation of the particle in the well. If this exact value of the normalization constant C is used in the rate formula derivation of Section 7.3, then Eq. (7.3.8) becomes

$$f = \nu(T) e^{-V(b)/kT}. \tag{7.4.10}$$

Therefore, the use of the exact normalization condition introduces a temperature-dependent frequency factor into the Arrhenius relation but leaves the activation energy unchanged. Since the exponential factor will dominate, it may be difficult to detect the temperature-dependent frequency factor predicted by Eq. (7.4.10). However, computer simulation experiments (Pear and Weiner, 1978) indicate that if sufficiently accurate experimental data are available to detect this temperature dependence, then it may be used to deduce additional information as to the shape of the potential $V(x)$.

7.5 MANY DEGREES OF FREEDOM

The one-dimensional rate theory of Sections 7.3 and 7.4 focused on a single degree of freedom of the diffusing impurity atom with the atoms of the host lattice regarded as fixed at their equilibrium sites. It ignored, therefore, the role of the thermal motion of the host atoms and also ignored important cooperative motion of host and impurity atoms. The latter is illustrated in Figure 7.7 in

---

[5]For $E > V(b)$, this is to be interpreted as twice the time required for the particle to travel from $x = -b$ to $x = b$.

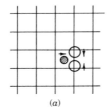 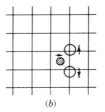

(a)   (b)

Figure 7.7   Required coordination in interstitial diffusion.

which atoms are represented not as geometric points but as spheres with some effective radii.[6] It is clear that it would be much more difficult for the impurity atom to exchange sites when host atoms 1 and 2 have moved together as in Figure 7.7a than when they have moved apart as in Figure 7.7b.

We consider next a rate theory for this class of processes which, in theory, includes as many of the degrees of freedom of the system (in this case impurity plus host atoms) as desired. As a specific example we continue to use the case of the diffusion of interstitial impurity atoms, although it is clear that the mathematical formulation applies unchanged to many other processes, for example, to the thermally activated motion of dislocations.[7] Assume again that the crystal contains a dilute concentration of impurity atoms. Without any significant change in the physical situation, we regard them as uniformly distributed so that the host crystal can be regarded as composed of a large number of identical crystallites, each containing one impurity atom in the same corresponding cell (Figure 7.8). Each crystallite has N atoms (including the impurity atom) and $n = 3N$ degrees of freedom. Mass-reduced coordinates, Eq. (4.4.4), are used and the Hamiltonian of each crystallite (with the same indexing of atoms used in each) is, as in Eq. (4.4.5),[8]

$$H(q, p) = \frac{1}{2} \sum_{i=1}^{n} p_i^2 + V(q_1,\ldots, q_n).$$

Our discussion parallels the treatment of the model with one degree of freedom given in Section 7.3. The crystallite has a stable equilibrium configuration S with the impurity atom at the center of the cell as shown in Figure 7.9a and another stable equilibrium configuration S' with the impurity atom in the center of the adjacent cell, Figure 7.9c. As shown in Figure 7.9, the presence of the impurity will result in distortion of the host lattice in its stable equilibrium configurations. (There are other adjacent stable equilibrium configurations but

---

[6] That is, repulsive interatomic forces become very large when the distance between a pair of atoms is less than the sum of the effective radii.

[7] This process is discussed in Weiner and Sanders (1964) and Weiner (1969).

[8] The Hamiltonian of Eq. (4.4.5), $H(q, p; E_{LM})$, includes the possible effect of an imposed deformation on the rate process. We return to this question at the end of this section.

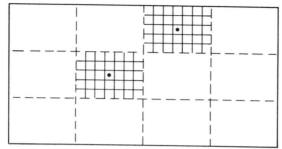

Figure 7.8 Conceptual collection of identical crystallites each containing impurity atom.

we are focusing on these two.) Between configurations S and S' there is an unstable equilibrium configuration, U, Figure 7.9b. In configuration space, Γ_q, the constant energy contours of $V(q_1,\ldots,q_n)$ must then appear as shown schematically in Figure 7.10. Points S and S' correspond to potential minima while U corresponds to a saddle point.

Thus far, our discussion has centered on a single crystallite. To describe the dynamical state of the collection of crystallites we use a distribution function

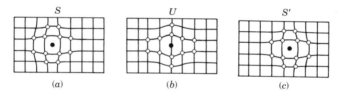

(a)	(b)	(c)

Figure 7.9 Stable configurations S and S' with intervening unstable configuration U.

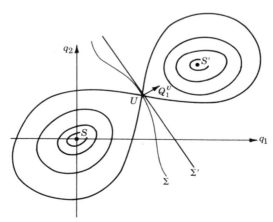

Figure 7.10 Stable configurations S and S' with intervening unstable configuration U shown in configuration space.

$\rho(q_1, \ldots, q_n, p_1, \ldots, p_n) = \rho(q, p)$ with the property that

$$\int_D \rho(q, p) \, dq \, dp$$

equals the fraction of crystallites in an arbitrary region D of phase space. Therefore, $\rho(q, p)$ must satisfy the normalization condition

$$\int_{D_s} dq \int_{\Gamma_p} dp \rho(q, p) = 1 \tag{7.5.1}$$

where D_s corresponds to the maximal region[9] in configuration space in which S is the only stable equilibrium configuration for the crystallite and U is the only other equilibrium configuration. Because we are using the same system of coordinates for all of the crystallites, they all occupy the region D_s of configuration space prior to any impurity atom transitions.

We may again regard the collection of crystallites as a physical representation of the concept of a canonical ensemble of replicas of a single crystallite, all in thermal equilibrium at temperature T.[10] Therefore,

$$\rho(q, p) = Ce^{-H(q, p)/kT} \tag{7.5.2}$$

with the constant C to be determined by the normalization condition of Eq. (7.5.1). We carry out this computation approximately, as in Section 7.3. In the vicinity of S, which we take at the origin of Γ_q, we express V in its harmonic approximation

$$V(q_1, \ldots, q_n) = \tfrac{1}{2} S_{ij} q_i q_j \tag{7.5.3}$$

where we have taken $V = 0$ at S and where, since S is a stable equilibrium configuration, S_{ij}, $i, j = 1, \ldots, n$, is a positive-definite matrix. For sufficiently low temperature levels, the major contribution to the integral over D_s in Eq. (7.5.1) comes from the region in which the harmonic approximation to V, Eq. (7.5.3), is valid and since the integrand is negligible in any case where this approximation is poor (see Figure 4.5), we may extend the integration employing it over all of Γ_q. Therefore,

$$C^{-1} = \int_{\Gamma_q} e^{-S_{ij}q_i q_j/2kT} \, dq \int_{\Gamma_p} e^{-p_i p_i/2kT} \, dp. \tag{7.5.4}$$

---

[9] In view of the approximations made in use of the normalization condition (7.5.1), the precise definition of D_s is not important.

[10] The correspondence is limited to their statistical properties. See Section 7.6.

The integral over Γ_q is evaluated, as in the calculations leading to Eq. (4.5.5), by transforming to normal coordinates so that

$$S_{ij}q_iq_j = \sum_{i=1}^{n} \lambda_i^s (Q_i^s)^2 \qquad (7.5.5)$$

where, since S_{ij} is positive-definite, its eigenvalues $\lambda_i^s > 0$, $i = 1,\ldots, n$. It is then found that

$$C^{-1} = (2\pi kT)^n \prod_{i=1}^{n} (\lambda_i^s)^{-1/2} = (2\pi kT)^n |S|^{-1/2} \qquad (7.5.6)$$

where $|S|$ is the determinant of the matrix S_{ij}.

Consider next the flux of replicas to the adjacent potential well. Let q_i^U be the coordinates of U and consider the harmonic approximation of V in the neighborhood of U,

$$V = V_U + \tfrac{1}{2}U_{ij}(q_i - q_i^U)(q_j - q_j^U). \qquad (7.5.7)$$

Since U is an unstable equilibrium configuration, the matrix U_{ij} must have at least one negative eigenvalue $\lambda_1^U < 0$, and we assume there is only one[11] so that $\lambda_i^U > 0$, $i = 2,\ldots, n$. Let Q_i^U be the normal coordinates for U_{ij}, with origin at U, with corresponding momenta P_i^U. Then Q_1^U is in the direction of maximum negative curvature of the saddle point in the potential energy surface at U; its sign is taken so that it points in the direction away from S and toward S' (Figure 7.10). It is next necessary to define a critical hypersurface Σ passing through U with the property that any trajectory that begins in D_s and crosses Σ goes on to the neighborhood of S'. If the temperature level is sufficiently low, then most of the transitions from S to S' will take place along trajectories that will pass through the neighborhood of the saddle point at U; therefore, we can take as the critical surface the hyperplane Σ' perpendicular to Q_1^U with coordinates Q_i^U, $i = 2,\ldots, n$ lying in Σ'. Let Γ' denote the $2(n-1)$ dimensional phase space corresponding to $Q_{i'}^U$, $P_{i'}^U$, $i' = 2,\ldots, n$. Then, by the same reasoning as used in Section 7.3 for the one-dimensional case, the fractional rate f of crossing the critical hyperplane Σ' is

$$f = \int_0^{\infty} P_1^U \, dP_1^U \int_{\Gamma'} \rho(0, P_1^U, Q_{i'}^U, P_{i'}^U) \prod_{i'=2}^{n} dQ_{i'}^U \, dP_{i'}^U. \qquad (7.5.8)$$

Again, by the same type of reasoning previously employed (e.g., Section 4.5 and Figure 4.5), if the temperature level is sufficiently low, then the principal

---

[11] This is equivalent to the assumption that the path through U leads to only one other stable equilibrium configuration S'.

contribution to the integral over Γ' comes from the neighborhood of U for which we can write

$$\rho\left(0, P_1^U; Q_{i'}^U, P_{i'}^U\right) = C \exp - \left\{\frac{1}{2} \sum_{i=1}^{n} \left(P_i^U\right)^2 + V_U + \frac{1}{2} \sum_{i'=2}^{n} \lambda_{i'}^U \left(Q_{i'}^U\right)^2\right\}/2kT,$$

(7.5.9)

and we may use this expression for ρ for integration over all of Γ' since the integrand is negligible where the approximation is poor. The integrations of Eq. (7.5.8) are then straightforward, with the result[12]

$$f = \frac{1}{2\pi} \left[\frac{|S|^{1/2}}{\displaystyle\prod_{i'=2}^{n} \left(\lambda_{i'}^U\right)^{1/2}} \right] e^{-V_U/kT},$$

$$= \frac{1}{2\pi} \left[\lambda_1^U \frac{|S|}{|U|} \right]^{1/2} e^{-V_U/kT}, \qquad (7.5.10)$$

$$= \frac{1}{2\pi} \left[\frac{\displaystyle\prod_{i=1}^{n} \omega_i^S}{\displaystyle\prod_{i'=2}^{n} \omega_{i'}^U} \right] e^{-V_U/kT}.$$

We have given three different forms of the expression by use of the relations,

$$\prod_{i=1}^{n} \lambda_i^U = |U|, \qquad (7.5.11)$$

where $|U|$ is the determinant of the matrix U_{ij} and

$$\omega_i^S = \left(\lambda_i^S\right)^{1/2}, \, i = 1,\ldots, n; \qquad \omega_{i'}^U = \left(\lambda_{i'}^U\right)^{1/2}, \, i' = 2,\ldots, n, \quad (7.5.12)$$

where we recall that we are using mass-reduced coordinates.

We see that the rate expression derived with the consideration of many degrees of freedom of the system is again of the Arrhenius form. The activation energy is given by the barrier height at the saddle point. The frequency factor

---

[12] The development of Eq. (7.5.10), with the process of diffusion in solids as motivation, was given by Vineyard (1957). The same expression has been derived with chemical reaction processes as motivation (see, e.g., Slater, 1959, p. 105).

is now, however, of a more complex form than obtained from the one degree of freedom analysis. We consider next a procedure which may aid in its calculation for specific models.

Computation of $|S|/|U|$

If n is large, then the direct computation of the determinants $|S|$ and $|U|$ for a specific atomistic model would be difficult. On the other hand, since in the present formulation each crystallite contains only a single localized defect, such as an impurity atom or a dislocation, we can expect that the matrices S_{ij} and U_{ij}, or S and U, will only differ substantially in relatively few entries. This fact may be used to simplify the computation of the determinantal quotient.

Let $D = U - S$ be the defect matrix that will have most of its elements of negligible magnitude. Then,

$$I = UU^{-1} = (S + D)U^{-1} = SU^{-1} + DU^{-1}$$

where I is the $n \times n$ identity matrix. Therefore,

$$SU^{-1} = I - DU^{-1}$$

and

$$|S|/|U| = |I - DU^{-1}|, \tag{7.5.13}$$

thus reducing the problem to the computation of the determinant of a sparse matrix. Examples of the use of Eq. (7.5.13) in the computation of the frequency factor for creep in an atomistic dislocation model may be found in Weiner and Sanders (1964) and for an atomistic model for vacancy diffusion in Weiner and Adler (1966).

Use of Thermodynamic Terminology

Rate processes in solids are frequently described using the terminology of macroscopic thermodynamics. The atomistic theory of this section may be recast in this language as follows:[13]

Equation (7.5.8) may be rewritten as

$$f = C \int_0^\infty P_1^U e^{-(P_1^U)^2/2kT} dP_1^U \int_{\Gamma'} e^{-H'(Q_{i'}^U, P_{i'}^U)/kT} \prod_{i'=2}^{n} dQ_{i'}^U dP_{i'}^U, \tag{7.5.14}$$

where $H'(Q_{i'}^U, P_{i'}^U)$ is the Hamiltonian of the system constrained to move in the hyperplane Σ' (Figure 7.10) so that it has only $n - 1$ degrees of freedom. The

[13] Vineyard (1957) and Wert and Zener (1949).

normalization constant $C = Z^{-1}$, where Z is the partition function of the system when it is in the vicinity of its equilibrium configuration [see Eq. (7.5.4)]. The integration with respect to P_1^U may be performed leading to the expression

$$f = \left(\frac{kT}{2\pi}\right)^{1/2} \frac{Z_{\Sigma'}}{Z},$$
(7.5.15)

where $Z_{\Sigma'}$ is the partition function corresponding to $H'(Q_{i'}^U, P_{i'}^U)$.

Let Σ_0 be a hyperplane passing through the equilibrium configuration at S parallel to Σ' (Figure 7.10), and let Z_{Σ_0} be the partition function of the system when constrained to move in Σ_0. Then Eq. (7.5.15) can be rewritten in the form,

$$f = \left(\frac{kT}{2\pi}\right)^{1/2} \frac{Z_{\Sigma_0}}{Z} \frac{Z_{\Sigma'}}{Z_{\Sigma_0}}.$$
(7.5.16)

We now regard the strains E_{LM} as imposed parameters on each crystallite so that all partition functions depend on E_{LM} and T, and formally apply Eq. (3.9.1) to $Z_{\Sigma'}$ and Z_{Σ_0}:

$$F'(E_{LM}, T) = -kT \log Z_{\Sigma'}(E_{LM}, T),$$
(7.5.17)

and

$$F_0(E_{LM}, T) = -kT \log Z_{\Sigma_0}(E_{LM}, T).$$
(7.5.18)

Then, Eq. (7.5.16) can be rewritten in the form

$$f = \tilde{\nu} e^{-\Delta F/kT}$$
(7.5.19)

where

$$\Delta F(E_{LM}, T) = F'(E_{LM}, T) - F_0(E_{LM}, T)$$
(7.5.20)

may be referred to as the free energy of activation and the frequency factor

$$\tilde{\nu} = \left(\frac{kT}{2\pi}\right)^{1/2} \frac{Z_{\Sigma_0}}{Z}.$$
(7.5.21)

If the stresses T_{LM} are regarded as imposed parameters, then the Helmholtz free energy $F(E_{LM}, T)$ is replaced by the Gibbs free energy $G(T_{LM}, T)$ in Eqs. (7.5.19) and (7.5.20).

The frequency factor $\tilde{\nu}$ may be related to the frequency factor

$$\nu^* = \frac{1}{2\pi} \left[\frac{\prod_{i=1}^{n} \omega_i^S}{\prod_{i'=2}^{n} \omega_{i'}^U} \right]$$
(7.5.22)

of Eq. (7.5.10) in the following way: Since $\Delta F = \Delta U - T\Delta S$, if we identify ΔU with V_U, the difference in potential energy between the unstable and stable configurations, then the comparison of Eqs. (7.5.10) and (7.5.19) leads to

$$\nu^* = \tilde{\nu} e^{\Delta S/k}. \qquad (7.5.23)$$

Although the use of the terminology of macroscopic thermodynamics may have heuristic value, it must be emphasized that the transcription presented here is purely formal. Since there are no macroscopic means for imposing the constraints confining a crystallite to either of the hyperplanes Σ_0 or Σ', the functions $F_0(E_{LM}, T)$ and $F'(E_{LM}, T)$ have no macroscopic counterparts. For this reason it appears best to accept the basic atomistic character of rate processes and the corresponding terminology, as in Eq. (7.5.10), which can be evaluated in terms of specific atomistic models.

7.6 TRANSITION-STATE ASSUMPTION

The rate theories of Sections 7.3 and 7.5 are both based on the assumption of the existence of a critical surface with the property that any trajectory that crosses it goes on to complete the transition. The state of the system at this surface, for example, at the barrier peak in the one-dimensional theory, is referred to as a transition-state and theories based on this assumption are called transition-state theories.

To understand the implications and shortcomings of this approach, consider the simple one-dimensional theory of Section 7.3. There, we regarded the collection of impurity atoms as statistically equivalent to a canonical ensemble of replicas of a system consisting of a single impurity atom in weak interaction with a heat bath—in this case, the host crystal. We now recall two aspects of the development of the canonical ensemble concept in Sections 2.6 and 2.7 which are of importance here:

1 In the resulting expression for the canonical ensemble, $\rho = C\exp - (H/kT)$, $H(q, p; \mathscr{A})$ is the Hamiltonian of the small component in weak interaction with the heat bath. The parameters $\mathscr{A}$ describe a small number of time-independent controllable characteristics of the heat bath. The time-dependent part of the weak interaction of the small component with the heat bath, that due to the thermal motion of the atoms of the heat bath, does not appear in H. Nevertheless, the canonical distribution accurately describes the statistical aspects of the motion of the small component in its phase space, that is, the fraction of time spent by it in any region of its phase space.

2 The trajectory of the small component, on the other hand, is profoundly affected by the time-dependent part of the weak interaction with its heat bath, and the small component does not follow the trajectory based on its Hamiltonian $H(q, p; \mathscr{A})$. This is shown in Figure 7.11 for the case of the impurity

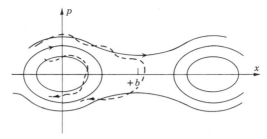

Figure 7.11 Effect of thermal interactions with remainder of crystal on impurity atom trajectories. Solid line, trajectories with interactions neglected; dashed line, trajectories showing effects of interactions.

atom treated as a system with a single degree of freedom as in Section 7.3. The trajectories computed according to $H(x, p)$ of Eq. (7.3.5) are shown, along with a schematic representation of the way the actual trajectories are perturbed due to weak interactions with the host crystal. Among these is shown one trajectory that crosses the barrier at $x = b$ but then is caused to return by its interaction with the crystal.[14]

The analysis of Section 7.3, particularly that leading to Eq. (7.3.3), is based only on the statistical aspects of the impurity atom's motion in its phase space. Since these are accurately described by the canonical ensemble, the transition-state theory represents correctly the rate with which the collection of impurity atoms cross the critical barrier at $x = b$. It fails, however, to account for those that cross and return[15] before completing the transition.

In order to go beyond transition-state theory, it is necessary to include in the model description some indication of the nature and strength of the interactions between the small component and the heat bath. One approach to this problem is to model these interactions as in the theory of Brownian motion and we turn next to a brief outline of this subject.

7.7 BROWNIAN MOTION

The theory of Brownian motion can be presented on various levels of mathematical sophistication and in its most abstract form it is part of the modern subject of stochastic processes. In our discussion we will follow the older

---

[14] The fact that the impurity atoms do not follow the trajectories predicted by the Hamiltonian $H(x, p)$ does not affect the analysis of Section 7.4; there, these latter trajectories are merely used as the basis for an alternate coordinate system for the purposes of phase space integration.

[15] Transition-state theory also does not address the possibility of an impurity atom persisting in motion in the periodic potential after surmounting the first barrier. In our discussions here, we are assuming that interactions with the crystal prevent this from occurring. The question is treated by Weiner and Forman (1974), Risken and Vollmer (1979), Nozières and Iche (1979), and Vollmer and Risken (1980).

treatment of Chandrasekhar (1943) which places greater emphasis on the physical ideas.

The phenomenom receives its name from its description[16] by the botanist Robert Brown who, in 1828, observed the irregular motion of pollen particles suspended in water and early controversy centered about whether the phenomenom was associated only with living matter. The quantitative[17] theory of Brownian motion relating it to the thermal motion of atoms of the liquid was first formulated by Einstein (1905). A mathematical model for the motion of a Brownian particle was presented by Langevin (1908) and it is this that we consider next.

Langevin Equation

Consider a particle of mass m subject to a potential V; for simplicity, we confine attention to motion in the x direction. If the particle is otherwise isolated, the equation of motion is simply

$$m\ddot{x} = -\frac{dV}{dx}. \tag{7.7.1}$$

Suppose next that the particle is immersed in a liquid at temperature T. Then, the liquid will exert a viscous force on the particle, $-\eta\dot{x}$. In addition, there will be complex time-dependent forces exerted by the liquid on the particle due to the thermal motion of the atoms of the liquid. If we think of the particle as a small component or system, in the sense of statistical mechanics, with the liquid as its heat bath, then these forces are due to the time-dependent portion of the interaction between them. In our past discussions, we have ignored any detailed effects of this interaction. However, if the particle is small enough, then these forces will have a nonvanishing resultant, which is responsible for the particle's irregular motion. This resultant is modeled by Langevin[18] as a time-dependent random force $R(t)$ whose statistical characteristics will be discussed subsequently. With the inclusion of the viscous and random forces, the equation of motion takes the form

$$m\ddot{x} + \eta\dot{x} + \frac{dV}{dx} = R(t),$$

or

$$\ddot{x} + \beta\dot{x} + \frac{1}{m}\frac{dV}{dx} = A(t), \tag{7.7.2}$$

[16]He was not the first to observe the phenomenom. For an interesting brief history see Nelson (1967).
[17]The hypothesis that Brownian motion is due to the thermal molecular motions of the liquid had been put forward earlier, for example, by Gouy in 1888.
[18]Langevin (1908).

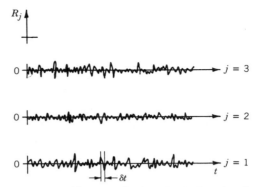

Figure 7.12 Different realizations $R_j(t)$ of random force.

where[19] $\beta = \eta/m$ and $A(t) = R(t)/m$. This is the Langevin equation for this process. It may be extended to other physical situations, for example, to particles with three degrees of freedom or to systems of particles, in a natural way.

There is currently much effort[20] devoted to derivations based on fundamental principles of the Langevin equation, or of generalizations of it, for various combinations of types of heat baths and Brownian particles, for example, for a harmonic lattice as heat bath containing a single heavy atom as Brownian particle. Here, we are postulating the equation as a mathematical model for the study of the effects on its trajectory of the interaction between a small component and its heat bath. As we shall see, the statistical character of the random force $R(t)$ is completely specified in terms of η and T; therefore, the Langevin equation models the strength of the interaction between a small component and its heat bath in terms of a single parameter, the viscosity.[21]

Concept of a Solution to the Langevin Equation

Since only statistical characteristics of the random force $R(t)$ are specified, we cannot expect to get a deterministic solution to the Langevin equation in the usual sense; the solution must also be phrased in statistical terms.

To clarify the ideas involved, consider a large number N of identical Brownian particles immersed in a liquid in a dilute suspension so that they do not interact with each other. Then, each particle trajectory $x_j(t)$ will satisfy an

[19] For convenience, we are following here the notation used by Chandrasekhar (1943). In this chapter, therefore, the symbol β is not used for $(kT)^{-1}$ as it is elsewhere.

[20] See, for example, Ford, Kac, and Mazur (1965), and Deutch and Silbey (1971).

[21] For the particular case of a Brownian particle in a liquid, the constant η is not the viscosity of the liquid but is proportional to it; the constant of proportionality depends on the shape and size of the particle. For a spherical particle of radius a in a fluid of viscosity μ, $\eta = 6\pi a\mu$, a relation obtained by the appropriate solution of the Navier–Stokes equation and referred to as Stokes' law.

equation of the form of Eq. (7.7.2), that is,

$$m\ddot{x}_j + \eta\dot{x}_j + \frac{dV}{dx}(x_j) = R_j(t), \qquad j = 1,\ldots, N \qquad (7.7.3)$$

where we now regard $R_j(t)$ as some rapidly fluctuating function of time, different for each particle, as shown schematically in Figure 7.12. We may now, subject to prescribed initial conditions, obtain the solution for $x_j(t)$ to Eq. (7.7.3) in terms of $R_j(t)$, that is, $x_j(t) = \mathcal{F}\{R_j(t)\}$, where $\mathcal{F}$ represents some functional of $R_j(t)$. If the statistical characteristics of $R_j(t)$ are known, then we can find the statistical characteristics of $x_j(t)$.

Statistical Characteristics of R(t)

In the language of probability theory,[22] for a given fixed instant of time, $R(t)$ is a random variable and $R_j(t)$ are realizations of it. Then,

$$\langle R(t) \rangle = \lim_{N \to \infty} \frac{1}{N} \sum_{j=1}^{N} R_j(t) \qquad (7.7.4)$$

is its mean and, in view of the physical nature of $R(t)$ we postulate[23] that $\langle R(t) \rangle = 0$.

In order to motivate the other statistical property of $R(t)$, we first recall the central limit theorem of probability (Section 5.4): under very broad conditions, the sum of n independent random variables, $X_n = \sum_{i=1}^{n} x_i$, has a probability distribution $p(X_n)$ which, with increasing n, approaches a normal or Gaussian distribution with $\langle X_n \rangle = \sum_{i=1}^{n} \langle x_i \rangle$ and $(\Delta X_n)^2 = \sum_{i=1}^{n}(\Delta x_i)^2$, where $(\Delta x_i)^2 = \langle x_i^2 \rangle - \langle x_i \rangle^2$, $(\Delta X_n)^2 = \langle X_n^2 \rangle - \langle X_n \rangle^2$. On physical grounds, we expect $R(t)$ to be a rapidly fluctuating function on the time scale of variation of other quantities, such as the displacement of the Brownian particle. We assume, therefore, that we can find time intervals Δt in which $R(t)$ undergoes many fluctuations but the other quantities in the Langevin equation, for example, $x(t)$, remain substantially constant. Consider next

$$B(t; \Delta t) = \frac{1}{m} \int_t^{t+\Delta t} R(\tau)\, d\tau = \int_t^{t+\Delta t} A(\tau)\, d\tau \qquad (7.7.5)$$

where we recall that $A(t) = R(t)/m$; B is therefore proportional to the impulse of the random force over the indicated time interval. We assume that the process is steady state so that $B(t; \Delta t) = B_{\Delta t}$, that is, the impulse depends only

---

[22] See, for example, Feller (1950).
[23] Note that the deterministic portion of the force on the Brownian particle due to its motion relative to the fluid is represented by the viscous force $-\eta\dot{x}$ in Eq. (7.7.2).

on Δt and is independent of t. Write $B_{\Delta t}$ in terms of an approximating sum as

$$B_{\Delta t} = \int_{t}^{t+\Delta t} A(\tau)\, d\tau = \sum_{i=1}^{n} A_i\, \delta t \qquad (7.7.6)$$

where $n(\delta t) = \Delta t$. If δt is a fixed interval on the order of the time scale of the fluctuations (see Figure 7.12), then it is reasonable to regard the values A_i as independent random values and to apply the central limit theorem. These heuristic considerations suggest that the random variable $B_{\Delta t}$ be regarded as normally distributed with $\langle B_{\Delta t} \rangle = 0$ and $\langle B_{\Delta t}^2 \rangle$ proportional[24] to Δt. Therefore, we postulate

$$\langle B_{\Delta t}^2 \rangle = q\, \Delta t, \qquad (7.7.7)$$

and the probability distribution $w(B_{\Delta t})$ is

$$w(B_{\Delta t}) = \frac{1}{(2\pi q\, \Delta t)^{1/2}} e^{-B_{\Delta t}^2/(2q\,\Delta t)}. \qquad (7.7.8)$$

Brownian Motion of Free Particle

In order to determine the appropriate value of the proportionality constant q in Eq. (7.7.7), we consider the special case of a collection of free particles, that is, $V(x) = 0$, immersed in a liquid as heat bath, which all start at $t = 0$ with the velocity u_0. The Langevin equation (7.7.2) then takes the form

$$\frac{du}{dt} + \beta u = A(t), \qquad (7.7.9)$$

with initial condition

$$u(0) = u_0. \qquad (7.7.10)$$

The formal solution to Eqs. (7.7.9) and (7.7.10) is

$$u(t) - u_0 e^{-\beta t} = \int_0^t e^{\beta(\xi - t)} A(\xi)\, d\xi. \qquad (7.7.11)$$

Since, for any given value of t, the right-hand side of Eq. (7.7.11) is a random variable, the same is true for the left-hand side and both have the same probability distribution. In preparation for the determination of the

---

[24] This proportionality is suggested by the fact that n, the number of terms in the approximating sum, is proportional to Δt with fixed δt. The argument is, of course, not rigorous.

probability distribution of the integral $\int_0^t e^{\beta(\xi-t)}A(\xi)\,d\xi$, consider the more general quantity

$$Y = \int_0^t \psi(\xi)A(\xi)\,d\xi \qquad (7.7.12)$$

where $\psi(t)$ is slowly varying and essentially constant in time during intervals of order Δt. Under these conditions, we may approximate Y as

$$Y \cong \sum_{j=0}^{n-1} \psi(j\Delta t)\int_{j\Delta t}^{(j+1)\Delta t} A(\xi)\,d\xi = \sum_{j=0}^{n-1} \psi_j B_{\Delta t}, \qquad (7.7.13)$$

where $n\,\Delta t = t$. Therefore, Y is the sum of n independent random variables, each normally distributed with zero mean and mean-square deviation $\psi_j^2\langle B_{\Delta t}^2\rangle = \psi_j^2 q\,\Delta t$ by use of Eq. (7.7.7). Therefore,[25] Y is normally distributed with $\langle Y\rangle = 0$ and

$$\langle Y^2\rangle = q\,\Delta t \sum_{j=0}^{n-1} \psi_j^2 \cong q\int_0^t \psi^2(\xi)\,d\xi, \qquad (7.7.14)$$

that is, the probability distribution $W(Y)$ is of the form

$$W(Y) = \frac{1}{(2\pi\langle Y^2\rangle)^{1/2}} e^{-Y^2/2\langle Y^2\rangle} \qquad (7.7.15)$$

with $\langle Y^2\rangle$ given in Eq. (7.7.14). For the case of the free particle, $\psi(\xi) = e^{\beta(\xi-t)}$ and

$$\langle Y^2\rangle = q\int_0^t \psi^2(\xi)\,d\xi = q\int_0^t e^{2\beta(\xi-t)}\,d\xi = \frac{q}{2\beta}(1 - e^{-2\beta t}). \qquad (7.7.16)$$

However, from Eq. (7.7.11), $Y = u(t) - u_0 e^{-\beta t}$ and, by substitution in Eq. (7.7.15), we find

$$W(u - u_0 e^{-\beta t}) = \frac{1}{\left(2\pi\cdot\frac{q}{2\beta}(1 - e^{-2\beta t})\right)^{1/2}} \exp\left(\frac{-(u - u_0 e^{-\beta t})^2}{\frac{q}{\beta}(1 - e^{-2\beta t})}\right)$$

or

$$W(u, t; u_0) = \frac{1}{(2\pi\sigma^2)^{1/2}} \exp\left(\frac{-(u - \bar{u}(t))^2}{2\sigma^2(t)}\right) \qquad (7.7.17)$$

---

[25] It is not necessary to assume here that n is large and to invoke the central limit theorem since the sum of any number of independent normally distributed random variables is normally distributed with the above relation between means and mean-square deviations. This result is readily derived by use of the Fourier transform as in Eqs. (5.5.1)–(5.5.3).

where

$$\bar{u}(t) = u_0 e^{-\beta t} \tag{7.7.18}$$

and

$$\sigma^2(t) = \frac{q}{2\beta}(1 - e^{-2\beta t}). \tag{7.7.19}$$

The probability distribution $W(u, t; u_0)$ for the particle velocity u for an ensemble of particles which all begin with velocity u_0 is shown in Figure 7.13 at time $t = 0$, at a later time t and in the limit at $t \rightarrow \infty$ when

$$\lim_{t \to \infty} W(u, t; u_0) = \left(\frac{\beta}{\pi q}\right)^{1/2} e^{-\beta u^2/q}. \tag{7.7.20}$$

This velocity distribution, which does not depend on the initial velocity, u_0, should correspond to that obtained for a canonical ensemble, namely,

$$\rho(u) = \left(\frac{m}{2\pi kT}\right)^{1/2} e^{-mu^2/2kT}; \tag{7.7.21}$$

that is, the prediction of equilibrium statistical mechanics is that

$$\lim_{t \to \infty} \sigma^2(t) = kT/m. \tag{7.7.22}$$

Agreement between Eqs. (7.7.20) and (7.7.21) requires that

$$q = \frac{2\beta kT}{m} = \frac{2\eta kT}{m^2}. \tag{7.7.23}$$

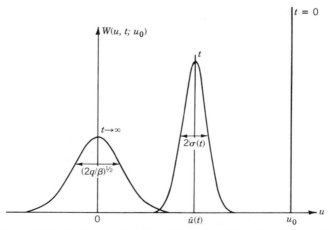

Figure 7.13 Evolution of velocity distribution of free Brownian particle.

This completes the determination of the constant of proportionality q and makes the specification of the statistical characteristics of the random force $R(t)$ complete. It may be shown (cf. Chandrasekhar, 1943) that the same value of q applies in the general case when $V(x) \neq 0$. Note that the value of q depends on both η and T. This is reasonable since η is a measure of the strength of the interaction between the Brownian particle and the liquid, and T is a measure of the thermal motion of the atoms of the liquid.

We may regard this problem as providing a simple model of the approach to equilibrium of an ensemble corresponding initially to a nonequilibrium state (all replicas with initial value u_0). It is seen from Eqs. (7.7.18)–(7.7.20) that the rate of approach to equilibrium varies with the parameter $\beta = \eta/m$; it is more rapid the larger the interaction of the small component with its heat bath and the smaller its mass.

Size of the Interval Δt

Given a particle in a liquid as heat bath, there are two time scales fixed by the nature of the system: (1) δt, the average interval between successive fluctuations of the random force exerted by the liquid on the particle (Figure 7.12), and (2) t_m, the time required for a small change in the particle's position or velocity. From the previous discussion, we see that the Brownian motion model and the Langevin equation will only be applicable if it is possible to find a time interval Δt such that $\delta t \ll \Delta t \ll t_m$.

Brownian Particle in a Quadratic Potential

As a second example, which will find application in our discussion of rate theory, we consider a Brownian particle subject to a quadratic potential

$$V(x) = \tfrac{1}{2}\kappa x^2 \qquad (7.7.24)$$

where κ may be either positive or negative. The Langevin equation, Eq. (7.7.2), takes the form

$$\frac{d^2x}{dt^2} + \beta\frac{dx}{dt} + \frac{\kappa}{m}x = A(t), \qquad (7.7.25)$$

with initial conditions

$$x(0) = x_0, \qquad \frac{dx}{dt}\bigg|_{t=0} = v_0. \qquad (7.7.26)$$

The formal solution to Eqs. (7.7.25) and (7.7.26) regarding $A(t)$ as a prescribed forcing function is readily obtained by the method of variation of the parameters. Details are given in Chandrasekhar (1943). The result may be written in the form

$$x(t) - \bar{x}(t) = \int_0^t \psi(\xi) A(\xi) \, d\xi \qquad (7.7.27)$$

where

$$\bar{x}(t) = \frac{1}{\mu_1 - \mu_2} \left[(v_0 - \mu_2 x_0) e^{\mu_1 t} + (x_0 \mu_1 - v_0) e^{\mu_2 t} \right] \qquad (7.7.28)$$

with

$$\mu_1 = -\frac{\beta}{2} + \left(\frac{\beta^2}{4} - \frac{\kappa}{m} \right)^{1/2}; \qquad \mu_2 = -\frac{\beta}{2} - \left(\frac{\beta^2}{4} - \frac{\kappa}{m} \right)^{1/2} \qquad (7.7.29)$$

and

$$\psi(\xi) = \frac{1}{\mu_1 - \mu_2} \left[e^{\mu_1(t-\xi)} - e^{\mu_2(t-\xi)} \right]. \qquad (7.7.30)$$

It will be recognized that $\bar{x}(t)$ is the deterministic motion that the particle would follow in the absence of thermal motion ($A(t) \equiv 0$). As in the previous example, the statistical distribution of $x(t) - \bar{x}(t)$ will be the same as that of $\int_0^t \psi(\xi) A(\xi) \, d\xi$; as shown in Eqs. (7.7.12)–(7.7.15), this quantity will be normally distributed with zero mean and with variance

$$\sigma^2 = q \int_0^t \psi^2(\xi) \, d\xi$$

$$= \frac{q}{(\mu_1 - \mu_2)^2} \left[\frac{1}{2\mu_1 \mu_2} \left(\mu_2 e^{2\mu_1 t} + \mu_1 e^{2\mu_2 t} \right) \right.$$

$$\left. - \frac{2}{\mu_1 + \mu_2} \left(e^{(\mu_1 + \mu_2)t} - 1 \right) - \frac{\mu_1 + \mu_2}{2\mu_1 \mu_2} \right]. \qquad (7.7.31)$$

Harmonic Oscillator

For the case of a harmonic oscillator, $\kappa > 0$, both μ_1 and μ_2 are negative, if real, or have negative real parts if complex, and

$$\lim_{t \to \infty} \sigma^2(t) = \frac{mq}{2\kappa\beta} = \frac{kT}{\kappa} \qquad (7.7.32)$$

where Eq. (7.7.23) has been employed. This limit is in agreement with the equilibrium distribution in configuration space predicted by the canonical distribution, namely,

$$\rho(x) = Ce^{-\kappa x^2/(2kT)}. \tag{7.7.33}$$

Parabolic Barrier

We turn next to the case in which $\kappa = -\kappa_b$, $\kappa_b > 0$. This corresponds to a parabolic potential barrier as shown in Figure 7.14. Let $x_0 < 0$ and $v_0 > 0$; we wish to determine the probability that the particle crosses the barrier peak at $x = 0$. Alternatively, we may regard the initial conditions to apply to a collection of Brownian particles and we seek the fraction of this collection which surmount the barrier. Let

$$W(x, t; x_0, v_0) = \frac{1}{(2\pi\sigma^2)^{1/2}} \exp\left(\frac{-(x - \bar{x})^2}{2\sigma^2}\right). \tag{7.7.34}$$

We denote by $K_\eta(x_0, v_0)$ the probability that a Brownian particle with the given initial conditions surpasses the barrier peak and remains in the region $x > 0$; that is,

$$K_\eta(x_0, v_0) = \lim_{t \to \infty} \int_0^\infty W(x, t; x_0, v_0)\, dx. \tag{7.7.35}$$

We see from Eq. (7.7.29) that for the present case of $\kappa < 0$, $\mu_1 > 0$ and $\mu_2 < 0$ as opposed to the case of the harmonic oscillator where both μ_1 and μ_2 have negative real parts. Therefore, both $\bar{x}(t)$ and $\sigma^2(t)$ grow indefinitely, as seen from Eqs. (7.7.28) and (7.7.31), and the limiting behavior arises from the competition between the motion of the mean and the spreading of the wave packet. This is shown schematically in Figure 7.14 for the case in which the initial conditions would not permit the particle to surmount the barrier in the absence of the random thermal force. At time t_1, the wave packet mean is shown at x_1, its furthest excursion to the right. At later times, the mean moves

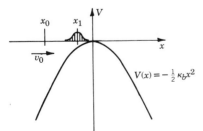

Figure 7.14 Motion of Brownian particle on parabolic barrier.

to the left indefinitely, but the accompanying spread of the packet leads to a finite probability of the particle being found in the region $x > 0$.

From Eq. (7.7.34),

$$\int_0^\infty W(x, t; x_0, v_0)\, dx = \frac{1}{(2\pi\sigma^2)^{1/2}} \int_0^\infty e^{-(x-\bar{x})^2/2\sigma^2}\, dx \qquad (7.7.36)$$

$$= \frac{1}{\sqrt{\pi}} \int_{\frac{-\bar{x}}{(2\sigma^2)^{1/2}}}^\infty e^{-y^2}\, dy = \tfrac{1}{2}\,\mathrm{erfc}\!\left(\frac{-\bar{x}}{(2\sigma^2)^{1/2}}\right).$$

From Eqs. (7.7.28) and (7.7.31),

$$\lim_{t \to \infty} \frac{-\bar{x}}{(2\sigma^2)^{1/2}} = \left(\frac{\mu_1}{q}\right)^{1/2}(\mu_2 x_0 - v_0)$$

$$= \left(\frac{\mu_1 m}{2\beta\kappa T}\right)^{1/2}(\mu_2 x_0 - v_0) \qquad (7.7.37)$$

where Eq. (7.7.23) has been used. Therefore,

$$K_\eta(x_0, v_0) = \tfrac{1}{2}\,\mathrm{erfc}\!\left\{\left(\frac{\mu_1 m}{2\beta k T}\right)^{1/2}(\mu_2 x_0 - v_0)\right\}. \qquad (7.7.38)$$

Since $\mu_1 > 0$, $\mu_2 < 0$, it is seen from Eq. (7.7.28) that $\lim_{t \to \infty} \bar{x}(t) = 0$ if and only if

$$v_0 = v_0^* = \mu_2 x_0, \qquad (7.7.39)$$

that is, v_0^* is the critical initial velocity at which the particle, in the absence of the effect of the thermal random force, will just reach the top of the barrier and come to rest; therefore, $K_\eta(x_0, v_0)$ may be rewritten in terms of v_0^* as

$$K_\eta(x_0, v_0) = \tfrac{1}{2}\,\mathrm{erfc}\!\left\{\left(\frac{\mu_1 m}{2\beta k T}\right)^{1/2}(v_0^* - v_0)\right\}. \qquad (7.7.40)$$

The nature of the transmission function $K(x_0, v_0)$ is shown in Figure 7.15.

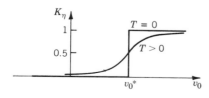

Figure 7.15 Transmission function K_η, Eq. (7.7.40), for Brownian particle on parabolic barrier.

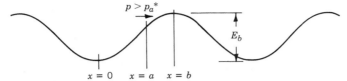

Figure 7.16 Alternate formulation of one-dimensional rate theory.

7.8 KRAMERS RATE FORMULA

In this section we generalize the one-dimensional transition-state rate theory of Section 7.3 to include, on the basis of the Brownian motion model, the effects of interaction of the system in question with a heat bath. The resulting rate expression, originally formulated to deal with chemical reaction rates, is due to Kramers (1940).[26]

In order to motivate the derivation, we consider first an alternate formulation for the one-dimensional, transition-state rate expression of Eq. (7.3.8). Instead of computing the rate with which impurity atoms cross the potential barrier at $x = b$ (Figure 7.16) with positive momentum, we compute the rate f with which they cross the plane $x = a, 0 < a < b$, with momentum sufficient to carry them over the barrier, that is, with $p > p_a^*$ where

$$p_a^* = [2m(V(b) - V(a))]^{1/2}. \qquad (7.8.1)$$

By the same reasoning that led to Eq. (7.3.3), we can express this rate as

$$f = \frac{1}{m} \int_{p_a^*}^{\infty} p\rho(a, p)\, dp. \qquad (7.8.2)$$

With the use of Eqs. (7.3.4) and (7.3.5), this leads to

$$
\begin{aligned}
f_{TS} &= \frac{C}{m} e^{-V(a)/kT} \int_{p_a^*}^{\infty} p \exp\left(-\frac{p^2}{2mkT}\right) dp \\
&= \frac{C}{m} \cdot mkT \cdot \exp\left[-\left(V(a) + \frac{(p_a^*)^2}{2m}\right)/kT\right]
\end{aligned} \qquad (7.8.3)
$$

which, with the aid of Eq. (7.3.7) for the approximate normalization constant C, and by use of Eq. (7.8.1), leads to

$$f_{TS} = \nu_0 \exp\left(-\frac{V(b)}{kT}\right) = \nu_0 \exp\left(\frac{-E_b}{kT}\right) \qquad (7.8.4)$$

[26] The original derivation of Kramers employed the Fokker–Planck formalism (cf. Chandrasekhar, 1943). We follow here the derivation given by Pear and Weiner (1978) which is based on the Langevin equation.

as previously derived. We have denoted the rate here as f_{TS} to emphasize that it is derived on the basis of the transition-state assumption. It is this assumption, in which the effect of interactions with the heat bath on the particle trajectory are neglected, which permitted us to state that all particles crossing $x = a$ with $p > p_a^*$ will surmount the barrier peak, and that none can cross if $p < p_a^*$.

We may restate this condition in terms of a transmission function $K_0(a, p)$ defined as

$$K_0(a, p) = 0, \qquad p < p_a^*$$

$$\qquad\qquad = 1, \qquad p > p_a^*. \qquad (7.8.5)$$

By use of this transmission function, Eq. (7.8.2) can be rewritten in the equivalent form,

$$f_{TS} = \frac{1}{m} \int_{-\infty}^{\infty} p K_0(a, p) \rho(a, p) \, dp. \qquad (7.8.6)$$

We next assume that we can regard the impurity atoms of the example of Section 7.3 as Brownian particles in interaction with the host lattice as heat bath, with the strength of interaction characterized by the viscosity parameter η. Then, the formulation of Eq. (7.8.6) must be modified since particles crossing $x = a$ with $p < p_a^*$ may still cross the barrier with the aid of thermal interactions and conversely those with $p > p_a^*$ may be turned back. For this purpose, we assume that the potential barrier in the region $x > a$ may be approximated by a quadratic function of the form

$$V(x) = -\tfrac{1}{2} \kappa_b (x - b)^2$$

and that the effect of the interactions with the heat bath may be incorporated in the formulation by replacing $K_0(a, p)$ in Eq. (7.8.6) by $K_\eta(a, p)$, the transmission function for a parabolic barrier as computed in Section 7.7. We see, from Eqs. (7.7.39) and (7.7.40), that in terms of the notation of the present section (which involves a shift in origin and use of momenta in place of velocities)

$$K_\eta(a, p) = \tfrac{1}{2} \operatorname{erfc}\left\{ \left(\frac{\mu_1}{2\eta kT}\right)^{1/2} (p_a^* - p_a) \right\} \qquad (7.8.7)$$

where now

$$p_a^* = m\mu_2(a - b) \qquad (7.8.8)$$

with μ_1, μ_2 defined in Eq. (7.7.29) with $\kappa = -\kappa_b$. The rate expression including the effects of interaction with the heat bath is then

$$f = \frac{1}{m} \int_{-\infty}^{\infty} p K_\eta(a, p) \rho(a, p) \, dp. \qquad (7.8.9)$$

When the approximate normalization constant C as given by Eq. (7.3.7) is used and the indicated integrations performed (by use of integration by parts), the result is

$$f = \nu_0\left(\sqrt{\xi^2 + 1} - \xi\right)\exp\left(\frac{-E_b}{kT}\right) \tag{7.8.10}$$

where, as before,

$$\nu_0 = \frac{1}{2\pi}\sqrt{\frac{\kappa_w}{m}} \tag{7.8.11}$$

is the natural frequency of oscillation of the particle in the harmonic region of the well, and

$$\xi = \frac{\eta}{2\sqrt{\kappa_b m}}. \tag{7.8.12}$$

Equation (7.8.10) is known as Kramers rate formula. Note that:

1   The activation energy E_b is left unchanged by the interaction with the heat bath. The frequency factor is reduced by the factor $\sqrt{\xi^2 + 1} - \xi$.

2   When the strength of the interaction goes to zero ($\eta \rightarrow 0$), Kramers rate formula, Eq. (7.8.10), reduces to the transition-state rate formula of Eq. (7.3.8).

3   The effect of increasing η is to decrease the frequency factor and the rate f. For large ξ, Eq. (7.8.10) assumes the approximate form

$$f \cong \frac{\nu_0}{2\xi}\exp\left(\frac{-E_b}{kT}\right) = \nu_0\frac{\sqrt{\kappa_b m}}{\eta}\exp\left(\frac{-E_b}{kT}\right). \tag{7.8.13}$$

4   A decrease in $\sqrt{\kappa_b m}$ with η fixed also causes a decrease in the effective rate of transition. This is understandable on physical grounds since a decrease in κ_b corresponds to a barrier peak that is flatter, and therefore the thermal random force can more easily return the particle after it has crossed the peak. A smaller particle mass also facilitates return.

5   The fact that the Kramers rate formula gives a more detailed description of the process than the one-dimensional transition-state rate formula of Eq. (7.3.8) is indicated by its dependence on two additional parameters: η, a measure of the strength of interaction with the heat bath; and κ_b, the curvature of the barrier peak. On the other hand, the value of $x = a$ (Figure 7.16), which may be regarded as the point of transition between the regions of positive and negative curvature of the potential function $V(x)$, drops out in the integration as it does in the transition-state analysis and does not appear in the final formula.

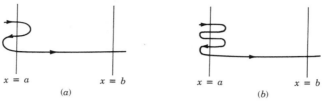

$x = a$ $x = b$ $x = a$ $x = b$

(a)   (b)

Figure 7.17 Multiple crossings of intermediate plane $x = a$ of trajectories that go on to cross barrier at $x = b$.

6   The increase in the range of integration from $0 \leqslant p < \infty$, for the transition-state analysis of Section 7.3, to the range $-\infty < p < \infty$ in Eq. (7.8.9) requires discussion. Consider the following decomposition of Eq. (7.8.9):

$$f = f_+ + f_-$$

where

$$f_+ = \frac{1}{m} \int_0^\infty pK_\eta(a, p)\rho(a, p)\, dp,$$

$$f_- = \frac{1}{m} \int_{-\infty}^0 pK_\eta(a, p)\rho(a, p)\, dp. \tag{7.8.14}$$

The portion f_+ describes the rate with which particles cross $x = a$ and then go on to overcome the barrier at $x = b$. Because of the effect of the random thermal force, some of these successful particles may first recross $x = a$ in the negative direction and then return to cross $x = a$ and $x = b$ as shown schematically in Figure 7.17a and b. Therefore, f_+ is an overestimate of the desired rate since the flux of particles crossing $x = a$ in the positive direction includes those with multiple crossings. This overestimate is due to the flux of particles across $x = a$ in the negative direction which then go on to cross $x = b$. The rate of barrier crossing by the latter particles is[27] $-f_-$ and the corrected rate is therefore $f_+ - (-f_-) = f$.

Exact Normalization

It is clear that if the exact value of the normalization constant C, as given by Eq. (7.4.8), is used in place of the approximate value given by Eq. (7.3.7), then Eq. (7.8.10) is replaced by

$$f = \nu(T)\left(\sqrt{\xi^2 + 1} - \xi\right)\exp\left(\frac{-E_b}{kT}\right) \tag{7.8.15}$$

---

[27]Note that $K_\eta(a, p)$, for $p < 0$, represents the small fraction of particles which cross $x = a$ going to the left but finally cross to the region $x > b$, and that $f_- < 0$.

where $\nu(T)$, the thermally averaged frequency of oscillation of the particle in the well, is defined in Eq. (7.4.9).

Computer Simulation Results

The simulation by digital computer of the Brownian motion of a particle both in a periodic and in a double-well potential was carried out by Pear and Weiner (1978) and some of the results serve to illustrate the physical ideas discussed here.

For ease in calculation, the potentials were taken as continuous, piecewise quadratic functions with continuous derivatives. The periodic potential is defined for the interval $-\gamma b \leqslant x \leqslant (2 - \gamma)b$ as

$$V_1(x) = \tfrac{1}{2}\kappa_w x^2, \qquad |x| \leqslant \gamma b,$$
$$= E_b - \tfrac{1}{2}\kappa_b(x - b)^2, \qquad \gamma b \leqslant x \leqslant (2 - \gamma)b, \qquad (7.8.16)$$

and is continued with period $2b$ for all x; γ is a parameter, $0 < \gamma < 1$, which may be selected to represent high, narrow barriers ($\gamma \approx 1$) or low, broad barriers ($\gamma \approx 0$). To ensure the continuity of the derivative of $V_1(x)$, it is necessary that

$$\kappa_b/\kappa_w = \gamma(1 - \gamma)^{-1} \qquad (7.8.17)$$

and, from the continuity of $V_1(x)$, the barrier height

$$E_b = \tfrac{1}{2}\kappa_w \gamma b^2. \qquad (7.8.18)$$

The double-well potential $V_2(x)$ is defined in a manner analogous to the periodic potential as

$$V_2(x) = \tfrac{1}{2}\kappa_w(|x| - b)^2, \qquad |x| \geqslant (1 - \gamma)b$$
$$= E_b - \tfrac{1}{2}\kappa_b x^2, \qquad |x| \leqslant (1 - \gamma)b. \qquad (7.8.19)$$

Eqs. (7.8.17) and (7.8.18) apply here as well.

Computer generated particle trajectories for the double-well potential are shown in Figure 7.18. For a low value[28] of η corresponding to $\eta/\sqrt{\kappa_w m} = 0.05$, it is seen in Figure 7.18a that every crossing of the barrier peak at $x = 0$ corresponds to an actual exchange of wells; in this case the transition-state rate would be correct. On the other hand, for $\eta/\sqrt{\kappa_w m} = 5$, it is seen in Fig. 7.18b that there are many crossings and recrossings of the barrier peak but only one effective exchange of wells has occurred in the time period of the simulation.

The computer program measured both transition-state rates and effective rates. For the case of the double-well potential, the former required only that

[28] Recall that critical damping for the particle oscillating in the well is given by $\eta/\sqrt{\kappa_w m} = 2$.

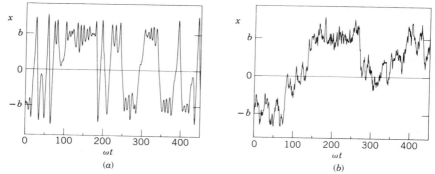

Figure 7.18 Computer generated trajectories for Brownian motion of particle in double well potential of Eq. (7.8.20); well minima are at $x = \pm b$ and barrier peak is at $x = 0$. (a) $\eta/\sqrt{\kappa_w m}$ = 0.05. (b) $\eta/\sqrt{\kappa_w m}$ = 5. (After Pear and Weiner, 1978.)

the particle cross the barrier peak at $x = 0$ with $\dot{x} > 0$ while the latter required that the particle first cross $x = -(1 - \gamma)b$ and then cross $x = (1 - \gamma)b$ before an effective jump was recorded. From the measured rates f at a given temperature, the corresponding frequency factors ν are obtained by use of the relation $f = \nu e^{-E_b/kT}$. The results are shown in Figure 7.19. It is seen that when the transition state rates are used the frequency factor is independent of η, whereas the frequency factor based on effective rates depends on η as predicted by Eq. (7.8.15).

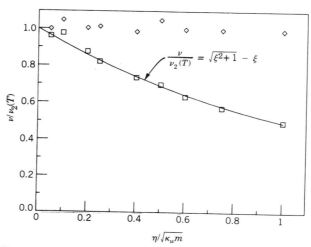

Figure 7.19 Frequency factor ν as determined from rates measured in computer simulation experiments, by recording transition-state rates ($\Diamond$) and effective rates ($\Box$). These are compared with the frequency factor $\nu_2(T)$, the theoretical transition-state frequency factor based on exact normalization, Eq. (7.4.9), computed for the double-well potential $V_2(x)$ of Eq. (7.8.19). The data shown is for $kT/E_b = 0.2$ and $\gamma = 0.3$. (After Pear and Weiner, 1978.)

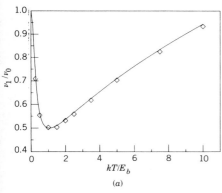
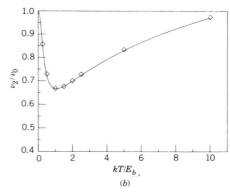

Figure 7.20   Comparison of frequency factors $\nu_1(T)$ and $\nu_2(T)$ based on exact normalization, Eq. (7.4.9), with $\nu_0 = 1/(2\pi)\sqrt{\kappa_w/m}$, based on approximate normalization, Eq. (7.3.7). Data points are from computer simulation experiments for $\eta/\sqrt{\kappa_w m} = 0.05$. (a) Periodic potential, $V_1(x)$, of Eq. (7.8.16) with $\gamma = 0.1$. (b) Double well potential, $V_2(x)$, of Eq. (7.8.19) with $\gamma = 0.1$.

The computer simulation also served to illustrate the role of exact normalization and the resultant temperature-dependent frequency factor $\nu(T)$. These results are shown in Figure 7.20 which show simulation results for $\eta/\sqrt{\kappa_b m} = 0.05$, so that transition-state theory is quite accurate, and for $\gamma = 0.1$, which corresponds to a low flat barrier. It is seen that the values of $\nu(T)$, as computed from Eq. (7.4.9) for the piecewise quadratic periodic potential $V_1(x)$ of Eq. (7.8.16) or the double-well potential $V_2(x)$ of Eq. (7.8.19) agree quite well with the computer simulation results. Note that for the periodic potential, the value of $\nu(T)$ decreases by a factor of 2 as the temperature goes from zero to $kT/E_b = 1$; the decrease for the corresponding case of the double well is less, but still substantial.

Systems with Several Degrees of Freedom

Extensions of Kramers rate theory to apply to systems with several degrees of freedom interacting with a heat bath have been made by Landauer and Swanson (1961) and by Helfand (1971).

Quantum Theory

CHAPTER EIGHT

Basic Concepts of Quantum Mechanics

8.1 INTRODUCTION

We have been concerned thus far with analyses based solely on classical mechanics and, as we have seen, many aspects of the statistical mechanics of elasticity can be treated adequately on this basis. However, in order to understand the nature and the location of the limits of the classical approach, it is necessary to go beyond these limits and to consider the treatment of parts of the subject on the basis of quantum mechanics.

There are three important aspects of the study of the mechanical behavior of solids from the atomistic viewpoint where quantum mechanics plays a central role:

1 Interatomic force laws In the classical discussions, an atomistic model of a solid consisted of a collection of particles or mass points interacting according to a specified force law. In order to go beyond these models, to endow these particles with the structure of atoms consisting of nuclei and electrons, and to understand the basis of the different types of interatomic force laws, it is necessary to utilize quantum mechanics.

2 Low-temperature elastic behavior Classical statistical mechanics is adequate for the treatment of the mechanical behavior of most materials provided the temperature level is not too low. Below these levels new effects appear which require the use of quantum statistical mechanics for their understanding.

3 Rate theory If it is desired to analyze rate processes in solids at low temperature levels, it is necessary to employ quantum statistical mechanics. If, in addition, particles of small mass are involved, as in the diffusion of hydrogen atoms in a crystal, then the description of the dynamics of the system requires quantum, rather than classical, mechanics.

These three topics are treated in the following chapters. We begin in this chapter with a brief discussion of the basic concepts of quantum mechanics, with emphasis on the changes in viewpoint from classical mechanics and the corresponding change in the mathematical formulation of the subject which is engendered by this new viewpoint.

The reader who is already familiar with the principles of quantum mechanics will find the present chapter superfluous. It is intended, rather, for the reader with little or no background in the subject and its purpose is to provide him with a relatively brief introduction to the new concepts and attitudes it requires. This introduction focuses on those topics needed for the discussion of the subsequent chapters. There are, of course, a large number of texts available that treat these topics at much greater length and may be used for supplementary reading. Among those, at an appropriate level for this purpose, are Blokhintsev (1964), Messiah (1964), Kemble (1937), Bohm (1951), Ikenberry (1962), Davydov (1965), and Cohen-Tannoudji, Diu, and Laloë (1977).

8.2   STRUCTURE OF CLASSICAL MECHANICS

In order to consider the basic ideas in their simplest setting, we begin with the example of a single particle of mass m constrained to move in a single direction x, subject to a potential $V(x)$. We have used the same example in Section 2.2 in our discussion of Hamiltonian mechanics. As we saw there, it is convenient to formulate the problem in terms of two first-order equations,

$$m\dot{x} = p \qquad (8.2.1)$$

$$\dot{p} = -\frac{dV}{dx} \qquad (8.2.2)$$

where p is the particle momentum, with initial conditions

$$x(t_0) = x_0, \qquad p(t_0) = p_0. \qquad (8.2.3)$$

The time evolution of the system may then be represented by a trajectory $(x(t), p(t))$ in the phase space whose coordinates are (x, p).

Thus far, we have considered this simple problem in classical mechanics purely as an example of a set of ordinary differential equations with prescribed initial conditions. We turn next to our understanding of the relationship of this formalism to the physical world. The setting of the initial conditions corresponds to an experimental observation that determines the particle position and momentum at $t = t_0$. We may also say that the experimental observation determines the particle's dynamical state at $t = t_0$ as a pair of numbers (x_0, p_0). The particle's subsequent dynamical state as it evolves in time is given by the set of functions $(x(t), p(t))$ which are solutions to Eqs. (8.2.1) and

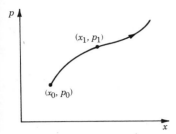

Figure 8.1   Classical trajectory in phase space.

(8.2.2) subject to the initial conditions, Eq. (8.2.3). If we observe the same particle at a later time $t = t_1$, we will observe the dynamical state (x_1, p_1) where $x_1 = x(t_1)$, $p_1 = p(t_1)$, the pair of numbers obtained by evaluating the solution functions $x(t)$, $p(t)$ at $t = t_1$. The equations of motion, Eqs. (8.2.1) and (8.2.2), serve therefore to predict, with complete certainty, the result of an ideal experimental observation at a later time t_1, for a system that has been observed in state (x_0, p_0) at time t_0. We may also use the values (x_1, p_1) as initial conditions for Eqs. (8.2.1) and (8.2.2) for the solution for $t \geq t_1$; the result will coincide in this time period with the solution for $t \geq t_0$ with initial conditions (x_0, p_0), Figure 8.1. In other words, in the classical mechanics framework, an intermediate observation of the particle's evolving dynamical state does not affect its subsequent behavior.

8.3   STRUCTURE OF QUANTUM MECHANICS

We next consider the same problem from the quantum viewpoint, beginning with the determination of the dynamical state of the particle at $t = t_0$. Its classical description in terms of the pair of numbers (x_0, p_0) implies that immediately after the experimental determination of these quantities, that is, before the passage of time permits the particle's dynamical state to change, we know both the position and the momentum of the particle with complete precision. This type of measurement seems operationally feasible on the basis of our physical intuition. This intuition, however, is built on experience with objects of macroscopic size and there is really no reason to trust it for phenomena on the atomic scale. In fact, a careful examination of the measurement process led Heisenberg[1] to the conclusion that it is not possible to determine simultaneously the particle's position and momentum, both with arbitrarily high precision, since the very act of measurement will perturb these quantities in a way that cannot be computed exactly. Therefore, from the quantum viewpoint, the determination of the dynamical state of a particle by a measurement at $t = t_0$ leads not to a pair of numbers (x_0, p_0) but to a pair of probability distribution functions $P_x(x, t_0 +)$, $P_p(p, t_0 +)$. We use the nota-

---

[1] A general account is contained in Heisenberg (1930).

tion $t_0 +$ to emphasize that this pair of functions embodies the knowledge regarding the particle's position and momentum obtained by the measurement at $t = t_0$ and provides, therefore, the quantum mechanical description of the dynamical state of the particle immediately *after* this measurement. These functions have the usual properties and significance of probability distributions in general.[2] In particular, they must satisfy the requirement of being everywhere nonnegative and the normalization requirements

$$\int_{-\infty}^{\infty} P_x(x, t_0 +) \, dx = \int_{-\infty}^{\infty} P_p(p, t_0 +) \, dp = 1. \tag{8.3.1}$$

The expected or mean values of the particle's position and momentum at t_0 are

$$\bar{x}(t_0 +) = \int_{-\infty}^{\infty} x P_x(x, t_0 +) \, dx \tag{8.3.2}$$

$$\bar{p}(t_0 +) = \int_{-\infty}^{\infty} p P_p(p, t_0 +) \, dp. \tag{8.3.3}$$

We will also use the notation $\langle x \rangle = \bar{x}$, $\langle p \rangle = \bar{p}$ for these means.[3] The expected or mean value $\bar{f}(t_0 +)$ of any function of position $f(x)$ is given by

$$\bar{f}(t_0 +) = \int_{\infty}^{\infty} f(x) P_x(x, t_0 +) \, dx \tag{8.3.4}$$

and similarly for any function of momentum $g(p)$

$$\bar{g}(t_0 +) = \int_{-\infty}^{\infty} g(p) P_p(p, t_0 +) \, dp. \tag{8.3.5}$$

The mean square deviations in these distributions at $t_0 +$

$$(\Delta x)^2 = \left\langle (x - \bar{x})^2 \right\rangle = \int_{-\infty}^{\infty} (x - \bar{x})^2 P_x(x, t_0 +) \, dx \tag{8.3.6}$$

$$(\Delta p)^2 = \left\langle (p - \bar{p})^2 \right\rangle = \int_{-\infty}^{\infty} (p - \bar{p})^2 P_p(p, t_0 +) \, dp \tag{8.3.7}$$

serve as a measure of the uncertainty regarding the particle's position and

---

[2] For a further discussion of probability and quantum mechanics see Newton (1980).
[3] It is convenient to have both notations available. The bar is generally used for simple quantities, such as $\bar{x}$, and allows easy indication of possible time dependence of the mean, for example, $\bar{x}(t)$. The brackets serve better for more cumbersome expressions such as $\left\langle (x - \bar{x})^2 \right\rangle$. This is the same notation we have used for expected or mean values in our discussion of classical statistical mechanics. It is important to recognize that the need for probability distributions arises from different sources in quantum mechanics and in classical statistical mechanics. This will be seen more clearly in Chapter 10, which treats quantum statistical mechanics, a discipline in which both sources of uncertainty are present simultaneously.

momentum immediately after the measurement at time t_0. The limitation on the possible precision of simultaneous measurement of position and momentum as embodied in Heisenberg's uncertainty[4] relation may be stated in terms of these quantities as follows:

$$\Delta x \cdot \Delta p \geqslant \hbar/2 \qquad (8.3.8)$$

where $\hbar = h/2\pi$ and h is Planck's constant, $h = 6.626 \times 10^{-27}$ ergs sec.[5] It is a fundamental postulate of quantum mechanics that the uncertainty relation (8.3.8) applies to all possible schemes that may be devised for the measurement of position and momentum. It is important to recognize that the uncertainty relation refers only to the product $\Delta x \cdot \Delta p$. It is possible, in theory, without violating this inequality, to devise a measurement that will provide information regarding the particle's position with arbitrarily small uncertainty Δx, but the uncertainty in the particle's momentum Δp must become correspondingly large, and similarly with the roles of position and momentum reversed.

Time Evolution of Dynamical State

We have seen that our measurement at time t_0 has led to the determination of the dynamical state of the particle as a pair of probability distribution functions $P_x(x, t_0 +)$, $P_p(p, t_0 +)$. With the passage of time, the dynamical state of the particle will evolve, and at a later time t, will be given by the pair of functions $P_x(x, t)$ and $P_p(p, t)$. We defer the discussion of the equation that governs the evolution of the functions $P_x(x, t)$ and $P_p(p, t)$ but note here that they retain their significance as probability distribution functions to which, therefore, Eqs. (8.3.1)–(8.3.7), written initially for t_0, apply as well. The functions $P_x(x, t)$ and $P_p(p, t)$ represent the state of our knowledge about the particle at time t which we have acquired as a result of a measurement at time $t = t_0$ and by the mathematical calculation of the evolution of these functions to the time t. It is clear, therefore, that the uncertainty relation, Eq. (8.3.8), which is a basic physical postulate applying to all measurements, must apply as well to the uncertainties $\Delta x(t)$ and $\Delta p(t)$ computed on the basis of $P_x(x, t)$ and $P_p(p, t)$, since we may regard the measurement at time t_0 and the calculation to the later time t as constituting a single measurement process.

Relationship between $P_x(x, t)$ and $P_p(p, t)$

The basic physical postulate embodied in the Heisenberg uncertainty principle requires that a relationship exist between the uncertainties $\Delta x(t)$ and $\Delta p(t)$ as computed on the basis of $P_x(x, t)$ and $P_p(p, t)$. The mathematical structure of

---

[4] The term uncertainty is used here in the sense of Eqs. (8.3.6) and (8.3.7), not as in the information theory discussion of Section 3.12.

[5] The fact that h has so small a numerical value when expressed in units appropriate to macroscopic phenomena makes clear that the inherent imprecision in any measurement due to the Heisenberg uncertainty principle is completely negligible for any process on the macroscopic scale.

quantum mechanics must, therefore, relate these two functions in a manner that guarantees this result. This is accomplished by first introducing functions $\psi_x(x, t)$ and $\psi_p(p, t)$, in general complex valued, such that

$$P_x(x, t) = |\psi_x(x, t)|^2,$$

$$P_p(p, t) = |\psi_p(p, t)|^2. \tag{8.3.9}$$

The relation that is postulated between $P_x(x, t)$ and $P_p(p, t)$ and that ensures the Heisenberg uncertainty relationship may now be stated very simply: The functions $\psi_x(x, t)$ and $\psi_p(p, t)$ are Fourier transforms of each other; explicitly[6]

$$\psi_p(p, t) = (2\pi\hbar)^{-1/2} \int_{-\infty}^{\infty} \psi_x(x, t) e^{-ipx/\hbar} \, dx \tag{8.3.10}$$

which, by the Fourier integral theorem, has the inverse relation

$$\psi_x(x, t) = (2\pi\hbar)^{-1/2} \int_{-\infty}^{\infty} \psi_p(p, t) e^{ipx/\hbar} \, dp. \tag{8.3.11}$$

Because of the postulated relation, Eq. (8.3.10), all of the information about the dynamical state of the particle at time t is contained in either of the functions $\psi_x(x, t)$ or $\psi_p(p, t)$. In particular, all of the knowledge regarding the dynamical state of the particle obtained by a measurement at time t_0 may be embodied in either the function $\psi_x(x, t_0 +)$ or the function $\psi_p(p, t_0 +)$. It will be convenient in the following discussion to make the former choice. Thus, the classical specification of the initial dynamical state as (x_0, p_0) is replaced in quantum mechanics by the specification of the function $\psi_x(x, t_0 +)$. In terms of $\psi_x(x, t)$, the normalization requirement of Eq. (8.3.1) takes the form

$$\int_{-\infty}^{\infty} |\psi_x(x, t)|^2 \, dx = 1. \tag{8.3.12}$$

Unless otherwise stated, we assume this normalization condition satisfied in the following discussions.

Schrödinger Equation

Classically, the subsequent time evolution of the dynamical state of the particle, the trajectory $(x(t), p(t))$ was obtained from the solution of the classical equations of motion, Eqs. (8.2.1) and (8.2.2), subject to the prescribed

---

[6] The role of Planck's constant h in the definition of the Fourier transforms of Eqs. (8.3.10, 11) will be clarified in the discussion of Section 8.4 where it will be shown that the Fourier transform relation implies the uncertainty relation. For the present we note merely that it serves to render the exponents nondimensional.

initial conditions. In quantum mechanics the subsequent time evolution of the dynamical state, $\psi_x(x, t)$, is obtained from the solution, subject to the prescribed initial condition, of the quantum equation of motion, Schrödinger's equation, which takes the form,[7] for the particle under consideration,

$$\frac{-\hbar^2}{2m} \frac{\partial^2 \psi_x}{\partial x^2} + V(x)\psi_x = i\hbar \frac{\partial \psi_x}{\partial t}. \tag{8.3.13}$$

Let the solution of Eq. (8.3.13), corresponding to the initial conditions $\psi_x(x, t_0 +)$, be $\psi_x(x, t)$ and consider a later instant of time t_1. Denote the value of the solution at this time by $\psi_x(x, t_1 -)$. In contrast to the classical picture, the nature of the time evolution of the particle's dynamical state for $t > t_1$ will depend on whether or not we observe its state at $t = t_1$. If we do not observe it, its behavior for $t > t_1$ is given by the original solution $\psi_x(x, t)$ (which may be regarded alternatively as the solution to Schrödinger's equation for $t > t_1$ with initial conditions $\psi_x(x, t_1 +) = \psi_x(x, t_1 -)$). However, if we do observe it at $t = t_1$, our knowledge regarding its dynamical state will be changed[8] so that after measurement its state will be $\psi_x(x, t_1 +) \neq \psi_x(x, t_1 -)$.

8.4 CONSEQUENCES OF THE FOURIER TRANSFORM RELATION BETWEEN $\psi_x(x)$ AND $\psi_p(p)$

As we noted in the previous section, the complex functions $\psi_x(x, t)$ and $\psi_p(p, t)$ are postulated to be Fourier transforms of each other. In this section we consider some important consequences of this relationship.

Some Standard Fourier Transform Results

We first record some standard Fourier transform results which we will need. Since time plays no role in this discussion, we drop the variable t and write $\psi_x(x)$ and $\psi_p(p)$. We adopt the notation $\psi_x(x) \cdot \supset \cdot \psi_p(p)$ for a Fourier transform pair defined as in Eqs. (8.3.10) and (8.3.11).

---

[7] The change from the ordinary differential equations of the classical formulation to the partial differential equation of the quantum case is in accord with the change in mode of description of the evolving dynamical state from the pair of functions of time $(x(t), p(t))$ to the single function of space and time $\psi_x(x, t)$. There is, of course, no question of the derivation of Eq. (8.3.13); Schrödinger's equation is a fundamental postulate of quantum mechanics just as Newton's is of classical mechanics. It is, nevertheless, of interest to consider the underlying motivation of the postulate (see, e.g., Blokhintsev, 1964, pp. 102–105) as well as the relationship between the two equations. The latter question is discussed in Section 8.6.

[8] The way in which our knowledge is changed depends on the nature of the measurement. It may, for example, due to the interaction of the measuring apparatus and the particle, increase the precision of our information regarding the particle's position but decrease our information regarding its momentum. The measurement process is discussed further in Section 8.8.

By differentiation of Eq. (8.3.11) with respect to x we obtain the following familiar result:[9]

$$\frac{\hbar}{i}\frac{\partial \psi_x}{\partial x} \cdot \supset \cdot p\psi_p.$$ (8.4.1)

This process can be repeated leading to the general result

$$\left(\frac{\hbar}{i}\right)^n \frac{\partial^n \psi_x}{\partial x^n} \cdot \supset \cdot p^n\psi_p.$$ (8.4.2)

A second standard result in Fourier transform theory which we will need is Parseval's theorem; in the present notation, it takes the form

$$\int_{-\infty}^{\infty} \psi_p^*(p)\phi_p(p)\,dp = \int_{-\infty}^{\infty} \psi_x^*(x)\phi_x(x)\,dx$$ (8.4.3)

where $\psi_x \cdot \supset \cdot \psi_p$, $\phi_x \cdot \supset \cdot \phi_p$ are any two sets of Fourier transform pairs and ψ_p^* denotes the complex conjugate of ψ_p.

Calculation of Means

We show next how the Fourier transform properties just enumerated permit the computation of $\bar{p}$, the expected or mean value of the momentum, in terms of the function $\psi_x(x)$. As originally defined in Eq. (8.3.3),

$$\bar{p} = \int_{-\infty}^{\infty} pP_p(p)\,dp = \int_{-\infty}^{\infty} p|\psi_p(p)|^2\,dp = \int_{-\infty}^{\infty} p\psi_p^*(p)\psi_p(p)\,dp.$$

However, if we now use the transform pair, Eq. (8.4.1), and Parseval's theorem, Eq. (8.4.3), with $p\psi_p$ playing the role of ϕ_p, we see immediately that

$$\bar{p} = \int_{-\infty}^{\infty} \psi_x^*(x)\frac{\hbar}{i}\frac{\partial \psi_x}{\partial x}\,dx.$$ (8.4.4)

We can compute $\overline{p^2} = \langle p^2 \rangle$ in a similar fashion.

$$\langle p^2 \rangle = \int_{-\infty}^{\infty} p^2 P_p(p)\,dp = \int_{-\infty}^{\infty} p^2|\psi_p(p)|^2\,dp = \int_{-\infty}^{\infty} \psi_p^*(p)p^2\psi_p(p)\,dp.$$

Then, by use of the transform pair $p^2\psi_p \cdot \supset \cdot (\hbar/i)^2\partial^2\psi_x/\partial x^2$, Eq. (8.4.2), and Parseval's theorem, Eq. (8.4.3), with now $p^2\psi_p$ playing the role of ϕ_p, we see

[9]See, for example, Carrier, Krook, and Pearson (1966, p. 312). Of course, Planck's constant h does not appear in the standard treatments of Fourier transforms, but the required modifications are minor.

that

$$\langle p^2 \rangle = \int_{-\infty}^{\infty} \psi_x^*(x)\left(\frac{\hbar}{i}\right)^2 \frac{\partial^2 \psi_x}{\partial x^2}\, dx. \tag{8.4.5}$$

It is clear now how this procedure extends to any power of p and therefore to any polynomial $g(p)$. We may state the result symbolically as:

$$\langle g \rangle = \int_{-\infty}^{\infty} \psi_x^*(x) g\left(\frac{\hbar}{i}\frac{\partial}{\partial x}\right)\psi_x(x)\, dx. \tag{8.4.6}$$

In this equation, $g(\frac{\hbar}{i}\frac{\partial}{\partial x})$ is the differential operator obtained by making the replacement $p \rightarrow (\hbar/i)\partial/\partial x$ in the polynomial $g(p)$; this differential operator acts only on the function following it, namely, ψ_x.

We recall now the procedure, Eq. (8.3.4), for computing the mean $\langle f \rangle$ of any function, $f(x)$, of particle position,

$$\langle f \rangle = \int_{-\infty}^{\infty} f(x)P_x(x)\, dx = \int_{-\infty}^{\infty} f(x)\psi_x^*(x)\psi_x(x)\, dx. \tag{8.4.7}$$

We can, therefore, combine Eqs. (8.4.6) and (8.4.7) to read

$$\langle f + g \rangle = \int_{-\infty}^{\infty} \psi_x^*(x)\left[f(x) + g\left(\frac{\hbar}{i}\frac{\partial}{\partial x}\right)\right]\psi_x(x)\, dx. \tag{8.4.8}$$

In most treatments of quantum mechanics, Eq. (8.4.8) is taken as a basic postulate and is expressed in terms of more general functions $F(x, p)$ as[10]

$$\langle F \rangle = \int_{-\infty}^{\infty} \psi_x^*(x)F\left(x, \frac{\hbar}{i}\frac{\partial}{\partial x}\right)\psi_x(x)\, dx. \tag{8.4.9}$$

We have followed a different, somewhat longer, route to arrive at the more restricted formula, Eq. (8.4.8), because this path is easier to motivate and is sufficiently general for our purposes.[11] In particular, it permits the calculation of the expected value, $\langle H \rangle$, of the total energy, $H(x, p)$, of the particle where

$$H(x, p) = \frac{p^2}{2m} + V(x), \tag{8.4.10}$$

as

$$\langle H \rangle = \int_{-\infty}^{\infty} \psi_x^*(x)\left[-\frac{\hbar^2}{2m}\frac{\partial^2}{\partial x^2} + V(x)\right]\psi_x(x)\, dx. \tag{8.4.11}$$

---

[10] Difficulties then arise in terms of the nature of the differential operator replacement for terms such as xp^2; these do not concern us here. See, for example, Messiah (1964).
[11] A presentation leading to Eq. (8.4.8) along a somewhat similar route to that followed here is given by Furry (1963).

Heisenberg Uncertainty Relation

We now show that the formalism developed in this section, which has been based on the Fourier transform relation between the functions $\psi_x(x)$ and $\psi_p(p)$, implies the Heisenberg uncertainty relation, Eq. (8.3.8). With the availability of Eq. (8.4.8), however, we no longer need to use, in most of the following discussion, both functions $\psi_x(x)$ and $\psi_p(p)$. We will generally use only the former and simplify the notation by writing $\psi_x(x) = \psi(x)$, returning to the previous notation only when both functions are under discussion.

We start by treating the special case in which $\langle x \rangle = \langle p \rangle = 0$ so that

$$(\Delta x)^2 = \left\langle (x - \langle x \rangle)^2 \right\rangle = \langle x^2 \rangle - \langle x \rangle^2 = \langle x^2 \rangle$$

$$= \int_{-\infty}^{\infty} \psi^*(x) x^2 \psi(x)\, dx \qquad (8.4.12)$$

and similarly

$$(\Delta p)^2 = \langle p^2 \rangle = -\hbar^2 \int_{-\infty}^{\infty} \psi^*(x) \frac{\partial^2 \psi}{\partial x^2}\, dx, \qquad (8.4.13)$$

by use of Eq. (8.4.5).

Let α be an arbitrary real number and consider the positive-definite integral,

$$I(\alpha) = \int_{-\infty}^{\infty} \left| \left(\alpha \hbar \frac{\partial}{\partial x} - x \right) \psi \right|^2 dx \geq 0. \qquad (8.4.14)$$

Expansion of the integrand leads to

$$I(\alpha) = \int_{-\infty}^{\infty} \left(\alpha \hbar \frac{\partial}{\partial x} - x \right) \psi^* \left(\alpha \hbar \frac{\partial}{\partial x} - x \right) \psi\, dx$$

$$= \alpha^2 \hbar^2 \int_{-\infty}^{\infty} \frac{\partial \psi^*}{\partial x} \frac{\partial \psi}{\partial x}\, dx - \alpha \hbar \left[\int_{-\infty}^{\infty} \frac{\partial \psi^*}{\partial x} x \psi\, dx + \int_{-\infty}^{\infty} x \psi^* \frac{\partial \psi}{\partial x}\, dx \right]$$

$$+ \int_{-\infty}^{\infty} x^2 \psi^* \psi\, dx.$$

By use of integration by parts and the condition[12] that $\lim_{x \to \pm\infty} \psi(x) = 0$ we see that

$$\hbar^2 \int_{-\infty}^{\infty} \frac{\partial \psi^*}{\partial x} \frac{\partial \psi}{\partial x}\, dx = -\hbar^2 \int_{-\infty}^{\infty} \psi^* \frac{\partial^2 \psi}{\partial x^2}\, dx = (\Delta p)^2.$$

[12]We adopt this condition as part of the requirement that the particle is localized to a finite region of space.

Similarly

$$\int_{-\infty}^{\infty} \frac{\partial \psi^*}{\partial x} x\psi \, dx = -\int_{-\infty}^{\infty} \psi^* \left(\psi + x\frac{\partial \psi}{\partial x} \right) dx = -1 - \int_{-\infty}^{\infty} \psi^* x \frac{\partial \psi}{\partial x} \, dx$$

where use has also been made of the normalization condition, Eq. (8.3.12).
Therefore, the polynomial $I(\alpha)$ becomes

$$I(\alpha) = \alpha^2 (\Delta p)^2 + \alpha\hbar + (\Delta x)^2. \tag{8.4.15}$$

Since $I(\alpha)$ is nonnegative, as seen from its definition in Eq. (8.4.14), this quadratic polynomial in α can have at most two equal roots. Therefore, its discriminant, $b^2 - 4ac \leqslant 0$, or

$$\hbar^2 - 4(\Delta p)^2 (\Delta x)^2 \leqslant 0,$$

thus leading directly to the Heisenberg uncertainty relation.
   If the means $\bar{x}$ and $\bar{p}$ are not zero the function $I(\alpha)$ is defined as

$$I(\alpha) = \int_{-\infty}^{\infty} \left| \left[\alpha \left(\hbar\frac{\partial}{\partial x} - i\bar{p} \right) - (x - \bar{x}) \right] \psi \right|^2 dx \geqslant 0 \tag{8.4.16}$$

in place of the definition given in Eq. (8.4.14) and it is readily verified that this leads to the same polynomial as in Eq. (8.4.15).

Minimum Uncertainty Measurement

As an illustrative example, we consider the simultaneous measurement of the position and momentum of a particle with an apparatus designed[13] to yield this information with the minimum uncertainty which is consistent with the Heisenberg uncertainty relation; that is, after this measurement

$$\Delta x \cdot \Delta p = \frac{\hbar}{2}. \tag{8.4.17}$$

This, in turn, implies that the discriminant of the polynomial $I(\alpha)$ defined in Eq. (8.4.15) is zero and that it, therefore, has a single real root, namely,

$$\alpha = \frac{-\hbar}{2(\Delta p)^2} = \frac{-2(\Delta x)^2}{\hbar} \tag{8.4.18}$$

where we have used Eq. (8.4.17). For this value of α, $I(\alpha) = 0$ and the integrand in Eq. (8.4.16) must be identically zero. Therefore, $\psi(x)$ satisfies the

---

[13] The experiment is hypothetical; it is not clear how this apparatus would be designed.

differential equation

$$\frac{\partial \psi}{\partial x} = \left(\frac{i\bar{p}}{\hbar} - \frac{(x - \bar{x})}{2(\Delta x)^2} \right) \psi \tag{8.4.19}$$

with the solution

$$\psi(x) = C \exp\left(\frac{i\bar{p}x}{\hbar} - \frac{(x - \bar{x})^2}{4(\Delta x)^2} \right) \tag{8.4.20}$$

with the arbitrary constant C determined to satisfy the normalization condition, Eq. (8.3.12). The final result is

$$\psi(x) = \frac{1}{(2\pi)^{1/4}(\Delta x)^{1/2}} \exp\left(\frac{i\bar{p}x}{\hbar} - \frac{(x - \bar{x})^2}{4(\Delta x)^2} \right). \tag{8.4.21}$$

It is of interest here to compute the Fourier transform $\psi_p(p)$ of the function $\psi_x(x) = \psi(x)$ in Eq. (8.4.21). The result, by application of Eq. (8.3.10), is

$$\psi_p(p) = \left(\frac{2}{\pi} \right)^{1/4} \left(\frac{\Delta x}{\hbar} \right)^{1/2} \exp\left(\frac{-i(p - \bar{p})\bar{x}}{\hbar} - \frac{(\Delta x)^2(p - \bar{p})^2}{\hbar^2} \right). \tag{8.4.22}$$

Therefore, the probability distributions of coordinates and momenta, $P_x(x)$ and $P_p(p)$, take similar forms, namely:

$$P_x(x) = \frac{1}{(2\pi)^{1/2} \Delta x} \exp\left(\frac{-(x - \bar{x})^2}{2(\Delta x)^2} \right), \tag{8.4.23}$$

$$P_p(x) = \frac{1}{\hbar}\left(\frac{2}{\pi} \right)^{1/2} \Delta x \exp\left(\frac{-2(\Delta x)^2(p - \bar{p})^2}{\hbar^2} \right),$$

$$= \frac{1}{(2\pi)^{1/2} \Delta p} \exp\left(\frac{-(p - \bar{p})^2}{2(\Delta p)^2} \right) \tag{8.4.24}$$

where, in the latter form of Eq. (8.4.24), we have made use of Eq. (8.4.17).

Both probability distributions are thus Gaussian and the state described by Eq. (8.4.21) is referred to as a Gaussian wave packet. The minimum uncertainty measurement provides a good illustration of the necessary trade-off in accuracy in the measurement of position and momentum. The subsequent time evolution of these states will be discussed in Section 10.5.

A More Compact Notation

We introduce at this point a more compact notation for the various infinite integrals such as those in Eq. (8.4.12) or (8.4.13) which have appeared repeatedly throughout this section. For any two functions $\psi(x)$ and $\phi(x)$ we write

$$\int_{-\infty}^{\infty} \psi^*(x)\phi(x)\, dx = (\psi, \phi). \qquad (8.4.25)$$

Note that the first function of the pair (ψ, ϕ) appears in the integral as $\psi^*(x)$, the complex conjugate of $\psi(x)$. It follows from the definition that

$$(\psi, \phi) = (\phi, \psi)^* \qquad (8.4.26)$$

$$(\psi, \phi_1 + \phi_2) = (\psi, \phi_1) + (\psi, \phi_2) \qquad (8.4.27)$$

$$(\psi, c\phi) = c(\psi, \phi), \qquad (c\psi, \phi) = c^*(\psi, \phi) \qquad (8.4.28)$$

where c is an arbitrary complex number. These properties form part of the definition of what is referred to as an inner product between two vectors in a linear vector space.[14] It is a generalization of the concept of the scalar product between two vectors in three-dimensional Euclidean space.

We also use the linear operator notation, writing

$$\frac{\hbar}{i}\frac{\partial}{\partial x}\psi(x) = \mathsf{p}\psi \qquad (8.4.29)$$

where the use of the notation p indicates the differential operator $(\hbar/i)\partial/\partial x$ acting on the function $\psi(x)$. More generally we use the notation

$$F\left(x; \frac{\hbar}{i}\frac{\partial}{\partial x}\right)\psi(x) = \mathsf{F}\psi. \qquad (8.4.30)$$

With this notation for differential operators, the Schrödinger time-dependent equation, Eq. (8.3.13), may be written in the compact form

$$\mathsf{H}\psi = i\hbar\frac{\partial\psi}{\partial t}. \qquad (8.4.31)$$

This operator equation may be regarded as the basic postulated form of the Schrödinger equation; it applies as well to more complex systems than here

---

[14]Also needed for the inner product definition is the property $(\phi, \phi) \geqslant 0$; $(\phi, \phi) = 0$ if and only if $\phi = 0$ (see Halmos, 1958, p. 121). The latter part of this property follows from Eq. (8.4.25) if, for example, we restrict attention to continuous ϕ.

considered, provided the proper interpretation is given to the operator H. Some generalizations will be considered in Section 8.5. With this notation, an integral such as in Eq. (8.4.9) can be written

$$\int_{-\infty}^{\infty} \psi^*(x) F\left(x, \frac{\hbar}{i} \frac{\partial}{\partial x}\right) \phi(x) \, dx = (\psi, \mathsf{F}\phi). \qquad (8.4.32)$$

Consider the integral

$$\int_{-\infty}^{\infty} \psi^*(x) \frac{\hbar}{i} \frac{\partial}{\partial x} \phi(x) \, dx = -\int_{-\infty}^{\infty} \frac{\hbar}{i} \frac{\partial \psi^*}{\partial x} \phi \, dx = \int_{-\infty}^{\infty} \left(\frac{\hbar}{i} \frac{\partial \psi}{\partial x}\right)^* \phi \, dx$$

$$(8.4.33)$$

where we have used integration by parts and the vanishing of ϕ and ψ at the infinite limits. This result may be restated as

$$(\psi, \mathsf{p}\phi) = (\mathsf{p}\psi, \phi). \qquad (8.4.34)$$

In quantum mechanics attention is limited to operators F (referred to as Hermitian or self-adjoint operators) which obey a similar equation for arbitrary ψ and ϕ, that is, for which[15]

$$(\psi, \mathsf{F}\phi) = (\mathsf{F}\psi, \phi). \qquad (8.4.35)$$

Observables

It is customary in quantum mechanics to refer to the Hermitian operator as an observable and to use the same terminology and notation for the physical property of the system which it represents. Thus, we speak of the expected value $\langle \mathsf{F} \rangle$ of the observable F when the system is in the state ψ as given by[16]

$$\langle \mathsf{F} \rangle = (\psi, \mathsf{F}\psi), \qquad (8.4.36)$$

as a replacement for the more extended terminology and notation of Eq. (8.4.9).

[15]By successive application of Eq. (8.4.34), $(\psi, \mathsf{p}^2\phi) = (\mathsf{p}\psi, \mathsf{p}\phi) = (\mathsf{p}^2\psi, \phi)$, we see that p^2 and similarly p^n are Hermitian operators. It is clear, therefore, that the operators assigned to functions of the form $f(x) + g(p)$, with $g(p)$ a polynomial, by the prescription given after Eq. (8.4.6), are in fact Hermitian.

[16]Because of Eq. (8.4.35), it does not matter which of the two functions, ψ and ϕ, we regard as being operated on by the Hermitian operator F in the expression $(\psi, \mathsf{F}\phi)$. This is the basis for another notation that enjoys wide currency in the quantum mechanics literature, the Dirac bracket notation in which the inner product (ψ, ϕ) is written as $\langle \psi | \phi \rangle$ and in which $(\psi, \mathsf{F}\phi)$ is denoted by $\langle \psi | \mathsf{F} | \phi \rangle$ (see Messiah, 1964).

Time Dependence of Observables

Consider the time-dependent dynamical state $\psi(x, t)$ of a particle where, therefore, $\psi(x, t)$ satisfies the time-dependent Schrödinger equation. The expectation or mean value $\langle H \rangle$ of the observable H, the Hamiltonian or total energy of the particle, is

$$\langle H \rangle = (\psi, H\psi). \qquad (8.4.37)$$

We confine attention to Hamiltonians that are time-independent and show that, in close analogy to the corresponding classical case [see Eq. (2.5.21)], $\langle H \rangle$ is constant. We, therefore, compute $d\langle H \rangle/dt$, starting from Eq. (8.4.37), and making use of the concrete definitions given above to justify the various steps, we find that

$$\frac{d\langle H \rangle}{dt} = \left(\frac{\partial \psi}{\partial t}, H\psi \right) + \left(\psi, H \frac{\partial \psi}{\partial t} \right)$$

$$= \left(\frac{\partial \psi}{\partial t}, H\psi \right) + \left(H\psi, \frac{\partial \psi}{\partial t} \right), \qquad (8.4.38)$$

where we have made use of the Hermitian character of H. Now substitute for $H\psi$ from the time-dependent Schrödinger equation in its symbolic form, Eq. (8.4.31). Then,

$$\frac{d\langle H \rangle}{dt} = \left(\frac{\partial \psi}{\partial t}, i\hbar \frac{\partial \psi}{\partial t} \right) + \left(i\hbar \frac{\partial \psi}{\partial t}, \frac{\partial \psi}{\partial t} \right) = 0, \qquad (8.4.39)$$

where we have made use of Eq. (8.4.28).

In a similar way we can compute the rate of change of the expected value $\langle A \rangle$ of any observable A. We assume that the operator A has no explicit time dependence. Then,

$$\langle A \rangle = (\psi, A\psi)$$

and

$$\frac{d}{dt} \langle A \rangle = \left(\frac{\partial \psi}{\partial t}, A\psi \right) + \left(\psi, A \frac{\partial \psi}{\partial t} \right).$$

By substitution from the time-dependent Schrödinger equation, Eq. (8.4.31),

$$\frac{d\langle A \rangle}{dt} = \left(-\frac{i}{\hbar} H\psi, A\psi \right) + \left(\psi, -\frac{i}{\hbar} AH\psi \right)$$

$$= \frac{i}{\hbar} \{ (H\psi, A\psi) - (\psi, AH\psi) \}$$

$$= \frac{i}{\hbar} (\psi, (HA - AH)\psi), \qquad (8.4.40)$$

where Eq. (8.4.28) and the Hermitian character of H have been employed. Eq.

(8.4.40) can be rewritten[17]

$$\frac{d\langle A \rangle}{dt} = \frac{i}{\hbar} \langle [H, A] \rangle \tag{8.4.41}$$

where

$$[H, A] = HA - AH \tag{8.4.42}$$

is known as the commutator of the two operators H and A. Therefore, the expected value $\langle A \rangle$ of any (time-independent) observable A that commutes with H is also a constant of the motion. It is clear that the previous result that $\langle H \rangle$ is a constant of the motion follows as a special case of this more general result.

8.5 EXTENSION TO THREE-DIMENSIONAL MOTION AND TO *N* PARTICLES

In our treatment of quantum mechanics thus far we have restricted attention to the case of a single particle moving in one fixed direction in order to present the basic concepts in their simplest form. In this section, we indicate how the concepts are generalized when the motion of a single particle in three dimensions is considered. It will be seen then that the further generalization to a system of N particles is, at least from the notational viewpoint, quite straightforward. For the most part, in what follows, it appears to be sufficient to simply list the forms certain key equations take when these generalizations are made.

Three-Dimensional Motion

Let the particle coordinates, referred to a rectangular coordinate system, be (x_1, x_2, x_3); as before we will use the notation $x_j, j = 1, 2, 3$ for these coordinates and the notation $\mathbf{x}$ for a vector with these components. The momentum $\mathbf{p}$ of the particle has components $p_j, j = 1, 2, 3$. The wave functions $\psi_x(x, t)$ and $\psi_p(p, t)$ for the one-dimensional motion are then generalized to corresponding functions of three variables which are denoted by $\psi_x(\mathbf{x}, t)$ and $\psi_p(\mathbf{p}, t)$. They are now three-dimensional Fourier transforms of each other:

$$\psi_\mathbf{p}(\mathbf{p}, t) = (2\pi\hbar)^{-3/2} \int_{-\infty}^{\infty} \psi_\mathbf{x}(\mathbf{x}, t) e^{-i\mathbf{p}\cdot\mathbf{x}/\hbar} \, d\mathbf{x} \tag{8.5.1}$$

$$\psi_\mathbf{x}(\mathbf{x}, t) = (2\pi\hbar)^{-3/2} \int_{-\infty}^{\infty} \psi_\mathbf{p}(\mathbf{p}, t) e^{i\mathbf{p}\cdot\mathbf{x}/\hbar} \, d\mathbf{p} \tag{8.5.2}$$

---

[17]The close resemblance to the Poisson bracket formulation of the equations of motion of classical mechanics (Goldstein, 1980, p. 405) may be noted.

where $dx = dx_1 dx_2 dx_3$, and the single integral denotes integration over $-\infty < x_j < \infty$, $j = 1, 2, 3$, etc. These wave functions give rise to probability distributions, $P_x(\mathbf{x}, t) = |\psi_x(\mathbf{x}, t)|^2$, $P_p(\mathbf{p}, t) = |\psi_p(\mathbf{p}, t)|^2$ as before. Following the same lines as in the one-dimensional argument, we may demonstrate that the Fourier transform relation again leads to the Heisenberg uncertainty relation which in three dimensions takes the form[18]

$$(\Delta x_n)(\Delta p_m) \geqslant \frac{\hbar}{2} \delta_{mn} \qquad (8.5.3)$$

where δ_{mn} is the Kronecker delta.

The expression of the expected values of polynomial functions of the momenta solely in terms of the function $\psi_x(\mathbf{x}, t)$ is again accomplished by use of properties of the Fourier transform relation, Eq. (8.5.1), as in Section 8.4. Analogously to the procedure followed there, we differentiate Eq. (8.5.2) with respect to x_j in order to demonstrate that

$$\frac{\hbar}{i} \frac{\partial \psi_x}{\partial x_j} \cdot \supset \cdot p_j \psi_p, \qquad j = 1, 2, 3, \qquad (8.5.4)$$

or, in an alternate notation,

$$\frac{\hbar}{i} \frac{\partial \psi_x}{\partial \mathbf{x}} \cdot \supset \cdot \mathbf{p} \psi_p \qquad (8.5.5)$$

are Fourier transform pairs. This relation, together with Parsevals relation in three dimensions, permits writing the expected value $\langle g \rangle$ of any polynomial $g(\mathbf{p})$ in a form analogous to Eq. (8.4.6), namely,

$$\langle g \rangle = \int_{-\infty}^{\infty} \psi_x^*(\mathbf{x}) g\left(\frac{\hbar}{i} \frac{\partial}{\partial \mathbf{x}}\right) \psi_x(\mathbf{x}) \, d\mathbf{x} \qquad (8.5.6)$$

and we note the generalization of Eq. (8.4.9), giving the mean $\langle F \rangle$ of a function $F(\mathbf{x}, \mathbf{p})$, as

$$\langle F \rangle = \int_{-\infty}^{\infty} \psi_x(\mathbf{x}) F\left(\mathbf{x}, \frac{\hbar}{i} \frac{\partial}{\partial \mathbf{x}}\right) \psi_x(\mathbf{x}) \, d\mathbf{x}. \qquad (8.5.7)$$

As in the one-dimensional case, we write $\psi_x(\mathbf{x}) = \psi(\mathbf{x})$ unless the discussion requires the use of both ψ_x and ψ_p.

As we noted in Section 8.4, the basic form of the time-dependent Schrödinger equation is the operator equation

$$\mathsf{H}\psi = i\hbar \frac{\partial \psi}{\partial t}.$$

---

[18] There is, therefore, no theoretical impediment to the precise measurement of a particle coordinate component and simultaneously measuring precisely a momentum component, provided these two components are not in the same direction.

Since the Hamiltonian or total energy of the system $H(\mathbf{x}, \mathbf{p})$ is

$$H(\mathbf{x}, \mathbf{p}) = \frac{1}{2m} \sum_{j=1}^{3} p_j^2 + V(x_1, x_2, x_3) = \frac{1}{2m} \mathbf{p} \cdot \mathbf{p} + V(\mathbf{x}) \quad (8.5.8)$$

and the differential operator corresponding to p_j is

$$\mathsf{p}_j = \frac{\hbar}{i} \frac{\partial}{\partial x_j} \quad (8.5.9)$$

the time-dependent Schrödinger equation in explicit differential operator form is

$$\mathsf{H}\psi = \frac{-\hbar^2}{2m} \nabla^2 \psi + V(\mathbf{x})\psi = i\hbar \frac{\partial \psi}{\partial t} \quad (8.5.10)$$

where

$$\nabla^2 = \frac{\partial^2}{\partial x_1^2} + \frac{\partial^2}{\partial x_2^2} + \frac{\partial^2}{\partial x_3^2} = \sum_{j=1}^{3} \frac{\partial^2}{\partial x_j^2}. \quad (8.5.11)$$

Motion of N Particles

Consider next the motion of N particles. By following the indexing system described in Section 2.2. which leads to the Hamiltonian of Eq. (2.2.15), together with the use of mass-reduced coordinates as described in Section 4.4 which leads to Eq. (4.4.5), we can write[19] the Hamiltonian of the N particles in the form

$$H(x_1, \ldots, x_n; p_1, \ldots, p_n) = \frac{1}{2m} \sum_{j=1}^{n} p^2 + V(x_1, \ldots, x_n) \quad (8.5.12)$$

or

$$H(\mathbf{x}, \mathbf{p}) = \frac{1}{2m} \mathbf{p} \cdot \mathbf{p} + V(\mathbf{x})$$

where $n = 3N$, $\mathbf{x}$ and $\mathbf{p}$ denote n-dimensional vectors and $V(\mathbf{x})$ describes the interaction potential among the N particles. The equations of the first part of this section now provide immediately the necessary generalizations to a system of N particles, provided it is understood that in each case the range of $j = 1, \ldots, n$. An additional point to be noted is that the normalization factor in Eqs. (8.5.1) and (8.5.2) depends on the dimensionality of the Fourier transform and for N particles becomes $(2\pi\hbar)^{-3N/2}$.

---

[19]In order to maintain the analogy with the Hamiltonian of a single particle, Eq. (8.5.8), the present definition of mass-reduced coordinates uses the ratio m_i/m in place of simply m_i as in Eq. (4.4.4); here, m is a reference mass chosen for convenience.

The compact notation introduced in Section 8.4 for particles with a single degree of freedom may also be extended to the multidimensional case in a natural way. For example, Eq. (8.4.25) takes the form

$$\int_{-\infty}^{\infty} \psi^*(\mathbf{x})\phi(\mathbf{x})\,d\mathbf{x} = (\psi, \phi) \tag{8.5.13}$$

where the integral is now $3N$-dimensional for a system of N particles. It is clear that Eqs. (8.4.26)–(8.4.28) apply in this case as well. An observable A is now a Hermitian operator A which acts on functions of $3N$ variables; an example for $N = 1$ is the Hamiltonian H defined in Eq. (8.5.10). With this understanding, Eqs. (8.4.35)–(8.5.42) also apply.

8.6   HYDRODYNAMIC ANALOGY TO QUANTUM MECHANICS

There is great value for some one approaching for the first time a subject such as quantum mechanics which is so far from the realm of everyday physical experience to see analogies to more familiar topics. The hydrodynamic analogy,[20] which we present in this section, should provide a particularly useful picture to those familiar with classical continuum mechanics.

We start by considering the case of a single particle of mass m moving in three dimensions subject to a potential $V(\mathbf{x})$. The quantum formulation of the previous section applies therefore and the Schrödinger equation for the wave function $\psi(\mathbf{x}, t)$ is given by Eq. (8.5.10). Write the complex function $\psi(\mathbf{x}, t)$ in terms of its modulus and phase, that is, in the form

$$\psi(\mathbf{x}, t) = A(\mathbf{x}, t)\exp\left[\frac{i}{\hbar}S(\mathbf{x}, t)\right]. \tag{8.6.1}$$

Then, the equations that the functions $A(\mathbf{x}, t)$ and $S(\mathbf{x}, t)$ must satisfy are obtained by substituting into Eq. (8.5.10) and equating to zero separately real and imaginary parts. The results are:

$$\frac{\partial S}{\partial t} = -V + \frac{\hbar^2}{2m}\frac{\nabla^2 A}{A} - \frac{1}{2m}(\nabla S)^2 \tag{8.6.2}$$

$$\frac{\partial A}{\partial t} = -\frac{1}{m}\nabla A \cdot \nabla S - \frac{1}{2m}A\nabla^2 S \tag{8.6.3}$$

---

[20] The analogy was first developed by Madelung (1926) shortly after the introduction by Schrödinger of the wave equation itself, and has been rediscovered by numerous writers since. It has also been studied and extended by many including Bohm and Vigier (1954), Takabayasi (1952), and Jánossy (1962). It has been used as a basis for the numerical solution of the Schrödinger equation by Weiner and Partom (1969), Weiner and Askar (1971b), Kim and Weiner (1973), Weiner and Forman (1974b), Terlecki, Grün and Scheid (1982), and for its perturbative analysis by Weiner and Askar (1971).

where, in the usual vector notation,

$$\nabla A \cdot \nabla S = \sum_{j=1}^{3} \frac{\partial A}{\partial x_j} \frac{\partial S}{\partial x_j} \tag{8.6.4}$$

and $(\nabla S)^2 = \nabla S \cdot \nabla S$. These equations are transformed by taking the gradient of the first and multiplying the second by A. The results are

$$\frac{\partial(\nabla S)}{\partial t} = -\nabla V + \nabla \left(\frac{\hbar^2}{2m} \frac{\nabla^2 A}{A} \right) - \frac{1}{m} \nabla S \cdot \nabla \nabla S \tag{8.6.5}$$

$$\frac{\partial A^2}{\partial t} = -\frac{1}{m} \nabla A^2 \cdot \nabla S - \frac{1}{m} A^2 \nabla^2 S. \tag{8.6.6}$$

We may now exhibit the hydrodynamic analogy by introducing the following notation:

$$\mathbf{v}(\mathbf{x}, t) = \frac{1}{m} \nabla S(\mathbf{x}, t) \tag{8.6.7}$$

$$\rho(\mathbf{x}, t) = A^2(\mathbf{x}, t) \tag{8.6.8}$$

$$V_{qu.}(\mathbf{x}, t) = -\frac{\hbar^2}{2m} \frac{\nabla^2 A}{A}. \tag{8.6.9}$$

Eqs. (8.6.5) and (8.6.6) take the following form:

$$m \frac{d\mathbf{v}}{dt} = -\nabla(V + V_{qu.}) \tag{8.6.10}$$

$$\frac{\partial \rho}{\partial t} + \nabla \cdot (\rho \mathbf{v}) = 0 \tag{8.6.11}$$

where

$$\frac{d\mathbf{v}}{dt} = \frac{\partial \mathbf{v}}{\partial t} + \mathbf{v} \cdot \nabla \mathbf{v}. \tag{8.6.12}$$

The physical interpretation of these equations is clear. They describe the flow of a continuum of particles with mass density $\rho(\mathbf{x}, t)$ and with the velocity $\mathbf{v}(\mathbf{x}, t)$ for the particle presently at position[21] $(\mathbf{x}, t)$. Equation (8.6.11) is the usual continuity equation for such a continuum [see Eqs. (2.5.18) and (2.5.19)]. From the equations of motion for the continuum, Eq. (8.6.10), we see that each particle is acted on by forces derived from a potential which consists of two

[21] That is, Eulerian coordinates are employed.

parts: $V(\mathbf{x})$, which is simply the prescribed potential, and $V_{qu}(\mathbf{x}, t)$, the equivalent quantum potential, which depends on the density variation of the continuum, according to Eq. (8.6.9).

This hydrodynamic analogy allows us to visualize the time evolution of the quantum state of a single particle in terms of the flow of a continuum whose density at a point is proportional to the probability density of the particle's location at that point. The analogy shows clearly the relation between the Schrödinger equation and the classical equation of motion and demonstrates that the predictions of quantum mechanics will be essentially indistinguishable from those of classical mechanics when dealing with particles of large mass and macroscopic distances. In this case, the quantum potential V_{qu} defined in Eq. (8.6.9) becomes negligible and if the particle is initially well localized on a macroscopic scale,[22] it will remain so, following the classical trajectory.

We can also reinterpret the expected or quantum mean energy, $\overline{H}$, in the light of the hydrodynamic analogy. As previously derived,

$$\overline{H} = (\psi, H\psi) = \int_{-\infty}^{\infty} \psi^*(\mathbf{x}, t)\left[\frac{-\hbar^2}{2m}\nabla^2 + V(x)\right]\psi(\mathbf{x}, t)\, d\mathbf{x}. \quad (8.6.13)$$

With $\psi = Ae^{iS/\hbar}$ as in Eq. (8.6.1) this takes the form

$$\overline{H} = \int_{-\infty}^{\infty}\left\{\frac{-\hbar^2}{2m}A\left(\nabla^2 A - \frac{A}{\hbar^2}(\nabla S)^2 + \frac{2i}{\hbar}\nabla A \cdot \nabla S + \frac{iA}{\hbar}\nabla^2 S\right) + A^2 V\right\} d\mathbf{x}.$$

$$(8.6.14)$$

From the Hermitian character of H it follows that the imaginary contribution to $\overline{H}$ must vanish. The nonvanishing parts of the integral may be reexpressed in terms of the hydrodynamic analogy by means of Eqs. (8.6.7)–(8.6.9) as:

$$\overline{H} = \int_{-\infty}^{\infty} \rho(\mathbf{x}, t)\left[V(\mathbf{x}) + V_{qu}(\mathbf{x}, t) + \frac{m}{2}|\mathbf{v}(\dot{\mathbf{x}}, t)|^2\right] d\mathbf{x}.$$

The total energy is, therefore, simply the sum of kinetic plus potential (including the quantum potential) energy of the equivalent continuum.

We have considered the hydrodynamic analogy to the quantum mechanical problem of a single particle moving in three-dimensional space and have been led to consideration of a three-dimensional continuum of particles. It is clear from the derivation and the discussion of Section 8.5 that the same analogy applies to the motion of N particles. In this case, however, it must be phrased in terms of a $3N$-dimensional continuum of particles moving in a $3N$-dimensional configuration space. The derivation is precisely the same as just given providing all vectors are understood to be $3N$-dimensional, ∇ the $3N$-dimensional gradient operator, etc.

---

[22] Note that the particle cannot be too sharply localized on an atomic scale or V_{qu} will not be small.

8.7   INITIAL-VALUE PROBLEMS

Consider the problem of the determination of the wave function $\psi(\mathbf{x}, t)$ which satisfies the differential equation

$$H\psi = -\frac{\hbar^2}{2m}\nabla^2\psi + V(\mathbf{x})\psi = i\hbar\frac{\partial\psi}{\partial t} \tag{8.7.1}$$

with the initial condition

$$\psi(\mathbf{x}, 0) = \psi_0(\mathbf{x}). \tag{8.7.2}$$

We assume, in accord with our general practice, that ψ_0 is normalized to unity. Since Eq. (8.7.1) is a linear[23] partial differential equation, it is natural to use the technique of separation of variables for its solution, that is, to seek a solution in the form

$$\psi(\mathbf{x}, t) = \phi(\mathbf{x})f(t). \tag{8.7.3}$$

Substitution into Eq. (8.7.1) and the separation of variables leads in the usual way to the equations

$$\frac{H\phi}{\phi} = \frac{i\hbar}{f}\frac{df}{dt} = E \tag{8.7.4}$$

with E a constant. The equation for $f(t)$ is readily solved and leads to the result that Eq. (8.7.1) has a solution of the form

$$\psi(\mathbf{x}, t) = \phi(\mathbf{x})e^{-iEt/\hbar} \tag{8.7.5}$$

provided $\phi(\mathbf{x})$ satisfies the equation[24]

$$H\phi = E\phi,$$

or

$$\frac{-\hbar^2}{2m}\nabla^2\phi + V(\mathbf{x})\phi = E\phi; \tag{8.7.6}$$

that is, ϕ must be an eigenfunction of the operator H and E is the corresponding eigenvalue. We will confine attention in this discussion to the case in which

---

[23] It is interesting to note that the corresponding classical problem, Eqs. (8.2.1) and (8.2.2), is in general nonlinear, and that when the Schrödinger equation is reformulated, as in the previous section, to stress its relation to the classical case, it too becomes nonlinear, Eqs. (8.6.2) and (8.6.3).
[24] Equation (8.7.6) is generally termed the time-independent Schrödinger equation, whereas Eq. (8.7.1) is termed the time-dependent Schrödinger equation.

H has a discrete spectrum,[25] that is, a countable set of eigenvalues E_n, $n = 0, 1, 2, \ldots$, which we will order with increasing magnitude of E, with corresponding eigenfunctions ϕ_n. The eigenfunctions ϕ_n are taken to be normalized to unity. If $E_n \neq E_m$ it is easy to demonstrate that the corresponding eigenfunctions are orthogonal, that is, $(\phi_n, \phi_m) = 0$. If an eigenvalue E_n is degenerate, that is, if there corresponds to it a set of linearly independent eigenfunctions, then linear combinations of the latter may be defined so that they too are mutually orthogonal. In this way it is possible to show that the eigenfunctions $\phi_n(x)$ form an orthonormal set, that is,

$$(\phi_n, \phi_m) = \delta_{nm}. \tag{8.7.7}$$

It can also be shown under broad conditions[26] that this set is complete over a suitable space of square-integrable functions; that is, it is possible to expand $\psi_0(x)$, assuming it belongs to this space, in terms of these functions as

$$\psi_0(x) = \sum_{n=0}^{\infty} c_n\phi_n(x) \tag{8.7.8}$$

where, by use of Eq. (8.7.6), it is seen that the expansion coefficients

$$c_n = (\phi_n, \psi_0). \tag{8.7.9}$$

Note that since $(\psi_0, \psi_0) = 1$, it follows from Eqs. (8.7.8) and (8.7.9) that

$$\sum_{n=0}^{\infty} |c_n|^2 = 1. \tag{8.7.10}$$

The solution to the initial-value problem of Eqs. (8.7.1) and (8.7.2) can now be obtained by the superposition of solutions of the form of Eq. (8.7.5) as[27]

$$\psi(x, t) = \sum_{n=0}^{\infty} c_n\phi_n(x)\exp\left(\frac{-iE_nt}{\hbar}\right). \tag{8.7.11}$$

[25] This will be the case if $V(x)$ increases sufficiently rapidly as $|x| \to \infty$ so that all solutions to Eq. (8.7.6) correspond to square integrable or to normalizable functions, as in Eq. (8.3.12). Conceptually, it is always possible to model any physical situation so that this is the case, that is, by enclosing the system by an isolating wall [as in Eq. (2.7.1) for example] at some large distance. On the other hand, for mathematical simplicity, it is frequently convenient to consider models that lead to functions that are not square integrable over the required infinite range and therefore cannot be normalized as in Eq. (8.3.12) and for which the operator H has a continuous spectrum. A simple example is provided by the model of a completely free particle, $V(x) \equiv 0$. Other models lead to a spectrum with both continuous and discrete portions. The continuous spectrum leads to conceptual and notational difficulties (see, e.g., Messiah, 1964), and we will confine attention to models in which it is absent.
[26] See, for example, Ikenberry (1962), p. 123.
[27] We are using here, and in what follows, a notation in which an m-fold degenerate eigenvalue E_n is written $E_n = E_{n+1} = \cdots = E_{n+m-1}$. Therefore, all sums, such as in Eq. (8.7.10), are sums over distinct eigenfunctions, not sums over distinct eigenvalues. In quantum mechanics the two alternatives are referred to as sum over states and sum over levels, respectively.

Stationary States

In spite of the apparent time dependence of the state ψ given by Eq. (8.7.5), we see that any observable A which is time-independent will have an expected value $\langle A \rangle = (\psi, A\psi)$ which will also be time independent. States of the form $\psi(\mathbf{x}, t)$ as defined in Eq. (8.7.5), as well as the eigenfunctions $\phi_n(\mathbf{x})$, are therefore referred to as stationary states. On the other hand, a sum of such states, as in Eq. (8.7.11), leads to time-dependent behavior.

8.8 ASPECTS OF THE MEASUREMENT PROCESS

With the availability of an explicit form of the solution to the time-dependent Schrödinger equation, we can return to a further consideration of some aspects of the measurement process which were alluded to in Section 8.3.

Principle of Immediately Successive Measurements

A postulate of quantum mechanics regarding the nature of the measurement process may be stated as follows:

Consider a measurement at time t_1 of a particular observable A of a system[28] which yields the value a_1 for this observable. A second measurement of the same observable immediately following the first will yield the same value a_1 with complete certainty.[29]

The postulate is clearly a very reasonable one. Any measurement takes place over a nonzero time period which can be conceptually divided in two and regarded as two successive measurements. If the postulate were false, the result of the measurement would depend on which time interval were used. Also, if it were false, it is not clear how it would be replaced in order that the statement "The observable A was measured at time t_1 and found to have the value a_1," convey information about the system with operational significance.

If $\psi_{1+} = \psi(\mathbf{x}, t_1 +)$ is the state of the system immediately after the measurement, it follows from the postulate that

$$(\Delta A)^2 \triangleq \left\langle (A - a_1)^2 \right\rangle = \left(\psi_{1+}, (A - a_1)^2 \psi_{1+} \right)$$

$$= ((A - a_1)\psi_{1+}, (A - a_1)\psi_{1+}) = 0, \qquad (8.8.1)$$

where we have used the fact that the operator A is Hermitian and that, therefore, a_1 is real and the operator $A - a_1$ is also Hermitian. It follows from

---

[28] The system can consist of a single particle or a collection of particles.

[29] The term "immediately" refers to a limiting process in which the time Δt between successive measurements goes to zero. Alternatively, we may say that the uncertainty ΔA as to the result of the second measurement has the property that $\lim_{\Delta t \to 0} \Delta A = 0$.

Eq. (8.8.1) that

$$A\psi_{1+} = a_1\psi_{1+}, \tag{8.8.2}$$

that is, ψ_{1+} must be an eigenfunction of A corresponding to the eigenvalue a_1. Therefore, the possible results of a measurement of an observable are limited to the spectrum of the corresponding operator A. If that spectrum is discrete, only these discrete values can be measured. This is one of the predictions of quantum mechanics which is most at variance with the physical intuition developed from the consideration of macroscopic phenomena, although it is a familiar result to an experimenter examining the spectrum of electromagnetic radiation from a collection of atoms.

Collapse of Wave Packet

As an example of the effect of a measurement upon the state of a system, consider the measurement of its energy; the corresponding operator is H. We suppose that the state of the system is $\psi(x, t)$ as defined in Eq. (8.7.11), obtained as the solution to the initial-value problem of Eqs. (8.7.1) and (8.7.2). We wish to measure its energy at some subsequent time t_1. *Before* making this measurement, we can calculate its expected value $\langle H \rangle_1$ from the equation

$$\langle H \rangle_1 = (\psi_1, H\psi_1) \tag{8.8.3}$$

where $\psi_1 = \psi(x, t_1)$ as given by Eq. (8.7.11). From that equation we find

$$\langle H \rangle_1 = \sum_{n=0}^{\infty} |c_n|^2 E_n \tag{8.8.4}$$

where we have made use of Eqs. (8.7.6) and (8.7.7) in the calculation.[30] The uncertainty ΔH in the prediction of Eq. (8.8.4) can also be calculated:

$$(\Delta H)^2 = \left\langle (H - \langle H \rangle_1)^2 \right\rangle = \left(\psi_1, (H - \langle H \rangle_1)^2 \psi_1 \right)$$

$$= \sum_{n=0}^{\infty} |c_n|^2 E_n^2 - \langle H \rangle_1^2. \tag{8.8.5}$$

Equations (8.8.4) and (8.8.5) represent the state of our knowledge of the system's energy at $t = t_1$ before we have made our measurement. The result of our measurement must be, as indicated above, one of the eigenvalues, E_n, of the operator H. Our *a priori* prediction of Eqs. (8.8.4) and (8.8.5) indicates that it is likely that E_n will lie in the interval $\langle H \rangle_1 - \Delta H < E_n < \langle H \rangle_1 + \Delta H$ but, of course, this need not be the case. Also, whereas the state of the system immediately before the measurement was $\psi(x, t_1)$ as given by Eq. (8.7.11), immediately afterward its state is $\psi(x, t_1 +) = \phi_n(x)$, where ϕ_n is an eigenfunction of H corresponding to the observed energy E_n. This discontinuous change

---

[30] Note that $\langle H \rangle_1$ is independent of the time t_1, in accord with the general result of Eq. (8.4.39).

in wave function due to the measurement process is referred to as the collapse of the wave packet.

Several further aspects of the measurement process should be noted:

1 If the observed value of the energy corresponds to a degenerate eigenvalue E_n, then the state of the system after the measurement will not be uniquely determined by the energy measurement alone. In order to determine its state uniquely, the results of the measurement of a number of different observables of the system will be required, where the required number[31] is characteristic of the given system (see, for example, the discussion in Messiah, 1964, pp. 202–204).

2 We have used the measurement of the energy of the system as a particular example. If the measurement of some other observable A of the system were performed at time t_1, a similar collapse of the system's wave function to an eigenfunction ϕ_n^A of the operator A would occur at $t_1 +$. In general, however, ϕ_n^A would not be an eigenfunction of H as well. Therefore, the state of the system would change and evolve for $t > t_1$ as predicted by the time-dependent Schrödinger equation, whereas after the measurement of energy the system is in a stationary state.

3 If we consider the role of the quantities $|c_n|^2$ in Eq. (8.8.4) for the expected value of the energy, $\langle H \rangle_1$, and in Eq. (8.8.5) for the variance $(\Delta H)^2$ in its measurement, then we see that it is reasonable to set

$$|c_n|^2 = p_n, \tag{8.8.6}$$

so that

$$\sum_{n=0}^{\infty} p_n = 1 \tag{8.8.7}$$

by Eq. (8.7.10), and regard p_n as the probability that a system in state $\psi(\mathbf{x}, t)$ given by Eq. (8.7.11) will be found, by an energy measurement, to have energy E_n and to be in the state $\phi_n(\mathbf{x})$ after the measurement.

8.9　SOME EXAMPLES OF STATIONARY STATES

We have seen in the previous two sections the importance of the eigenfunctions $\phi_n(\mathbf{x})$ of the energy operator H or, in terminology frequently employed in quantum mechanics, the importance of stationary states or solutions to the

---

[31] This concept of a characteristic number of observable measurements required to determine the state of a quantum system uniquely has its parallel in the concept of the number of degrees of freedom of a classical system. For a quantum system whose set of observables all have their classical counterparts in the corresponding classical system, the two numbers are equal. However, there are quantum observables such as electron spin (see Section 8.11) which do not have classical counterparts.

time-independent Schrödinger equation. In this section we consider three simple particular cases that will illustrate some important principles. We will not present all of the details of the calculations. They are readily found in any of the standard works (see Section 8.1), which also contain many other examples.

Square-Well Potential

This highly idealized model is invariably one of the first treated in elementary expositions of the principles of quantum mechanics since the required calculations are elementary and it serves to illustrate a number of important general principles. The model consists of a particle of mass m constrained to move in a single direction and subject to the potential

$$V(x) = 0; \quad 0 < x < a$$

$$= \infty; \quad x \leqslant 0, x \geqslant a. \tag{8.9.1}$$

Clearly, if the particle is to have finite energy it must have zero probability of being found outside of the interval $0 < x < a$; that is, any stationary state $\phi(x) = 0$ for $x \leqslant 0$ and $x \geqslant a$. Furthermore, we require that $\phi(x)$ and $d\phi/dx$ be continuous in $0 \leqslant x \leqslant a$ since otherwise the expected kinetic energy (which depends on $d^2\phi/dx^2$) would become infinite and we conclude[32] that $\phi(0) = \phi(a) = 0$. Therefore, the time-independent Schrödinger equation, Eq. (8.7.6), becomes for this case

$$\frac{-\hbar^2}{2m} \frac{d^2\phi}{dx^2} = E\phi, \quad 0 < x < a \tag{8.9.2}$$

subject to the boundary conditions

$$\phi(0) = \phi(a) = 0. \tag{8.9.3}$$

The general solution to Eq. (8.9.2) is

$$\phi(x) = A \sin kx + B \cos kx \tag{8.9.4}$$

where

$$k = \frac{(2mE)^{1/2}}{\hbar}. \tag{8.9.5}$$

From the boundary condition $\phi(0) = 0$ we conclude that the constant $B = 0$.

[32] These boundary conditions may be motivated in a more rigorous manner by first considering the solution to the problem with $V = V_0$ outside the interval $0 < x < a$ and letting $V_0 \to \infty$.

From the second boundary condition, $\phi(a) = 0$, we find that the permissible values of k are discrete, given by the relation[33]

$$k_n a = n\pi, \qquad n = 1, 2, \ldots \qquad (8.9.6)$$

so that, from Eq. (8.9.5), the eigenvalues, or permissible energy levels E_n, are

$$E_n = \frac{(\hbar k_n)^2}{2m} = \frac{(\hbar n\pi)^2}{2ma^2}, \qquad n = 1, 2, \ldots \qquad (8.9.7)$$

and the corresponding eigenfunctions, or stationary states, are

$$\phi_n(x) = A \sin k_n x = A \sin \frac{n\pi x}{a} = \sqrt{\frac{2}{a}} \sin \frac{n\pi x}{a} \qquad \text{for } 0 \leqslant x \leqslant a$$

$$= 0 \qquad \text{for } x < 0 \text{ and } x > a, \qquad (8.9.8)$$

where the constant A has been computed to satisfy the normalization requirement, Eq. (8.3.12). The form of $P_n(x) = |\phi_n(x)|^2$, the probability distributions in the stationary states, is shown in Figure 8.2 for $n = 1$, 2, and 3. Several important principles which have wider application are illustrated by this simple example:

1   The discrete character of the eigenvalues E_n is due to the boundary conditions $\phi(0) = \phi(a) = 0$, that is, it arises from the localization of the particle by the potential.

2   The minimum eigenvalue[34] $E_1 > 0$. The fact that the minimum possible observed energy of the particle is positive is a direct consequence of the Heisenberg uncertainty principle, Eq. (8.3.8). For if the observed energy were zero the particle must be located in the interval $0 < x < a$ with $\Delta p = 0$ in violation of the inequality of Eq. (8.3.8). This positive minimum energy is referred to as zero-point energy and is a general characteristic of localized systems. Its particular value for this simple model,

$$E_1 = \frac{(\hbar\pi)^2}{2ma^2} = \frac{h^2}{8ma^2}, \qquad (8.9.9)$$

is useful for estimating the magnitude of the zero-point energy in terms of the particle mass and the degree of localization imposed by the confining potential.

---

[33] Note that $n = 0$ is excluded since it leads to the trivial solution $\phi(x) = 0$, that is, no particle!
[34] Note that the energy datum is chosen to be zero in Eq. (8.9.1) and that it is convenient to index the energy eigenvalues E_n starting with $n = 1$ in this example.

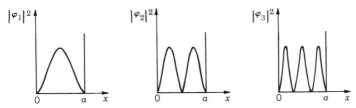

Figure 8.2 Probability distribution for first three states of particle in infinite square well potential.

The eigenfunction $\phi_1(x)$ corresponding to the minimum energy E_1 is referred to as the ground state of the system and eigenfunctions $\phi_n(x)$ for $n > 1$ are then referred to as excited states.

3 For low values of n the probability density $P_n(x)$ is highly nonuniform (Figure 8.2). As n increases, although $P_n(x)$ has an increasing number of zeros, the probability of finding the particle in any interval approaches uniformity. This large n behavior is in accord with the classical predictions for a particle in this potential, since the classical particle with prescribed energy has constant velocity and, therefore, uniform probability density of being found, over a long time period, at any position in the well. This is an example of the correspondence principle that states the behavior of a quantum system approaches that of the corresponding classical system for sufficiently high energy values.

4 If m and a in Eq. (8.9.7) are macroscopic in character, then n must be very large for E_n to be macroscopically measurable. Since

$$\frac{E_n - E_{n-1}}{E_n} = \frac{2n - 1}{n^2} \approx \frac{2}{n} \text{ for } n \gg 1, \qquad (8.9.10)$$

it follows that the possible observed energy values would appear continuous on a macroscopic scale.

5 The stationary states $\phi_n(x)$ defined in Eq. (8.9.8) may be rewritten in the form

$$\phi_n(x) = \frac{1}{\sqrt{2a}}(e^{ik_n x} + e^{-ik_n x}) \text{ for } 0 < x < a,$$

$$= 0 \text{ for } x \leqslant 0 \text{ and } x \geqslant a. \qquad (8.9.11)$$

It is then instructive to apply the hydrodynamic analogy of Section 8.6 separately to each complex exponential. From Eqs. (8.6.1) and (8.6.7) it is seen that v_n, the particle velocity of the analogy corresponding to $e^{\pm ik_n x}$, is $\pm \hbar k_n/m$ and $\tilde{p}_n = mv_n$, the analog particle momentum corresponding to $e^{\pm ik_n x}$, is

$$\tilde{p}_n = \pm \hbar k_n. \qquad (8.9.12)$$

Therefore, in a phase space representation with coordinates x and $\tilde{p}$, the hydrodynamic analogy for $\phi_n(x)$ takes the form shown in Figure 8.3. From Eq. (8.9.7)

$$E_n = \frac{\tilde{p}^2}{2m} \tag{8.9.13}$$

just as in the classical case, so for this simple model the phase space appearance of the two cases is identical for all n. However, only orbits corresponding to the discrete values of E_n are possible in the quantum case. Furthermore, it must be emphasized that in the quantum case, interference effects in the computation of $P_n(x)$ from $\phi_n(x)$, Eq. (8.9.11), make this probability distribution for low n greatly different from the corresponding classical case.

Harmonic Oscillator

The example of the harmonic oscillator is of great importance because of its many areas of application. We again consider a particle of mass m constrained to move in a single direction, subject now to the quadratic potential

$$V(x) = \tfrac{1}{2}\kappa x^2, \quad -\infty < x < \infty \tag{8.9.14}$$

so that the classical circular frequency of the particle is

$$\omega = \sqrt{\kappa/m}. \tag{8.9.15}$$

The time-independent Schrödinger equation, Eq. (8.7.6), for this model is

$$-\frac{\hbar^2}{2m}\frac{d^2\phi}{dx^2} + \tfrac{1}{2}\kappa x^2\phi = E\phi. \tag{8.9.16}$$

It can be put in the form

$$\frac{d^2\phi}{dx^2} + (k^2 - \lambda^2 x^2)\phi = 0, \tag{8.9.17}$$

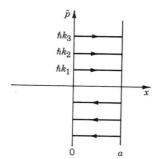

Figure 8.3 Phase plane (with coordinates $x, \tilde{p}$) representation of first three states of particle in infinite square well potential.

where

$$k^2 = \frac{2mE}{\hbar^2} \text{ and } \lambda = \frac{m\omega}{\hbar}. \tag{8.9.18}$$

It is seen that for large $|x|$ the solution to Eq. (8.9.17) behaves asymptotically as $\phi(x) \sim e^{\pm \frac{1}{2}\lambda x^2}$ and the negative sign is needed for a normalizable solution. It is, therefore, convenient to write

$$\phi(x) = e^{-\frac{1}{2}\lambda x^2} v(x) \tag{8.9.19}$$

where, by substitution into Eq. (8.9.17), $v(x)$ must satisfy the equation

$$\frac{d^2v}{dx^2} - 2\lambda x \frac{dv}{dx} + (k^2 - \lambda)v = 0. \tag{8.9.20}$$

A solution to Eq. (8.9.20) is obtained by the method of Frobenius, that is, by substitution of the series

$$v(x) = \sum_{j=0}^{\infty} a_j x^j \tag{8.9.21}$$

into Eq. (8.9.20) and obtaining the recurrence relation

$$a_{j+2} = \frac{\lambda(2j + 1) - k^2}{(j + 2)(j + 1)} a_j. \tag{8.9.22}$$

It may be verified that if this recurrence relation is nonterminating, it leads to a function $v(x)$ defined by the infinite series of Eq. (8.9.21) which behaves asymptotically as $v(x) \sim e^{\lambda x^2}$ and, from Eq. (8.9.19), to a non-normalizable $\phi(x)$. In order that $\phi(x)$ be normalizable, therefore, it is necessary that the recurrence relation lead to $a_{j+2} = 0$ for finite j. This will be the case if

$$k_n^2 = \lambda(2n + 1), \quad n = 0, 1, 2, \ldots \tag{8.9.23}$$

or, by use of Eq. (8.9.18), if

$$E_n = (n + \tfrac{1}{2})\hbar\omega, \quad n = 0, 1, 2, \ldots. \tag{8.9.24}$$

For these values of E_n, $v_n(x)$ will be a polynomial[35] of order n. The normalized

---

[35] They are the Hermite polynomials.

eigenfunctions $\phi_n(x)$ are then of the form

$$\phi_0(x) = \left(\frac{\lambda}{\pi}\right)^{1/4} e^{-\frac{1}{2}\lambda x^2},$$

$$\phi_1(x) = \left(\frac{4\lambda^3}{\pi}\right)^{1/4} x e^{-\frac{1}{2}\lambda x^2},$$

$$\phi_2(x) = \left(\frac{\lambda}{4\pi}\right)^{1/4} (1 - 2\lambda x^2) e^{-\frac{1}{2}\lambda x^2}, \qquad \text{etc.} \qquad (8.9.25)$$

The functions ϕ_0 and ϕ_1 are shown in Figure 8.4.

We may make some observations regarding the harmonic oscillator which parallel to some extent those made for the square-well potential:

1 The discrete character of the eigenvalues E_n is again due to the localization of the particle by the potential.

2 The zero-point energy, $E_0 = \hbar\omega/2$, is again a consequence of the Heisenberg uncertainty relation. That the minimum energy cannot be zero is clear since the latter would require the particle at rest at the bottom of the well, that is, $\Delta p = \Delta x = 0$. Its value arises from an energy minimizing process which may be seen from an examination of the ground state $\phi_0(x)$. This function corresponds to a stationary and centered Gaussian wave packet, that is, Eq. (8.4.21) with $\bar{p} = \bar{x} = 0$, and with

$$\Delta x = \left(\frac{\hbar}{2m\omega}\right)^{1/2}. \qquad (8.9.26)$$

It may be verified (Section 10.5) that this is the uncertainty Δx that corresponds to the minimum expected energy for the wave packet. The expected

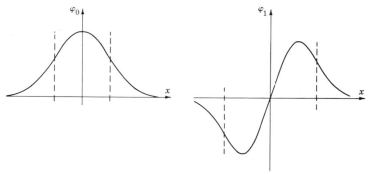

Figure 8.4   Ground state ϕ_0 and first excited state ϕ_1 of harmonic oscillator. Vertical dashed lines indicate limits of excursion of classical particle with given energy.

potential energy can be decreased by decreasing Δx and so increasing the likelihood that the particle be found near the well minimum, but then, in order to satisfy the uncertainty relation, Δp would increase and therefore the expected kinetic energy would increase.

3 For large n, the probability density $P_n(x)$ approaches the distribution to be expected from the classical viewpoint (see, e.g., Dicke and Wittke, 1960, p. 59, Fig. 3-14). However, this probability density differs greatly from the classical calculated probability density for low n.

4 As with the square-well potential, it is possible to write the stationary states $\phi_n(x)$ for the harmonic oscillator as a sum of complex states. The corresponding phase plane representation (with coordinates x and $\tilde{p}$) is closer in appearance to the classical case for low n than is the case for the real states $\phi_n(x)$ shown in Figure 8.4 (see, e.g., Weiner, 1978, Fig. 3).

5 The quantum mechanical discussion of the harmonic oscillator has particular relevance for the mechanical behavior of crystals since, in the harmonic approximation, the crystal Hamiltonian in terms of normal-mode coordinates, Eq. (4.4.19), describes a collection of harmonic oscillators. From the relation, Eq. (4.4.18), between the normal-mode coordinates and the atom coordinates, it follows that the zero-point energy of the collection of oscillators gives rise to zero-point energy of the atoms as well. From the quantum viewpoint, therefore, the atoms of a crystal cannot be regarded as at rest at the lattice sites even at $T = 0$.

We have noted the close connection between normal modes and traveling lattice waves in Section 4.9. In the harmonic approximation, the crystal Hamiltonian can be written in terms of traveling-wave coordinates in place of normal-mode coordinates[36] and it again takes the form of a collection of harmonic oscillators. It therefore follows that the energy associated with a traveling wave of frequency ω can only have values of the form $(N + \frac{1}{2})\hbar\omega$, with $N = 0, 1, 2, \dots$. If the energy of a wave of particular type (i.e., with given polarization vector and wave vector) has energy $(N + \frac{1}{2})\hbar\omega$, then there are said to be N phonons of the given type in the crystal. The term phonon[37] is generally used in place of lattice wave and, for example, the term phonon dispersion relation is used in place of lattice wave dispersion relation as discussed in Section 4.9.

Hydrogenic Atom

We next consider the hydrogenic (or hydrogen-like) atom which consists of two particles, a nucleus of mass M and electrical charge $+Ze$ and an electron of mass μ and charge $-e$, with the two interacting through the Coulomb

---

[36]See, for example, Maradudin, Montroll, and Weiss (1963, pp. 32–34).

[37]The term conveys the idea that lattice waves have particle characteristics just as the term photon emphasizes the particle characteristics of electromagnetic radiation; for a brief discussion, see Smith (1961, pp. 97–99).

potential. With $Z = 1$, this corresponds to the hydrogen atom; with $Z = 2$, it corresponds to He^+, the positively charged ion that results when the helium atom loses one electron; with $Z = 3$, it corresponds to Li^{2+}, etc.

The problem of finding the stationary states for this system is treated in detail in all of the standard texts. Here, we only outline the mathematical formulation of the problem, the general method of solution, and the nature of the results.

Since the mass of the nucleus is so large compared to that of the electron, we can regard it as localized and fixed at the origin and treat only the electron quantum mechanically. Its Hamiltonian is

$$H(\mathbf{r}, \mathbf{p}) = \frac{|\mathbf{p}|^2}{2\mu} - \frac{Ze^2}{|\mathbf{r}|} \tag{8.9.27}$$

and the corresponding time-independent Schrödinger equation is

$$H\psi = \frac{-\hbar^2}{2\mu}\nabla^2\psi - \frac{Ze^2}{|\mathbf{r}|}\psi = E\psi. \tag{8.9.28}$$

Let x, y, z be the Cartesian coordinates of $\mathbf{r}$. Because of the spherical symmetry of the Coulomb potential, it is convenient to rewrite Eq. (8.9.28) in terms of a spherical coordinate system (r, θ, ϕ), with z the polar axis. It then takes the form

$$\frac{-\hbar^2}{2\mu}\left[\frac{1}{r^2}\frac{\partial}{\partial r}\left(r^2\frac{\partial}{\partial r}\right) + \frac{1}{r^2\sin\theta}\frac{\partial}{\partial\theta}\left(\sin\theta\frac{\partial}{\partial\theta}\right) + \frac{1}{r^2\sin^2\theta}\frac{\partial^2}{\partial\phi^2}\right]\psi$$

$$- \frac{Ze^2}{r}\psi = E\psi. \tag{8.9.29}$$

We seek solutions of the form $\psi(r, \theta, \phi) = R(r)\Theta(\theta)\Phi(\phi)$ and use the technique of separation of variables in two steps, first separating out the variable ϕ and then separating r and θ. In this way we are led to two separation constants, m^2 and λ, and the following equations:

$$\frac{d^2\Phi}{d\theta^2} + m^2\Phi = 0, \tag{8.9.30}$$

$$\frac{1}{\sin\theta}\frac{d}{d\theta}\left(\sin\theta\frac{d\Theta}{d\theta}\right) + \left(\lambda - \frac{m^2}{\sin^2\theta}\right)\Theta = 0, \tag{8.9.31}$$

$$\frac{\hbar^2}{2\mu}\frac{1}{r^2}\frac{d}{dr}\left(r^2\frac{dR}{dr}\right) + \left(E + \frac{Ze^2}{r} - \frac{\hbar^2\lambda}{2\mu r^2}\right)R = 0. \tag{8.9.32}$$

We wish localized solutions, with proper limiting behavior as $r \to \infty$, which are everywhere finite, continuous, and single valued. These requirements are satisfied only for discrete values of the constants m^2, λ, and E. How these requirements lead to discrete values is seen most readily for Eq. (8.9.30) for which the solution is

$$\Phi(\phi) = Ce^{im\phi}, \qquad (8.9.33)$$

which will be consistent with a single-valued and continuous $\psi(\mathbf{r})$ only if $m = 0, \pm 1, \pm 2, \ldots$. The restriction on the constants in Eq. (8.9.31) arises from the requirement that $\Theta(\theta)$ remain finite at $\theta = 0, \pi$ and the restrictions on the constants in Eq. (8.9.32) arise from the requirement[38] that $\lim_{r\to\infty} R(r) = 0$. Because λ and m^2 both appear in Eq. (8.9.31) and E and λ both appear in Eq. (8.9.32), the permissible values of these constants are interrelated. The final results for the permitted values are

$$E_n = \frac{-Z^2}{n^2}\tilde{E}_1, \qquad n = 1, 2, 3, \ldots, \qquad (8.9.34)$$

$$\lambda = \ell(\ell + 1), \qquad \ell = 0, 1, \ldots, n - 1, \qquad (8.9.35)$$

$$m = 0, \pm 1, \pm 2, \ldots, \pm \ell \qquad (8.9.36)$$

where

$$\tilde{E}_1 = \frac{\mu e^4}{2\hbar^2} = 13.55 \text{ eV}. \qquad (8.9.37)$$

The solution corresponding to a particular permitted set of n, ℓ, and m is denoted by $\psi_{n\ell m}(r, \theta, \phi) = R_{n\ell}(r)\Theta_{\ell m}(\theta)\Phi_m(\phi)$ where

$$R_{n\ell}(r) = C\rho^{\ell}f_{n\ell}(\rho)e^{-\rho/n}, \qquad (8.9.38)$$

$f_{n\ell}(\rho)$ is a polynomial of degree $n - \ell - 1$, $\rho = r/a_0$ with

$$a_0 = \frac{\hbar^2}{\mu e^2} = 0.529 \text{ Å}; \qquad (8.9.39)$$

$$Y_{\ell m}(\theta, \phi) = \Theta_{\ell m}(\theta)\Phi_m(\phi) = \left(\frac{(\ell - |m|)!(2\ell + 1)}{(\ell + |m|)!4\pi}\right)^{1/2} P_\ell^{|m|}(\cos\theta)e^{im\phi},$$

$$(8.9.40)$$

where the functions $Y_{\ell m}(\theta, \phi)$ are called spherical harmonics and $P_\ell^{|m|}(\cos\theta)$

---

[38] Details of the solution for $R(r)$ will be found, for example, in Blokhintsev (1964, pp. 184–189) and for $\Theta(\theta)$ (*ibid.*, pp. 586–589).

are the associated Legendre polynomials where, for $m \geqslant 0$,

$$P_\ell^m(\xi) = \frac{!}{2^\ell \ell!} (1 - \xi^2)^{m/2} \frac{d^{m+\ell}}{d\xi^{m+\ell}} (\xi^2 - 1)^\ell. \qquad (8.9.41)$$

As examples, we list the first few states explicitly:

$$\psi_{100} = \frac{1}{\sqrt{\pi}} \left(\frac{Z}{a_0} \right)^{3/2} e^{-Zr/a_0}, \qquad (8.9.42)$$

$$\psi_{200} = \frac{1}{4\sqrt{2\pi}} \left(\frac{Z}{a_0} \right)^{3/2} \left(2 - \frac{Zr}{a_0} \right) e^{-Zr/2a_0}, \qquad (8.9.43)$$

$$\psi_{210} = \frac{1}{4\sqrt{2\pi}} \left(\frac{Z}{a_0} \right)^{3/2} \frac{Zr}{a_0} e^{-Zr/2a_0} \cos\theta, \qquad (8.9.44)$$

$$\psi_{21\pm1} = \frac{1}{8\sqrt{\pi}} \left(\frac{Z}{a_0} \right)^{3/2} \frac{Zr}{a_0} e^{-Zr/2a_0} \sin\theta\, e^{\pm i\phi}, \qquad (8.9.45)$$

$$\psi_{300} = \frac{1}{81\sqrt{3\pi}} \left(\frac{Z}{a_0} \right)^{3/2} \left(27 - 18\frac{Zr}{a_0} + 2\frac{Z^2 r^2}{a_0^2} \right) e^{-Zr/3a_0}. \qquad (8.9.46)$$

Figures showing the radial and angular dependence of the probability distributions that correspond to these states may be found in all of the standard texts. As a particular example, it is readily verified that for the ground state of the H atom, the radial probability density, $r^2 |\psi_{100}|^2$, is maximum at $r = a_0$. This distance, defined in Eq. (8.9.39), is known as the Bohr radius and is a fundamental dimension on the atomic level.

In the case of the hydrogenic atom, as opposed to the two previous examples of stationary states considered in this section, it is not a question of understanding why the minimum energy is not zero but rather why the energy does not become negatively infinite as the electron collapses into the nucleus. The reason is again to be found in the Heisenberg uncertainty relation: as the expected potential energy is decreased by increased localization of the electron near the nucleus, the expected kinetic energy must increase.

Quantum Numbers

We have seen that $\psi_{n\ell m}$ is an eigenfunction of H

$$H\psi_{n\ell m} = E_n \psi_{n\ell m}; \qquad (8.9.47)$$

this was the starting point of the calculation in Eq. (8.9.28). It can be shown that $\psi_{n\ell m}$ is also an eigenfunction of the observable L^2, corresponding to the square of the orbital angular momentum of the electron, and also of the observable L_z, corresponding to the component of electron angular momentum about the z-axis. According to the general principles for obtaining the differential operators corresponding to classical quantities, Eq. (8.5.7),

$$L_z = -i\hbar\left(x\frac{\partial}{\partial y} - y\frac{\partial}{\partial x}\right), \tag{8.9.48}$$

$$L^2 = -\hbar^2\left[\left(y\frac{\partial}{\partial z} - z\frac{\partial}{\partial y}\right)^2 + \left(z\frac{\partial}{\partial x} - x\frac{\partial}{\partial z}\right)^2 + \left(x\frac{\partial}{\partial y} - y\frac{\partial}{\partial x}\right)^2\right].$$

$$\tag{8.9.49}$$

Transcribed to spherical coordinates, they take the form

$$L_z = -i\hbar\frac{\partial}{\partial \phi}, \tag{8.9.50}$$

$$L^2 = -\hbar^2\left[\frac{1}{\sin\theta}\frac{\partial}{\partial\theta}\left(\sin\theta\frac{\partial}{\partial\theta}\right) + \frac{1}{\sin^2\theta}\frac{\partial^2}{\partial\phi^2}\right]. \tag{8.9.51}$$

It may then be verified that

$$L^2\psi_{n\ell m} = \ell(\ell + 1)\hbar^2\psi_{n\ell m}, \tag{8.9.52}$$

and

$$L_z\psi_{n\ell m} = m\hbar\psi_{n\ell m}. \tag{8.9.53}$$

Therefore, measurements of these three observables, H, L^2, and L_z, can lead to only a set of discrete values[39] which are in accordance with Eqs. (8.9.34)–(8.9.36). The indices n, ℓ, and m are referred to as the quantum numbers that identify the state: n is called the principal quantum number, ℓ, the orbital angular momentum or the azimuthal quantum number and m is the magnetic[40] quantum number. From Eqs. (8.9.34)–(8.9.36) it is seen that, for a given principal quantum number n, there are

$$\sum_{\ell=0}^{n-1}(2\ell + 1) = n^2 \tag{8.9.54}$$

distinct states $\psi_{n\ell m}$ possible, that is, E_n has degeneracy n^2.

[39] We are excluding the possibility of ionization which leads to a continuous spectrum of energy values.
[40] This terminology is used because electron angular momentum about a given axis (here denoted by the z-axis) is associated with a magnetic moment proportional to the angular momentum.

8.10 TENSOR PRODUCT OF TWO SPACES

The concept of the tensor product of two spaces proves useful when a given system is permitted to acquire additional degrees of freedom or when two systems are put together to form a composite system. We illustrate the two cases by means of simple examples.

Increase in Degrees of Freedom

Consider a particle constrained to move in a single direction denoted here by x_1 and confined to the interval $0 \leqslant x_1 \leqslant a_1$ by an infinite square well potential as in Eq. (8.9.1). (The notation employed is the same as in Section 8.9, except for the addition throughout of an index to define the coordinate direction.) The stationary states $\phi_n^{(1)}(x_1)$ are then as given in Eq. (8.9.8) and any possible state $\psi^{(1)}(x_1)$ of the particle can be written as a sum over these stationary states as

$$\psi^{(1)}(x_1) = \sum_{r=1}^{\infty} c_r \phi_r^{(1)}(x_1). \tag{8.10.1}$$

We may describe this situation by the statement that the possible states $\psi^{(1)}(x_1)$ lie in the space[41] $\mathscr{E}_1$ spanned by the basis set $\phi_r^{(1)}(x_1)$, $r = 1, 2, \ldots$.

If, instead, the particle were constrained to move in the x_2 direction and confined to the interval $0 \leqslant x_2 \leqslant a_2$, then any possible state $\psi^{(2)}(x_2)$ of the particle would lie in the space $\mathscr{E}_2$ spanned by the basis set $\phi_r^{(2)}(x_2)$, $r = 1, 2, \ldots$.

Consider next the case in which the particle has two degrees of freedom, free to move in the x_1 and x_2 directions, and confined to the region $0 \leqslant x_1 \leqslant a_1$, $0 \leqslant x_2 \leqslant a_2$ by an infinite square well potential. It is readily verified that the Hamiltonian $H_{12}(x_1, x_2, p_1, p_2)$ for this case is

$$H_{12}(x_1, x_2, p_1, p_2) = H_1(x_1, p_1) + H_2(x_2, p_2), \tag{8.10.2}$$

where H_1, H_2 are the Hamiltonians for the one-dimensional problems, and therefore the corresponding operators also satisfy this relation:

$$\mathsf{H}_{12} = \mathsf{H}_1 + \mathsf{H}_2. \tag{8.10.3}$$

It may then be verified that

$$\phi_{rs}^{(12)}(x_1, x_2) = \phi_r^{(1)}(x_1)\phi_s^{(2)}(x_2), \quad r, s = 1, 2, \ldots \tag{8.10.4}$$

---

[41]We do not give here the additional mathematical details required to connect this discussion to the concept of Hilbert space and to related structures. Such discussions may be found, for example, in Böhm (1979) or Jammer (1974).

are a complete set of eigenfunctions of H_{12} and that any state $\psi^{(12)}(x_1, x_2)$ may be written therefore as a sum

$$\psi^{(12)}(x_1, x_2) = \sum_{r, s = 1}^{\infty} c_{rs} \phi_{rs}^{(12)}(x_1, x_2)$$

$$= \sum_{r, s = 1}^{\infty} c_{rs} \phi_r^{(1)}(x_1) \phi_s^{(2)}(x_2). \qquad (8.10.5)$$

In the terminology previously introduced, the possible states $\psi^{(12)}(x_1, x_2)$ of the particle with motion possible in the x_1 and x_2 direction lie in the space $\mathscr{E}_{12}$ spanned by the basis set $\phi_{rs}^{(12)}(x_1, x_2) = \phi_r^{(1)}(x_1)\phi_s^{(2)}(x_2)$, r, $s = 1, 2 \ldots$. $\mathscr{E}_{12}$ is said to be the tensor product of the spaces $\mathscr{E}_1$ and $\mathscr{E}_2$; this is frequently written

$$\mathscr{E}_{12} = \mathscr{E}_1 \otimes \mathscr{E}_2. \qquad (8.10.6)$$

Inner products between two states of $\mathscr{E}_{12}$ are defined in the same way as in the spaces $\mathscr{E}_1$ and $\mathscr{E}_2$. We use the following notation:

$$\int_{-\infty}^{\infty} \int_{-\infty}^{\infty} \psi^{(12)*}(x_1, x_2) \chi^{(12)}(x_1, x_2) \, dx_1 \, dx_2 = \left(\psi^{(12)}, \chi^{(12)} \right)_{12} \quad (8.10.7)$$

in $\mathscr{E}_{12}$, while in $\mathscr{E}_1$,

$$\int_{-\infty}^{\infty} \psi^{(1)*}(x_1) \chi^{(1)}(x_1) \, dx_1 = \left(\psi^{(1)}, \chi^{(1)} \right)_1 \qquad (8.10.8)$$

and similarly in $\mathscr{E}_2$. For states $\psi^{(12)}$, $\chi^{(12)}$ that are of the form

$$\psi^{(12)} = \psi^{(1)} \psi^{(2)}, \qquad \chi^{(12)} = \chi^{(1)} \chi^{(2)} \qquad (8.10.9)$$

it follows directly from the definition that

$$\left(\psi^{(12)}, \chi^{(12)} \right)_{12} = \left(\psi^{(1)}, \chi^{(1)} \right)_1 \left(\psi^{(2)}, \chi^{(2)} \right)_2. \qquad (8.10.10)$$

For states that are sums of terms of the type of Eq. (8.10.9), the linearity of the inner product can be used to evaluate inner products in $\mathscr{E}_{12}$ in terms of inner products in $\mathscr{E}_1$ and $\mathscr{E}_2$.

Suppose next that the particle with motion possible in the x_1 and x_2 direction is in a state $\psi^{(12)}(x_1, x_2) = \psi^{(1)}(x_1)\psi^{(2)}(x_2)$ where $(\psi^{(1)}, \psi^{(1)})_1 = (\psi^{(2)}, \psi^{(2)})_2 = 1$. It then follows from Eq. (8.10.10) that $(\psi^{(12)}, \psi^{(12)})_{12} = 1$ as well. If we consider an observable A_1 that depends only on x_1, then its expected value for the system in state $\psi^{(12)}$ is

$$\langle A_1 \rangle = \left(\psi^{(12)}, A_1 \psi^{(12)} \right)_{12} = \left(\psi^{(1)}, A_1 \psi^{(1)} \right)_1 \left(\psi^{(2)}, \psi^{(2)} \right)_2$$

$$= \left(\psi^{(1)}, A_1 \psi^{(1)} \right)_1;$$

that is, if we confine attention to observables that depend only on x_1, it is sufficient to describe the system by states in $\mathscr{E}_1$. Only if we wish to consider observables A_{12} that depend on x_2 as well as on x_1 is it necessary to consider states in the enlarged space $\mathscr{E}_{12}$. We have arrived at this conclusion on the basis of a simple particular example, but it embodies an important general principle that we will make use of in our discussion of electron spin in the next section.

We have, in the discussion of this example, focused on particles governed by the square-well Hamiltonian H_1, H_2, and $H_{12} = H_1 + H_2$. It should be noted that, from a more general viewpoint, the role of these Hamiltonians is simply to provide a complete basis for the spaces $\mathscr{E}_1$, $\mathscr{E}_2$, and $\mathscr{E}_{12}$. The elements $\psi^{(1)}$, $\psi^{(2)}$, and $\psi^{(12)}$ in these spaces may be used to describe a particle governed by other Hamiltonians[42] of the appropriate dimensionality.

Increase in Number of Particles

Our previous discussion has shown how an increase in the scope of experiments to include measurements of observables that depend on an additional degree of freedom leads to the use of the appropriate tensor product space. We next consider the case in which we have two particles, each constrained to move in the same single direction denoted by x and each confined to the same interval $0 \leqslant x < a$ by an infinite square well potential. We now let x_1 and x_2 denote the position of each particle in the x direction and the preceding discussion, with $a_1 = a_2 = a$, may be applied directly to this case. We conclude that a general state of the two particles $\psi^{(12)}(x_1, x_2)$ will be an element of the space $\mathscr{E}_{12}$. As in the previous discussion it should be noted here that the Hamiltonian $H_{12} = H_1 + H_2$ simply provides a complete basis for the space $\mathscr{E}_{12}$ and the two particle state $\psi^{(12)}(x_1, x_2)$ may refer to a pair of particles governed by a more general Hamiltonian, for example, one that involves interaction between the two particles.

8.11 ELECTRON SPIN

In addition to an electrical charge of $-e$, an electron also has an intrinsic magnetic moment μ or, in more picturesque language, carries with it a magnetic dipole μ. The magnitude $|\mu|$ of this dipole is fixed but its orientation is not. Therefore, the electron is said to have internal degrees of freedom corresponding to the dipole orientation in addition to the external degrees of freedom corresponding to the position of the electron in space.

To gain some appreciation of the nature of the intrinsic magnetic moment of the electron we consider a type of experiment first performed by Stern and

---

[42] These Hamiltonians must, however, also impose the requirement that $\psi^{(1)}$ vanish outside the interval $0 \leqslant x_1 \leqslant a_1$, and similarly for the other cases. If this is too restrictive, other bases, for example, harmonic oscillator states, can be employed.

Gerlach in 1921. Since the energy of a magnetic dipole μ in a magnetic field $\mathbf{H}$ is

$$V = -\mu \cdot \mathbf{H} \tag{8.11.1}$$

there will be a force

$$\mathbf{F} = -\nabla V = -\nabla(\mu \cdot \mathbf{H}) \tag{8.11.2}$$

exerted on the dipole in a nonuniform magnetic field. In the Stern–Gerlach experiment a beam of electrons[43] is passed through a highly nonuniform magnetic field as shown schematically in Figure 8.5. The resultant force on the electron's magnetic moment causes the beam to deflect by an amount that is measured by noting where they impinge on a screen. Let the direction of the magnetic field be denoted by z. Then, an analysis of the force acting on the magnetic dipole (cf. Cohen-Tannoudji, 1977) shows that this force also acts in the z direction and is proportional to μ_z, the component of μ in the magnetic field direction. If we think of the dipole from a classical viewpoint, we would expect its orientation to be continuously distributed over the electron beam with $-|\mu| \leqslant \mu_z \leqslant +|\mu|$ and that, therefore, the beam would impinge on the screen over an elongated narrow strip in the z direction of finite length. Surprisingly, what is found is that the beam splits in two and that there are two distinct spots aligned in the z direction and equidistant from the beam axis (Figure 8.5). We are, therefore, led to the conclusion that if we attempt to measure the component of μ in an arbitrary direction, called here the z direction, the observed values of μ_z will be either $+\mu_0$ or $-\mu_0$ with μ_0 the same value for all measurements. More specifically, it is found that

$$\mu_z = \pm \frac{e\hbar}{2m_e c} \tag{8.11.3}$$

where m_e is the electron mass and c is the speed of light.

The intrinsic magnetic moment μ is regarded as due to the spin of the electron about an axis parallel to μ so that the electron has spin[44] angular momentum s and

$$\mu = -\frac{e}{m_e c}\mathbf{s}. \tag{8.11.4}$$

[43] Our description of the Stern–Gerlach experiment is highly schematic. In the original experiment the electrons were carried along as part of a beam of silver atoms. For more detail see, for example, Cohen-Tannoudji (1977, Vol. I, p. 387 *et seq.*).

[44] The term spin angular momentum or intrinsic angular momentum, which should be taken only in a figurative sense and not visualized in terms of a classical picture, is used to distinguish it from the electron's angular momentum about a fixed point due to its motion in space. The latter is termed its orbital angular momentum (Section 8.9). The existence of the intrinsic magnetic moment and the intrinsic angular momentum of the electron and the relation between them may be understood on the basis of relativistic quantum mechanics.

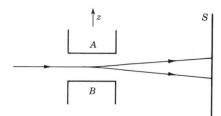

Figure 8.5 Schematic representation of Stern–Gerlach experiment. Poles A and B of magnet are shaped to produce nonuniform magnetic field, $\partial H_z/\partial z \neq 0$, in gap. Resulting force on electrons' magnetic moment splits beam and produces two distinct spots on screen S.

Because of the relation of Eq. (8.11.4), we may regard the Stern–Gerlach experiment as measuring the component s_z of the electron spin in an arbitrary direction by imposing a magnetic field in that direction. From Eqs. (8.11.3) and (8.11.4) it follows that the possible values of s_z are

$$s_z = \pm \frac{\hbar}{2} \qquad (8.11.5)$$

and the electron is spoken of as being a particle of spin one-half.[45] If the value $s_z = +\hbar/2$ is found, the electron is said to have spin up and for $s_z = -\hbar/2$ it is said to have spin down.

Spin Space

Since the property s_z has only two possible values, it follows from the general principles of quantum mechanics that there is a corresponding Hermitian operator S_z with $\pm\hbar/2$ as its only two eigenvalues. Further considerations indicate that these eigenvalues are nondegenerate and the corresponding eigenvectors are denoted χ^+, χ^- so that

$$S_z\chi^+ = +\frac{\hbar}{2}\chi^+,$$

$$S_z\chi^- = -\frac{\hbar}{2}\chi^-. \qquad (8.11.6)$$

The vectors χ^+, χ^- span a two-dimensional linear vector space, termed $\mathscr{E}_s$, the spin space of a single electron. An inner product is introduced[46] into $\mathscr{E}_s$ by taking the vectors χ^+, χ^- to be an orthonormal set, that is, by stating

$$(\chi^+, \chi^+)_s = (\chi^-, \chi^-)_s = 1$$

$$(\chi^+, \chi^-)_s = 0. \qquad (8.11.7)$$

[45] Other particles have spin which are an integer or other half-integer multiples of $\hbar$.

[46] Because of the linearity of the inner product, Eqs. (8.4.26)–(8.4.28), an inner product is defined on a linear vector space when its values are defined for all pairs of a basis of the space. The definitions of Eqs. (8.11.7) are required to conform to the probabilistic interpretations of the states $\chi +$ and $\chi -$; this is shown in Eqs. (8.11.8)–(8.11.10).

An arbitrary spin state χ can be written, therefore, as

$$\chi = c_+\chi^+ + c_-\chi^- \tag{8.11.8}$$

where normalization of χ, $(\chi, \chi)_s = 1$, leads by use of Eq. (8.11.7), to

$$|c_+|^2 + |c_-|^2 = 1. \tag{8.11.9}$$

The expected value of s_z when the electron spin is in state χ is then

$$\langle S_z \rangle = (\chi, S_z\chi)_s = \left(c_+\chi^+ + c_-\chi^-, \frac{\hbar}{2}(c_+\chi^+ - c_-\chi^-) \right)_s$$

$$= \left(|c_+|^2 - |c_-|^2 \right)\frac{\hbar}{2}. \tag{8.11.10}$$

Therefore, in light of Eq. (8.11.9), we can interpret $|c_+|^2$ as p_+, the probability of finding the electron with spin up when its spin is in state χ given by Eq. (8.11.8), and correspondingly $|c_-|^2 = p_-$.

Simultaneous Consideration of External and Internal Degrees of Freedom

As long as we are concerned with experiments that depend on the electron spin orientation alone, it is sufficient to confine attention to states in the spin space $\mathscr{E}_s$. If we are concerned with properties that depend only on the electron position x, we need to consider only states $\psi(x)$ in the space[47] $\mathscr{E}_x$ spanned by a suitable basis $\phi_r(x)$, $r = 1, 2, \ldots$. On the other hand, if we wish to consider properties that depend simultaneously on both electron position x and spin s, then it is necessary to consider the tensor-product space $\mathscr{E}_{xs} = \mathscr{E}_x \otimes \mathscr{E}_s$, which is spanned by the elements $\phi_r(x)\chi^+$ and $\phi_r(x)\chi^-$, $r = 1, 2, \ldots$.

Consider a typical element Φ in $\mathscr{E}_{xs}$. It can be written in terms of this basis as

$$\Phi = \sum_{r=1}^{\infty} c_r^+ \phi_r(x)\chi^+ + \sum_{r=1}^{\infty} c_r^- \phi_r(x)\chi^-$$

or

$$\Phi = \psi^+(x)\chi^+ + \psi^-(x)\chi^- \tag{8.11.11}$$

where $\psi^+(x)$ and $\psi^-(x)$ are elements of $\mathscr{E}_x$. The statement that Φ is normalized

[47]In Section 8.10 we used the notation $\mathscr{E}_1$ for the space spanned by a suitable basis $\phi_r(x_1)$, $r = 1, 2, \ldots$. In the notation of that section, $\mathscr{E}_x = \mathscr{E}_1 \otimes \mathscr{E}_2 \otimes \mathscr{E}_3$.

to unity takes the form

$$1 = (\Phi, \Phi)_{xs} = (\psi^+\chi^+ + \psi^-\chi^-, \psi^+\chi^+ + \psi^-\chi^-)_{xs}$$

$$= (\psi^+\chi^+, \psi^+\chi^+)_{xs} + (\psi^+\chi^+, \psi^-\chi^-)_{xs}$$

$$+ (\psi^-\chi^-, \psi^+\chi^+)_{xs} + (\psi^-\chi^-, \psi^-\chi^-)_{xs} \qquad (8.11.12)$$

by the linearity of the inner product. But

$$(\psi^+\chi^+, \psi^+\chi^+)_{xs} = (\psi^+, \psi^+)_x(\chi^+, \chi^+)_s = (\psi^+, \psi^+)_x, \qquad (8.11.13)$$

by Eq. (8.11.7), and the other terms of Eq. (8.11.12) are treated similarly. The final result is

$$1 = (\Phi, \Phi)_{xs} = (\psi^+, \psi^+)_x + (\psi^-, \psi^-)_x = |\psi^+(\mathbf{x})|^2 + |\psi^-(\mathbf{x})|^2.$$

$$(8.11.14)$$

By the same reasoning as applied to the state defined in Eq. (8.11.8), we can interpret $|\psi^+(\mathbf{x})|^2$ as the probability density for finding an electron at $\mathbf{x}$ with spin up and $|\psi^-(\mathbf{x})|^2$ as the probability density for finding it there with spin down.

8.12   IDENTICAL PARTICLES AND THE PAULI PRINCIPLE

Consider a collection of identical particles, for example, a collection of electrons. All of their properties are identical and each would behave in the same way in the same experimental situation. From the classical viewpoint it is, nevertheless, still possible to distinguish between two identical particles on the basis of their location at some reference time t_0. Since classical particles follow well-defined trajectories $\mathbf{x}_1(t)$ and $\mathbf{x}_2(t)$, a particle that is observed at position $\mathbf{x}_1(t)$ at $t > t_0$ can be identified unambiguously as that particle which was at $\mathbf{x}_1(t_0)$ at time t_0 (Figure 8.6a).

The situation is different if the particles are described by quantum mechanics. Consider again the case of two identical particles. We can, in principle, determine their locations precisely at some reference time t_0 and speak of particle 1 as that which was at position $\mathbf{x}_1$ at t_0 and of particle 2 which was at position $\mathbf{x}_2$ at t_0. Suppose that we now attempt to treat the particles as two distinct and separate systems and to describe their subsequent time evolution by wave functions $\psi_1(\mathbf{x}_1, t)$ and $\psi_2(\mathbf{x}_2, t)$; these will be of the form of moving and spreading wave packets as shown schematically in Figure 8.6b. At $t = t_1$, after only a short time has elapsed, there is no significant overlap between these wave packets. Therefore, an experiment at $t = t_1$ that locates a particle within the region in which only $|\psi_1(\mathbf{x}_1, t_1)|^2$ has any appreciable value can be

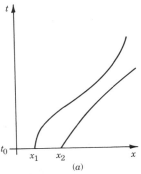
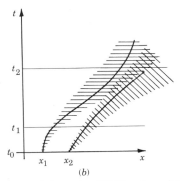

Figure 8.6 Motion of two identical particles. (*a*) Classical viewpoint. (*b*) Quantum viewpoint; shading indicates spread of wave packets.

said, with a high degree of certainty, to have detected particle 1. However, at a still later time t_2, when there is substantial overlap between the wave packets, an experimental measurement may detect a particle but there are no longer any means available for determining which particle has been detected. The individual wave functions $\psi_1(\mathbf{x}_1, t)$ and $\psi_2(\mathbf{x}_2, t)$ then lose their operational significance and the state of the two particles must be described by a wave function $\psi(\mathbf{x}_1, \mathbf{x}_2, t)$ that depends on both arguments. In terms of the concept of tensor products, for short times the initially localized particles can be represented by elements in $\mathscr{E}_{\mathbf{x}_1}$ and $\mathscr{E}_{\mathbf{x}_2}$; for long times the particle pair must be described at any instant by an element in $\mathscr{E}_{\mathbf{x}_1\mathbf{x}_2} = \mathscr{E}_{\mathbf{x}_1} \otimes \mathscr{E}_{\mathbf{x}_2}$. If the particles have spin, for example if we are dealing with a pair of electrons, then the general two-particle state is described at a given instant t by an element $\Phi(1, 2)$ in $\mathscr{E}_{\mathbf{x}_1 s_1 \mathbf{x}_2 s_2} = \mathscr{E}_{\mathbf{x}_1} \otimes \mathscr{E}_{s_1} \otimes \mathscr{E}_{\mathbf{x}_2} \otimes \mathscr{E}_{s_2} = \mathscr{E}_{\mathbf{x}_1\mathbf{x}_2} \otimes \mathscr{E}_{s_1 s_2}$. An element in this space takes the form

$$\Phi(1, 2) = \psi_1(\mathbf{x}_1, \mathbf{x}_2)\chi_1^+\chi_2^+ + \psi_2(\mathbf{x}_1, \mathbf{x}_2)\chi_1^-\chi_2^-$$
$$+ \psi_3(\mathbf{x}_1, \mathbf{x}_2)\chi_1^+\chi_2^- + \psi_4(\mathbf{x}_1, \mathbf{x}_2)\chi_1^-\chi_2^+, \qquad (8.12.1)$$

where χ_1^+ is the element in $\mathscr{E}_{s_1}$ describing electron 1 with spin up, etc. Consider next the state $\Phi(2, 1)$ defined as

$$\Phi(2, 1) = \psi_1(\mathbf{x}_2, \mathbf{x}_1)\chi_2^+\chi_1^+ + \psi_2(\mathbf{x}_2, \mathbf{x}_1)\chi_2^-\chi_1^-$$
$$+ \psi_3(\mathbf{x}_2, \mathbf{x}_1)\chi_2^+\chi_1^- + \psi_4(\mathbf{x}_2, \mathbf{x}_1)\chi_2^-\chi_1^+.$$

It is a fundamental postulate for systems of identical particles that the interchange of labels used in the description of identical particles can have no operational result; that is, the states $\Phi(1, 2)$ and $\Phi(2, 1)$ must both give the same expected value for any observable. This will be the case if

$$\Phi(2, 1) = \lambda\Phi(1, 2) \qquad (8.12.2)$$

for λ an arbitrary complex number. To determine the possible values of λ, we introduce the permutation operator P_{12} which interchanges the indices 1 and 2 in the description of any two-particle state on which it acts, that is, $P_{12}\Phi(1,2) = \Phi(2,1)$. Then Eq. (8.12.2) becomes

$$P_{12}\Phi(1,2) = \lambda\Phi(1,2). \tag{8.12.3}$$

We apply the operator P_{12} to both sides of Eq. (8.12.3), obtaining

$$P_{12}^2\Phi(1,2) = \lambda P_{12}\Phi(1,2).$$

Since the twice-repeated application of P_{12} to a state returns it to its original form, we find by use of Eq. (8.12.3) that

$$\Phi(1,2) = \lambda^2\Phi(1,2), \tag{8.12.4}$$

and therefore that

$$\lambda = \pm 1. \tag{8.12.5}$$

This argument may be extended to n-particle states $\Phi(1,2,\ldots,n)$. The permutation operator P_{ij} interchanges the indices i and j in the description of any n-particle state on which it acts and, in accord with the postulate of quantum mechanics stated previously, for n identical particles,

$$P_{ij}\Phi(1,2,\ldots,i,\ldots,j,\ldots,n) = \lambda\Phi(1,2,\ldots,i,\ldots,j,\ldots,n) \tag{8.12.6}$$

and, by the same argument used for $n = 2$, $\lambda = \pm 1$. Furthermore it is readily verified (Blokhintsev, 1964, p. 471) that the same value of λ applies for all pairs (i,j), so that the state $\Phi(1,2,\ldots,n)$ for n identical particles is either completely symmetric ($\lambda = +1$) or completely antisymmetric ($\lambda = -1$).

Thus far, the discussion has dealt with a particular instant of time. We now make explicit the time dependence of the state $\Phi(1,2,\ldots,n;t)$ which is an eigenfunction of P_{ij} with eigenvalue $\lambda = \pm 1$. The possibility remains that $\lambda = \lambda(t)$ and that the same collection of n identical particles will at some periods of time be described by a completely symmetric state and at other periods by a completely antisymmetric state. We now rule out this possibility.

Note first that at any instant t, the expected value of the observable P_{ij}.

$$\langle P_{ij}\rangle = (\Phi, P_{ij}\Phi) = (\Phi, \lambda\Phi) = \lambda. \tag{8.12.7}$$

Furthermore, if H is the Hamiltonian operator for n identical particles, all quantities depending on properties of particle i (its momentum, position, charge, spin, etc.) must appear in the definition of H in precisely the same manner as those depending on particle j. Therefore,

$$P_{ij}H\Phi(1,2,\ldots,n;t) = HP_{ij}\Phi(1,2,\ldots,n;t), \tag{8.12.8}$$

that is, the operators commute or their commutator $[H, P_{ij}] = 0$. It follows from Eq. (8.4.41) that $\langle P_{ij} \rangle = \lambda$ is constant in time. Note that Eq. (8.4.41) and Eq. (8.12.8) are valid for time-dependent and well as time-independent Hamiltonians so that the result applies no matter what operations are performed on the particles. We are, therefore, led to the conclusion that there is one class of identical particles that must always be described by symmetric states and another class that must always be described by antisymmetric states. It is found that the class to which a given type of particle belongs is determined by its intrinsic spin. If the spin is integer, it belongs to the class described by symmetric states and it is called a *boson*; if the spin is a half-odd integer, it belongs to the class described by antisymmetric states and it is called[48] a *fermion*. Thus electrons are fermions and many-electron systems must always be described by antisymmetric states.

Pauli Exclusion Principle

Let $\mathscr{E}_n^e$ denote the space of all states of a system of n electrons which are consistent with this antisymmetry requirement. For the case of a single electron no such requirement exists and $\mathscr{E}_1^e = \mathscr{E}_{xs}$ defined in Section 8.11; it is spanned by a basis of the form $\phi_r(x)\chi^+$ and $\phi_r(x)\chi^-$, $r = 1, 2, \ldots$. To simplify the notation, we denote the basis for $\mathscr{E}_1^e$ by ξ_r, $r = 1, 2, \ldots$, so that ξ_r is a state that carries both coordinate and spin information, for example, $\xi_1 = \phi_1(x)\chi^+$, $\xi_2 = \phi_1(x)\chi^-$, $\xi_3 = \phi_2(x)\chi^+$, etc. It is also necessary to introduce notation that provides labels for the n electrons and we write $\xi_r(p)$ for the statement that the pth electron is in state ξ_r, for example, $\xi_1(p) = \phi_1(x_p)\chi_p^+$, $p = 1, \ldots, n$.

An appropriate normalized basis for $\mathscr{E}_n^e$ which ensures the required antisymmetry is then

$$\xi_{r_1 r_2 \ldots r_n} = \frac{1}{\sqrt{n!}} \sum_p (-1)^{\mathscr{P}_p} \xi_{r_1}(p_1)\xi_{r_2}(p_2)\ldots\xi_{r_n}(p_n) \qquad (8.12.9)$$

where $r_1 r_2 \ldots r_n$ is an n-tuple with $r_j = 1, 2, \ldots$, and the sum is over all possible permutations $(p_1 p_2 \ldots p_n) = p$ of the integers $1, 2, \ldots, n$; $\mathscr{P}_p = 0$ if the permutation p is even and $\mathscr{P}_p = 1$ if this permutation is odd. From its definition $\xi_{r_1 r_2 \ldots r_n}$ can also be written as a determinant (called a Slater determinant)

$$\xi_{r_1 r_2 \ldots r_n} = \frac{1}{\sqrt{n!}} \begin{vmatrix} \xi_{r_1}(1) & \xi_{r_2}(1) & \cdots & \xi_{r_n}(1) \\ \xi_{r_1}(2) & \xi_{r_2}(2) & \cdots & \xi_{r_n}(2) \\ \vdots & \vdots & & \vdots \\ \xi_{r_1}(n) & \xi_{r_2}(n) & \cdots & \xi_{r_n}(n) \end{vmatrix}. \qquad (8.12.10)$$

It is clear, particularly from the second definition, that the basis states $\xi_{r_1 r_2 \ldots r_n}$ are completely antisymmetric with respect to the interchange of two

---

[48] The particle classes are named after the physicists S. N. Bose and E. Fermi.

electron labels since that corresponds to the interchange of two rows in the determinant. Therefore, any state in $\mathscr{E}_n^{\varrho e}$ will also be completely antisymmetric. It is also clear from Eq. (8.12.10) that $\xi_{r_1 r_2 \ldots r_n} = 0$ if $r_j = r_k$ for any particular pair of subscripts since the determinant would then have two identical columns.

The states, stationary or time dependent, corresponding to any n-electron Hamiltonian, H, can be described by elements in $\mathscr{E}_n^{\varrho e}$. If, in addition, the interaction between the electrons is neglected so that $H = H(1) + H(2) + \ldots + H(n)$, the sum of n one-electron Hamiltonians, then a basis state $\xi_{r_1 r_2 \ldots r_n}$ of $\mathscr{E}_n^{\varrho e}$, consisting of a Slater determinant of the corresponding one-electron states, is a stationary state of H. The statement that $\xi_{r_1 r_2 \ldots r_n} = 0$ if any particular pair $r_j = r_k$ then implies that the description of the stationary state of n electrons, with the neglect of electron–electron interaction, requires n distinct one-electron states. This, in turn, is usually rephrased as "No two electrons can occupy the same state" and is referred to as the Pauli exclusion principle.

Periodic Table

The Pauli exclusion principle plays a central role in the understanding of the grouping in the periodic table of the elements with common chemical properties. This grouping is governed by the change in the ground state of the electrons in the atoms as a function of the atomic number Z, where Ze is the charge on the nucleus and, therefore, Z is the number of electrons in the neutral atom.

For H, $Z = 1$, the ground state of the single electron is either $\psi_{100} \chi^+$ or $\psi_{100} \chi^-$, where ψ_{100} is given by Eq. (8.9.42) with $Z = 1$. (In what follows, $\psi_{n\ell m}$ refers to the coordinate wave function for the hydrogenic atom (Section 8.9) evaluated for the Z under discussion.)

Consider next He, $Z = 2$. If we neglect the interaction between the electrons, as we will do in this discussion, we can describe the ground state of the two electrons by means of a Slater determinant, Eq. (8.12.10), formed from the two states $\psi_{100} \chi^+$ and $\psi_{100} \chi^-$.

We recall, Eq. (8.9.54), that there are n^2 coordinate wave functions $\psi_{n\ell m}$ for a given principal quantum number n and therefore $2n^2$ states, $\psi_{n\ell m} \chi^+$ and $\psi_{n\ell m} \chi^-$, when spin is included. Therefore, for Li, $Z = 3$, since there are no more states with $n = 1$ available, it is necessary[49] to add to the basis for $\mathscr{E}_3^{\varrho e}$ a higher energy state [see Eq. (8.9.34)] corresponding to $n = 2$; the ground state of the three electrons would then be given by the Slater determinant formed from the three one-electron states, $\psi_{100} \chi^+, \psi_{100} \chi^-, \psi_{200} \chi^+$. This step is generally described by the statement that the $n = 1$ shell is filled in He, and it is

---

[49] Were it not for the Pauli exclusion principle, therefore, the ground state of all atoms would be similar and they would have similar chemical properties. To quote from Weisskopf (1975), "We owe the variety of nature largely to the exclusion principle."

necessary to add the next electron state in the $n = 2$ shell. It is also general terminology to omit the word "state" in these descriptions and to speak of the electrons in the closed shell and of the electrons in the open shell, although, as we have seen, all three electrons are simultaneously in the state described by the Slater determinant based on the three one-electron states. Nevertheless, the terminology is valuable for qualitative discussions, and we may say, for example, that it is the more loosely bound open-shell electrons, the valence electrons, which determine the chemical behavior of an atom. We return briefly to this question in Section 9.6.

If the progression is continued in this way[50] it is found that Na, $Z = 11$, has two closed shells ($n = 1$ with $2n^2 = 2$ electrons, $n = 2$ with $2n^2 = 8$ electrons) with the remaining electron in the open shell state $\psi_{300}\chi^+$. Since the open shell states of Li and Na are similar, except for the shell number, they are in the same group of the periodic table and have similar chemical behavior.

Electron Pairs

We consider next the case of two electrons and wish to examine the effect of their spin states on the required symmetry of their coordinate-state description. For this purpose we write the permutation operator P_{12} as a product:

$$P_{12} = P_{12}^x P_{12}^s, \qquad (8.12.11)$$

where P_{12}^x interchanges the particle labels only in the coordinate state description and P_{12}^s interchanges these labels only in the spin-state description.

Any state of an electron pair is an element of $\mathscr{E}_2^e = \mathscr{E}_{x_1 s_1 x_2 s_2} = \mathscr{E}_{x_1 x_2} \otimes \mathscr{E}_{s_1 s_2}$. The spin space for two electrons, $\mathscr{E}_{s_1 s_2}$, is four-dimensional and the basis $\xi_{r_1}\xi_{r_2}$ for $\mathscr{E}_2^e$ as defined previously carries with it the orthonormal basis $\chi_1^+\chi_2^+, \chi_1^-\chi_2^-, \chi_1^+\chi_2^-, \chi_1^-\chi_2^+$ for spin space. The first two of these are eigenvectors of P_{12}^s but the last two are not. It is convenient for this discussion, therefore, to choose a new orthonormal basis for $\mathscr{E}_{s_1 s_2}$ composed of states Ξ_j, $j = 1, \ldots, 4$ which are all eigenvectors of P_{12}^s; this is easily accomplished as follows:

$$\Xi_1 = \chi_1^+\chi_2^+$$

$$\Xi_2 = \chi_1^-\chi_2^-$$

$$\Xi_3 = \frac{1}{\sqrt{2}}[\chi_1^+\chi_2^- + \chi_1^-\chi_2^+]$$

$$\Xi_4 = \frac{1}{\sqrt{2}}[\chi_1^+\chi_2^- - \chi_1^-\chi_2^+]. \qquad (8.12.12)$$

[50] For a thorough discussion of the periodic table, see Blokhintsev (1964, pp. 518–528); see also Cohen-Tannoudji (1977, pp. 1410–1417). The effect of electron–electron interaction changes, in some places, the progression of electron states which would be expected if it is ignored.

It is seen that

$$\mathbf{P}_{12}^s \Xi_j = \lambda_j \Xi_j, \quad j = 1, \dots, 4 \qquad (8.12.13)$$

with

$$\lambda_j = +1, \ j = 1, 2, 3 \text{ and } \lambda_4 = -1. \qquad (8.12.14)$$

The first three states are referred to as triplet states and the fourth is called a singlet state. Furthermore, a calculation (see, e.g., Cohen-Tannoudji, 1977, p. 1008) of the expected values of the sum of the spin angular momenta for the electron pair for each of the states Ξ_j shows that the triplet states correspond to parallel spins and the singlet state corresponds to antiparallel spins.

Consider now the state of an electron pair in the form $\Phi(1, 2) = \psi(\mathbf{x}_1, \mathbf{x}_2)\Xi_j$. Of necessity,

$$P_{12}\Phi(1, 2) = -\Phi(1, 2). \qquad (8.12.15)$$

However, by use of Eqs. (8.12.11) and (8.12.13) we can rewrite this as

$$\mathbf{P}_{12}^x P_{12}^s \psi(\mathbf{x}_1, \mathbf{x}_2)\Xi j = P_{12}^x(\mathbf{x}_1, \mathbf{x}_2)\lambda_j \Xi_j = -\psi(\mathbf{x}_1, \mathbf{x}_2)\Xi_j. \qquad (8.12.16)$$

It follows from Eq. (8.12.14) that

$$P_{12}^x\psi(\mathbf{x}_1, \mathbf{x}_2) = \psi(\mathbf{x}_2, \mathbf{x}_1) = -\psi(\mathbf{x}_1, \mathbf{x}_2) \qquad (8.12.17)$$

if the spins are in a triplet (parallel spin) state and

$$P_{12}^x\psi(\mathbf{x}_1, \mathbf{x}_2) = \psi(\mathbf{x}_2, \mathbf{x}_1) = +\psi(\mathbf{x}_1, \mathbf{x}_2) \qquad (8.12.18)$$

if the spins are in a singlet (antiparallel spin) state. The spin state, therefore, controls the symmetry of the coordinate portion of the electron-pair description, and we shall see in Section 9.2 that this has an important effect on interatomic interaction.

CHAPTER NINE

Interatomic Interactions

9.1 INTRODUCTION

In the classical discussions of Part 1, the formulation of an atomistic model of a solid involved the assumption of a Hamiltonian describing a collection of mass points that interact with a specified force law. As we have noted, quantum mechanics provides the fundamental basis for understanding the origin and the nature of the interatomic force laws.

The previous chapter provided an introduction to the basic concepts of quantum mechanics, including the Heisenberg uncertainty principle and the Pauli exclusion principle. The former is responsible for the need for the use of probability distributions, particularly when dealing with very light particles such as electrons. The latter is responsible for the great diversity in the electronic ground states and, therefore, in the different chemical behavior of the various elements.

Although it is easy to formulate the Schrödinger equation for systems of interacting atoms, the resulting mathematical problem is too complex for exact solution and must be treated approximately. Numerous schemes have been developed for this purpose. It is beyond the scope of this book to enter into a discussion of these methods and we treat, in this chapter, only some basic aspects of the problem. We start, in Section 9.2, with a discussion of the H_2 molecule, the simplest example of a covalent bond and one that illustrates the important role of electron spin in interatomic interaction.

We turn next to two important general considerations: the adiabatic approximation (Section 9.3) and the Hellmann–Feynman theorem (Section 9.4). The former provides the theoretical basis for the type of Hamiltonian used in Part 1. The latter indicates that although the nature of the electron distribution must be determined on the basis of quantum mechanics, the resulting interatomic force can be interpreted on the basis of classical electrostatics. As an example, the Hellmann–Feynman theorem is used in Section 9.5 as the basis for computing the harmonic elastic moduli of centrosymmetric crystals directly in terms of the electron density distribution. Finally, we turn in Section 9.6 to a general discussion of different types of interatomic interaction and the corresponding characteristics of empirical interatomic potentials.

9.2 HYDROGEN MOLECULE

The hydrogen molecule, H_2, presents one of the simplest[1] examples of a binding interaction between atoms. The molecule consists of two interacting hydrogen atoms, a system of two protons and two electrons. Since the protons are so much more massive than the electrons (the mass ratio is 1836:1), it is a good approximation[2] to consider the protons as perfectly localized and fixed in space at positions $\mathbf{R}_A$ and $\mathbf{R}_B$ (Figure 9.1) and to treat only the two electrons quantum mechanically. The Hamiltonian for the two electrons is written

$$H(\mathbf{x}_1, \mathbf{x}_2, \mathbf{p}_1, \mathbf{p}_2; \mathbf{R}_A, \mathbf{R}_B) = \frac{1}{2m_e}\left(|\mathbf{p}_1|^2 + |\mathbf{p}_2|^2\right) + V(\mathbf{x}_1, \mathbf{x}_2; \mathbf{R}_A, \mathbf{R}_B),$$

$$(9.2.1)$$

where m_e is the electron mass, $\mathbf{x}_1, \mathbf{x}_2$ are the positions of the two electrons, $\mathbf{p}_1, \mathbf{p}_2$ are their momenta, and V is the Coulomb potential energy between the electrons and between the electrons and the fixed protons. That is (Figure 9.1),

$$V(\mathbf{x}_1, \mathbf{x}_2; \mathbf{R}_A, \mathbf{R}_B)$$

$$= e^2\left(\frac{1}{|\mathbf{x}_1 - \mathbf{x}_2|} - \frac{1}{|\mathbf{x}_1 - \mathbf{R}_A|} - \frac{1}{|\mathbf{x}_1 - \mathbf{R}_B|} - \frac{1}{|\mathbf{x}_2 - \mathbf{R}_A|} - \frac{1}{|\mathbf{x}_2 - \mathbf{R}_B|}\right).$$

$$(9.2.2)$$

The Hamiltonian of Eq. (9.2.1) is not complete since it considers only the electrostatic interactions of the electrons with the protons and with each other. It neglects the magnetic interactions entered into by the intrinsic magnetic moments of the electrons; these interactions are between the intrinsic moments themselves (referred to as spin–spin interactions) and between the intrinsic moments and the magnetic moment due to the orbital motion of the electrons (spin–orbit interactions). However, an estimation of the magnitude of these

---

[1] The only simpler example is the singly ionized hydrogen molecule ion, H_2^+, that is, a hydrogen molecule that has lost one electron. However, since H_2^+ has only a single electron, its behavior does not illustrate the important role of the spin state of an electron pair in interatomic bonds.

[2] The nature of this approximation will be considered in greater detail in Section 9.3.

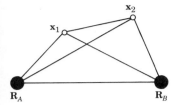

Figure 9.1 Hydrogen molecule configuration.

magnetic terms[3] reveals that they are very small compared to the electrostatic terms and may be neglected with very small loss of accuracy in most calculations, for example, in a calculation of the ground state energy of the molecule. Because of the neglect of these terms, the function defined in Eq. (9.2.1) is referred to as a "spin-free" Hamiltonian.

The operator H corresponding to the Hamiltonian of Eq. (9.2.1) is obtained in the standard way and leads to the following time-independent Schrödinger equation for $\psi(x_1, x_2)$, the coordinate portion of the stationary states of the two electrons:

$$H\psi = \frac{-\hbar^2}{2m_e}(\nabla_1^2 + \nabla_2^2)\psi + V(x_1, x_2; R_A, R_B)\psi = E\psi, \qquad (9.2.3)$$

where ∇_1^2, ∇_2^2 are the three-dimensional Laplacian operators with respect to x_1 and x_2, respectively.

Although we have indicated both R_A and R_B as specified parameters, it is clear from the translational and rotational invariance of V that the stationary state ψ and the corresponding energy E of the electron pair will depend only on the parameter $R = |R_A - R_B|$, the internuclear distance.

Variational Method for Approximate Solutions

Although it has a deceptively simple appearance, the exact solution of Eq. (9.2.3) has not yet been achieved. A great deal of effort has been expended, however, on obtaining approximate solutions to it[4] and to the equations for more complex atomic and molecular systems; the development of these approximate computational techniques is one of the central activities of the field know as quantum chemistry.

Many of the computational techniques of quantum chemistry are variational in character. Their basis lies in the following simple consideration:

Let the exact normalized eigenfunctions and eigenvalues of Eq. (9.2.3) be $\varphi_j(x_1, x_2; R)$, $E_j(R)$, $j = 0, 1, 2, \ldots$, with the energies E_j labeled in order of increasing magnitude. Let $\psi(x_1, x_2; R)$ be an approximation to the ground

---

[3] See, for example, Davydov (1965, p. 335).
[4] The techniques developed are capable of producing extremely accurate approximate solutions; see, for example Kolos and Wolniewicz (1968), where agreement of 0.01% between the calculated and experimental values of the dissociation energy of the H_2 molecule is reported.

state wave function. Since the set φ_j are a complete orthonormal basis for $\mathscr{E}_{\mathbf{x}_1\mathbf{x}_2}$,

$$\psi = \sum_{j=0}^{\infty} c_j\varphi_j \qquad (9.2.4)$$

with [Eq. (8.7.10)]

$$\sum_{j=0}^{\infty} |c_j|^2 = 1. \qquad (9.2.5)$$

The expected value of the energy of the electrons corresponding to the approximate state ψ is

$$E = (\psi, H\psi) = \sum_{j=0}^{\infty} |c_j|^2 E_j. \qquad (9.2.6)$$

It follows that[5]

$$E \geqslant \sum_{j=0}^{\infty} |c_j|^2 E_0 = E_0 \qquad (9.2.7)$$

where we have used the fact that $E_j \geqslant E_0$, $j > 0$ and the final equality follows from Eq. (9.2.5).

We have arrived at the result that the exact ground state energy E_0 is a lower bound to the expected energy corresponding to any approximate state ψ. The proof made use of the exact energy states φ_j which we know exist but whose form we do not know. The result suggests, however, the following approximate scheme. Define an approximate ground state wave function

$$\psi = \sum_{j=0}^{m} c_j u_j$$

where $u_j = u_j(\mathbf{x}_1, \mathbf{x}_2)$ is some convenient set of functions. Determine the expansion coefficients c_j so as to minimize the expected energy corresponding to ψ. The functions u_j may be drawn from a complete basis set for $\mathscr{E}_{\mathbf{x}_1\mathbf{x}_2}$ but this need not be the case. Clearly, the efficiency of the procedure depends on the choice of the function u_j; also, the accuracy is improved by increasing the number of basis functions employed.[6]

We have described the variational procedure in terms of the H_2 molecule; it is clear, however, that the same principles apply to more general cases as well.

---

[5] This is a particular case of what is known as the Ritz theorem; see, for example, Cohen-Tannoudji (1977, p. 1149).
[6] In the calculations for the H_2 molecule of Kolos and Wolniewicz (1968), 80 to 100 terms were used.

Variational Solution for H_2 Molecule

We consider a variational solution with only two functions in the basis set:

$$u_1(x_1, x_2) = \varphi_A(x_1)\varphi_B(x_2)$$
$$u_2(x_1, x_2) = \varphi_A(x_2)\varphi_B(x_1) \qquad (9.2.8)$$

where $\varphi_A(x_1)$ denotes the electron ground state for a hydrogen atom consisting of electron one interacting with the proton at $\mathbf{R}_A$, with corresponding definitions for the other functions.[7] That is, from Eq. (8.9.42),

$$\varphi_A(x_1) = \frac{1}{\sqrt{\pi a_0^3}} e^{-\rho_{A1}} \qquad (9.2.9)$$

where

$$\rho_{A1} = |x_1 - \mathbf{R}_A|/a_0 \qquad (9.2.10)$$

and $a_0 = 0.529\text{Å}$ as defined in Eq. (8.9.39). The approximate state function for the electron pair is taken as a linear combination of u_1 and u_2

$$\psi(x_1, x_2) = c_1 u_1(x_1, x_2) + c_2 u_2(x_1, x_2) \qquad (9.2.11)$$

with real coefficients c_1 and c_2. Although u_1 and u_2 are normalized to unity, ψ is not. A normalized approximate solution, $\psi^N(x_1, x_2)$, is readily obtained as

$$\psi^N = \frac{\psi}{(\psi, \psi)^{1/2}} \qquad (9.2.12)$$

where

$$(\psi, \psi) = (c_1 u_1 + c_2 u_2, c_1 u_1 + c_2 u_2) = c_1^2 + c_2^2 + 2c_1 c_2 S \quad (9.2.13)$$

and where

$$S = (u_1, u_2) \qquad (9.2.14)$$

is know as the overlap integral. It then follows that the expected energy value E corresponding to ψ^N is

$$E = \langle H \rangle = (\psi^N, H\psi^N) = \frac{c_1^2 H_{11} + c_2^2 H_{22} + 2c_1 c_2 H_{12}}{c_1^2 + c_2^2 + 2c_1 c_2 S}, \qquad (9.2.15)$$

---

[7]Heitler and London (1927) were the first to use these functions for the approximate solution of the H_2 molecule. Their use is suggested by the fact that each electron can be regarded as associated with either nucleus.

where

$$H_{ij} = (u_i, \mathsf{H} u_j), \quad i, j = 1, 2 \tag{9.2.16}$$

and $H_{11} = H_{22}$, $H_{12} = H_{21}$ because both electron labels enter H in a symmetric manner. It is seen that E depends only on $A = c_2/c_1$;

$$E = \frac{(1 + A^2)H_{11} + 2AH_{12}}{1 + A^2 + 2AS} \tag{9.2.17}$$

and setting

$$\frac{dE}{dA} = 0 \tag{9.2.18}$$

for stationary values leads to the result that $A = \pm 1$. These values correspond to two approximate states[8]

$$\psi_s(\mathbf{x}_1, \mathbf{x}_2) = u_1(\mathbf{x}_1, \mathbf{x}_2) + u_2(\mathbf{x}_1, \mathbf{x}_2)$$
$$\psi_a(\mathbf{x}_1, \mathbf{x}_2) = u_1(\mathbf{x}_1, \mathbf{x}_2) - u_2(\mathbf{x}_1, \mathbf{x}_2) \tag{9.2.19}$$

with ψ_s symmetric and ψ_a antisymmetric with respect to electron label interchange. Therefore, from the discussion of Section 8.12, we see that ψ_s is appropriate for an electron pair in a singlet state (antiparallel spins) and ψ_a is appropriate for an electron pair in a triplet state (parallel spins). The corresponding values of $E = E(R)$ are obtained[9] from Eq. (9.2.17), with $A = +1$ for ψ_s and $A = -1$ for ψ_a. The quantity $E(R)$ thus obtained is the expected value of the energy of the electrons. To obtain the total energy of interaction of the H_2 molecule, it is necessary to add $V_{nn}(R)$ to $E(R)$, where

$$V_{nn}(R) = \frac{e^2}{R} \tag{9.2.20}$$

is the repulsive Coulomb interaction energy between the two protons. The total interaction energy

$$V(R) = E(R) + V_{nn}(R) \tag{9.2.21}$$

is shown schematically in Figure 9.2 for ψ_s and ψ_a. At very large separations, $V(R)$ approaches $-2E_1$, the ground state energy for two isolated hydrogen atoms, where E_1 is given in Eq. (8.9.37). It is seen that only when the electron pair is in a singlet state (antiparallel spins) is binding between a pair of hydrogen atoms to produce a stable hydrogen molecule possible; the stable state is exhibited by the minimum in the energy $V(R)$ which occurs at $R = R_0$.

---

[8] These are the unnormalized states, corresponding to Eq. (9.2.11).
[9] We do not give the details here for the integral evaluations necessary for the calculation of H_{11}, H_{12} and S; see Davydov (1965, pp. 478–485).

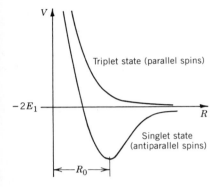

Figure 9.2 Interaction energy between two hydrogen atoms.

Although the electron spins do not appear in the Hamiltonian of the problem and, therefore, have no direct effect on the energy of the system, we see that the spins, nevertheless, have a decisive effect on the interatomic interaction in the H_2 molecule through their control of the symmetry of the coordinate wave function. In the case of antiparallel spins, the wave function is symmetric in the coordinates of the two electrons. This symmetry results in a high probability density for the electrons between the two nuclei. For parallel spins, on the other hand, the required antisymmetry leads to low probability density for the electrons, or, more briefly, low electron density between the nuclei. The bonding and antibonding characteristics of the two spin states may be traced to this difference in electron density distribution.[10]

Covalent Bond

The bond in the hydrogen molecule formed by the electron pair in the singlet state, characterized by a localized region of high electron density between the two nuclei, is the simplest example of what is referred to as a covalent bond. Such bonds also form between some other types of atoms, but the presence of more than one electron per atom makes the analysis more complex.[11]

9.3 ADIABATIC APPROXIMATION

In the previous section, the interaction between two hydrogen atoms was considered. In the analysis the two protons were regarded as fixed in space and the ground state energy of the electrons, with the interproton distance as parameter, was determined quantum mechanically.

[10] For figures showing the electron density distributions in the two cases and a further discussion of this point, see Blokhintsev (1964, p. 542).
[11] For a brief discussion see Davydov (1965, pp. 486–499) or Cohen-Tannoudji (1977, pp. 841–855). For a more extensive discussion see Slater (1963).

A theoretical basis for this approach is provided by what is known as the adiabatic approximation.[12] It is discussed in this section for the more general case of a collection of atoms consisting of N_n nuclei and N_e electrons. The Hamiltonian of the system may be written in the form

$$H(\mathbf{r}^e, \mathbf{p}^e; \mathbf{r}^n, \mathbf{p}^n) = \sum_{i=1}^{N_e} \frac{|\mathbf{p}_i^e|^2}{2m_e} + \sum_{l=1}^{N_n} \frac{|\mathbf{p}_l^n|^2}{2M_l} + V_{ee}(\mathbf{r}^e) + V_{en}(\mathbf{r}^e, \mathbf{r}^n) + V_{nn}(\mathbf{r}^n)$$

$$(9.3.1)$$

where $\mathbf{r}_i^e, \mathbf{p}_i^e, i = 1, \ldots, N_e$ are the electron coordinates and momenta, $\mathbf{r}_l^n, \mathbf{p}_l^n$, $l = 1, \ldots, N_n$ are the nuclei coordinates and momenta, m_e is the electron mass, M_l is the mass of the nucleus l, and we have used the collective argument $\mathbf{r}^e = (\mathbf{r}_1^e, \ldots, \mathbf{r}_{N_e}^e)$, etc. $V_{ee}(\mathbf{r}^e)$, $V_{en}(\mathbf{r}^e, \mathbf{r}^n)$, and $V_{nn}(\mathbf{r}^n)$ are, respectively, the Coulomb interaction energies between the electrons, between the electrons and the nuclei, and between the nuclei:

$$V_{ee} = \sum_{\substack{i,j=1 \\ i>j}}^{N_e} \frac{e^2}{s_{ij}}; \qquad s_{ij} = |\mathbf{r}_i^e - \mathbf{r}_j^e|$$

$$V_{en} = -\sum_{i=1}^{N_e} \sum_{l=1}^{N_n} \frac{q_l e}{s_{il}}; \qquad s_{il} = |\mathbf{r}_i^e - \mathbf{r}_l^n| \qquad (9.3.2)$$

$$V_{nn} = \sum_{\substack{l,l'=1 \\ l>l'}}^{N_n} \frac{q_l q_{l'}}{s_{ll'}}; \qquad s_{ll'} = |\mathbf{r}_l^n - \mathbf{r}_{l'}^n|$$

where q_l is the charge on nucleus l. The time-dependent Schrödinger equation for the system is

$$-\frac{\hbar^2}{2} \left[\frac{1}{m_e} \sum_{j=1}^{N_e} \nabla_j^2 \psi + \sum_{l=1}^{N_n} \frac{1}{M_l} \nabla_l^2 \psi \right]$$

$$+ \left(V_{ee}(\mathbf{r}^e) + V_{en}(\mathbf{r}^e, \mathbf{r}^n) + V_{nn}(\mathbf{r}^n) \right) \psi = i\hbar \frac{\partial \psi}{\partial t}. \qquad (9.3.3)$$

Here, the notation ∇_j^2 is the three-dimensional Laplacian with respect to $\mathbf{r}_j^e$ and ∇_l^2 has the corresponding significance with respect to $\mathbf{r}_l^n$. We seek an approxi-

---

[12] The adiabatic approximation was developed in detail by Born and Oppenheimer (1927) (see also Born and Huang, 1954, pp. 166–173) for the case in which the nuclei are oscillating in the vicinity of a stable equilibrium configuration; in that context, the adiabatic approximation is frequently referred to as the Born–Oppenheimer approximation.

mate solution to Eq. (9.3.3) in the form

$$\psi(\mathbf{r}^e, \mathbf{r}^n, t) = \psi^e(\mathbf{r}^e, \mathbf{r}^n)\psi^n(\mathbf{r}^n, t). \qquad (9.3.4)$$

Substitution of this expression into Eq. (9.3.3) leads to the result

$$-\frac{\hbar^2}{2}\left[\frac{1}{m_e}\psi^n\sum_{j=1}^{N_e}\nabla_j^2\psi^e + \sum_{l=1}^{N_n}\frac{1}{M_l}\left(\psi^e\nabla_l^2\psi^n + 2\nabla_l\psi^e\cdot\nabla_l\psi^n + \psi^n\nabla_l^2\psi^e\right)\right]$$

$$\qquad\qquad (1)\qquad\qquad\qquad (2)\qquad\qquad (3)\qquad\quad (4)$$

$$+ (V_{ee} + V_{en} + V_{nn})\psi^e\psi^n = i\hbar\psi^e\frac{\partial\psi^n}{\partial t} \qquad (9.3.5)$$

where ∇_l is the three-dimensional gradient with respect to $\mathbf{r}_l^n$. We now make use of the fact that the electron mass is very small compared to the mass of a nucleus. We assume that all derivatives of ψ^e are of comparable magnitude and, therefore, neglect terms (3) and (4) of Eq. (9.3.5), which are multiplied by $1/M_l$, in comparison[13] with term (1) which is multiplied by $1/m_e$. The approximate equation that results is

$$-\frac{\hbar^2}{2}\left[\frac{1}{m_e}\psi^n\sum_{j=1}^{N_e}\nabla_j^2\psi^e + \psi^e\sum_{l=1}^{N_n}\frac{1}{M_l}\nabla_l^2\psi^n\right]$$

$$+ (V_{ee} + V_{en} + V_{nn})\psi^e\psi^n = i\hbar\psi^e\frac{\partial\psi^n}{\partial t}. \qquad (9.3.6)$$

In addition we assume that $\psi^e(\mathbf{r}^e, \mathbf{r}^n)$ satisfies the eigenvalue equation

$$H_e\psi^e \triangleq -\frac{\hbar^2}{2m_e}\sum_{j=1}^{N_e}\nabla_j^2\psi^e + (V_{ee} + V_{en})\psi^e = E\psi^e. \qquad (9.3.7)$$

In this equation, the nuclear coordinates $\mathbf{r}_l^n$ play the role of parameters since derivatives with respect to them are absent. For any set of values for these coordinates, Eq. (9.3.7) determines both the eigenvalues $E_i(\mathbf{r}^n)$ and the corresponding eigenfunctions $\psi_i^e(\mathbf{r}^e; \mathbf{r}^n)$, where we have made explicit the dependence of both quantities on the nuclear coordinates as parameters. We choose the minimum eigenvalue, $E_0(\mathbf{r}^n)$, and the corresponding eigenfunction, $\psi_0^e(\mathbf{r}^e; \mathbf{r}^n)$, and substitute Eq. (9.3.7) into Eq. (9.3.6). The common factor of

---

[13] The same reasoning would appear to dictate neglect of term (2) as well. This is not done since it is proportional to ψ^e; this will appear as a common factor in the equation of ψ^n.

$\psi_0^e(\mathbf{r}^e; \mathbf{r}^n)$ can then be cancelled, leading to the following equation for $\psi^n(\mathbf{r}^n, t)$:

$$-\frac{\hbar^2}{2} \sum_{l=1}^{N_n} \frac{1}{M_l} \nabla_l^2 \psi^n + \left(V_{nn}(\mathbf{r}^n) + E_0(\mathbf{r}^n) \right) \psi^n = i\hbar \frac{\partial \psi^n}{\partial t}. \qquad (9.3.8)$$

The electron coordinates have completely disappeared from Eq. (9.3.8) and we see that it corresponds to the time-dependent Schrödinger equation for a system of N_n particles with Hamiltonian

$$H(\mathbf{r}^n, \mathbf{p}^n) = \sum_{l=1}^{N_n} \frac{|\mathbf{p}_l|^2}{2M_l} + V(\mathbf{r}^n) \qquad (9.3.9)$$

where

$$V(\mathbf{r}^n) = E_0(\mathbf{r}^n) + V_{nn}(\mathbf{r}^n). \qquad (9.3.10)$$

This equation is the generalization of Eq. (9.2.21), derived for the H_2 molecule.

Having arrived, through the use of the adiabatic approximation, at the effective Hamiltonian $H(\mathbf{r}^n, \mathbf{p}^n)$ for the system of N_n nuclei, we may now choose to treat them in subsequent calculations either from the quantum or the classical viewpoint. In many cases, particularly if the nuclei are all relatively massive particles, it is permissible and convenient to exercise the latter option; this is the procedure we have adopted throughout Part 1 of this book. In this case, we can describe the physical nature of the adiabatic approximation in the following way: Because the electron mass is so much smaller than the mass of the nuclei, the latter move relatively slowly so that the electrons' state changes quasi-statically, remaining always in the ground state[14] corresponding to the instantaneous positions of the nuclei. The total energy of the electrons (kinetic plus potential) is $E_0(\mathbf{r}^n)$ and is, therefore, determined solely by the positions of the nuclei; when it is added to the internuclear potential $V_{nn}(\mathbf{r}^n)$, we obtain the total potential energy $V(\mathbf{r}^n)$ for the system of nuclei. If, on the other hand, we treat the nuclei quantum mechanically, then the simple physical picture just presented as descriptive of the adiabatic approximation is not strictly applicable since it involves the motion of the nuclei along a definite trajectory in configuration space.

In this discussion of the adiabatic approximation we have focused on its physical interpretation and have not presented any analysis that indicates clearly the class of problems for which its use is justified. This type of analysis remains the subject of current research.[15] The approximation appears to be a reasonable one for the study of insulators and semiconductors where a finite

[14] This property is the origin of the nomenclature, "adiabatic approximation" for the method: the electrons do not make a transition from the lowest energy level to a higher energy level.
[15] Cf. Seiler (1973).

energy gap exists between the electron ground state and the first excited state; it is clearly less accurate for metals, where this gap vanishes, but is still useful as a starting point in the discussion.

9.4   HELLMANN–FEYNMAN THEOREM

As we saw in the previous section, it is a consequence of the adiabatic approximation that we may express the wave function $\psi(\mathbf{r}^e, \mathbf{r}^n, t)$ for a collection of nuclei and electrons in the form[16] $\psi_e(\mathbf{r}^e, \mathbf{r}^n)\psi_n(\mathbf{r}^n, t)$. From the electronic portion, $\psi_e(\mathbf{r}^e, \mathbf{r}^n)$, of this wave function we can, as we shall see, derive the concept of a distributed electron density $\rho(\mathbf{r})$ in ordinary three-dimensional space[17] in the vicinity of the nuclei which are at the positions $\mathbf{r}_l^n, l = 1, \ldots, N_n$ and are regarded as point charges. Although it is essential to determine $\psi_e(\mathbf{r}^e; \mathbf{r}^n)$ by the laws of quantum mechanics, it is the content of the Hellmann–Feynman theorem (Hellmann, 1937; Feynman, 1939) that the forces exerted by the corresponding distributed charge density $\rho(\mathbf{r})$ on the nuclei may be interpreted and computed simply in terms of classical electrostatics.

If the system contains only a single electron, then $|\psi_e(\mathbf{r}; \mathbf{r}^n)|^2 = P_e(\mathbf{r}; \mathbf{r}^n)$, the probability density for finding an electron at the position $\mathbf{r}$. This probability density may be reinterpreted as the density of a "smeared-out" electron at that point and referred to as the electron density. Consider next a system containing N_e electrons. The electron density, $\rho_k(\mathbf{r})$, at position $\mathbf{r}$ due to the kth electron, without regard to the possible position of any of the other electrons, is

$$\rho_k(\mathbf{r}) = \int_{\mathbb{R}_{3(N_e-1)}} \psi_e \psi_e^* d\mathbf{r}_1^e \ldots d\mathbf{r}_{k-1}^e d\mathbf{r}_{k+1}^e \ldots d\mathbf{r}_{N_e}^e \qquad (9.4.1)$$

where $\mathbf{r}_k^e = \mathbf{r}$ in ψ_e and where $\mathbb{R}_{3(N_e-1)}$ is the $3(N_e - 1)$ dimensional configuration space for the system of all but the kth electron. The electron density, $\rho(\mathbf{r})$, due to all of the electrons is then

$$\rho(\mathbf{r}) = \sum_{k=1}^{N_e} \rho_k(\mathbf{r}). \qquad (9.4.2)$$

Because of the required symmetry of ψ_e in the electron positions, $\mathbf{r}_k^e$, the electron densities $\rho_k(\mathbf{r})$ are the same for all k.

---

[16] In the previous section the notation $\psi^e(\mathbf{r}^e, \mathbf{r}^n)\psi^n(\mathbf{r}^n, t)$ was employed because the subscript position was needed for electron state designation.

[17] The distinction in notation should be emphasized: $\mathbf{r}$ is a three-dimensional vector as are $\mathbf{r}_l^e$ and $\mathbf{r}_l^n$, whereas $\mathbf{r}^e = (\mathbf{r}_1^e, \ldots, \mathbf{r}_{N_e}^e)$, $\mathbf{r}^n = (\mathbf{r}_1^n, \ldots, \mathbf{r}_{N_n}^n)$.

Within the context of the adiabatic approximation the interatomic potential $V(\mathbf{r}^n)$ can be written [Eq. (9.3.10)] as

$$V(\mathbf{r}^n) = E_0(\mathbf{r}^n) + V_{nn}(\mathbf{r}^n) \tag{9.4.3}$$

so that the force $\mathbf{f}_l$ acting on the lth nucleus is

$$\mathbf{f}_l = -\nabla_l V = -\nabla_l E_0 - \nabla_l V_{nn} \tag{9.4.4}$$

where, as previously defined, ∇_l is the three-dimensional gradient with respect to $\mathbf{r}_l^n$. The second term gives the ordinary Coulomb electrostatic repulsion of the remaining nuclei acting on the lth nucleus. We wish now to give a similar interpretation in terms of Coulomb electrostatics to the first term. As developed in the adiabatic approximation, $E_0(\mathbf{r}^n)$ is the ground state energy corresponding to the wave function $\psi_e(\mathbf{r}^e, \mathbf{r}^n)$ for a system of N_e electrons in the presence of N_n fixed nuclei at positions $\mathbf{r}^n = (\mathbf{r}_1^n, \ldots, \mathbf{r}_{N_n}^n)$, that is, for a system with Hamiltonian

$$H_e(\mathbf{r}^e, \mathbf{p}^e; \mathbf{r}^n) = \sum_{j=1}^{N_e} \frac{|\mathbf{p}_j|^2}{2m_e} + V_{ee}(\mathbf{r}^e) + V_{en}(\mathbf{r}^e, \mathbf{r}^n). \tag{9.4.5}$$

Therefore,

$$E_0(\mathbf{r}^n) = (\psi_e, H_e \psi_e) = \int_{\mathbb{R}_{3N_e}} \psi_e^*(H_e \psi_e)\, d\mathbf{r}_1^e \ldots d\mathbf{r}_{N_e}^e \tag{9.4.6}$$

where it is important to note that the inner product involves integration only over the $3N_e$-dimensional configuration space of the electrons, since the nuclear coordinates $\mathbf{r}^n$ act as parameters. By the usual rules for differentiating such an integral we find that[18]

$$\nabla_l E_0 = (\nabla_l \psi_e, H_e \psi_e) + (\psi_e, H_e \nabla_l \psi_e) + (\psi_e, (\nabla_l H_e)\psi_e). \tag{9.4.7}$$

Consider the first two terms in this equation. Since H_e is Hermitian and since $H_e \psi_e = E_0(\mathbf{r}^n)\psi_e$, they may be written

$$(\nabla_l \psi_e, H_e \psi_e) + (\psi_e, H_e \nabla_l \psi_e) = (\nabla_l \psi_e, H_e \psi_e) + (H_e \psi_e, \nabla_l \psi_e)$$

$$= E_0(\mathbf{r}^n)[(\nabla_l \psi_e, \psi_e) + (\psi_e, \nabla_l \psi_e)].$$

$$\tag{9.4.8}$$

---

[18] The validity of Eq. (9.4.7) is easily verified by an extended computation based on the multiple integral definition of the inner product and the explicit definition of H_e as a differential operator.

However, the electronic wave function ψ_e is normalized for all values of $\mathbf{r}^n$; that is,

$$(\psi_e, \psi_e) = \int_{\mathbf{R}_{3N_e}} \psi_e^*(\mathbf{r}^e, \mathbf{r}^n)\psi_e(\mathbf{r}^e, \mathbf{r}^n)\, d\mathbf{r}_1^e \ldots d\mathbf{r}_{N_e}^e = 1. \qquad (9.4.9)$$

Therefore,

$$\nabla_l(\psi_e, \psi_e) = (\nabla_l\psi_e, \psi_e) + (\psi_e, \nabla_l\psi_e) = 0 \qquad (9.4.10)$$

so that the sum of the first two terms in Eq. (9.4.7) vanishes. We turn next to the remaining term in that equation. Since the portions of the operator H_e which correspond to the electron kinetic energy and the interelectron potential energy, $V_{ee}(\mathbf{r}^e)$, both do not depend on the nuclear coordinates,

$$\nabla_l H_e = \nabla_l V_{en}(\mathbf{r}^e, \mathbf{r}^n). \qquad (9.4.11)$$

As previously defined [Eq. (9.3.2)],

$$V_{en}(\mathbf{r}^e, \mathbf{r}^n) = -\sum_{j=1}^{N_e}\sum_{l=1}^{N_n}\frac{q_l e}{s_{jl}}; \qquad s_{jl} = |\mathbf{r}_j^e - \mathbf{r}_j^n|$$

and therefore

$$\nabla_l V_{en} = -eq_l\sum_{j=1}^{N_e}\nabla_l s_{jl}^{-1}. \qquad (9.4.12)$$

It follows that

$$\nabla_l E_0(\mathbf{r}^n) = (\psi_e, (\nabla_l H_e)\psi_e) = (\psi_e, (\nabla_l V_{en})\psi_e)$$

$$= -eq_l\sum_{j=1}^{N_e}\int_{\mathbf{R}_{3N_e}}\nabla_l s_{jl}^{-1}\psi_e^*\psi_e\, d\mathbf{r}_1^e \ldots d\mathbf{r}_{N_e}^e. \qquad (9.4.13)$$

Since s_{jl}^{-1} depends only on $\mathbf{r}_j^e$ and $\mathbf{r}_l^n$, the $3N_e$-fold integral may be written as

$$\nabla_l E_0(\mathbf{r}^n) = -eq_l\sum_{j=1}^{N_e}\int_{\mathbf{R}_3}\nabla_l s_{jl}^{-1}\left[\int_{\mathbf{R}_{3(N_e-1)}}\psi_e^*\psi_e\, d\mathbf{r}_1^e \ldots d\mathbf{r}_{j-1}^e\, d\mathbf{r}_{j+1}^e \ldots d\mathbf{r}_{N_e}^e\right]d\mathbf{r}_j^e$$

$$= -eq_l\sum_{j=1}^{N_e}\int_{\mathbf{R}_3}\nabla_l s_{jl}^{-1}\rho_j(\mathbf{r}_j^e)\, d\mathbf{r}_j^e \qquad (9.4.14)$$

where Eq. (9.4.1) has been used. But we now recognize that, for l fixed, ∇s_{jl}^{-1} is the same function of $\mathbf{r}_j^e$ for all j, and that in each integral the variable $\mathbf{r}_j^e$ simply acts as variable of integration for the three-dimensional configuration space $\mathbb{R}_3$. In place of $\mathbf{r}_j^e$, we now introduce $\mathbf{r}$ as notation for this variable of integration, write

$$s_{lr} = |\mathbf{r}_l^n - \mathbf{r}| \qquad (9.4.15)$$

and rewrite Eq. (9.4.14) as

$$-\nabla_l E_0(\mathbf{r}^n) = eq_l \nabla_l \int_{\mathbb{R}_3} s_{lr}^{-1}(\mathbf{r}_l^n, \mathbf{r}) \sum_{j=1}^{N_e} \rho_j(\mathbf{r})\, d\mathbf{r}$$

$$= eq_l \nabla_l \int_{\mathbb{R}_3} s_{lr}^{-1}(\mathbf{r}_l^n, \mathbf{r}) \rho(\mathbf{r})\, d\mathbf{r} \qquad (9.4.16)$$

where we have utilized Eq. (9.4.2) for $\rho(\mathbf{r})$, the electron density at $\mathbf{r}$. We have thus arrived at an expression for $-\nabla_l E_0$, the force on nucleus l due to the electrons, which is of precisely the same form as computed on the basis of classical Coulomb electrostatics.

9.5 HARMONIC ELASTIC MODULI BASED ON HELLMANN–FEYNMAN THEOREM[19]

We return to a consideration of the harmonic elastic moduli $\tilde{C}_{LMNK}$ which have been discussed in Section 4.6, confining attention here to centrosymmetric crystals. As in that section, we focus on an interior region I together with E_{in}, the thin layer of surrounding atoms which interact with the atoms of I (see Figure 4.3). Let $\mathbf{X}_l$ (with components $X_L(l)$) $l = 1, \ldots, N$ be the lattice sites in the reference configuration, $\mathbf{x}_l$ (with components $x_i(l)$) those in the deformed configuration, with the two related by the affine transformation a_{iL}:

$$x_i(l) = a_{iL} X_L(l), \qquad l = 1, \ldots, N. \qquad (9.5.1)$$

Let $V_0(\mathbf{x}_1, \ldots, \mathbf{x}_N)$ be the potential energy of the atoms of $I + E_{in}$ when all of their nuclei are at the deformed lattice sites. Then, as seen in the previous section,

$$V_0(\mathbf{x}_1, \ldots, \mathbf{x}_N) = V_{nn}(\mathbf{x}_1, \ldots, \mathbf{x}_N) + \int_v V_{en} \rho\, d\mathbf{r} \qquad (9.5.2)$$

where

$$V_{nn} = \sum_{\substack{l, l'=1 \\ l > l'}}^{N} q_l q_{l'} s_{ll'}^{-1} \qquad (9.5.3)$$

[19] Weiner (1981).

with q_l the charge on nucleus l and

$$s_{ll'} = |\mathbf{x}_l - \mathbf{x}_{l'}| \qquad (9.5.4)$$

$$V_{en} = V_{en}(\mathbf{r}; \mathbf{x}_1, \ldots, \mathbf{x}_N) = -e \sum_l q_l s_{lr}^{-1} \qquad (9.5.5)$$

with $-e$ the charge on the electron and

$$s_{lr} = |\mathbf{x}_l - \mathbf{r}|; \qquad (9.5.6)$$

$$\rho = \rho(\mathbf{r}; \mathbf{x}_1, \ldots, \mathbf{x}_N) \qquad (9.5.7)$$

is the electron density at position $\mathbf{r}$. The integration in Eq. (9.5.2) is carried out over the region v occupied by $I + E_{in}$ in the deformed configuration.[20] It is a consequence of the Hellmann–Feynman theorem that

$$\frac{\partial V_0}{\partial x_i(l)} = \frac{\partial V_{nn}}{\partial x_i(l)} + \int_v \frac{\partial V_{en}}{\partial x_i(l)} \rho \, d\mathbf{r}. \qquad (9.5.8)$$

That is, in computing the first partial derivative of V_0 with respect to the coordinate of any nucleus, the electron density ρ is not differentiated.[21] We now make use of this result to compute the stress tensor T_{LM} acting on I in its deformed state.

Let [Eq. (1.2.27)]

$$E_{LM} = \tfrac{1}{2}(a_{iL} a_{iM} - \delta_{LM}) \qquad (9.5.9)$$

be the material strain tensor corresponding to the affine deformation a_{iL}. Given any function $f(\mathbf{x}(1), \ldots, \mathbf{x}(N))$, it follows from Eqs. (9.5.1) and (9.5.9) that

$$\frac{\partial f}{\partial E_{LM}} = A_{Li} \frac{\partial f}{\partial a_{iM}} = A_{Li} \sum_{l=1}^{N} \frac{\partial f}{\partial x_i(l)} X_M(l) \qquad (9.5.10)$$

where A_{Li} is the matrix inverse to a_{iL}. Then, in the classical harmonic

---

[20] Since $\rho(\mathbf{r}; \mathbf{x}_1, \ldots, \mathbf{x}_N)$ is the density only of those electrons associated with the atoms of $I + E_{in}$, its value is negligible outside of the region v. Alternatively, therefore, we could regard the integration in Eq. (9.5.2) as extending over all space.

[21] There is also no need to consider the variation of the volume v in this differentiation. This can be verified by a change in variable of integration (see Eq. (9.5.14)) to make the range of integration fixed; see also footnote 20.

approximation at temperature $T = 0$ [Eq. (4.5.7)]

$$\mathscr{V} T_{LM} = \frac{\partial V_0}{\partial E_{LM}} = A_{Li} \sum_{l=i}^{N} \frac{\partial V_0}{\partial x_i(l)} X_M(l)$$

$$= A_{Li} \sum_{l=1}^{N} \left[\frac{\partial V_{nn}}{\partial x_i(l)} + \int_v \frac{\partial V_{en}}{\partial x_i(l)} \rho \, d\mathbf{r} \right] X_M(l) \qquad (9.5.11)$$

where $\mathscr{V}$ is the volume occupied by I + E_{in} in the reference configuration and where we have made use of the Hellmann–Feynman theorem in the form of Eq. (9.5.8). Having done so, we can now use Eq. (9.5.10) again and return to derivatives with respect to E_{LM},

$$\mathscr{V} T_{LM} = \frac{\partial V_{nn}}{\partial E_{LM}} + \int_v \frac{\partial V_{en}}{\partial E_{LM}} \rho \, d\mathbf{r}. \qquad (9.5.12)$$

To obtain the harmonic elastic moduli $\tilde{C}_{LMNK}$ it is necessary to differentiate Eq. (9.5.12) with respect to E_{NK}. The Hellmann–Feynman dispensation of the differentiation of ρ applies, of course, only to first partials; it is now necessary to take into account the dependence of the electron density on the nuclei positions. The result is

$$\mathscr{V} \tilde{C}_{LMNK} = \mathscr{V} \frac{\partial T_{LM}}{\partial E_{NK}} = \frac{\partial^2 V_{nn}}{\partial E_{LM} \partial E_{NK}} + \int_v \frac{\partial^2 V_{en}}{\partial E_{LM} \partial E_{NK}} \rho \, d\mathbf{r} + \int_v \frac{\partial V_{en}}{\partial E_{LM}} \frac{\partial \rho}{\partial E_{NK}} \, d\mathbf{r}$$

$$(9.5.13)$$

where $\partial \rho / \partial E_{NK}$ is to be computed on the basis of Eq. (9.5.10)

It is now convenient to make a change of variable of integration for the integrals in Eq. (9.5.13) from $\mathbf{r}$ (components r_i) to $\mathbf{R}$ (components R_L) where

$$r_i = a_{iL} R_L. \qquad (9.5.14)$$

Let

$$\tilde{\rho}(\mathbf{R}; \mathbf{x}_1, \ldots, \mathbf{x}_N) = \rho(\mathbf{r}(\mathbf{R}); \mathbf{x}_1, \ldots, \mathbf{x}_N) |a_{iL}|, \qquad (9.5.15)$$

where $|a_{iL}|$ is the determinant of a_{iL} and is, Eq. (1.2.24), the ratio of corresponding volumes in the deformed and undeformed crystal. It is seen that $\tilde{\rho}(\mathbf{R}; \mathbf{x}_1, \ldots, \mathbf{x}_N)$ is the electron density in the deformed crystal, at the point in space $\mathbf{r}$ obtained from the argument $\mathbf{R}$ by Eq. (9.5.14) (see Figure 9.3) and expressed per unit of undeformed crystal volume.

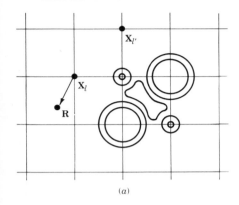

(a)

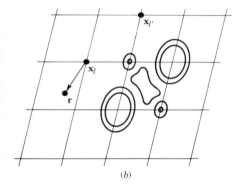

(b)

Figure 9.3 Crystal in reference (a) and deformed (b) configurations. Position vectors $\mathbf{R}$ and $\mathbf{r}$ are related by same affine deformation which takes lattice sites $\mathbf{X}_l$ into $\mathbf{x}_l$. Constant electron density curves before and after deformation are shown schematically. (After Weiner 1981.)

With this change of variable of integration, Eq. (9.5.13) takes the form

$$\mathscr{V}\tilde{C}_{LMNK} = \frac{\partial^2 V_{nn}}{\partial E_{LM} \partial E_{NK}} + \int_{\mathscr{V}} \frac{\partial^2 V_{en}}{\partial E_{LM} \partial E_{NK}} \tilde{\rho} \, d\mathbf{R} + \int_{\mathscr{V}} \frac{\partial V_{en}}{\partial E_{LM}} \frac{\partial \tilde{\rho}}{\partial E_{NK}} \, d\mathbf{R}.$$

$$(9.5.16)$$

Cauchy Relations

We have thus arrived at an explicit formula for the harmonic elastic moduli in terms of the electron density distribution and its change upon crystal deformation. We now use this result to derive a sufficient condition for the Cauchy relations which is stated in terms of the electron density distribution rather than in terms of the interatomic force law as in Section 4.6.

For this purpose it is convenient, as in the discussion of Section 4.6, to regard V_{nn} and V_{en} as functions of $\xi_{ll'} = s_{ll'}^2$ and $\xi_{l\mathbf{r}} = s_{l\mathbf{r}}^2$, respectively, writing

$$V_{nn} = \sum_{\substack{l,l'=1 \\ l>l'}}^{N} \varphi_{ll'}(\xi_{ll'}) \tag{9.5.17}$$

and

$$V_{en} = \sum_{l=1}^{N} \Phi_l(\xi_{l\mathbf{r}}) \tag{9.5.18}$$

where the definitions of $\varphi_{ll'}(\xi)$ and $\Phi_l(\xi)$ follow from comparison with Eqs. (9.5.3) and (9.5.5):

$$\varphi_{ll'}(\xi) = \frac{q_l q_{l'}}{\sqrt{\xi}}, \quad \Phi_l(\xi) = \frac{-e q_l}{\sqrt{\xi}}. \tag{9.5.19}$$

Let

$$\Delta X_L(ll') = X_L(l) - X_L(l') \tag{9.5.20}$$

and

$$\Delta X_L(l\mathbf{R}) = X_L(l) - R_L. \tag{9.5.21}$$

Then [Eq. (1.2.9)]

$$s_{ll'}^2 - S_{ll'}^2 = 2E_{LM}\Delta X_L(ll')\Delta X_M(ll'), \tag{9.5.22}$$

and

$$s_{l\mathbf{r}}^2 - S_{l\mathbf{R}}^2 = 2E_{LM}\Delta X_L(l\mathbf{R})\Delta X_M(l\mathbf{R}) \tag{9.5.23}$$

where

$$S_{ll'}^2 = \Delta X_L(ll')\Delta X_L(ll'), \quad S_{l\mathbf{R}}^2 = \Delta X_L(l\mathbf{R})\Delta X_L(l\mathbf{R}) \tag{9.5.24}$$

are the squared distances in the reference configuration corresponding, respectively, to $s_{ll'}^2$ and $s_{l\mathbf{r}}^2$ in the deformed configuration. We may now compute the derivatives appearing in Eq. (9.5.16) with the result [compare with Eq. (4.6.14)]

$$\mathscr{V}\tilde{C}_{LMNK} = 4 \sum_{\substack{ll'=1 \\ l>l'}}^{N} \varphi_{ll'}''(\xi_{ll'})\Delta X_L(ll')\Delta X_M(ll')\Delta X_N(ll')\Delta X_K(ll')$$

$$+ 4 \sum_{l=1}^{N} \int_{\mathscr{V}} \Phi_l''(\xi_{l\mathbf{r}})\Delta X_L(l\mathbf{R})\Delta X_M(l\mathbf{R})\Delta X_N(l\mathbf{R})\Delta X_K(l\mathbf{R})\tilde{\rho}\, d\mathbf{R}$$

$$+ 2 \sum_{l=1}^{N} \int_{\mathscr{V}} \Phi_l'(\xi_{l\mathbf{r}})\Delta X_L(l\mathbf{R})\Delta X_M(l\mathbf{R})\frac{\partial \tilde{\rho}}{\partial E_{NK}}\, d\mathbf{R}, \tag{9.5.25}$$

where $\xi_{l\mathbf{r}} = \xi_{l\mathbf{r}(\mathbf{R})}$. We conclude from Eq. (9.5.25) that the Cauchy relations will be satisfied if

$$\frac{\partial \tilde{\rho}}{\partial E_{NK}} \equiv 0 \text{ for } \mathbf{R} \in \mathscr{V} \tag{9.5.26}$$

or equivalently, if

$$\tilde{\rho}(\mathbf{R}; \mathbf{x}_1, \dots, \mathbf{x}_N) = \tilde{\rho}(\mathbf{R}; \mathbf{X}_1, \dots, \mathbf{X}_N). \tag{9.5.27}$$

Since $\mathbf{r}$ is related to $\mathbf{R}$ by the same affine transformation as deforms the lattice of nuclei, we may restate this result as follows: If, in a centrosymmetric crystal, the electron density distribution undergoes the same affine deformation as does the lattice of nuclei, the harmonic moduli will satisfy the Cauchy relations.

9.6 CATEGORIES OF INTERATOMIC FORCE LAWS

In the previous section we have seen that the Hellmann–Feynman theorem may be used to express the harmonic elastic moduli of centrosymmetric crystals in terms of the electron density distribution $\rho(\mathbf{r})$. This theorem has been used also for studies[22] of lattice vibrations based directly on $\rho(\mathbf{r})$. However, most studies of the mechanical behavior of crystalline and polymeric solids are based on empirical interatomic potentials. Since the Hellmann–Feynman theorem shows that for a given $\rho(\mathbf{r})$ the interatomic forces can be understood in terms of classical electrostatics, it is convenient to distinguish four general classes of electron density distributions and to describe the nature of the interatomic force law which each class implies. These categories are idealizations; the bonding among specific collections of atoms generally will not fall neatly into a single class but will have characteristics common to two or more of them.

We can visualize the development of the electron density distribution about a collection of atoms by first considering these atoms sufficiently far apart so that the charge distribution in the vicinity of each corresponds to that of a neutral isolated atom. The atoms are then brought closer together and interaction between them[23] will cause changes in the individual charge distributions about each atom. The nature of these changes will depend on the types of atoms involved and in particular on the states of their valence electrons: how

---

[22] DeCicco and Johnson (1969), Johnson (1974), Johnson and Moore (1974).

[23] That is, when they are sufficiently close to each other the electron states must be determined from a Schrödinger equation, which treats the electrons of the various atoms simultaneously. These states will then depend, in the adiabatic approximation, on the relative positions of the nuclei. This method of discussing interatomic bonding is due to Hellmann (1937); see also Peierls (1955). It applies to the formation of molecules (including polymers) or crystals. In all cases the atoms are regarded as maintained in a geometrically similar array as they are brought together to their final configuration.

tightly they are bound, that is how much energy must be supplied to remove them or, conversely, how easily will the atoms accept additional valence electrons. These properties depend upon the position of the type of atom in the periodic table (Section 8.12).[24]

We can distinguish four categories of bonding in terms of the changes in charge distribution which take place as the collection of atoms approach each other.

1 No charge transfer takes place and the atoms remain as overall neutral charge distributions. However, the solution[25] to the Schrödinger equation, which treats the electrons of the various atoms simultaneously, leads to a distortion of the charge distributions about each atom and therefore to a weak electrostatic force between them. This is known as the Van der Waals force. It is the mode of interaction, for example, between the atoms of rare gas solids.

2 At the other extreme, we have the case in which there is the complete transfer of one electron from each of one set of the atoms to each of the other set. Therefore, each atom now can be characterized as an ion with a charge distribution corresponding to a net positive or negative charge of magnitude e. The strong electrostatic interaction between these ions is referred to as ionic bonding; examples are provided by the alkali halide crystals such as LiF, NaCl, etc.

3 There is shared localized electron density between atoms. This is known as covalent bonding. Examples are provided by the hydrogen molecule (Section 9.2), in which the electron pair with opposed spins have a high localized density between the atoms, or by the bonding with a carbon atom whose four valence electrons[26] pair with four other valence electrons and have high localized charge density in the carbon-bonding directions (see Figure 5.3).

4 Some valence electrons leave their atoms and assume delocalized states so that there is a relatively uniform charge density associated with these electrons. These electron states are highly mobile in response to an electric field and give rise to high electrical conductivity. The system is then often described, in picturesque terms, as one corresponding to a collection of positive ions in a negative sea of electrons and the bonding is referred to as metallic. The familiar metals, Fe, Cu, Ni, etc., fall into this category.

Characteristics of Interatomic Potentials

We have seen in Section 9.3 that the adiabatic approximation leads, for a group of N atoms, to the existence of a potential energy function $V(\mathbf{r}_1^n, \ldots, \mathbf{r}_N^n)$

[24]See, for example, Zhdanov (1965, pp. 68–81) for a more extended discussion.
[25]An approximate solution, using perturbation techniques, for a pair of hydrogen atoms (at sufficiently large separation so that negligible charge sharing occurs) may be found in most texts on quantum mechanics; see, for example, Cohen-Tannoudji (1977, Vol. II, p. 1130 ff.).
[26]It is not obvious from its position in the periodic table that carbon has four electrons that can participate in covalent bonds. For a quantum mechanical discussion see, for example, Davydov (1965, pp. 489–490) or Cohen-Tannoudji (1977, pp. 854–855).

[as in Eq. (9.3.10)] which depends on the positions $r_1^n, \ldots, r_N^n$ of the atoms' nuclei. With this theoretical background for the existence of this function, but faced with the computational difficulties of calculating its specific definition from basic principles, we are frequently led to postulating empirical potentials. When discussing empirical potentials we write $r_l^n = r_l$ and, with the adiabatic approximation in mind, regard the atoms as mass points at the positions formerly ascribed to their nuclei. This is the viewpoint we adopted throughout Part 1. The empirical potentials are then formulated to have the characteristics indicated by the type of atoms being considered. Some of the characteristics of importance and their relation to the categories of interatomic bonding just enumerated are as follows:

(a)   Two or Many-Body Interaction

An interatomic potential $V(r_1, \ldots, r_N)$ is said to be a two-body potential if it can be written in the form

$$V(r_1, \ldots, r_N) = \sum_{\substack{l, l'=1 \\ l > l'}}^{N} \varphi_{ll'}(r_l, r_{l'}). \qquad (9.6.1)$$

A many-body potential is one that cannot be decomposed in this fashion. Of the four bonding classes, it appears that only the Van der Waals interaction can be represented accurately by a two-body potential. However, ionic interactions are also frequently modeled by two-body Coulomb potentials as though each ion corresponded to a spherically symmetric charge distribution. This approximation (sometimes called the rigid ion approximation) neglects the change in interaction between an ion pair at fixed separation, due to the change in the polarization of their charge distributions by the approach of a third atom. This is shown schematically in Figure 9.4 where it is seen that the interaction between ions A and B will depend on the position of ion C. To account for these difficulties, models[27] for ionic interaction have been developed in which each ion is described both by its position r_l and by its polarization h_l. With this expanded description for each ion, we may return to a two-body potential of the form $\varphi_{ll'}(r_l, r_{l'}; h_l, h_{l'})$. The potential energy function V for the full system is obtained by summing these two-body potentials as in Eq. (9.6.1) so that $V = V(r_1, \ldots, r_N; h_1, \ldots, h_N)$. Note that this inclusion of a partial description of the electron charge distribution is still within the framework of the adiabatic approximation. There is no inertia associated with polarization change and the values of h_l for a given set of $(r_1, \ldots, r_N)$ are determined by solution of the $3N$ equations

$$\nabla_{h_l} V = 0$$

---

[27]These are referred to as "shell models" because the electron charge is regarded figuratively as distributed uniformly on a spherical shell, which can be displaced relative to the positive nucleus in order to represent the ion polarization. For discussions of the shell model see Cochran (1973); its quantum mechanical foundation is studied by Niedermann and Wagner (1976).

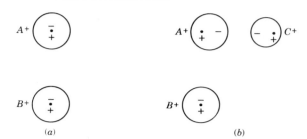

Figure 9.4 (*a*) Two positively charged interacting ions A^+ and B^+. (*b*) Approach of third ion C^+ changes polarization of A^+ and affects interaction between A^+ and B^+.

where $\nabla_{\mathbf{h}_l}$ is the three-dimensional gradient with respect to the components of $\mathbf{h}_l$. These $3N$ equations may be used to eliminate the variables $\mathbf{h}_l$ from V, thus returning to a potential which depends solely on the atomic positions $\mathbf{r}_l$ as in the usual form of the adiabatic approximation. However, when this is done, the two-body character of the interaction will be lost.

Covalent bonding is, in general,[28] not two-body in character since the potential energy of interaction depends on the relative orientation of all of the atoms that share localized electron distributions between them. A good example is provided by the bonding in a polymer such as polyethylene (Section 5.3). There, the interaction energy for a carbon atom depends on the position of its two neighboring carbon atoms along the backbone chain and on the positions of the hydrogen atoms which form its side group (see Figure 5.4). This sensitivity to the relative positions of covalently bonded atoms is sometimes described in terms of the presence of "bond-bending" forces in addition to "bond-stretching" forces; however, it must be recognized that the description of bond bending requires the designation of the positions of three atoms.

In metallic bonding the energy of the delocalized electrons will increase upon a decrease in the volume of the crystal. This increase is a consequence of both the Heisenberg uncertainty relation and the Pauli exclusion principle; a decrease in uncertainty of electron position must be accompanied by an increase in the uncertainty of its momentum and, therefore, in its expected kinetic energy, and when many electrons occupy the same region, the exclusion principle, in effect, assigns to each electron only a fraction of that volume.[29] For this reason, metallic bonding is frequently modeled by two-body potentials between the positive ions plus a volume-dependent energy for the delocalized electrons; therefore, the overall interaction is not two-body.

(b) Central or Noncentral Forces

If the force exerted by atom l' on atom l acts always along the line connecting these two atoms, the force is said to be central.

---

[28]An exception occurs when covalent bonding occurs between only two atoms, as in the H_2 molecule.

[29]See, for example, Weisskopf (1975, p. 606).

If the force law for a collection of atoms is derived from a general many-body potential $V(\mathbf{r}_1, \ldots, \mathbf{r}_N)$, then, while the force $\mathbf{f}_l$ on a given atom is clearly defined by the appropriate partial derivative of V evaluated at $(\mathbf{r}_1, \ldots, \mathbf{r}_N)$, it cannot be described as a force exerted by another atom l' on l or by a sum of such forces. Only if the potential is two-body, Eq. (9.6.1), is such a decomposition possible and, therefore, it is only for this category of potentials that the concept of central forces is defined.

On the other hand, a two-body potential $\varphi_{ll'}(\mathbf{r}_l, \mathbf{r}_{l'})$ is a scalar function with vector arguments. As such, it must be expressible in the form

$$\varphi_{ll'}(\mathbf{r}_l, \mathbf{r}_{l'}) = \varphi_{ll'}(|\mathbf{r}_l - \mathbf{r}_{l'}|) \tag{9.6.2}$$

and therefore must correspond to a central force law.

It follows that noncentral force laws cannot be derived from interatomic potentials of the form $V(\mathbf{r}_1, \ldots, \mathbf{r}_N)$ in which atoms are modeled as structureless mass points completely described by their position $\mathbf{r}_l$. We consider next the possibility of defining two-body noncentral forces directly in terms of vector-valued functions, without recourse to a potential energy function.

Toward this end consider a collection of atoms which interact with a two-body force law defined by the relations

$$\mathbf{f}_{ll'} = \mathbf{H}(\mathbf{r}_l, \mathbf{r}_{l'}), \quad l, l' = 1, \ldots, N. \tag{9.6.3}$$

[To keep the notation simple, we are considering a collection of like atoms. The same argument applies to a collection containing several types of atoms; in this case the vector function in Eq. (9.6.3) would be denoted by $\mathbf{H}_{ll'}(\mathbf{r}_l, \mathbf{r}_{l'})$.] If we wish this interatomic force law to apply to any arbitrary configuration of the atoms, then it follows that it must, in fact, describe a central force law.[30] To see this, consider two configurations of the collection of atoms, denoted by configurations (a) and (b), which differ only by a rigid body motion, that is, all interatomic distances are the same. Consider first the case in which configurations (a) and (b) differ by a pure translation corresponding to the vector $\mathbf{c}$. Then,

$$\mathbf{f}_{ll'}^{(a)} = \mathbf{H}(\mathbf{r}_l, \mathbf{r}_{l'})$$

$$\mathbf{f}_{ll'}^{(b)} = \mathbf{H}(\mathbf{r}_l + \mathbf{c}, \mathbf{r}_{l'} + \mathbf{c}). \tag{9.6.4}$$

Since the vector function $\mathbf{H}$ describes an interatomic force law, we require $\mathbf{f}_{ll'}^{(a)} = \mathbf{f}_{ll'}^{(b)}$. Therefore, $\mathbf{H}(\mathbf{r}_l, \mathbf{r}_{l'}) = \mathbf{H}(\mathbf{r}_l + \mathbf{c}, \mathbf{r}_{l'} + \mathbf{c})$ for an arbitrary vector $\mathbf{c}$. Take $\mathbf{c} = -\mathbf{r}_{l'}$. Then, $\mathbf{H}(\mathbf{r}_l, \mathbf{r}_{l'}) = \mathbf{H}(\mathbf{r}_l - \mathbf{r}_{l'}, 0)$ and can be rewritten as $\mathbf{H}(\mathbf{r}_{ll'})$ where $\mathbf{r}_{ll'} = \mathbf{r}_l - \mathbf{r}_{l'}$.

---

[30] The argument parallels the treatment of the principle of material indifference in continuum mechanics (see Truesdell and Noll, 1965).

Consider next a rigid body motion relating configurations (a) and (b) which corresponds to a rotation, that is,

$$\mathbf{r}_{ll'}^{(b)} = \mathbf{Q}\mathbf{r}_{ll'}^{(a)} \tag{9.6.5}$$

where $\mathbf{Q}$ is an arbitrary orthogonal transformation. Again, if $\mathbf{f}_{ll'}$ has the physical significance of an interatomic force law, it must rotate with the body (Figure 9.5), so that $\mathbf{f}_{ll'}^{(b)} = \mathbf{Q}\mathbf{f}_{ll'}^{(a)}$. But $\mathbf{f}_{ll'}^{(b)} = \mathbf{H}(\mathbf{r}_{ll'}^{(b)}) = \mathbf{H}(\mathbf{Q}\mathbf{r}_{ll'}^{(a)})$ and $\mathbf{f}_{ll'}^{(a)} = \mathbf{H}(\mathbf{r}_{ll'}^{(a)})$. Therefore,

$$\mathbf{H}(\mathbf{Q}\mathbf{r}_{ll'}^{(a)}) = \mathbf{Q}\mathbf{H}(\mathbf{r}_{ll'}^{(a)}) \tag{9.6.7}$$

and this is a functional relation that $\mathbf{H}(\mathbf{r}_{ll'})$ must satisfy for arbitrary $\mathbf{Q}$. Let $\mathbf{Q}_r$ be the special orthogonal transformation that corresponds to a rotation through an arbitrary angle about $\mathbf{r}_{ll'}^{(a)}$. The only vectors $\mathbf{Q}_r$ leaves invariant are vectors parallel to $\mathbf{r}_{ll'}^{(a)}$. From the preceding considerations

$$\mathbf{f}_{ll'}^{(b)} = \mathbf{Q}_r\mathbf{f}_{ll'}^{(a)} = \mathbf{H}(\mathbf{Q}_r\mathbf{r}_{ll'}^{(a)}) = \mathbf{H}(\mathbf{r}_{ll'}^{(a)}) = \mathbf{f}_{ll'}^{(a)}. \tag{9.6.8}$$

That is, the force $\mathbf{f}_{ll'}$ is unchanged by $\mathbf{Q}_r$ and must, therefore, be parallel to $\mathbf{r}_{ll'}$, that is, it is a central force. It is then readily shown in the usual way that the force must be derivable from a two-body potential.

Two points about this demonstration of the equivalence of a two-body force law to one derivable from a two-body potential should be noted:

1 The demonstration is applicable only to a general force law, that is, one regarded as valid for arbitrarily large displacements of the atoms. It does not apply to a restricted theory specifically framed to be limited to the treatment of small atomic displacements from a stated reference configuration. (A similar situation arises in continuum mechanics. The theory of anisotropic linear elasticity does not violate the principle of material indifference because only infinitesimal rotations are permitted from the reference state; an analogous theory for anisotropic fluids with restrictions on the magnitude of rotations

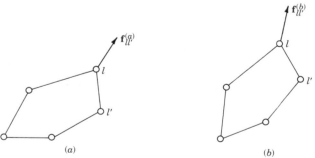

(a) (b)

Figure 9.5 Atoms interacting with two-body force law subjected to a rigid body motion.

would not be useful.) The demonstration also does not apply to a restricted two-dimensional theory in which a planar set of atoms, with the atomic motion constrained to lie in the given plane, is treated.[31]

2 The demonstration applies to force laws of the form $\mathbf{f}_{ll'} = \mathbf{H}(\mathbf{r}_l, \mathbf{r}_{l'})$ in which atoms are regarded as structureless mass points, described only by their position. It does not apply to the case in which atoms are regarded as having additional internal structure.

(c) Long- or Short-Range Forces

This characteristic is most readily defined for two-body force laws where it refers to the rapidity of the decay of f, the magnitude of the interatomic force, with r, the interatomic distance. For Van der Waals' bonding, $f \sim r^{-7}$ and the interaction is short ranged. For ionic bonding, on the other hand, $f \sim r^{-2}$, and the interaction is long ranged.

For a force law described by a many-body potential $V(\mathbf{r}_1, \ldots, \mathbf{r}_N)$, this characteristic may be described in the following way: The force on an arbitrary atom is

$$\mathbf{f}_l = - \nabla_l V(\mathbf{r}_1, \ldots, \mathbf{r}_N).$$

Consider all of the atomic positions, $\mathbf{r}_{l'}$, $l' \neq l$, confined to a sphere and $\mathbf{r}_l$ outside this sphere at a minimum distance d from its boundary. Then, the long- or short-range character of the force law refers to the decay of $|\mathbf{f}_l|$ with d.

[31]An example is provided by the work of Sanders (1962) on a two-dimensional atomistic model of a crystal dislocation.

CHAPTER TEN

Quantum Statistical Effects

10.1 INTRODUCTION

Our discussions in Part 1 of the role of temperature in the elastic behavior of crystalline and polymeric solids, and in rate processes in solids, were based on classical statistical mechanics. To gain an understanding of the range of validity of these treatments, we turn in this chapter to a study of quantum statistical mechanics, focusing on those portions particularly relevant to our areas of concern.

We begin in Section 10.2 with a discussion of the basic principles of quantum statistical mechanics. Our treatment is brief and draws on the close analogies with the classical subject, which was treated in greater detail in Chapters 2 and 3. The development of the quantum canonical ensemble follows the information theory approach of Jaynes (1957).

Quantum statistical effects in crystal elasticity are discussed in Section 10.3 and those in polymer elasticity are discussed in Section 10.4. The final three sections are directed toward quantum effects in rate processes in solids. There are several different approaches to this subject, which is one of much current research activity. We describe one approach, based on coherent states, which serves to illustrate the twofold role of quantum mechanics in rate processes in modifying both the statistics and the dynamics of the system undergoing a transition.

10.2 QUANTUM STATISTICAL MECHANICS

In order to have a specific physical situation in mind, we start our discussion of quantum statistical mechanics with the example of a crystal subjected to an imposed deformation and in interaction with a heat bath, the same case treated in detail on the basis of classical statistical mechanics in Chapter 4.

As discussed in Section 4.3 (see Figure 4.3), we focus our attention on an interior portion I of the crystal; its atoms will be treated explicitly on the basis of statistical mechanics, with the remainder of the crystal, designated by E, regarded as heat bath. The Hamiltonian of I takes the form [see Eq. (4.3.12)]

$$H(\mathbf{r}, \mathbf{p}; a_{iL}) = \frac{1}{2} \sum_{l \in I} \frac{|\mathbf{p}(l, t)|^2}{m(l)} + V(\mathbf{r}; a_{iL}) \tag{10.2.1}$$

where a_{iL} is the imposed deformation matrix and V is the potential energy of interaction of the atoms of I with each other and with the atoms of E_{in} (the interacting layer of E, see Figure 4.3) regarded as fixed at the deformed lattice sites. There is, therefore, the additional interaction energy $\Delta V_{I,E}(\mathbf{r}, \mathbf{r}')$ between I and E, defined in Eq. (4.3.9), which is due to the thermal motion of the atoms of E in the vicinity of their deformed lattice sites. Here, as in Section 4.3, $\mathbf{r}$ denotes the set of coordinates of all of the atoms of I, and $\mathbf{r}'$ those of E.

Let $\psi(\mathbf{r}, t)$ be the wave function describing the state of I at time t. Its time evolution is governed by the equation

$$(H + H')\psi = i\hbar \frac{\partial \psi}{\partial t} \tag{10.2.2}$$

where H is the operator corresponding to the Hamiltonian H defined in Eq. (10.2.1) and H' corresponds[1] to the thermal interaction $\Delta V_{I,E}(\mathbf{r}, \mathbf{r}')$.

Let $\varphi_n(\mathbf{r}; a_{iL})$, $E_n(a_{iL})$, $n = 0, 1, 2, \ldots$ be the eigenfunctions and eigenvalues[2] of H,

$$H\varphi_n = E_n\varphi_n, \quad n = 0, 1, 2, \ldots. \tag{10.2.3}$$

In the absence of any interaction with a heat bath (H' = 0), the general solution to Eq. (10.2.2) could be written in the form (Section 8.7) of Eq. (8.7.11),

$$\psi = \sum_{n=0}^{\infty} c_n \varphi_n e^{-iE_n t/\hbar}, \tag{10.2.4}$$

with constant expansion coefficients c_n. With the presence of nonzero interaction, we seek a solution of the same form but now with $c_n = c_n(t)$. By substitution of Eq. (10.2.4) into (10.2.2) and use of Eq. (10.2.3) we find

$$\sum_{n=0}^{\infty} c_n H' \varphi_n e^{-iE_n t/\hbar} = i\hbar \sum_{n=0}^{\infty} \dot{c}_n \varphi_n e^{-iE_n t/\hbar}. \tag{10.2.5}$$

---

[1] At this point in the discussion we regard the variables $\mathbf{r}'$ as specified functions of time. A further assumption regarding H' will be made subsequently.

[2] We are using the convention that the index n denotes distinct eigenfunctions; an m-fold degenerate eigenvalue is indicated by the notation $E_n = E_{n+1} = \cdots = E_{n+m-1}$.

We take the inner product of both sides of this equation with φ_m and find

$$\dot{c}_m = \frac{-i}{\hbar} \sum_{n=0}^{\infty} H'_{mn} c_n e^{i(E_m - E_n)t/\hbar} \qquad (10.2.6)$$

where we have used the orthonormality of the set φ_n and where

$$H'_{mn} = (\varphi_m, H'\varphi_n). \qquad (10.2.7)$$

Consider next some physical property of the interior crystal I described by a phase function $F(q, p)$ from the classical viewpoint and with F the corresponding quantum operator. At time t, with the crystal I in the state $\psi(\mathbf{r}, t)$, the expected value of this property is

$$\langle F \rangle(t) = (\psi, F\psi)$$

$$= \sum_{n, m=0}^{\infty} c_n^* c_m F_{nm} e^{i(E_n - E_m)t/\hbar} \qquad (10.2.8)$$

where we have used Eq. (10.2.4) and where

$$F_{nm} = (\varphi_n, F\varphi_m). \qquad (10.2.9)$$

As in classical statistical mechanics, we are not interested in the time-dependent $\langle F \rangle(t)$, which fluctuates very rapidly with respect to usual macroscopic time scales, but rather in its long-time average, which we denote here by double carats. That is,

$$\langle\langle F \rangle\rangle = \lim_{t \to \infty} \frac{1}{t} \int_0^t \langle F \rangle(\tau) \, d\tau$$

$$= \lim_{t \to \infty} \frac{1}{t} \int_0^t \sum_{n, m=0}^{\infty} c_n^* c_m F_{nm} e^{i(E_n - E_m)\tau/\hbar} \, d\tau. \qquad (10.2.10)$$

Consider next the nature of time dependence of the terms appearing under the integral in this equation. From the harmonic approximation to the Hamiltonian H, we may estimate that $E_n \sim n\hbar\omega$ where ω is of the order of lattice vibration frequencies. On the other hand, we see from Eq. (10.2.6) that $\dot{c}_n(t)$ decreases with the strength of the interaction H' between the crystal I and its heat bath. Therefore the nature of the time dependence of the terms in Eq. (10.2.10) is as shown schematically in Figure 10.1, and, for sufficiently weak interaction,[3] cancellation of the rapidly oscillatory terms will result in the

---

[3] As in the classical case, it is the assumption of weak interaction which eliminates the need for knowledge of the detailed motion $\mathbf{r}'(t)$ of the heat bath atoms.

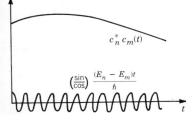

Figure 10.1 Schematic representation of time dependence of terms in Eq. (10.2.10).

integral having negligible value except for $n = m$. This leads to the result

$$\langle\langle F\rangle\rangle = \lim_{t \to \infty} \frac{1}{t} \int_0^t \sum_{n=0}^{\infty} |c_n|^2 F_{nn} d\tau,$$

$$= \sum_{n=0}^{\infty} \left(\lim_{t \to \infty} \frac{1}{t} \int_0^t |c_n|^2 d\tau \right) F_{nn},$$

or,

$$\langle\langle F\rangle\rangle = \sum_{n=0}^{\infty} \widehat{|c_n|^2}\langle F\rangle_n \tag{10.2.11}$$

where $\widehat{|c_n|^2}$ is the time average of $|c_n|^2$ and

$$\langle F\rangle_n = F_{nn} = (\varphi_n, F\varphi_n) \tag{10.2.12}$$

is the expected value of F when the system is in the state φ_n.

Since $\sum_{n=0}^{\infty}|c_n|^2 = 1$, [Eq. (8.7.10)], we can interpret $\widehat{|c_n|^2} = p_n$ as either the fraction of time that the system spends in the state φ_n or as the probability that the system is found in state φ_n at an arbitrary instant, and we can rewrite Eq. (10.2.11) as[4]

$$\langle\langle F\rangle\rangle = \sum_{n=0}^{\infty} p_n\langle F\rangle_n. \tag{10.2.13}$$

Equation (10.2.13) is the quantum analog of the basic Eq. (2.4.5) for classical

---

[4] Note that the physical picture which we have used as a basis for these calculations involves the state of the system $\psi(\mathbf{r}, t)$ varying continuously, as in Eq. (10.2.4), through states that are time-dependent superpositions of the energy states φ_n. It is only the cancellations that occur in the integrals of Eq. (10.2.10) which lead to the simple result of Eq. (10.2.13) and the possible interpretation of p_n as the fraction of time that the system spends in state φ_n. Particularly relevant here is the following quotation from Schrödinger (1946, p. 90): "Taken literally, this [interpretation of p_n] would mean that a physical process, even when no observing 'subject' interferes with it, consists of continual sequences of fits and jerks, the successive transfers of energy parcels between microsystems. This view, when given serious thought, cannot pass for anything but a sometimes convenient metaphor."

statistical mechanics which expresses the phase average $\bar{F}$ of any phase function $F(q, p)$ in terms of a probability distribution function $\rho(q, p)$. Here, the latter function is replaced by the set of discrete probabilities p_n. In classical statistical mechanics the statistical aspect of the calculation enters only through the function $\rho(q, p)$ and is, for the canonical distribution, a reflection of the information that is missing because of the incomplete specification of the interaction between the system and its heat bath. This basis for statistical reasoning is present in the quantum case as well and is represented by the probabilities p_n. However, there is also present the statistical aspect, which is fundamental to quantum mechanics (Section 8.3), and which limits us to the computation of the expected value $\langle F \rangle_n$ in state φ_n in place of the deterministic phase function value $F(q, p)$ at point (q, p) in classical phase space. The twofold role of statistics in quantum statistical mechanics is emphasized by the double-carat notation of Eq. (10.2.13).

Canonical Distribution of p_n

We turn next to the determination of the probabilities p_n for the canonical ensemble, that is, for a system in contact with a heat bath. The analogous derivation in the classical case was carried through in Chapter 2 by considering the given system as a small component of a large isolated system. Here, we will follow Jaynes (1957) and calculate the value of p_n as a problem in statistical inference to be solved by use of the principle of maximum uncertainty outlined in Section 3.12.

We will confine our attention to the case of a strain ensemble in which a set of kinematical parameters $(\mathscr{A}_1, \ldots, \mathscr{A}_\nu) = \mathscr{A}$ is imposed. The stress ensemble is treated in an analogous fashion. As we have seen, the prescribed values of the kinematical parameters serve to describe the deterministic portion of the effect of the heat bath on the system. It is also necessary to specify one parameter that characterizes, sufficiently well for the purpose of a macroscopic thermodynamics description, the effect of the thermal motion of the heat bath atoms on the system. In the classical derivation the common temperature of the system and the heat bath was used for this purpose; here, it is convenient to choose the internal energy U or, equivalently, the mean energy $\langle\langle H \rangle\rangle$ of the system.

Then, the determination of the probabilities p_n on the basis of the principle of maximum uncertainty requires the maximization of the uncertainty [Eq. (3.12.18)]

$$\mathscr{H}(p_1, p_2, \ldots) = -K \sum_{n=0}^{\infty} p_n \log p_n \qquad (10.2.14)$$

subject to the constraints

$$\sum_{n=0}^{\infty} p_n = 1 \qquad (10.2.15)$$

and, by use of Eqs. (10.2.3) and (10.2.13),

$$\sum_{n=0}^{\infty} p_n E_n = \langle\langle \mathsf{H} \rangle\rangle. \qquad (10.2.16)$$

The calculation is performed by use of the technique of Lagrange multipliers. That is, we consider the maximization of $\mathscr{H} - \lambda\Sigma_{n=0}^{\infty} p_n - \mu\Sigma_{n=0}^{\infty} p_n E_n$, with λ and μ Lagrange multipliers or, what is notationally more convenient, we use $\lambda - K$ and μ as multipliers and consider the equations

$$\frac{\partial}{\partial p_m}\left[-K\sum_{n=0}^{\infty} p_n \log p_n - (\lambda - K)\sum_{n=0}^{\infty} p_n - \mu\sum_{n=0}^{\infty} p_n E_n \right] = 0,$$

$$m = 0, 1, 2, \dots . \qquad (10.2.17)$$

The solutions are found to be

$$p_n = \exp - \left(\frac{\lambda + \mu E_n}{K} \right)$$

or

$$p_n = \exp\left(\frac{\psi - E_n}{\theta} \right); \qquad (10.2.18)$$

we have introduced the new notation $-\lambda/K = \psi/\theta$ and $\mu/K = 1/\theta$ in order to emphasize that the quantum canonical distribution thus arrived at is the discrete analog of the classical canonical distribution [Eq. (3.1.1)].

From this point on, the discussion relating the parameters ψ and θ to macroscopic thermodynamics parallels closely the discussion of the classical case in Chapter 3, the major change being the replacement of integrals by sums in the quantum case. For this reason we will omit details and only summarize the results.

As in the classical case it is possible by the consideration of suitable thought experiments to make the identifications $\theta = kT$ and $\psi = F(\mathscr{A}, T)$, where F is the Helmholtz free energy expressed as function of $\mathscr{A} = (\mathscr{A}_1, \dots, \mathscr{A}_\nu)$, the imposed kinematical parameters, and temperature. Then, the probabilities p_n take the form

$$p_n(\mathscr{A}, T) = \exp\left\{ \frac{F(\mathscr{A}, T) - E_n(\mathscr{A})}{kT} \right\}. \qquad (10.2.19)$$

The normalization requirement

$$\sum_{n=0}^{\infty} p_n = 1 \qquad (10.2.20)$$

leads, as in the classical case, to the result that

$$F(\mathscr{A}, T) = -kT \log Z(\mathscr{A}, T) \tag{10.2.21}$$

where

$$Z(\mathscr{A}, T) = \sum_{\substack{n \\ \text{states}}} \exp\left[-\frac{E_n(\mathscr{A})}{kT} \right] \tag{10.2.22}$$

is the quantum partition function. We have emphasized in our notation that the summation index n refers to the distinct quantum states of the system so that the same energy value $E_n = E_{n+1} = \cdots = E_{n+m-1}$ appears m times in the sum for the case of m-fold degeneracy. It is also convenient to group these terms, denoting distinct energy levels by $E_{n'}$ and letting $g_{n'}$ be the degeneracy of the n' level. Then, the quantum partition function of Eq. (10.2.22) may be written as

$$Z(\mathscr{A}, T) = \sum_{\substack{n' \\ \text{levels}}} g_{n'} \exp\left[-\frac{E_{n'}(\mathscr{A})}{kT} \right]. \tag{10.2.23}$$

The close relationship between the quantum partition function, as defined in Eq. (10.2.23), and the classical partition function, as given in Eq. (3.6.19), is apparent. From a computational viewpoint, therefore, the difference between using quantum or classical statistical mechanics to compute a macroscopic property is simply a question of using the appropriate partition function. Once this is done, the identification with macroscopic thermodynamics is made by means of Eq. (10.2.21) which applies equally well to both cases as do the other relations between the partition function and thermodynamic functions listed in Section 3.9. As discussed there, it is also convenient on occasion to utilize thermodynamic terminology and the relations of Section 3.9 for the discussion of small systems. Alternatively, thermodynamic terminology can be bypassed and mean quantities computed directly in terms of the partition function by use, for example, of the quantum equivalents of Eqs. (3.8.7) and (3.8.12). In order to show the close relation between the classical and quantum formalisms and to indicate the nature of the changes in going from one to the other. we repeat in Table 10.1, pp. 380–381, the classical derivation of Eqs. (3.8.7) and (3.8.12) and the corresponding quantum derivation, leading to the corresponding Eqs. (10.2.28) and (10.2.29), in parallel computations.

Density Matrix Formulation

The quantum statistical mechanical formalism for computing the expected value $\langle\langle F \rangle\rangle$ of an observable F as developed in this section for the canonical ensemble may be summarized as follows:

$$\langle\langle F\rangle\rangle = \sum_{\substack{n \\ \text{states}}} p_n \langle F\rangle_n$$

$$= Z^{-1} \sum_{\substack{n \\ \text{states}}} e^{-\beta E_n}(\varphi_n, F\varphi_n) \qquad (10.2.24)$$

where $\beta = (kT)^{-1}$, Z is the partition function defined in Eq. (10.2.22), $\varphi_n(\mathbf{r})$ are the eigenfunctions of H, the Hamiltonian operator of the system, and E_n are the corresponding eigenvalues.

It is convenient for some purposes to restate this formulation in terms of a function $\rho(\mathbf{r}', \mathbf{r})$ defined as

$$\rho(\mathbf{r}', \mathbf{r}) = Z^{-1} \sum_{\substack{n \\ \text{states}}} \varphi_n(\mathbf{r}')\varphi_n^*(\mathbf{r})e^{-\beta E_n}. \qquad (10.2.25)$$

The calculation of $\langle\langle F\rangle\rangle$ by means of Eq. (10.2.24) may be described in terms of $\rho(\mathbf{r}', \mathbf{r})$ by the following prescription: Compute $F\rho(\mathbf{r}', \mathbf{r})$ where the operator F acts only on the variable $\mathbf{r}'$. Then set $\mathbf{r}' = \mathbf{r}$ and integrate over all values of $\mathbf{r}$. The result is $\langle\langle F\rangle\rangle$. Symbolically,

$$\langle\langle F\rangle\rangle = \int_{-\infty}^{\infty} [F\rho(\mathbf{r}', \mathbf{r})]_{\mathbf{r}'=\mathbf{r}} \, d\mathbf{r}. \qquad (10.2.26)$$

The function $\rho(\mathbf{r}', \mathbf{r})$ is known as the *density matrix*[5] for the system. It is important because it contains within it all of the information necessary for the computation of the expected value of any observable of the system. We shall make use of it in Section 10.6 to provide another interpretation of the canonical ensemble for a harmonic oscillator.

Partition Function for Systems in Weak Interaction

It is easily verified that the product relation [Eq. (3.6.22)] for the classical partition function for systems in weak interaction applies to the quantum case as well. Let $H_{A+B} = H_A + H_B$ be the operators corresponding to the Hamiltonians of Eq. (3.6.21), φ_n^A, E_n^A, the eigenfunctions and eigenvalues of H_A, and φ_m^B, E_m^B the eigenfunctions and eigenvalues of H_B. Then,

$$H_{A+B}(\varphi_n^A \varphi_m^B) = (E_n^A + E_m^B)\varphi_n^A \varphi_m^B \qquad (10.2.27)$$

---

[5] The terminology follows from a more abstract formulation of the concept; see, for example, Cohen-Tannoudji (1977). We are paralleling the simpler description given by Feynman and Hibbs (1965, p. 273).

Table 10.1 Comparison of Classical and Quantum Calculations

	Classical

1 System described by Hamiltonian $H(x_1,\ldots,x_n,p_1,\ldots,p_n;\mathscr{A}_1,\ldots,\mathscr{A}_\nu)$, a function of $2n$ variables $(x_1,\ldots,x_n,p_1,\ldots,p_n)=(x,p)$ with ν kinematical parameters, $(\mathscr{A}_1,\ldots,\mathscr{A}_\nu)=\mathscr{A}$.

2 Energy of system when it is in microstate (x,p) with parameters $\mathscr{A}$ is value of function H at that point, that is, $H(x,p;\mathscr{A})$.

3 Let $\mathscr{F}_\alpha{}^m$ be force conjugate to $\mathscr{A}_\alpha$ when system is in state (x,p). We wish to determine the function $\mathscr{F}_\alpha{}^m(x,p;\mathscr{A})$.

4 Consider system in a fixed microstate (x,p) and give kinematical parameters a differential increment $d\mathscr{A}_\alpha$, $=1,\ldots,\nu$.

5

$$dH = \sum_{\alpha=1}^{\nu} \left.\frac{\partial H}{\partial \mathscr{A}_\alpha}\right|_{(x,p)} d\mathscr{A}_\alpha = \sum_{\alpha=1}^{\nu} \mathscr{F}_\alpha{}^m d\mathscr{A}_\alpha.$$

Therefore, $\mathscr{F}_\alpha{}^m = \dfrac{\partial H}{\partial \mathscr{A}_\alpha}$.

6 $Z(\mathscr{A},T)=\int_\Gamma \exp\,[-\beta H(x,p;\mathscr{A})]\,dx\,dp.$

7

$$-kT\frac{\partial}{\partial\mathscr{A}_\alpha}\log Z = Z^{-1}\int_\Gamma \frac{\partial H}{\partial\mathscr{A}_\alpha}\exp(-\beta H)\,dx\,dp$$

$$= \int_\Gamma \mathscr{F}_\alpha{}^m \rho\,dx\,dp = \langle\mathscr{F}_\alpha{}^m\rangle. \tag{3.8.7}$$

8

$$-\frac{\partial}{\partial\beta}\log Z = Z^{-1}\int_\Gamma H\exp(-\beta H)\,dx\,dp$$

$$= \int_\Gamma H\rho\,dx\,dp = \langle H\rangle. \tag{3.8.12}$$

Table 10.1 continued

Quantum

---

1 System described by differential operator H which acts on space of functions $\psi(x_1, \ldots, x_n) = \psi(x)$. $H = H(x_1, \ldots, x_n, \frac{\hbar}{i}\frac{\partial}{\partial x_1}, \ldots, \frac{\hbar}{i}\frac{\partial}{\partial x_n}; \mathscr{A}_1, \ldots, \mathscr{A}_\nu)$.

2 Expected energy when system is in (normalized) state ψ is $\langle H \rangle = (\psi, H\psi)$.

3 Let $\langle F_\alpha^m \rangle$ be expected value of force conjugate to $\mathscr{A}_\alpha$ when system is in state $\psi(x)$. We wish to determine the operator F_α^m.

4 Consider system in fixed state $\psi(x)$ and give kinematical parameters a differential increment $d\mathscr{A}_\alpha$, $\alpha = 1, \ldots, \nu$.

5

$$d\langle H \rangle = \sum_{\alpha=1}^{\nu} \left(\psi, \frac{\partial H}{\partial \mathscr{A}_\alpha} \psi \right) d\mathscr{A}_\alpha = \sum_{\alpha=1}^{\nu} \langle F_\alpha^m \rangle \, d\mathscr{A}_\alpha.$$

Therefore, $F_\alpha^m = \dfrac{\partial H}{\partial \mathscr{A}_\alpha}$.

6 $Z(\mathscr{A}, T) = \sum_{\substack{n \\ \text{states}}} \exp - \beta E_n(\mathscr{A})$ where $E_n(\mathscr{A})$ are eigenvalues of H corresponding to normalized eigenstates $\varphi_n(x; \mathscr{A})$.

$$E_n = (\varphi_n, H\varphi_n)$$

$$\frac{\partial E_n}{\partial \mathscr{A}_\alpha} = \left(\frac{\partial \varphi_n}{\partial \mathscr{A}_\alpha}, H\varphi_n \right) + \left(\varphi_n, H\frac{\partial \varphi_n}{\partial \mathscr{A}_\alpha} \right) + \left(\varphi_n, \frac{\partial H}{\partial \mathscr{A}_\alpha} \varphi_n \right)$$

$$= \left(\varphi_n, \frac{\partial H}{\partial \mathscr{A}_\alpha} \varphi_n \right) = \langle F_\alpha^m \rangle_n.$$

[Sum of first two terms vanish as in Eqs. (9.4.7) and (9.4.10).]

7

$$-kT\frac{\partial}{\partial \mathscr{A}_\alpha} \log Z = Z^{-1} \sum_{\substack{n \\ \text{states}}} \frac{\partial E_n}{\partial \mathscr{A}_\alpha} \exp(-\beta E_n)$$

$$= \sum_{\substack{n \\ \text{states}}} \langle F_\alpha^m \rangle_n p_n = \langle\langle F_\alpha^m \rangle\rangle. \qquad (10.2.28)$$

8

$$-\frac{\partial}{\partial \beta} \log Z = Z^{-1} \sum_{\substack{n \\ \text{states}}} E_n \exp(-\beta E_n)$$

$$= \sum_{\substack{n \\ \text{states}}} \langle H \rangle_n p_n = \langle\langle H \rangle\rangle. \qquad (10.2.29)$$

---

and $\varphi_n^A \varphi_m^B$, $n, m = 0, 1, 2 \ldots$ are a complete set of eigenfunctions of H_{A+B} with corresponding energies $E_n^A + E_m^B$. Therefore,

$$Z_{A+B} = \sum_{\substack{n, m \\ \text{states}}} \exp - \frac{\left(E_n^A + E_m^B \right)}{kT} = \sum_{\substack{n \\ \text{states}}} \exp - \frac{E_n^A}{kT} \sum_{\substack{m \\ \text{states}}} \exp - \frac{E_m^B}{kT}$$

$$= Z_A Z_B. \tag{10.2.30}$$

In some cases, the spacings between energy levels in one system may be much smaller than in the other, for example $\Delta E^B \ll \Delta E^A$. Therefore, there will exist temperature ranges for which $\Delta E^B/kT \ll 1$, so that the partition function Z_B may be replaced by its classical expression,[6] while $\Delta E^A/kT$ remains sufficiently large so that quantum statistics must still be employed. In this case, we may write the partition function in mixed quantum–classical form as

$$Z_{A+B} = \int_{\Gamma_B} \sum_{\substack{n \\ \text{states of } A}} \exp\left[- \frac{E_n^A}{kT} \right] \exp\left[- \frac{H_B(q, p)}{kT} \right] dq_B \, dp_B.$$

$$\tag{10.2.31}$$

We have included the terms involving E_n^A under the integral sign since in some situations, for example, where use is made of the adiabatic approximation, $E_n^A = E_n^A(q_B)$.

Partition Function for Harmonic Oscillator

For the harmonic oscillator (Section 8.9) the energy levels are $E_n = (n + \frac{1}{2})\hbar\omega$, $n = 0, 1, 2, \ldots$ [Eq. (8.9.24)] and are all nondegenerate. Therefore, its partition function is

$$Z_{qu} = e^{-\hbar\omega/2kT} \sum_{n=0}^{\infty} e^{-n\hbar\omega/kT} = \frac{e^{-\hbar\omega/2kT}}{1 - e^{-\hbar\omega/kT}} = \left(2 \sinh \frac{\hbar\omega}{2kT} \right)^{-1},$$

$$\tag{10.2.32}$$

where we have written Z_{qu} to emphasize that the partition function has been computed on the basis of quantum mechanics. For temperature levels sufficiently high so that $\hbar\omega/kT \ll 1$, it is seen from Eq. (10.2.32) that

$$Z_{qu} \sim \frac{kT}{\hbar\omega}, \tag{10.2.33}$$

[6]An example of the approach at high temperature levels of the quantum to the classical partition function (within a multiplicative constant) is provided by the harmonic oscillator, Eqs. (10.2.32)–(10.2.34); for the general case, see Münster (1969, pp. 134–137).

which differs from $Z_{cl} = 2\pi kT/\omega$, the classical partition function for ·a harmonic oscillator as given in Eq. (3.6.20), only by a multiplicative constant. That is, at high temperature levels

$$\frac{Z_{qu}}{Z_{cl}} \sim \frac{1}{2\pi\hbar} = \frac{1}{h}. \tag{10.2.34}$$

Since the computation of macroscopic thermodynamic functions from the partition function involves the logarithm of the latter (see Section 3.9), any multiplicative constant in the partition function definition produces only a change in datum for the corresponding thermodynamic function. As we are only concerned with changes in these functions, the choice of datum is unimportant.[7] Nevertheless, in many treatments the definition of the classical partition function given in Eq. (3.6.18) is modified by multiplication by h^{-n}, n the number of degrees of freedom of the system, in order to secure the high-temperature equivalence of Z_{cl} with Z_{qu}.

Thermodynamic Functions of Harmonic Oscillator

We next use Eqs. (3.9.1), (3.9.3), and (3.9.5) applied to Eq. (10.2.32) in order to compute the thermodynamic functions U, S, and F for a single harmonic oscillator.[8]

$$U = -\frac{\partial}{\partial\beta}\log Z = \left(\frac{1}{2} + \frac{1}{e^x - 1}\right)\hbar\omega, \tag{10.2.35}$$

$$S = k\left[\log Z - \beta\frac{\partial}{\partial\beta}\log Z\right] = k\left[\frac{x}{e^x - 1} - \log(1 - e^{-x})\right], \tag{10.2.36}$$

$$F = -kT\log Z = \frac{\hbar\omega}{2} + kT\log(1. - e^{-x}), \tag{10.2.37}$$

where

$$x = \frac{\hbar\omega}{kT}. \tag{10.2.38}$$

Consider the internal energy U which, as seen by Eq. (10.2.29), is the same as $\langle\langle H \rangle\rangle$, the mean energy of the oscillator. Its temperature variation is shown

---

[7]See the discussion of this point in Jackson (1968, p. 88 and Appendix D, pp. 229–231).
[8]See Section 3.9 for the motivation of the use of thermodynamic terminology for a single oscillator. These functions will find application in the next section in our discussion of the thermodynamics of a crystal in the quasi-harmonic approximation.

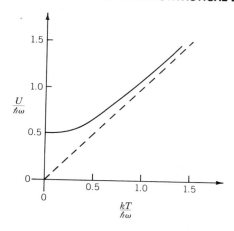

Figure 10.2 Mean energy $\ll H \gg = U$, Eq. (10.2.35), for quantum harmonic oscillator. Dashed line shows classical value.

in Figure 10.2. At very low temperature levels, $x \gg 1$, $U \cong \hbar\omega/2$, the zero-point energy of the oscillator, while at high-temperature levels, $x \ll 1$, $U \cong kT$, as predicted on the basis of classical statistical mechanics. This behavior of U is reflected in the temperature dependence of the specific heat of the oscillator,

$$C = \frac{dU}{dT} = T\frac{dS}{dT} = \frac{kx^2 e^x}{(e^x - 1)^2} \tag{10.2.39}$$

shown in Figure 10.3; the specific heat is zero at $T = 0$ and approaches the classical value, $C = k$, at high temperatures. Note that it is reasonably close to the classical value for $x = 1$; therefore, for temperatures greater than

$$T_c = \hbar\omega/k \tag{10.2.40}$$

classical statistical mechanics provides reasonably accurate results for these quantities.

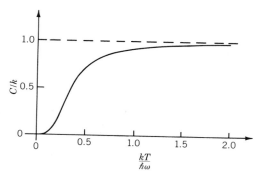

Figure 10.3 Specific heat of quantum harmonic oscillator, Eq. (10.2.39). Dashed line shows classical value.

Quantum Statistical Mechanics for Identical Particles

In our development of the quantum canonical ensemble describing a system I in weak interaction with a heat bath E, we assumed that the state of the system I could be described in terms of a wave function $\psi(\mathbf{r}, t)$ depending solely on the coordinates of I [see Eq. (10.2.2)]. This implies (Section 8.12) that it is possible to distinguish between the particles of I and the particles of the heat bath E, either because they are particles of different types or because they are localized by strong potentials to different regions of space.

However, the derivation does not require the ability to distinguish between the particles of I. The previous analysis applies, therefore, to the system I consisting of the collection of nonlocalized or conduction electrons in a metal with the remaining ions of the metal and its surroundings acting as the heat bath E. Let there be N nonlocalized electrons in I with stationary states $\xi_j^{(N)}$ and corresponding energies $E_j^{(N)}$, $j = 1, 2, \ldots$. The superscript (N) has been added to emphasize that these are N-electron states. Then, as previously derived, the probability $p_j^{(N)}$ associated with the state $\xi_j^{(N)}$ is

$$p_j^{(N)} = Z_{(N)}^{-1} e^{-\beta E_j^{(N)}} \tag{10.2.41}$$

with the partition function

$$Z_{(N)} = \sum_{\substack{j \\ \text{states}}} e^{-\beta E_j^{(N)}}. \tag{10.2.42}$$

In the sense that Eqs. (10.2.41) and (10.2.42) are in accord with the general theory, we may say that the identity of the free electrons introduces no new fundamental principles into quantum statistical mechanics. The fact that electrons are fermions appears in this formulation only through the requirement that the states $\xi_j^{(N)}$, which include both coordinate and spin information for the N electrons, must be antisymmetric with respect to electron label interchange. If, for example, we neglect the interaction between the conduction electrons, the independent electron approximation, then each state $\xi_j^{(N)}$ can be written as a single Slater determinant, Eq. (8.12.10), constructed from N distinct one electron states $\xi_j^{(1)}$, with the latter ordered, as usual, in terms of increasing energy. This requirement that N distinct one-electron states be employed embodies the Pauli exclusion principle and has, as one consequence, the result that even the ground state $\xi_0^{(N)}$ of the N conduction electrons makes use of one-electron states $\xi_j^{(1)}$, $j = 1, \ldots, N$, some of which correspond to high energies $E_j^{(1)}$. Since, in the absence of electron–electron interaction,

$$E_0^{(N)} = \sum_{j=1}^{N} E_j^{(1)}, \tag{10.2.43}$$

the ground state energy $E_0^{(N)}$ will be high. In a typical metal[9]

$$\frac{E_0^{(N)}}{NkT_R} \sim 200 \text{ for } T_R = 300 \ K. \qquad (10.2.44)$$

The first excited state $\xi_1^{(N)}$ is formed by leaving unchanged all of the 1-electron states utilized in the Slater determinant for $\xi_0^{(N)}$ except for $\xi_N^{(1)}$; the latter is replaced by $\xi_{N+1}^{(1)}$. Therefore, $E_1^{(N)} = E_0^{(N)} + (E_{N+1}^{(1)} - E_N^{(1)})$, and differs very little from $E_0^{(N)}$. Similarly, there are many other excited N-electron states obtained by the change in occupation of only a few 1-electron states from those with energies just below $E_0^{(N)}$ to those with energies just above E_0^N.

When the system of N electrons interacts with a heat bath, say at temperatures $T_R = 300$ K, it may be seen from Eqs. (10.2.41 and 44) that it is only these excited states with energies $E_j^{(N)}$ very close to $E_0^{(N)}$ which are occupied with any substantial probability $p_j^{(N)}$. Furthermore, it might be expected that temperature changes in the vicinity of T_R will have only a small effect on the mean energy of the conduction electrons. This turns out to be the case, and their specific heat is only about 1% of the value, $3Nk/2$, to be expected if they behaved classically.

A quantitative analysis, in the independent electron approximation, requires the determination of the one-electron statistics. These cannot be derived by simply regarding a single conduction electron as a small system in a heat bath of the remaining $N - 1$ conduction electrons and applying the previous analysis, since they are indistinguishable. They can, however, be derived by starting from Eqs. (10.2.41) and (10.2.42) and employing the Pauli exclusion principle. The resulting one-electron statistics[10] are called Fermi–Dirac statistics.

10.3 QUANTUM STATISTICAL EFFECTS IN CRYSTALS

As developed in Section 4.4, in the harmonic approximation the Hamiltonian of the interior portion I of a deformed crystal takes the form

$$H_h(Q, P; E_{LM}) = V_0(E_{LM}) + \frac{1}{2} \sum_{r=1}^{3N} \left(P_r^2 + \omega_r^2 Q_r^2 \right) \qquad (10.3.1)$$

where N is the number of atoms in I; E_{LM} is the material strain tensor describing the deformation of the lattice sites of the crystal from a designated reference lattice; $V_0(E_{LM})$ is the potential energy of I (including its energy of interaction with the surrounding crystal E) when all of the atoms of I + E are at the deformed reference sites; Q_r, P_r are normal coordinates and momenta

---

[9]See, for example, Ashcroft and Mermin (1976, p. 38).
[10]For the derivation, see, for example, Ashcroft and Mermin (1976, pp. 40–42).

describing the rth normal mode of vibratory motion of the atoms of I in the neighborhood of the deformed lattice sites; ω_r is the frequency of this mode and, in the quasi-harmonic approximation which we use throughout this section, $\omega_r = \omega_r(E_{LM})$.

This Hamiltonian describes a collection of $3N$ harmonic oscillators in weak interaction with each other and with the surrounding crystal which acts as heat bath. By application of Eq. (10.2.30), extended to many systems in weak interaction, the partition function of these $3N$ oscillators is the product of the partition functions of the individual oscillators. The potential energy $V_0(E_{LM})$ acts as a shift in datum for the energy of this system of oscillators and, as seen from Eq. (10.2.22), this shift multiplies their partition function by $\exp -(V_0/kT)$. Therefore, the quantum partition function of the crystal I is

$$Z_{qu}(E_{LM}, T) = e^{-V_0(E_{LM})/kT} \prod_{r=1}^{3N} Z_r(E_{LM}, T) \qquad (10.3.2)$$

where

$$Z_r(E_{LM}, T) = \frac{e^{-x_r/2}}{1 - e^{-x_r}} \qquad (10.3.3)$$

is the quantum partition function for the rth oscillator with

$$x_r = \frac{\hbar \omega_r}{kT}. \qquad (10.3.4)$$

By application of Eqs. (3.9.3), (3.9.5), and (3.9.1) to Eq. (10.3.2), we find

$$U(E_{LM}, T) = V_0(E_{LM}) + \sum_{r=1}^{3N} U_r(E_{LM}, T), \qquad (10.3.5)$$

$$S(E_{LM}, T) = \sum_{r=1}^{3N} S_r(E_{LM}, T), \qquad (10.3.6)$$

$$F(E_{LM}, T) = V_0(E_{LM}) + \sum_{r=1}^{3N} F_r(E_{LM}, T) \qquad (10.3.7)$$

where U_r, S_r, and F_r are the thermodynamic functions for the rth oscillator as given in Eqs. (10.2.35)–(10.2.37), with x replaced by x_r.

Specific Heat at Constant Deformation

From Eq. (10.3.5), the specific heat at constant deformation,

$$C_e = \frac{\partial U}{\partial T}\bigg|_{E_{LM}} = \sum_{r=1}^{3N} \frac{\partial U_r}{\partial T}\bigg|_{E_{LM}} = \sum_{r=1}^{3N} T \frac{\partial S_r}{\partial T}\bigg|_{E_{LM}} = \sum_{r=1}^{3N} C_r \qquad (10.3.8)$$

where C_r is given by Eq. (10.2.39), with x replaced by x_r, and represents the contribution of the rth normal mode to the specific heat of the crystal. It follows from the behavior of C_r, Figure 10.3, that at high temperatures, $C_\varepsilon \cong 3Nk$ in agreement with the classical quasi-harmonic prediction, Eq. (4.5.15), and from Eq. (10.2.40), that this will be a good approximation for $T > \hbar\omega_m/k$, where ω_m is the maximum modal frequency. The detailed nature of the dependence of C_ε on temperature will depend on the distribution of the frequencies ω_r for the given crystal. We turn next to two idealized models of this distribution.

Einstein and Debye Models

In the Einstein model of a crystal,[11] all of the normal mode frequencies are assumed equal,

$$\omega_r = \omega_E, \qquad r = 1,\ldots, 3N. \tag{10.3.9}$$

The resulting specific heat is then, from Eqs. (10.2.39) and (10.3.8),

$$C_\varepsilon = \frac{3Nkx_E^2 e^{x_E}}{\left(e^{x_E} - 1\right)^2} \tag{10.3.10}$$

where

$$x_E = \frac{\hbar\omega_E}{kT}. \tag{10.3.11}$$

By a suitable choice of ω_E, the Einstein model gives excellent qualitative and semiquantitative agreement with the observed decline of the specific heat of crystals as the temperature is decreased. This is a reflection of the fact that the temperature dependence of material properties that depend on sums over many normal modes, such as the specific heat, are relatively insensitive to the details of the dispersion relation; the major step toward the qualitative understanding of the low-temperature behavior of these properties is the incorporation of the quantum statistics of the harmonic oscillator in place of its classical statistics. Good quantitative agreement with experiment, however, requires further refinement of the model.

[11] Einstein (1907). This paper gave the first explanation of the observed variation of specific heats at low temperatures and provided important evidence that the quantum concept, introduced by Planck in 1900 in connection with electromagnetic radiation, had broad application. In a later paper, Einstein (1911) used the observed temperature dependence of C_ε for silver together with Eq. (10.3.10) to obtain a value for ω_E. He compared this frequency with that obtained on the basis of a simple atomistic model relating the bulk modulus of silver to its interatomic forces. Einstein termed the agreement ($\sim 20\%$) between these two frequencies "wahrhaft überraschend [truly surprising]" and one providing evidence for the close connection between lattice vibrations and elasticity, a relation suggested earlier by Madelung (1909) and Sutherland (1910).

One way in which the Einstein model is significantly in error is in the manner in which it predicts $C_\varepsilon \to 0$ as $T \to 0$. From Eq. (10.3.10), it is seen that for sufficiently small $T(x_E \gg 1)$ the temperature variation of C_ε is dominated by $\exp[-(\hbar\omega_E)/(kT)]$; experiments show a more gradual approach to zero. The Debye model[12] amends this difficulty and we turn next to its description.

Consider a composite crystal containing N atoms, n cells, with s atoms/cell, so that $N = sn$. Because of the relation of the normal modes to traveling waves (Section 4.9), we can designate the normal mode frequencies, ω_r, $r = 1,\dots, 3N$, by the alternate notation $\omega(\mathbf{f}_k, j)$, $k = 1,\dots, n$ and $j = 1,\dots, 3s$, where $\mathbf{f}_k$ is an allowed wave vector, one for which the traveling wave satisfies the specified periodic boundary condition, and j specifies the polarization of the wave. Therefore, the internal energy of the crystal can be written in the equivalent forms

$$U(E_{LM}, T) = V_0(E_{LM}) + \sum_{r=1}^{3N} \hbar\omega_r\left(\frac{1}{2} + \frac{1}{e^{x_r} - 1}\right), \qquad x_r = \frac{\hbar\omega_r}{kT}$$

$$= V_0(E_{LM}) + \sum_{j=1}^{3s} \sum_{k=1}^{n} \hbar\omega(\mathbf{f}_k, j)\left(\frac{1}{2} + \frac{1}{e^{x_{k,j}} - 1}\right),$$

$$x_{k,j} = \frac{\hbar\omega(\mathbf{f}_k, j)}{kT}. \tag{10.3.12}$$

For the purpose of specific heat computation, we need consider only that portion of $U(E_{LM}, T)$ which depends on T, namely,[13]

$$\tilde{U}(E_{LM}, T) = \sum_{j=1}^{3s} \sum_{k=1}^{n} g(\mathbf{f}_k, j) \tag{10.3.13}$$

where

$$g(\mathbf{f}_k, j) = \frac{\hbar\omega(\mathbf{f}_k, j)}{e^{x_{k,j}} - 1}. \tag{10.3.14}$$

The allowed wave vectors $\mathbf{f}_k$ are distributed uniformly throughout the first Brillouin zone with density $\mathscr{V}/(2\pi)^3$ (Section 4.9), where $\mathscr{V}$ is the volume of crystal I, so that each allowed wave vector has associated with it a volume $(2\pi)^3/\mathscr{V}$ in wave vector or reciprocal space. For $\mathscr{V}$ of macroscopic size, this corresponds to a dense distribution and it is natural to consider replacing the

---

[12] Debye (1912). For an interesting account of the background of this work, see Debye (1965).
[13] $\tilde{U}$ depends on the strains E_{LM} as well as on T since, in the quasi-harmonic approximation $\omega_r = \omega_r(E_{LM})$.

sum over k by an integral over the first Brillouin zone, writing

$$\tilde{U} = \frac{\mathscr{V}}{(2\pi)^3} \sum_{j=1}^{3s} \sum_{k=1}^{n} g(\mathbf{f}_k, j) \cdot \frac{(2\pi)^3}{\mathscr{V}} \cong \sum_{j=1}^{3s} \frac{\mathscr{V}}{(2\pi)^3} \int_{BZ} g(\mathbf{f}, j) \, d\mathbf{f}.$$

(10.3.15)

The replacement of the sum by an integral is justified providing the integrand is approximately constant over a volume $(2\pi)^3/\mathscr{V}$. As seen from Eq. (10.3.12) and (10.3.14), the rate of variation of g depends on T and is greater the smaller the value of T. We next estimate the value of $T_{\min}$ below which the replacement of sum by integral becomes excessively inaccurate. Consider the crystal to be a cube of side L. The change $\Delta\omega$ in frequency ω between two adjacent volume elements in wave vector space may be estimated as

$$\Delta\omega \sim \frac{d\omega}{df} \cdot \frac{(2\pi)}{L} = \frac{2\pi c}{L}$$

(10.3.16)

where c is of the order of magnitude of a sound speed in the crystal. Then, setting $\hbar(\Delta\omega)/kT_{\min} = 1$ leads to

$$T_{\min} = \frac{hc}{kL}.$$

(10.3.17)

For crystals of macroscopic size, this estimate leads to an exceedingly small value for $T_{\min}$. If, for example, we take $c = 5 \times 10^5$ cm sec^{-1} and $L = 1$ cm, $T_{\min} = 2.4 \times 10^{-5}$°K.

Assume next that T is sufficiently large to justify the replacement of sum by integral but sufficiently small so that $\hbar\omega_m/kT \gg 1$, where ω_m is the maximum frequency. At these low temperature levels the major contribution to the integral comes from the frequencies corresponding to the acoustic branches, $j = 1, 2, 3$, and from the low frequency, long wavelength portions of these branches in which

$$\omega(\mathbf{f}, j) = c_j f$$

(10.3.18)

where $f = |\mathbf{f}|$ and $c_j = c_j(\hat{\mathbf{f}})$ is the speed of the wave with polarization j in the direction $\hat{\mathbf{f}} = \mathbf{f}/f$. It is, therefore, convenient to rewrite the integral in terms of spherical coordinates f, θ, φ in wave vector space,

$$\tilde{U} = \sum_{j=1}^{3} \frac{\mathscr{V}}{(2\pi)^3} \int_{BZ} g(c_j f) f^2 \, df \, d\Omega = \sum_{j=1}^{3} \frac{\mathscr{V}}{(2\pi)^3} \int_S d\Omega \int_0^\infty g(c_j f) f^2 \, df$$

(10.3.19)

where $d\Omega = \sin^2\theta \, d\theta \, d\varphi$, S is the surface of the unit sphere, and where in the latter integral we have extended the integration with respect to f to $0 < f < \infty$ since at sufficiently low temperature levels the added portion is negligible. We may now use Eq. (10.3.18) to replace f by ω as variable of integration so that

$$\tilde{U} = \sum_{j=1}^{3} \frac{\mathscr{V}}{(2\pi)^3} \int_S d\Omega \int_0^\infty \frac{g(\omega)\omega^2\, d\omega}{c_j^3(\hat{\mathbf{f}})} \tag{10.3.20}$$

where the unit vector $\hat{\mathbf{f}} = \hat{\mathbf{f}}(\theta, \varphi)$.

We define an average reciprocal-cube wave speed, $\overline{c^{-3}}$,

$$\overline{c^{-3}} = \frac{1}{3} \sum_{j=1}^{3} \frac{1}{4\pi} \int_S \frac{d\Omega}{c_j^3(\hat{\mathbf{f}})}, \tag{10.3.21}$$

that is, the average is taken over the three acoustic branches and all possible directions $\hat{\mathbf{f}}$ of wave propagation. Then, by use of Eqs. (10.3.14), (10.3.20), and (10.3.21),

$$\tilde{U} = \frac{3\mathscr{V}\,\hbar\,\overline{c^{-3}}}{2\pi^2} \int_0^\infty \frac{\omega^3\, d\omega}{e^{\hbar\omega/kT} - 1} \tag{10.3.22}$$

or

$$\tilde{U} = \frac{3\mathscr{V}\,\overline{c^{-3}}(kT)^4}{2\pi^2\hbar^3} \int_0^\infty \frac{x^3}{e^x - 1}\, dx$$

$$= \frac{\pi^2 \mathscr{V}\,\overline{c^{-3}}(kT)^4}{10\hbar^3} = aT^4 \tag{10.3.23}$$

where we have used the result

$$\int_0^\infty \frac{x^3}{e^x - 1}\, dx = \frac{\pi^4}{15}. \tag{10.3.24}$$

We may conclude from Eq. (10.3.23) that at sufficiently low temperature levels,[14]

$$C_\varepsilon = \frac{\partial \tilde{U}}{\partial T}\bigg|_{E_{LM}} = 4aT^3. \tag{10.3.25}$$

Early experiments carried out on various solids in the temperature range 10–50°K appeared to verify this T^3 dependence of C_ε. Subsequent analyses by

[14] Recall that $\tilde{U} = \tilde{U}(E_{LM}, T)$; the strain dependence appears in $\overline{c^{-3}}$.

Blackman (1935) showed that this agreement was fortuitous, and that the theoretical T^3 dependence could only be expected at much lower temperature levels.[15]

The analysis thus far has assumed only that $T > T_{min}$, Eq. (10.3.17), so that the sum of Eq. (10.3.15) may be replaced by an integral, and that T is sufficiently small so that the range of integration in Eq. (10.3.19) or (10.3.20) may be extended to infinity; it is otherwise exact.[16] Of course, the resulting expressions for $\tilde{U}$ and C_ε, Eqs. (10.3.22) and (10.3.25) do not approach the correct classical limits at high temperature levels. To see the reason for this failure we reinterpret Eq. (10.3.22) as the replacement of a sum by an integral according to the scheme

$$\sum_{r=1}^{3N} \frac{\hbar\omega_r}{e^{\hbar\omega_r/kT} - 1} = \int_0^\infty \frac{\rho(\omega)\hbar\omega}{e^{\hbar\omega/kT} - 1} d\omega \tag{10.3.26}$$

where $\rho(\omega)d\omega$ is the number of normal-mode frequencies in the interval ω to $\omega + d\omega$. It follows from Eq. (10.3.22) that the low temperature approximation corresponds to

$$\rho(\omega) = A\omega^2, \, \omega > 0 \tag{10.3.27}$$

with

$$A = \frac{3\mathcal{V}c^{-3}}{2\pi^2}. \tag{10.3.28}$$

This frequency distribution function corresponds to an infinite number of normal modes and this is the reason why the correct classical limit cannot be attained. The Debye model remedies this deficiency by replacing Eq. (10.3.27) by

$$\rho(\omega) = A\omega^2, \quad 0 < \omega < \omega_D$$

$$= 0, \quad \text{for } \omega > \omega_D \tag{10.3.29}$$

where the frequency ω_D is determined by the requirement that $\rho(\omega)$ corresponds to the correct number of normal modes;

$$\int_0^{\omega_D} \rho(\omega) \, d\omega = 3N \tag{10.3.30}$$

---

[15] For a further discussion, see Born and Huang (1954, pp. 63–66). Note also that the deduction of the T^3 dependence requires the replacement of the sum in Eq. (10.3.15) by an integral; strictly speaking, therefore, it applies only for $T > T_{min}$.

[16] Similar results may be obtained for other thermodynamic functions as discussed later in this section. This permits the low-temperature description of the mechanical properties of crystals to be described in terms of macroscopic second- and third-order elastic moduli. (The latter enter the formulations when derivatives of thermodynamic functions with respect to strains are required.) See Sheard (1958), Garber and Granato (1975), and Gilder and Ganne (1980).

so that

$$A = 9N/\omega_D^3 \qquad (10.3.31)$$

or, by use of Eq. (10.3.28),

$$\omega_D = (9N/A)^{1/3} = \left(\frac{6\pi^2 N}{\mathcal{V}\overline{c^{-3}}}\right)^{1/3} = \left(\frac{6\pi^2 N}{\mathcal{V}}\right)^{1/3} \bar{c} \qquad (10.3.32)$$

where

$$\bar{c} \triangleq \left(\overline{c^{-3}}\right)^{-1/3}. \qquad (10.3.33)$$

With this assumption, Eq. (10.3.22) takes the form

$$\tilde{U} = A\hbar \int_0^{\omega_D} \frac{\omega^3 \, d\omega}{e^{\hbar\omega/kT} - 1}. \qquad (10.3.34)$$

Therefore, at high temperature levels

$$\tilde{U} \sim A\hbar \int_0^{\omega_D} \frac{\omega^3}{(\hbar\omega/kT)} \, d\omega = AkT \int_0^{\omega_D} \omega^2 \, d\omega = 3NkT, \qquad (10.3.35)$$

by use of Eq. (10.3.31), as it should. The Debye expression for $\tilde{U}$ for arbitrary temperature level, Eq. (10.3.34), may be put in the form

$$\tilde{U} = A\hbar \left(\frac{kT}{\hbar}\right)^4 \int_0^{\Theta_D/T} \frac{x^3}{e^x - 1} \, dx \qquad (10.3.36)$$

where

$$\Theta_D = \frac{\hbar\omega_D}{k} = \frac{\hbar\bar{c}}{k} \left(\frac{6\pi^2 N}{\mathcal{V}}\right)^{1/3} \qquad (10.3.37)$$

is known as the Debye temperature of the solid. Note that since c_j correspond to wave speeds for the acoustic branches in the long wavelength limit, they correspond to wave speeds computed on the basis of macroscopic elasticity. In the original Debye model, the solid was taken as isotropic and $\bar{c}$ was computed by the relation

$$\frac{1}{\bar{c}^3} = \frac{1}{3}\left(\frac{2}{c_t^3} + \frac{1}{c_l^3}\right) \qquad (10.3.38)$$

where c_t and c_l are the velocities of transverse and longitudinal waves in the solid. In more recent work[17] $c_j(\hat{\mathbf{f}})$ have been computed on the basis of anisotropic elasticity and $\bar{c}$ determined by the numerical integration of Eq. (10.3.21).

By introduction of the Debye function

$$D(y) = \frac{3}{y^3} \int_0^y \frac{x^3}{e^x - 1} dx, \tag{10.3.39}$$

and the use of Eqs. (10.3.31), (10.3.37) and (10.3.39), the expression for $\tilde{U}$ may be put in the form

$$\tilde{U} = 3NkTD\left(\frac{\Theta_D}{T}\right) \tag{10.3.40}$$

so that

$$C_\varepsilon = \frac{\partial \tilde{U}}{\partial T}\bigg|_{E_{LM}} = 3Nk\left[D\left(\frac{\Theta_D}{T}\right) - \frac{\Theta_D}{T}D'\left(\frac{\Theta_D}{T}\right)\right]. \tag{10.3.41}$$

The Debye model has been developed to give correct results at both low and high temperature levels. It provides a very good fit to experimental data at intermediate temperature levels as well, particularly when the Debye temperature Θ_D is used as an adjustable parameter. In this case the Debye temperature becomes an experimentally determined quantity, Θ_D^{exp}, which may be compared with the theoretical Θ_D^{th} computed from Eq. (10.3.37), using macroscopic elasticity to compute $\bar{c}$. For example, for NaCl, it is found[18] that $\Theta_D^{exp} = 281°K$ and $\Theta_D^{th} = 305°K$. This parameter provides a useful indication of the approximate temperature level that separates the quantum statistical and classical statistical regimes for a particular crystalline solid.

It is, of course, possible to fit either experimental data for $C_\varepsilon(T)$ or theoretical values of $C_\varepsilon(T)$ computed on the basis of detailed lattice models by means of Eq. (10.3.41) to any desired degree of accuracy by allowing Θ_D to vary with T, and presentations of the temperature dependence of the Debye temperature for experimental results for a given material or for theoretical calculations for a given lattice model are common. They provide a sensitive indication of the nature of the deviation from the predictions of the Debye model.

By use of the Einstein and Debye frequency distributions it is possible to express other thermodynamic functions in simplified form. Thus, by use of Eqs. (10.2.37), (10.3.7), and either Eq. (10.3.9) or Eq. (10.3.29), we see that the

[17]See, for example, Sheard (1958).
[18]Born and Huang (1954, p. 48).

Helmholtz free energy may be written as

$$F(E_{LM}, T) = V_0(E_{LM}) + Tg\left(\frac{\Theta}{T}\right) \qquad (10.3.42)$$

where, for the Einstein model,

$$\Theta = \Theta_E = \hbar\omega_E/k, \qquad (10.3.43)$$

$$g(x) = 3Nk\left(\frac{x}{2} + \log(1 - e^{-x})\right). \qquad (10.3.44)$$

and for the Debye model,

$$\Theta = \Theta_D = \hbar\omega_D/k \qquad (10.3.45)$$

$$g(x) = 3Nk\left(\frac{3}{x^3}\right)\int_0^x y^2\left[\frac{y}{2} + \log(1 - e^{-y})\right] dy. \qquad (10.3.46)$$

Grüneisen Tensor

The Grüneisen tensor has been discussed from the viewpoint of macroscopic thermodynamics in Section 1.8. We can now consider its characteristics when computed on the basis of the quantum quasiharmonic approximation. From its definition, Eq. (1.8.3), and from Eq. (10.3.6),

$$\gamma_{LM} = \frac{1}{C_\varepsilon} \frac{\partial S}{\partial E_{LM}}\bigg|_T = \frac{1}{C_\varepsilon} \sum_{r=1}^{3N} \frac{\partial S_r}{\partial E_{LM}}\bigg|_T \qquad (10.3.47)$$

or

$$\gamma_{LM} = \frac{1}{C_\varepsilon} \sum_{r=1}^{3N} C_r\gamma_{LM}^r \qquad (10.3.48)$$

where C_r, Eq. (10.3.8), is the specific heat of the rth mode and

$$\gamma_{LM}^r \triangleq \frac{1}{C_r} \frac{\partial S_r}{\partial E_{LM}}\bigg|_T \qquad (10.3.49)$$

is called the Grüneisen tensor for the rth mode. Since $S_r(E_{LM}, T) = S_r(x_r)$ where $x_r = \hbar\omega_r(E_{LM})/kT$, we see that

$$\frac{\partial S_r}{\partial E_{LM}}\bigg|_T = \frac{\hbar}{kT} \frac{dS_r}{dx_r} \frac{\partial\omega_r}{\partial E_{LM}}, \qquad \text{no sum on } r, \qquad (10.3.50)$$

and

$$C_r = T \left. \frac{\partial S_r}{\partial T} \right|_{E_{LM}} = - \frac{dS_r}{dx_r} \frac{\hbar \omega_r}{kT}, \qquad \text{no sum on } r, \qquad (10.3.51)$$

so that

$$\gamma_{LM}^r = - \frac{1}{\omega_r} \frac{\partial \omega_r}{\partial E_{LM}} = - \frac{\partial}{\partial E_{LM}} \log \omega_r; \qquad (10.3.52)$$

that is, the modal Grüneisen tensors are temperature independent. However, since the modal specific heats C_r vary with temperature in a manner dependent on ω_r, it follows from Eq. (10.3.48) that the Grüneisen tensor γ_{LM} will generally be temperature dependent. Two exceptions may be noted as follows.

At temperature levels sufficiently high so that classical mechanics applies, $C_r = k$ for all $r, C_\varepsilon = 3Nk$, and it follows from Eq. (10.3.48) that γ_{LM} is temperature independent in this temperature range.

We can also compute γ_{LM} based on either the Einstein or Debye model, by use of the common form of the free energy, Eq. (10.3.42), in which we regard the parameter $\Theta = \Theta(E_{LM})$. Since, by Eq. (1.5.13),

$$S = - \left. \frac{\partial F}{\partial T} \right|_{E_{LM}}$$

$$C_\varepsilon = T \left. \frac{\partial S}{\partial T} \right|_{E_{LM}} = - T \left. \frac{\partial^2 F}{\partial T^2} \right|_{E_{LM}} = - \left(\frac{\Theta}{T} \right)^2 g'', \qquad (10.3.53)$$

and

$$\gamma_{LM} = \frac{1}{C_\varepsilon} \left. \frac{\partial S}{\partial E_{LM}} \right|_T = - \frac{1}{C_\varepsilon} \frac{\partial^2 F}{\partial E_{LM} \partial T}$$

$$= - \frac{\Theta}{T^2} \frac{\partial \Theta}{\partial E_{LM}} g'' \bigg/ \left(\left(\frac{\Theta}{T} \right)^2 g'' \right) = - \frac{\partial \log \Theta}{\partial E_{LM}}. \qquad (10.3.54)$$

Therefore, the Grüneisen tensor γ_{LM} is temperature independent at all temperature levels when computed on the basis of either the Einstein or Debye models.[19]

Experimentally it is found that γ_{LM} is roughly constant over a wide range of temperature for many crystalline solids. Since the elastic moduli are only moderately temperature dependent, it follows from Eq. (1.8.10) that the

---

[19]An Einstein model was assumed in the original work of Grüneisen (1912).

thermal expansion tensor for these materials will then have roughly the same temperature dependence[20] as C_ε.

Specific Heat at Constant Stress

By use of Eq. (10.3.48), which gives the Grüneisen tensor γ_{LM} on the basis of the quasi-harmonic approximation, together with Eq. (1.8.22) of macroscopic thermodynamics, we find

$$C_\sigma = C_\varepsilon + \alpha_{LM}T \sum_{r=1}^{3N} C_r \gamma_{LM}^r. \tag{10.3.55}$$

It is also possible to return to the basic definition of C_σ and to write

$$C_\sigma = T \left. \frac{\partial S}{\partial T} \right|_{T_{LM}} = T \sum_{r=1}^{3N} \frac{dS_r}{dx_r} \left(-\frac{\hbar \omega_r}{kT^2} + \frac{\hbar}{kT} \left. \frac{\partial \omega_r}{\partial T} \right|_{T_{LM}} \right) \tag{10.3.56}$$

where

$$\left. \frac{\partial \omega_r}{\partial T} \right|_{T_{LM}} = \frac{\partial \omega_r}{\partial E_{RS}} \left. \frac{\partial E_{RS}}{\partial T} \right|_{T_{LM}}. \tag{10.3.57}$$

As an example of the study of a specific heat based on a detailed analysis of the frequency distribution rather than on a model relation we may refer to the work of Miiller and Brockhouse (1971). They computed C_σ for copper by use of Eq. (10.3.56), utilizing values of ω_r and $\partial \omega_r/\partial T|_{T_{LM}}$ determined for a large number of points in the first Brillouin zone by the technique of slow neutron scattering. The predicted values of C_σ which they obtained is shown in Figure 10.4 together with values of C_σ measured by direct experiment. The small discrepancy at high temperature levels is ascribed to the fact that the electrons in a metal do not remain in the ground state as the temperature increases, as is assumed in the adiabatic approximation. This small additional effect is called the electronic specific heat whereas that based on the Hamiltonian of the adiabatic approximation is called the specific heat due to lattice vibrations.

Also shown in Figure 10.4 is the straight line that results if the classical limit $C_\varepsilon = 3Nk$ is employed together with Eq. (1.8.23). This leads[21] to the predicted

[20]Examples of materials for which this is not the case are provided by germanium and silicon, which have negative coefficients of thermal expansion at low temperatures. See Dolling and Cowley (1966) or the brief account in Cochran (1973), p. 104. A comprehensive review of the thermal expansion of solids at low temperature ($1-100°K$), including both theory and experiment is given by Barron, Collins, and White (1980).

[21]We outline the numerical basis of Eq. (10.3.58). Copper has cubic symmetry so that $\gamma_{LM} = \gamma\delta_{LM}$, $\alpha_{LM} = \alpha\delta_{LM}$. Then, Eq. (1.8.23) becomes $C_\sigma - C_\varepsilon = \mathcal{V}\alpha^2 C_{LLNN}^T = \mathcal{V}\alpha^2(3C_{11}^T + 6C_{12}^T)$, using Voigt notation and Eq. (4.6.3). Assume one mole of copper, $N = N_{av} = 6.023 \times 10^{23}$ atoms, $Nk = R = 1.987$ cal deg^{-1} mole^{-1}, $\mathcal{V}$ (molar volume of copper) $= 7.12$ cm^3 mole^{-1}, $\alpha = 0.16 \times 10^{-4}/°K$, $C_{11} = 1.685 \times 10^{12}$ dyn/cm^2, $C_{12} = 1.215 \times 10^{12}$ dyn/cm^2. The temperature variation of $\mathcal{V}$, α, C_{11}, C_{12} is neglected in this calculation.

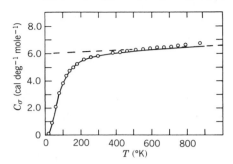

Figure 10.4   Specific heat C_σ of copper at fixed (zero) applied stress. Solid curve is computed according to Eq. (10.3.56); dashed line is classical result, Eq. (10.3.58); circles are experimental values. (After Miiller and Brockhouse, 1971) with permission.

classical variation

$$C_\sigma(\text{cal mole}^{-1}\ \text{deg}^{-1}) = 5.96\ \text{cal deg}^{-1}\ \text{mole}^{-1} + 5.38 \times 10^{-4}\ T. \quad (10.3.58)$$

The highest lattice mode frequency in copper is[22] $\nu \cong 7 \times 10^{12}\ \text{sec}^{-1}$. Therefore, as previously discussed, the classical approximation may be expected to be reasonably accurate above

$$T_c = \frac{\hbar\omega}{k} = \frac{h\nu}{k} \cong 335\ °\text{K}$$

and this is seen to be the case.

Thermoelastic Stress–Strain Relation

For the purpose of discussing quantum statistical effects on the thermoelasticity of crystals, it is convenient to rewrite the Helmholtz free energy of Eq. (10.3.7) in the form

$$F(E_{LM}, T) = V_0(E_{LM}) + kT \sum_{r=1}^{3N} f\left(\frac{\hbar\omega_r}{kT}\right) \quad (10.3.59)$$

where

$$f(x) = \frac{x}{2} + \log(1 - e^{-x}). \quad (10.3.60)$$

By use of Eq. (10.3.59) we find

$$T_{LM}(E_{RS}, T) = \frac{1}{\mathcal{V}} \frac{\partial F}{\partial E_{LM}} = \frac{1}{\mathcal{V}}\left[\frac{\partial V_0}{\partial E_{LM}} + \hbar \sum_{r=1}^{3N} f'(x_r)\frac{\partial\omega_r}{\partial E_{LM}}\right]$$

$$(10.3.61)$$

[22] Miiller and Brockhouse (1971, p. 714).

where

$$f'(x) = \frac{1}{2} + \frac{1}{e^x - 1}. \qquad (10.3.62)$$

Within the limitations of the quasi-harmonic approximation, the thermo-elastic relation of Eq. (10.3.61) applies for arbitrary strain and temperature. Since

$$\lim_{T \to 0} f'(x) = \lim_{x \to \infty} f'(x) = \frac{1}{2}, \qquad (10.3.63)$$

the stress–strain relation at $T = 0$ °K is

$$T_{LM}(E_{RS}, 0) = \frac{1}{\mathcal{V}}\left[\frac{\partial V_0}{\partial E_{LM}} + \frac{\hbar}{2} \sum_{r=1}^{3N} \frac{\partial \omega_r}{\partial E_{LM}} \right]$$

$$= \frac{1}{\mathcal{V}} \frac{\partial}{\partial E_{LM}}\left[V_0 + \sum_{r=1}^{3N} \frac{\hbar \omega_r}{2} \right], \qquad (10.3.64)$$

that is, at $T = 0$ °K, the stress depends on the variation of the sum of the potential energy of the atoms in their static deformed configuration plus their zero-point energy. Therefore, the zero-stress configuration at $T = 0$ °K corresponds to the minimum of this sum, not to the minimum of $V_0(E_{RS})$ alone.

For sufficiently high temperature levels, $x_r \ll 1$ all r. Since

$$f'(x) \cong \frac{1}{2} + \left(\frac{1}{x} - \frac{1}{2} + \dots \right) \cong \frac{1}{x} \quad \text{for } x \ll 1, \qquad (10.3.65)$$

Eq. (10.3.61) assumes the form

$$T_{LM}(E_{RS}, T) = \frac{1}{\mathcal{V}}\left[\frac{\partial V_0}{\partial E_{LM}} + kT \sum_{r=1}^{3N} \frac{\partial \log \omega_r}{\partial E_{LM}} \right] \qquad (10.3.66)$$

in agreement with Eq. (4.5.7) obtained on the basis of classical statistical mechanics.

Elastic Moduli

We consider next the isothermal elastic moduli used in the linear thermoelastic relation for small strains and temperature changes from the reference state consisting of the designated reference lattice from which the strains are measured and the reference temperature T.

$$C^T_{LMNK} = \frac{1}{\mathscr{V}} \frac{\partial^2 F}{\partial E_{LM} \partial E_{NK}}\bigg|_0$$

$$= \frac{1}{\mathscr{V}} \left[\frac{\partial^2 V_0}{\partial E_{LM} \partial E_{NK}}\bigg|_0 + \hbar \sum_{r=1}^{3N} f'(x_r^0) \frac{\partial^2 \omega_r}{\partial E_{LM} \partial E_{NK}}\bigg|_0 \right.$$

$$+ \frac{\hbar^2}{kT} \sum_{r=1}^{3N} f''(x_r^0) \frac{\partial \omega_r}{\partial E_{LM}}\bigg|_0 \frac{\partial \omega_r}{\partial E_{NK}}\bigg|_0 \Bigg], \qquad (10.3.67)$$

where the subscript 0 indicates evaluation at the reference state ($E_{RS} \equiv 0$, and temperature T),

$$x_r^0 = \frac{\hbar \omega_r^0}{kT} \qquad (10.3.68)$$

where ω_r^0 are the normal mode frequencies at $E_{RS} = 0$, and

$$f''(x) = \frac{-e^x}{(e^x - 1)^2}. \qquad (10.3.69)$$

Since

$$\lim_{T \to 0} f''(x) = \lim_{x \to \infty} f''(x) = 0, \qquad (10.3.70)$$

it follows that at $T = 0$

$$C^T_{LMNK} = \frac{1}{\mathscr{V}} \left[\frac{\partial^2 V_0}{\partial E_{LM} \partial E_{NK}}\bigg|_0 + \frac{\hbar}{2} \sum_{r=1}^{3N} \frac{\partial^2 \omega_r}{\partial E_{LM} \partial E_{NK}}\bigg|_0 \right]. \qquad (10.3.71)$$

At sufficiently high temperature levels, $x_r^0 \ll 1$. Since

$$f''(x) \sim -\frac{1}{x^2} \text{ for } x \ll 1, \qquad (10.3.72)$$

we find

$$C^T_{LMNK} = \frac{1}{\mathscr{V}} \left[\frac{\partial^2 V_0}{\partial E_{LM} \partial E_{NK}}\bigg|_0 + kT \sum_{r=1}^{3N} \frac{\partial^2 \log \omega_r}{\partial E_{LM} \partial E_{NK}}\bigg|_0 \right] \qquad (10.3.73)$$

in agreement with the classical result, Eq. (4.5.8).

Elastic Moduli for Einstein and Debye Models

In order to consider the nature of the transition from the quantum behavior at low temperature levels to the high-temperature classical behavior, we return to the special form of the free energy, Eq. (10.3.42), which applies to either the Einstein or Debye models. For this form of the free energy,

$$C_{LMNK}^T = \tilde{C}_{LMNK} + \frac{1}{\mathscr{V}} \left[\frac{\partial^2 \Theta}{\partial E_{LM} \partial E_{NK}} g' + \frac{1}{T} \frac{\partial \Theta}{\partial E_{LM}} \frac{\partial \Theta}{\partial E_{NK}} g'' \right]$$

$$(10.3.74)$$

where

$$\tilde{C}_{LMNK} = \frac{1}{\mathscr{V}} \frac{\partial^2 V_0}{\partial E_{LM} \partial E_{NK}} \bigg|_0 \qquad (10.3.75)$$

are the harmonic elastic moduli, and where all functions are evaluated at the reference state, $E_{RS} \equiv 0$ and temperature T. Similarly,

$$b_{LM} = \frac{1}{\mathscr{V}} \frac{\partial^2 F}{\partial E_{LM} \partial T} \bigg|_0 = -\frac{1}{\mathscr{V}} \frac{\Theta}{T^2} \frac{\partial \Theta}{\partial E_{LM}} g''. \qquad (10.3.76)$$

The adiabatic moduli may be determined by use of the relation, Eq. (1.8.18),

$$C_{LMNK}^S = C_{LMNK}^T + \frac{\mathscr{V} T b_{LM} b_{NK}}{C_\varepsilon}. \qquad (10.3.77)$$

By use of Eqs. (10.3.76) and (10.3.77) and of Eq. (10.3.53) which gives C_ε for these models,

$$C_{LMNK}^S = C_{LMNK}^T - \frac{1}{\mathscr{V} T} \frac{\partial \Theta}{\partial E_{LM}} \frac{\partial \Theta}{\partial E_{NK}} g'' \qquad (10.3.78)$$

so that, by use of Eq. (10.3.74),

$$C_{LMNK}^S = \tilde{C}_{LMNK} + \frac{1}{\mathscr{V}} \frac{\partial^2 \Theta}{\partial E_{LM} \partial E_{NK}} g'. \qquad (10.3.79)$$

In particular, for the Einstein model we find, by use of Eqs. (10.3.43), (10.3.44), and (10.3.79), that

$$C_{LMNK}^S = \tilde{C}_{LMNK} + \frac{3N\hbar}{\mathscr{V}} \frac{\partial^2 \omega_E}{\partial E_{LM} \partial E_{NK}} \left[\frac{1}{2} + \left(\exp\left(\frac{\hbar \omega_E}{kT} \right) - 1 \right)^{-1} \right].$$

$$(10.3.80)$$

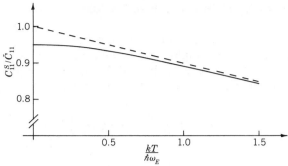

Figure 10.5   Temperature dependence of adiabatic elastic moduli based on Einstein model, Eq. (10.3.81), with $\delta\zeta = -0.1$. Dashed line shows linear classical behavior.

To consider the nature of the temperature dependence, consider a particular component, for example $C^S_{1111} = C^S_{11}$ in Voigt notation. Then, Eq. (10.3.80) can be put in the form

$$\frac{C^S_{11}}{\tilde{C}_{11}} = 1 + \delta\zeta\left(\frac{1}{2} + \frac{1}{e^x - 1}\right) \qquad (10.3.81)$$

where

$$\delta = \frac{3N\hbar\omega_E}{\mathcal{V}\tilde{C}_{11}} \qquad (10.3.82)$$

is the ratio of the zero-point energy to the elastic energy at unit strain,

$$\zeta = \frac{1}{\omega_E}\frac{\partial^2\omega_E}{\partial E^2_{11}} \qquad (10.3.83)$$

is a measure of the anharmonicity, and $x = \hbar\omega_E/kT$. The manner of temperature variation of C^S_{11} is the same as that of the energy of a harmonic oscillator of frequency ω_E, Eq. (10.2.35) and Figure 10.2. It is shown in Figure 10.5 for illustrative values of δ and ζ and it is seen to give rise to the type of temperature variation of elastic parameters observed experimentally (Figure 4.6).

Use of the Debye model would be more appropriate in order to obtain a quantitative fit for a given set of experimental data. In this case, the value of Θ^{exp}_D that gives the best fit to elastic moduli data would generally be different from that obtained by fitting specific heat data.[23]

---

[23] See, for example, Huntington (1958), p. 254.

10.4   QUANTUM STATISTICS FOR POLYMER MODELS

The thermomechanical behavior of stressed polymer chains was discussed in Chapter 6 on the basis of classical statistical mechanics. Two types of models were treated there: (a) rigid models in which the strong covalent bonds between backbone atoms were represented by geometric constraints in the model Hamiltonian prior to the calculation of the partition function, and (b) flexible models in which these bonds were modeled by stiff springs with spring constants taken as arbitrarily large after the partition function was calculated. As we saw there, when very short chains were considered, the classical analysis predicted different mechanical behavior for the two types of models; in this section we reexamine this question from the quantum viewpoint.

We begin with the Hamiltonian of Eq. (6.6.6)

$$H_F(q^i, p_i) = \tfrac{1}{2}g^{ij}p_i p_j + \tfrac{1}{2}\kappa a_{AB}q^A q^B + V(q^\alpha) \qquad (10.4.1)$$

for a chain with N atoms free to undergo thermal motion. We refer to Chapter 6 for a full discussion of the notation used but recall here that the coordinates $q^i, i = 1,\ldots, n = 3N$ are divided into two groups: $q^\alpha, \alpha = 1,\ldots, f$ represent soft variables (e.g., dihedral angles) and $q^A, A = f + 1,\ldots, n$ represent hard variables (e.g., bond lengths). The potential $V(q^\alpha)$ corresponds therefore to low rotational energy barriers, while the potential $\tfrac{1}{2}\kappa a_{AB}q^A q^B$ is the strong potential representing the covalent bonds. It is reasonable to write the latter in its quadratic approximation, with a_{AB} a constant matrix, since the displacements q^A from their equilibrium values are very small at reasonable temperature levels and since it is not expected from the nature of covalent bonding that the matrix a_{AB} should depend on the soft variables q^α.

The kinetic energy $K = \tfrac{1}{2}g^{ij}p_i p_j$ may be written as

$$K = \tfrac{1}{2}g^{\alpha\beta}p_\alpha p_\beta + \tfrac{1}{2}g^{AB}p_A p_B + g^{\alpha A}p_\alpha p_A \qquad (10.4.2)$$

where we see that the last term represents kinematic coupling between the soft and hard variables. We assume that we may neglect this coupling. Furthermore, since the q^A excursions are small, we assume that we can neglect their effect on $g^{\alpha\beta}$ and g^{AB} and write

$$H_F(q^i, p_i) \cong H_s(q^\alpha, p_\alpha) + H_h(q^A, p_A; q^\alpha) \qquad (10.4.3)$$

where

$$H_s(q^\alpha, p_\alpha) = \tfrac{1}{2}g^{\alpha\beta}p_\alpha p_\beta + V(q^\alpha) \qquad (10.4.4)$$

$$H_h(q^A, p_A; q^\alpha) = \tfrac{1}{2}g^{AB}p_A p_B + \tfrac{1}{2}\kappa a_{AB}q^A q^B \qquad (10.4.5)$$

with both $g^{\alpha\beta}$ and g^{AB} evaluated at arbitrary q^α but with $q^A \equiv 0$.

The Hamiltonian H_h corresponds to a collection of harmonic oscillators described in terms of a nonorthogonal coordinate system. We may determine their frequencies, ω_A, by considering the classical equations of motion,

$$\dot{q}^A = \frac{\partial H}{\partial p_A} = g^{AB}p_B, \qquad \dot{p}_B = -\frac{\partial H}{\partial q^B} = -\kappa a_{BC}q^C, \qquad (10.4.6)$$

so that

$$\ddot{q}^A + \kappa g^{AB}a_{BC}q^C = 0. \qquad (10.4.7)$$

The squared frequencies, ω_A^2, are therefore (Section 4.4) the eigenvalues of the matrix $\kappa g^{AB}a_{BC}$ so that, in particular,

$$\prod_{A=f+1}^{n} \omega_A^2 = \kappa^c|g^{AB}\|a_{BC}| \qquad (10.4.8)$$

where $c = f - n$. Because of the strength of covalent bonding, these frequencies are generally sufficiently high in polymer molecules so that $\hbar\omega_A/kT > 1$ for room-temperature levels.[24] It follows from the discussion of Section 10.2 that quantum statistics should be employed for an accurate treatment of the hard variables q^A.

On the other hand, the energy level spacing for the system of soft variables q^α will be very much smaller than for the system of hard variables q^A. Therefore, except for very low temperature levels, the quantum partition function Z_{qu} corresponding to H_F of Eq. (10.4.3) can be written, as discussed in Section 10.2, in mixed quantum–classical form as

$$Z_{qu}(T) = \int_{\Gamma_\alpha} Z_{h,qu}(q^\alpha, T)e^{-H_s(q^\alpha, p_\alpha)/kT} \prod_{\alpha=1}^{f} dq^\alpha \, dp_\alpha \qquad (10.4.9)$$

where

$$Z_{h,qu}(q^\alpha, T) = \prod_{A=f+1}^{n} g\left(\frac{\hbar\omega_A(q^\alpha)}{kT}\right) \qquad (10.4.10)$$

and

$$g(x) = \frac{e^{-x/2}}{1-e^{-x}} \qquad (10.4.11)$$

in accord with the definition of the quantum partition function given in Eq.

[24] See, for example, the discussion in Gō and Scheraga (1976).

(10.2.32). The integration over the momenta p_α may be performed to give the expression,

$$Z_{qu}(T) = (2\pi kT)^{f/2} \int_{\Gamma_{q^\alpha}} Z_{h,qu}(q^\alpha, T) |g_{\alpha\beta}|_0^{1/2} e^{-V(q^\alpha)/kT} \prod_{\alpha=1}^{f} dq^\alpha.$$

$$(10.4.12)$$

High-Temperature Behavior

At temperature levels sufficiently high so that $\hbar\omega_A/kT \ll 1$, it follows from Eq. (10.4.11) that $g(x) \sim 1/x$ so that

$$Z_{h,qu}(q^\alpha, T) \cong \prod_{A=f+1}^{n} \left(\frac{kT}{\hbar\omega_A}\right) = \left(\frac{2\pi kT}{h}\right)^c \prod_{A=f+1}^{n} \omega_A^{-1}. \quad (10.4.13)$$

We use Eq. (10.4.8) in Eq. (10.4.13) and substitute into Eq. (10.4.12), to see that the high-temperature behavior of $Z_{qu}(T)$ is

$$Z_{qu}(T) \cong h^{-c}(2\pi kT)^{(n+c)/2} \kappa^{-c/2} |a_{BC}|^{-1/2}$$

$$\times \int_{\Gamma_{q^\alpha}} |g^{AB}|_0^{-1/2} |g_{\alpha\beta}|_0^{1/2} e^{-V(q^\alpha)/kT} \prod_{\alpha=1}^{f} dq^\alpha. \quad (10.4.14)$$

By use of Eq. (6.3.18), it then follows that the high-temperature limit of $Z_{qu}(T)$ agrees (except for the irrelevant constant h^{-c}) with the classical partition function for the flexible model, Eq. (6.6.8).

Low-Temperature Behavior

We consider next the form of $Z_{qu}(T)$ for temperature levels sufficiently low so that $\hbar\omega_A/kT \gg 1$, while kT remains sufficiently large relative to the energy level spacings of the soft variables so that we may continue to treat the latter classically. Under these conditions, it follows from Eqs. (10.4.10), and (10.4.12) that

$$Z_{qu}(T) \cong (2\pi kT)^{f/2} \int_{\Gamma_{q^\alpha}} \prod_{A=f+1}^{n} \exp\left[-\frac{\hbar\omega_A}{2kT}\right] |g_{\alpha\beta}|_0^{1/2} e^{-V(q^\alpha)/kT} \prod_{\alpha=1}^{f} dq^\alpha.$$

$$(10.4.15)$$

By comparison of Eqs. (10.4.15) and (6.6.5), we see that the low-temperature form of $Z_{qu}(T)$ differs from $Z_R(T)$, the classical partition function for the rigid model, by the presence of the terms involving $\hbar \omega_A / 2$ in the integral defining Z_{qu}. These represent the contribution of the zero-point energy of the hard variables to the quantum partition function.

We are thus led to the conclusion that at room-temperature levels both classical forms of the partition function, $Z_R(T)$ and $Z_F(T)$, are in error relative to the quantum partition function. Z_F is in error because it is obtained by replacing $Z_{h,qu}$ by its high-temperature limit, although $\hbar \omega_A / kT > 1$ at room-temperature levels. In fact, these ratios are sufficiently high so that the low-temperature limit of $Z_{h,qu}$ is a better approximation. However, in this case, the zero-point energy contributions remain under the integral, as in Eq. (10.4.15), since, from Eq. (10.4.8), the frequencies $\omega_A = \omega_A(q^\alpha)$, with the dependence on q^α arising from the corresponding dependence of $|g^{AB}|$. Only if these frequencies are treated as strict constants is the low-temperature behavior of Z_{qu}, Eq. (10.4.15), equivalent to Z_R, Eq. (6.6.5), the partition function for the classical rigid model.

Gō and Scheraga (1976) analyzed the two classes of error for the case of a polymer molecule in solution and came to the conclusion that the classical flexible model provides a better approximation. For the case of stressed polymers, and in particular for molecules with imposed end-to-end vector $\mathbf{r}$, there is the added question of the effect of possible $\mathbf{r}$ dependence of ω_A.

A preliminary study of this question has been made by Perchak and Weiner (1982) based on quantum calculations for a flexible model of a freely jointed chain with $N = 2, 3,$ and 4 bonds. They find that the quantum force–length relation is already in good agreement with the classical result for the flexible model at room-temperature levels; the low-temperature behavior does not approach the classical rigid model because of the dependence of the zero-point energy on the end-to-end length.

10.5 GAUSSIAN WAVE PACKET DYNAMICS

The concept of a Gaussian wave packet was introduced in Section 8.4 where it was seen to arise as a consequence of a minimum uncertainty measurement. We wish now to make application of this concept in quantum statistical mechanics and in rate theory. For these purposes we begin in this section with the study of the dynamics of a particle, constrained to move in one dimension, whose state is described by a time-dependent Gaussian wave packet. The particle is subject to the quadratic potential

$$V(x) = \tfrac{1}{2}\kappa x^2, \qquad (10.5.1)$$

where κ may be positive (harmonic well), zero (free particle), or negative (parabolic barrier). The time-dependent Schrödinger equation, Eq. (8.3.13), then takes the form

$$-\frac{\hbar^2}{2m}\frac{\partial^2 \psi}{\partial x^2} + \frac{1}{2}\kappa x^2 = i\hbar\frac{\partial \psi}{\partial t} \qquad (10.5.2)$$

and we are seeking a solution $\psi(x, t)$ subject to the initial condition [see Eq. (8.4.21)]

$$\psi(x, t_0) = \frac{1}{(2\pi\chi_0)^{1/4}} \exp\left(\frac{i\bar{p}_0 x}{\hbar} - \frac{(x - \bar{x}_0)^2}{4\chi_0}\right). \qquad (10.5.3)$$

It may be verified by direct substitution that the wave function $\psi(x, t)$ continues to evolve as a Gaussian wave packet, that is, that a solution may be found in the form

$$\psi(x, t) = \frac{1}{(2\pi\chi)^{1/4}} \exp\left(\frac{iS(x, t)}{\hbar} - \frac{(x - \bar{x})^2}{4\chi}\right) \qquad (10.5.4)$$

where it is seen by comparison with Eq. (8.4.21) that

$$\chi(t) = (\Delta x)^2 \qquad (10.5.5)$$

and where

$$S(x, t) = \frac{1}{2}a(x - \bar{x})^2 + b(x - \bar{x}) + c \qquad (10.5.6)$$

with $\bar{x}$, χ, a, b, and c suitably chosen functions of time. Before giving the equations that govern the time dependence of these quantities, it will be convenient to introduce some additional notation.

The expected energy $\langle H \rangle$ corresponding to $\psi(x, t)$ of Eq. (10.5.4) is found, by carrying out the integrations indicated in Eq. (10.5.7), to be

$$\langle H \rangle = (\psi, H\psi) = \int_{-\infty}^{\infty} \psi^*(x, t)\left[-\frac{\hbar^2}{2m}\frac{\partial^2}{\partial x^2} + \frac{1}{2}\kappa x^2\right]\psi(x, t)\, dx$$

$$= E_{\text{cl}} + \mathcal{E} \qquad (10.5.7)$$

where

$$E_{\text{cl}} = \frac{1}{2}(m\dot{\bar{x}}^2 + \kappa\bar{x}^2) \qquad (10.5.8)$$

is the energy of the corresponding classical particle moving on the trajectory $\bar{x}(t)$ and

$$\mathcal{E} = \frac{a^2\chi}{2m} + \frac{\hbar^2}{8m\chi} + \frac{1}{2}\kappa\chi. \qquad (10.5.9)$$

We can now return to the equations which the functions $\bar{x}$, χ, a, b, and c must satisfy. These are determined by substitution of ψ, Eqs. (10.5.4) and (10.5.6), into the time-dependent Schrödinger equation, Eq. (10.5.2); the exponential then appears as a common factor multiplying terms proportional to x^0, x^1, and x^2. When the real and imaginary parts of the coefficients of these terms are set individually equal to zero the following equations result:

$$m\ddot{\bar{x}} = -\kappa\bar{x} \tag{10.5.10}$$

$$m\ddot{\chi} = -4\kappa\chi + 4\mathscr{E} \tag{10.5.11}$$

$$a = \tfrac{1}{2}m\dot{\chi}/\chi \tag{10.5.12}$$

$$b = m\dot{\bar{x}} \tag{10.5.13}$$

$$\dot{c} = E_{cl} - \frac{\hbar^2}{4m\chi}. \tag{10.5.14}$$

From the basic equation for the quantum mean momentum $\bar{p}$, Eq. (8.4.4), applied to the wave function of Eqs. (10.5.4) and (10.5.6), we find that $\bar{p} = b$ so that Eq. (10.5.13) may be rewritten

$$\bar{p} = m\dot{\bar{x}}. \tag{10.5.15}$$

This, coupled with Eq. (10.5.10), leads to the result that the quantum means $\bar{x}$, $\bar{p}$ for a Gaussian wave packet subject to a quadratic potential follow the same trajectory in phase space as does the corresponding classical particle. One consequence of this fact is that E_{cl}, defined in Eq. (10.5.8), will be a constant for the quantum case as well as for the classical case[25] and, since $\langle H \rangle$ is conserved, the quantity $\mathscr{E}$ defined in Eqs. (10.5.9) will also be a constant.

We turn next to an examination of the time dependence of the uncertainties Δx and Δp and introduce, in addition to the notation $\chi(t) = (\Delta x)^2$, the notation

$$\Omega(t) = (\Delta p)^2. \tag{10.5.16}$$

For the wave function defined in Eqs. (10.5.4) and (10.5.6) we find that

$$\Omega(t) = \frac{\hbar^2}{4\chi} + a^2\chi \tag{10.5.17}$$

so that

$$\chi(t)\Omega(t) = \frac{\hbar^2}{4} + a^2\chi^2 = \frac{\hbar^2}{4} + \frac{m^2\dot{\chi}^2}{4} \tag{10.5.18}$$

---

[25] Note that this is only true when $V(x)$ is quadratic.

by use of Eq. (10.5.12). It follows that a minimum uncertainty measurement at $t = t_0$ requires that

$$a(t_0) = \dot{\chi}(t_0) = 0 \qquad (10.5.19)$$

and that, in general, the wave function will not continue to correspond to one of minimum uncertainty for $t > t_0$. The time dependence of $\chi(t)$ is determined by Eq. (10.5.11) subject to the initial conditions $\chi(t_0) = \chi_0$ and $\dot{\chi}(t_0) = 0$. The form of the solution depends on κ and is

$\kappa > 0$ (potential well):

$$\chi(t) = \left(\chi_0 - \frac{\mathscr{E}}{\kappa} \right) \cos 2\omega t + \frac{\mathscr{E}}{\kappa}; \qquad \omega = \left(\frac{\kappa}{m} \right)^{1/2} \qquad (10.5.20)$$

$\kappa = 0$ (free particle):

$$\chi(t) = \frac{2\mathscr{E}}{m} t^2 + \chi_0 \qquad (10.5.21)$$

$\kappa < 0$ (parabolic barrier):

$$\chi(t) = \left(\chi_0 + \frac{\mathscr{E}}{\kappa_b} \right) \cosh 2\mu t - \frac{\mathscr{E}}{\kappa_b} \qquad (10.5.22)$$

where $\kappa = -\kappa_b$, $\kappa_b > 0$, $\mu = (\kappa_b/m)^{1/2}$ and $\mathscr{E} = \langle H \rangle - E_{cl}$ has been defined in Eq. (10.5.9). Since $\mathscr{E}$ is a constant, it may be evaluated at $t = t_0$ with the result

$$\mathscr{E} = \frac{\hbar^2}{8m\chi_0} + \tfrac{1}{2}\kappa\chi_0. \qquad (10.5.23)$$

Coherent States

For a particle represented by a Gaussian wave packet oscillating in a harmonic potential well, we see from Eq. (10.5.20) that $\chi(t)$ is oscillatory in general, but is constant for the particular value

$$\chi_0 = \frac{\mathscr{E}}{\kappa} = \frac{\hbar^2}{8m\kappa\chi_0} + \tfrac{1}{2}\chi_0,$$

that is, for

$$\chi_0 = \chi_c = \frac{\hbar}{2(m\kappa)^{1/2}} = \frac{\hbar}{2m\omega} \qquad (10.5.24)$$

where $\omega = (\kappa/m)^{1/2}$. Therefore, for this initial value of χ, a minimum uncertainty measurement leads to a Gaussian wave packet that oscillates back and forth in the harmonic potential well without change in shape. In this case it is referred to as a coherent state.[26] Since, as follows from Eq. (10.5.12), $a \equiv 0$ for a coherent state, we may rewrite Eqs. (10.5.4) and (10.5.6) for this case as follows:

$$\psi(x, t) = \frac{1}{(2\pi\chi_c)^{1/4}} \exp\left(\frac{i\bar{p}x}{\hbar} - \frac{(x - \bar{x})^2}{4\chi_c} \right) \qquad (10.5.25)$$

where χ_c is defined in Eq. (10.5.24) and we have used Eqs. (10.5.13) and (10.5.15). A multiplying factor

$$\exp\frac{i(\bar{p}\bar{x} + c)}{\hbar}$$

has been omitted in going from Eq. (10.5.4) and (10.5.6) to Eq. (10.5.25), since it is independent of x and has unit modulus; it therefore has no effect on the expectation of any observable computed on the basis of ψ.

From Eqs. (8.9.26) and (10.5.24), we see that Eq. (10.5.25) describes a Gaussian wave packet with the same width Δx as the ground state wave function for the particle in the harmonic potential well. Therefore, the coherent state for this case can also be described as the ground state $\varphi_0(x)$ given in Eq. (8.9.25), for which $\bar{x} = 0$, displaced without change of shape so that $\bar{x} \neq 0$, and subsequently oscillating back and forth without change of shape.

Tunneling through Parabolic Barrier

As seen from Eq. (10.5.22), motion of a Gaussian wave packet on a parabolic barrier is accompanied by an indefinite spreading of the wave packet. This gives rise to the phenomenon of the possibility of quantum mechanical tunneling of a particle through a barrier, even when its classical energy is insufficient to carry it over the barrier.

Consider a particle subject to the potential $V(x) = -\frac{1}{2}\kappa_b x^2$ in a Gaussian wave packet state, with conditions at $t = 0$ corresponding to $\bar{x}_0 < 0$, $\dot{\bar{x}}_0 > 0$, $\chi(0) = \chi_0$, $\dot{\chi}(0) = 0$. Then, the wave packet mean $\bar{x}(t)$ follows the classical equations

$$\bar{x}(t) = \bar{x}_0 \cosh \mu t + \frac{\dot{\bar{x}}_0}{\mu} \sinh \mu t \qquad (10.5.26)$$

with $\mu = (\kappa_b/m)^{1/2}$ and $\chi(t)$ is given by Eq. (10.5.22).

---

[26] This property of an appropriate Gaussian wave packet in a harmonic well was already noted by Schrödinger (1926). The theory of coherent states has been extensively studied in recent years particularly in connection with quantum aspects of optical phenomena (see Glauber, 1963; Klauder and Sudershan, 1968; Louisell, 1973).

The probability $P(t)$ of finding the particle at time t on the other side of the barrier peak in the region $x > 0$ is

$$P(t) = \int_0^\infty |\psi(x, t)|^2 \, dx = \frac{1}{(2\pi\chi)^{1/2}} \int_0^\infty \exp\left[-\frac{(x - \bar{x})^2}{2\chi}\right] dx$$

$$= \frac{1}{2} \text{erfc}\left[\frac{-\bar{x}(t)}{(2\chi(t))^{1/2}}\right] \tag{10.5.27}$$

where we have made use of Eq. (10.5.4). If the classical energy of the particle is insufficient to carry it over the barrier, its mean position $\bar{x}(t)$ will reach a maximum value $\bar{x}_{max} < 0$ and then return down the barrier, moving indefinitely to the left. At the same time, however, the wave packet is spreading, as seen from Eq. (10.5.22), and the particle tunneling results from the competition between these processes. From Eqs. (10.5.22) and (10.5.26),

$$\lim_{t \to \infty} \frac{-\bar{x}(t)}{(2\chi(t))^{1/2}} = B\left(v_0^* - \dot{\bar{x}}_0\right) \tag{10.5.28}$$

where

$$B = \frac{1}{2\mu}\left(\frac{\chi_0}{2} + \frac{\hbar^2}{8m\kappa_b\chi_0}\right)^{-1/2} \tag{10.5.29}$$

and

$$v_0^* = -\left(\frac{\kappa_b}{m}\right)^{1/2} \bar{x}_0 \tag{10.5.30}$$

is the critical initial velocity that would just carry the classical particle to the barrier top. Therefore, the quantum transmission function $K_{qu}(\bar{x}_0, \dot{\bar{x}}_0) = \lim_{t \to \infty} P(t)$ is

$$K_{qu}(\bar{x}_0, \dot{\bar{x}}_0) = \tfrac{1}{2}\text{erfc}\left[B\left(v_0^* - \dot{\bar{x}}_0\right)\right]. \tag{10.5.31}$$

There is a close analogy between the quantum mechanical tunneling of a Gaussian wave packet through a parabolic barrier and the overcoming of such a barrier of a classical particle with the aid of Brownian motion. This analogy[27] extends both to the physical picture of the process and to its mathematical formulation, as may be seen by comparing the quantum treatment of this section with the Brownian motion study of Section 7.7.

----

[27]The analogy between quantum mechanics and Brownian motion extends to other aspects of these subjects and has been widely studied. For a review see Jammer (1974, Chapter 9).

10.6   CANONICAL ENSEMBLE IN TERMS OF COHERENT STATES

Consider a harmonic oscillator with Hamiltonian

$$H(x, p) = \frac{p^2}{2m} + \tfrac{1}{2}\kappa x^2 = \frac{1}{2m}(p^2 + m^2\omega^2 x^2). \tag{10.6.1}$$

The density matrix $\rho(x', x)$ for its canonical ensemble is [Eq. (10.2.25)]

$$\rho(x', x) = Z^{-1}\sum_{n=0}^{\infty} \varphi_n(x')\varphi_n(x)e^{-\beta E_n}$$

$$= D\sum_{n=0}^{\infty} \varphi_n(x')\varphi_n(x)e^{-\bar{\beta}n} \tag{10.6.2}$$

where Z is given in Eq. (10.2.32),

$$\bar{\beta} = \frac{\hbar\omega}{kT} \tag{10.6.3}$$

$$D = 1 - e^{-\bar{\beta}} \tag{10.6.4}$$

and $\varphi_n(x)$ are the stationary states of the harmonic oscillator,[28] Eq. (8.9.25), with corresponding energy values $E_n = (n + \tfrac{1}{2})\hbar\omega$, $n = 0, 1, 2, \ldots$.

Let $\psi(x, t)$, as defined in Eq. (10.5.25), describe a coherent state of the oscillator. Since it defines a Gaussian wave packet that moves without change of width, the time dependence of $\psi(x, t)$ is due only to the variation of the means $\bar{x}$ and $\bar{p}$ and we can alternatively describe the coherent state as $\psi(x; \bar{x}, \bar{p})$; that is,

$$\psi(x; \bar{x}, \bar{p}) = \frac{1}{(2\pi\chi_c)^{1/4}}\exp\left(\frac{i\bar{p}x}{\hbar} - \frac{(x - \bar{x})^2}{4\chi_c}\right) \tag{10.6.5}$$

with $\chi_c = \hbar/(2m\omega)$.

We now wish to express the density matrix $\rho(x', x)$ as a superposition of coherent states. That is, we seek a function $\bar{\rho}(\bar{x}, \bar{p})$ such that

$$\int_{-\infty}^{\infty}\int_{-\infty}^{\infty} \bar{\rho}(\bar{x}, \bar{p})\psi(x'; \bar{x}, \bar{p})\psi^*(x; \bar{x}, \bar{p})\,d\bar{x}\,d\bar{p} = \rho(x', x) \quad (10.6.6)$$

where

$$\int_{-\infty}^{\infty}\int_{-\infty}^{\infty} \bar{\rho}(\bar{x}, \bar{p})\,d\bar{x}\,d\bar{p} = 1 \tag{10.6.7}$$

---

[28] Note that these stationary states are real, so that the complex conjugate is not needed in Eq. (10.6.2) as in the general definition of the density matrix in Eq. (10.2.25).

and where $\rho(x', x)$ is the same function of its arguments as given in Eq. (10.6.2).

Before deriving the precise form of the function $\bar{\rho}(\bar{x}, \bar{p})$, we note that Eqs. (10.6.2) and (10.6.6) lead to two different physical pictures if we think of the density matrix $\rho(x', x)$ as representing an ensemble of replicas of the harmonic oscillator. In the first, each replica is in some stationary state $\varphi_n(x)$, $n = 0, 1, 2, \ldots$ and the fraction of replicas of the ensemble in a given stationary state φ_m is $Z^{-1}e^{-\beta E_m}$. In the second, each replica is in a coherent state $\psi(x; \bar{x}, \bar{p})$; this state is time dependent since the means $\bar{x}(t)$, $\bar{p}(t)$ follow a classical trajectory in a phase space with coordinates $\bar{x}$, $\bar{p}$. The density of replicas at $(\bar{x}, \bar{p})$ is $\bar{\rho}(\bar{x}, \bar{p})$.

Although the two physical pictures are quite different, they both lead to the same expected values $\langle\langle F\rangle\rangle$ for any observable F since they are both equivalent to the same density matrix. That is

$$\langle\langle F\rangle\rangle = \int_{-\infty}^{\infty} [F\rho(x', x)]_{x'=x}\, dx \qquad (10.6.8)$$

where, according to the basic density matrix formalism (Eq. 10.2.26), F acts only on the variable x'. If the definition of Eq. (10.6.2) is used for $\rho(x', x)$, we find

$$\langle\langle F\rangle\rangle = Z^{-1} \sum_{n=0}^{\infty} e^{-\beta E_n}\langle F\rangle_n \qquad (10.6.9)$$

where $\langle F\rangle_n = (\varphi_n, F\varphi_n)$. If the definition of Eq. (10.6.6) is used for $\rho(x', x)$,

$$\langle\langle F\rangle\rangle = \int_{-\infty}^{\infty}\int_{-\infty}^{\infty} \bar{\rho}(\bar{x}, \bar{p})\langle F\rangle(\bar{x}, \bar{p})\, d\bar{x}\, d\bar{p} \qquad (10.6.10)$$

where $\langle F\rangle(\bar{x}, \bar{p}) = (\psi_{\bar{x}, \bar{p}}, F\psi_{\bar{x}, \bar{p}})$ is the quantum mean of F when the system is in the coherent state $\psi(x; \bar{x}, \bar{p}) = \psi_{\bar{x}, \bar{p}}$. It is clear that the coherent state ensemble provides a close analog to the classical formalism.

Computation[29] of $\bar{\rho}(\bar{x}, \bar{p})$

Let

$$X = \left(\frac{m\omega}{\hbar}\right)^{1/2} x,$$

$$P = (\hbar m\omega)^{-1/2} p. \qquad (10.6.11)$$

Then, the coherent state $\psi(x; \bar{x}, \bar{p})$ may be rewritten in terms of these new

[29]A computation based on an operator formalism for treating coherent states will be found in Glauber (1963); see also Klauder and Sudershan (1968) and Louisell (1973). We follow here the analytical approach of Weiner (1968).

variables as

$$\psi(X; \overline{X}, \overline{P}) = \frac{1}{(2\pi\chi_c)^{1/4}} \exp\left(i\overline{P}X - \tfrac{1}{2}(X - \overline{X})^2\right). \quad (10.6.12)$$

Similarly, the stationary states $\varphi_n(x)$ are rewritten as functions of these variables, $\varphi_n(X)$. Since the latter form a complete set, we may express the coherent states $\psi(X; \overline{X}, \overline{P})$ in terms of them. The expansion takes the following form (see Messiah, 1964, p. 492)

$$\psi(X; \overline{X}, \overline{P}) = \exp\left\{-\left[\tfrac{1}{4}(\overline{X}^2 + \overline{P}^2) - \tfrac{1}{2}i\overline{P}\overline{X}\right]\right\} \sum_{n=0}^{\infty} \frac{(\overline{X} + i\overline{P})^n}{(n!)^{1/2}2^{n/2}} \varphi_n(X).$$

$$(10.6.13)$$

Let

$$\xi = \tfrac{1}{2}(\overline{P}^2 + \overline{Q}^2) = H(\overline{x}, \overline{p})/\hbar\omega = E_{cl}/\hbar\omega, \quad (10.6.14)$$

where E_{cl} is the classical energy corresponding to the trajectory $\overline{x}(t)$, $\overline{p}(t)$ and, as we have noted in Section 10.4, is a constant on the trajectory, which is, as seen from Eq. (10.6.14), a circle of radius $(2\xi)^{1/2}$ in the $\overline{Q}, \overline{P}$ plane. We write

$$\overline{Q} + i\overline{P} = (2\xi)^{1/2}e^{i\theta} \quad (10.6.15)$$

and use ξ, θ as parameters in place of $\overline{Q}, \overline{P}$, writing the coherent states $\psi(X; \overline{X}, \overline{P}) = \psi(X; \xi, \theta)$. Then, Eq. (10.6.13) takes the form

$$\psi(X; \xi, \theta) = \exp\left\{-\tfrac{1}{2}\xi(1 + i\sin 2\theta)\right\} \sum_{n=0}^{\infty} \frac{\xi^{n/2}e^{in\theta}}{(n!)^{1/2}} \varphi_n(X). \quad (10.6.16)$$

We also use ξ, θ as coordinates for the phase space $\overline{\Gamma}$ and rewrite Eq. (10.6.6) as[30]

$$\int_0^{2\pi} d\theta \int_0^{\infty} \overline{\rho}(\xi, \theta)\psi(X'; \xi, \theta)\psi^*(X; \xi, \theta)\, d\xi = \rho(X', X). \quad (10.6.17)$$

[30] The distribution functions $\overline{\rho}_{\overline{X}, \overline{P}}(\overline{X}, \overline{P})$ and $\overline{\rho}_{\xi, \theta}(\xi, \theta)$ are related by the equation

$$\overline{\rho}_{\overline{X}, \overline{P}} = \overline{\rho}_{\xi, \theta} \frac{\partial(\xi, \theta)}{\partial(\overline{X}, \overline{P})}$$

where $\partial(\xi, \theta)/\partial(\overline{X}, \overline{P})$ denotes the Jacobian. For simplicity, we are writing $\overline{\rho}_{\overline{X}, \overline{P}}(\overline{X}, \overline{P}) = \overline{\rho}(\overline{X}, \overline{P})$ and similarly for other coordinate systems.

We assume

$$\bar{\rho}(\xi, \theta) = \frac{1}{2\pi}\bar{\rho}(\xi), \qquad (10.6.18)$$

that is, that the phase angles θ are uniformly distributed. Equation (10.6.17) then takes the form

$$\int_0^\infty \bar{\rho}(\xi)e^{-\xi}\sum_{n=0}^\infty \frac{\xi^n}{n!}\varphi_n(X')\varphi_n(X)\,d\xi = \rho(X', X) \qquad (10.6.19)$$

where we have made use of Eq. (10.6.16). Comparison of Eqs. (10.6.19) and (10.6.2) shows that $\bar{\rho}(\xi)$ must satisfy the equation

$$\int_0^\infty e^{-\xi}\xi^n\bar{\rho}(\xi)\,d\xi = n!De^{-\bar{\beta}n}, \qquad \text{for } n = 0, 1, 2, \ldots. \qquad (10.6.20)$$

This integral equation is readily solved by rewriting the right-hand side by use of the integral representation of the Γ function:

$$n!e^{-\bar{\beta}n} = \Gamma(n + 1)e^{-\bar{\beta}n} = \int_0^\infty (e^{-\beta}y)^n e^{-y}\,dy$$

$$= b\int_0^\infty \xi^n e^{-b\xi}\,d\xi, \qquad (10.6.21)$$

where $b = e^{\bar{\beta}}$. Comparison of Eqs. (10.6.20) and (10.6.21) then shows that

$$\bar{\rho}(\xi) = Dbe^{-(b-1)\xi} = (b - 1)e^{-(b-1)\xi} = ce^{-c\xi}, \qquad (10.6.22)$$

where

$$c = b - 1 = e^{\bar{\beta}} - 1. \qquad (10.6.23)$$

We next express the distribution function $\bar{\rho}(\xi, \theta) = (2\pi)^{-1}\bar{\rho}(\xi)$ in terms of $\bar{x}, \bar{p}$,

$$\bar{\rho}(\bar{x}, \bar{p}) = \frac{\partial(\xi, \theta)}{\partial(\bar{x}, \bar{p})}\bar{\rho}(\xi, \theta) = \hbar^{-1}\bar{\rho}(\xi, \theta)$$

$$= \frac{c}{2\pi\hbar}\exp\left\{-\frac{c(\bar{p}^2/m + \kappa\bar{x}^2)}{2\hbar\omega}\right\}. \qquad (10.6.24)$$

For high temperature levels such that $\bar{\beta} = \dfrac{\hbar\omega}{kT} \ll 1, c \sim \bar{\beta}$ and

$$\bar{\rho}(\bar{x}, \bar{p}) \cong \frac{\omega}{2\pi kT}\exp\left\{-\frac{(\bar{p}^2/m + \kappa\bar{x}^2)}{2kT}\right\} = \rho_{cl}(\bar{x}, \bar{p}) \qquad (10.6.25)$$

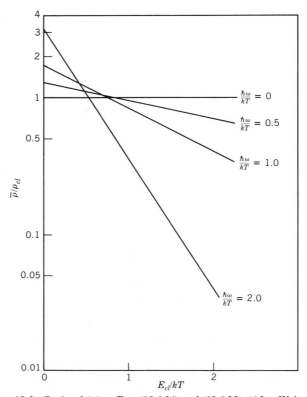

Figure 10.6   Ratio of $\bar{\rho}/\rho_{cl}$, Eqs. (10.6.24) and (10.6.25). (After Weiner 1970.)

where $\rho_{cl}(\bar{x}, \bar{p})$ is the classical canonical distribution function for a harmonic oscillator.

In Figure 10.6 we show the ratio of $\bar{\rho}/\rho_{cl}$ for various values of $\hbar\omega/kT$. It is seen that at low temperature levels, quantum statistics favor the low values of E_{cl} and make large values of E_{cl} much less probable than do classical statistics.

10.7   QUANTUM EFFECTS ON RATE PROCESSES

The discussions of rate theory in solids presented in Chapter 7 were purely classical in nature; classical statistical mechanics was used to describe the condition of thermal equilibrium in the potential well and classical mechanics was used to describe the dynamics of the system in overcoming the potential barrier.

In this section we wish to assess the importance of quantum effects on rate processes and, for this purpose, consider a quantum generalization of the simple classical rate theory presented in Section 7.3. We again use as an example the physical process of the diffusion of interstitial impurity atoms in a crystal and our discussion parallels the classical treatment of that section.

We assume that at a given instant of time, at sufficiently low temperature levels, the overwhelming majority of impurity atoms will be found in the harmonic portion of the potential well in their respective lattice cells and that the quantum state of each impurity atom can be described by a coherent state $\psi(x; \bar{x}, \bar{p})$ as defined in Eq. (10.6.5). Here $\chi_c = \hbar/(2m\omega)$, with m the mass of the impurity atom and ω the circular frequency of its oscillation in the potential well.

To describe the instantaneous state of the entire collection of impurity atoms in the harmonic well, we use the distribution function $\bar{\rho}(\bar{x}, \bar{p})$, given in Eq. (10.6.24), which defines a canonical ensemble in terms of coherent states.

A wave packet corresponding to a coherent state moves without change of shape only so long as the wave packet remains in the harmonic region of the well. When the wave packet moves onto the potential barrier it begins to spread. We now assume that when a wave packet of the ensemble crosses $\bar{x} = 0$ with $\dot{\bar{x}} = \bar{p}/m > 0$, the subsequent probability that the particle will be found beyond the barrier peak at $x = b$ is given by the quantum transmission function $K_{qu}(0, \dot{\bar{x}})$ defined in Eq. (10.5.31), with[31]

$$v_0^* = \left(\frac{2E_b}{m}\right)^{1/2} = \left(\frac{\kappa_b}{m}\right)^{1/2} b \tag{10.7.1}$$

with E_b, the barrier height; κ_b, the barrier curvature; and $\chi_0 = \chi_c = \hbar/2m\omega$. By the same reasoning followed in Sections 7.3 and 7.8 we are, therefore, led to the following expression for the rate of barrier crossing:

$$f_{qu} = \frac{1}{m} \int_0^\infty \bar{p} K_{qu}\left(0, \frac{\bar{p}}{m}\right) \bar{\rho}(0, \bar{p}) \, d\bar{p}. \tag{10.7.2}$$

With Eqs. (10.5.31) and (10.7.1) employed for K_{qu} and Eq. (10.6.24) employed for $\bar{\rho}$, the result of carrying out the integration is

$$f_{qu} = \frac{\omega}{2\pi}\left[\tfrac{1}{2}\mathrm{erfc}\, U + \tfrac{1}{2}(1 + \tfrac{1}{2}c)^{-1/2} e^{-U_c^2/(2+c)}\mathrm{erfc}\left(-U\left(1 + \frac{c}{2}\right)^{-1/2}\right)\right] \tag{10.7.3}$$

where

$$U = (2E_b/\hbar\omega)^{1/2} \tag{10.7.4}$$

[31]This method of computing the tunneling probability corresponds to the simplifying assumption that the wave packet enters on a parabolic barrier with curvature κ_b as soon as its mean crosses $x = 0$. Numerical computations presented in Weiner and Partom (1969) indicate that this procedure is reasonably accurate for sufficiently large $E_b/\hbar\omega$, say $E_b/\hbar\omega > 2$. For smaller values of the parameter $E_b/\hbar\omega$, the computation of the tunneling probability must take into account the gradual transition in potential curvature from its positive value in the potential well to the negative value on the barrier. An approximate analytical procedure for this purpose is also presented in this reference.

and, as previously defined in Eq. (10.6.23)

$$c = e^{\bar{\beta}} - 1 = e^{\hbar\omega/kT} - 1. \tag{10.7.5}$$

Numerical values for f_{qu} are shown in Figure 10.7. It is seen that at high temperature levels the rate expression provides a straight line Arrhenius plot characteristic of classical behavior. At low temperature levels, however, the Arrhenius plot exhibits a positive curvature due to tunneling effects. This type of curvature is observed in Arrhenius plots of experimental data in situations where tunneling is expected to play an important role, for example, in the diffusion of hydrogen in metals. A review of experimental data for this latter process has been given by Völkl and Alefeld (1975); as they note, the theory of such quantum rate processes has not yet progressed to the point where it can quantitatively explain all aspects of the observed phenomena.

The rate theory formulation of Eq. (10.7.2) incorporates the effect of quantum statistics for the description of thermal equilibrium in the well and the effect of quantum dynamics in the description of the motion of the system on the potential barrier. We can examine the result of including only one of these quantum aspects of the process by replacing either the quantum distribution function $\bar{\rho}$ by its classical limit ρ_{cl}, Eq. (10.6.25), or the quantum transmission function K_{qu} by its classical counterpart K_{cl} where

$$K_{cl}(0, \bar{p}/m) = 0 \quad \text{if } \bar{p} < (2mE_b)^{1/2}$$

$$= 1 \quad \text{if } \bar{p} > (2mE_b)^{1/2}. \tag{10.7.6}$$

In this way we can compute

$$f_{QS,CD} = \frac{1}{m} \int_0^{\infty} \bar{p} K_{cl}(0, \bar{p}/m)\bar{\rho}(0, \bar{p}) \, d\bar{p}, \tag{10.7.7}$$

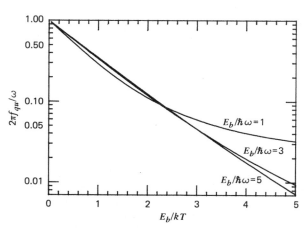

Figure 10.7 Quantum rate of barrier crossing, Eq. (10.7.3). (After Weiner 1970.)

incorporating quantum statistics (QS) but classical dynamics (CD), or

$$f_{CS,QD} = \frac{1}{m} \int_0^\infty \bar{p} K_{qu}(0, \bar{p}/m) \rho_{cl}(0, \bar{p}) \, d\bar{p}, \qquad (10.7.8)$$

incorporating quantum dynamics (QD) but classical statistics (CS). The results are shown in Figure 10.8 together with $f_{QS,QD} = f_{qu}$ [Eqs. (10.7.2) and (10.7.3)] and $f_{CS,CD} = f_{cl}$ [Eq. (7.3.8)]. The parameter value $E_b/\hbar\omega = 1$ (barrier height only twice the zero-point energy) was chosen to emphasize quantum effects. It is seen that $f_{QS,CD}$ exhibits negative curvature in an Arrhenius plot; the effect of quantum statistics causes the rate to decrease more rapidly with decreasing temperature than do classical statistics. On the other hand, $f_{CS,QD}$ exhibits positive curvature due to the rate-enhancing effect of tunneling. The combined effects lead to substantially straight-line behavior for f_{qu} at high temperature levels, with tunneling effects controlling at low temperature levels.

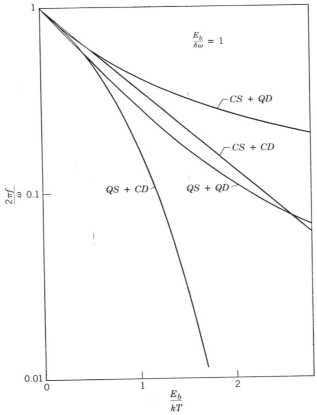

Figure 10.8 Comparison of different ways of computing barrier-crossing rates. CS, classical statistics; CD, classical dynamics; QS, quantum statistics; QD, quantum dynamics.

Additional References

Quantum rate theory is the subject of much current research. References to some of this work will be found in Sussmann (1971), Flynn (1972), and Fain (1980). A generalization of the approach described in this section to systems with many degrees of freedom is given by Weiner and Partom (1970). Different approaches to the quantum generalization of Kramers rate theory, Section 7.8, will be found in Ishioka (1980) and in Wolynes (1981).

References

Arnold, V. I., *Mathematical Methods of Classical Mechanics*, Springer-Verlag, New York (1978).

Arnold, V. I. and Avez, A., *Ergodic Problems of Classical Mechanics*, Benjamin, New York (1968).

Ashcroft, N. W. and Mermin, N. D., *Solid State Physics*, Holt, Rinehart and Winston, New York (1976).

Barber, M. N., and Ninham, B. W., *Random and Restricted Walks*, Gordon and Breach, New York (1970).

Barron, T. H. K., Collins, J. G., and White, G. K., "Thermal expansion of solids at low temperatures," *Adv. Phys.* **29**, 609–730 (1980).

Barron, T. H. K., and Klein, M. L., "Second-order elastic constants of a solid under stress," Proc. Phys. Soc. **85**, 523–532 (1965).

Begbie, G. H., and Born, M., "Thermal scattering of X-rays by crystals I. Dynamical foundation," *Proc. R. Soc. London, Ser. A* **188**, 179–188 (1947).

Birkhoff, G., and MacLane, S., *A Survey of Modern Algebra*, Macmillan, New York (1944).

Birshtein, T. M., and Ptitsyn, O. B., *Conformations of Macromolecules*, S. M. Timasheff and M. J. Timasheff, Trans., Wiley-Interscience, New York (1966).

Blackman, M., "Contributions to the theory of specific heat. III—On the existence of pseudo-T^3 regions in the specific heat of a crystal," *Proc. R. Soc. London, Ser. A* **149**, 117–125 (1935).

Blokhintsev, D. I., *Principles of Quantum Mechanics*, Trans. by Scripta Technica, Inc., Edited by S. Bjorklund, Allyn and Bacon, Boston, Massachusetts (1964).

Boggs, F. W., "Statistical mechanics of rubber," *J. Chem. Phys.* **20**, 632–636 (1952).

Böhm, A., *Quantum Mechanics*, Springer-Verlag, New York (1979).

Bohm, D., *Quantum Theory*, Prentice-Hall, Englewood Cliffs, New Jersey (1951).

Bohm, D., and Vigier, J. P., "Model of the causal interpretation of quantum theory in terms of a fluid with irregular fluctuations," *Phys. Rev.* **96**, 208–216 (1954).

Boley, B. A., and Weiner, J. H., *Theory of Thermal Stresses*, Wiley, New York, (1960).

Boltzmann, L., "Über das Warmegleich-gewicht zwischen mehratomigen Gasmolekülen," *Sitzber. Akad. Wiss. Wien* **63**, 397–418 (1871a).

Boltzmann, L., "Einige allgemeine Satze über Warmegleichgewicht," *Sitzber. Akad. Wiss. Wien* **63**, 679–711 (1871b).

Boltzmann, L., "Über die mechanischen Analogien des zweiten Hauptsatzes der Thermodynamik," *J. Reine Angew. Math.* **100**, 201–212 (1887).

Born, M., *Natural Philosophy of Cause and Chance*, Clarendon Press, Oxford (1949).

Born, M., and Huang, K., *Dynamical Theory of Crystal Lattices*, Clarendon Press, Oxford (1954).

Born, M. and Oppenheimer, R., "Zur Quantentheorie der Molekeln," *Ann. d. Phys.* **84**, 457–484 (1927).

Brillouin, L., *Tensors in Mechanics and Elasticity*, Academic Press, New York, (1964).

Buchdahl, H. A., *The Concepts of Classical Thermodynamics*, Cambridge University Press (1966).

Buchdahl, H. A., "Energy fluctuations of thermodynamic systems: Higher moments," *Int. J. Theoret. Phys.* **21**, 369–381 (1982).

Callen, H. B., *Thermodynamics*, Wiley, New York (1960).

Carrier, G. F., Krook, M. and Pearson, C. E., *Functions of a Complex Variable*, McGraw–Hill, New York (1966).

Chandrasekhar, S., "Stochastic problems in physics and astronomy," *Rev. of Mod. Phys.* **15**, 1–89 (1943); reprinted in *Selected Papers on Noise and Stochastic Processes*, N. Wax, Ed., Dover, New York (1954).

Cochran, W., *The Dynamics of Atoms in Crystals*, Crane, Russak, New York (1973).

Cohen-Tannoudji, C., Diu, B., and Laloë, F., *Quantum Mechanics*, Vols. I and II, Wiley, New York (1977).

Cowley, R. A., "The lattice dynamics of an anharmonic crystal," *Adv. Phys.* **12**, 421–480 (1963).

Davydov, A. S., *Quantum Mechanics*, D. ter Haar, Trans. Ed., Pergamon Press, New York (1965).

Deam, R. T., and Edwards, S. F., "The theory of rubber elasticity," *Philos. Trans. R. Soc. London, Ser. A* **280**, 317–353 (1976).

Debye, P., "The early days of lattice dynamics," pp. 9–13 in *Lattice Dynamics*, *J. Phys. Chem. Sol., Suppl.* 1, R. F. Wallis, Ed., Pergamon Press, Oxford (1965).

Debye, P., "Zur Theorie der spezifischen Wärmen," *Ann. Phys.* **39**, 798–839 (1912).

DeCicco, P. D., and Johnson, F. A., "The quantum theory of lattice dynamics. IV," *Proc. R. Soc. London, Ser. A* **310**, 111–119 (1969).

de Gennes, P. G., *Scaling Concepts in Polymer Physics*, Cornell University Press, Ithaca, New York, (1979).

Deutch, J. M., and Silbey, R., "Exact generalized Langevin equation for a particle in a harmonic lattice," *Phys. Rev. A* **3**, 2045–2052 (1971).

Dicke, R. H., and Wittke, J. P., *Introduction to Quantum Mechanics*, Addison-Wesley, Reading, Massachusetts (1960).

Dolling, G. and Cowley, R. A., "The thermodynamic and optical properties of germanium, silicon, diamond and gallium arsenide," *Proc. Phys. Soc.* **88**, 463–494 (1966).

Dossin, L. M. and Graessley, W. W., "Rubber elasticity of well-characterized polybutadiene networks," *Macromolecules*, **12**, 123–130 (1979).

Dym, H., and McKean, H. P., *Fourier Series and Integrals*, Academic Press, New York (1972).

Eichinger, B. E., "Elasticity theory. 5. Mean field solution of the network collapse problem," *Macromolecules* **14**, 1071–1076 (1981).

Einstein, A., "Über die von der molekularkinetischen Theorie der Wärme geforderte Bewegung von in ruhenden Flussigkeiten suspendierten Teilchen," *Ann. Phys.* (*4*) **17**, 549–560 (1905).

Einstein, A., "Die Plancksche Theorie der Strahlung und die Theorie der spezifischen Warme," *Ann. Phys.* **22**, 180–190 (1907).

Einstein, A., "Eine Beziehung zwischen dem elastischen Verhalten und der spezifischen Wärme bei festen Korpern mit einatomigen Molekül," *Ann. Phys.* **34**, 170–174 (1911).

Ericksen, J. L., "On the symmetry and stability of thermoelastic solids," *J. Appl. Mech.* **45**, 740–744 (1978).

Fain, B., *Theory of Rate Processes in Condensed Media*, Vol. 20, in *Lecture Notes in Chemistry*, Edited by G. Berthier et al., Springer-Verlag, New York (1980).

Falk, G., "Axiomatik der Thermodynamik" in *Handbuch der Physik*, S. Flügge, Ed., Vol. III/2, p. 119, Springer-Verlag, New York (1959).

Farquhar, I. E., *Ergodic Theory in Statistical Mechanics*, Wiley-Interscience, New York (1964).

Feller, W., *An Introduction to Probability Theory and Its Applications*, Vol. I, Wiley, New York (1950).

Fermi, E., Pasta, J., and Ulam, S., Los Alamos Scientific Lab. Rep. LA-1940 (1955). Reprinted *in* Enrico Fermi, Collected Papers, Vol. II, pp. 978–989, University of Chicago Press (1965).

Feynman, R. P., and Hibbs, A. R., *Quantum Mechanics and Path Integrals*, McGraw-Hill, New York (1965).

Feynman, R. P., "Forces in molecules," *Phys. Rev.* **56**, 340–343 (1939).

Fixman, M., "Classical statistical mechanics of constraints: A theorem and application to polymers," *Proc. Natl. Acad. Sci. U.S.A.* **71**, 3050–3053 (1974).

Flory, P. J., *Principles of Polymer Chemistry*, Cornell University Press, Ithaca, New York (1953).

Flory, P. J., *Statistical Mechanics of Chain Molecules*, Wiley-Interscience, New York (1969).

Flory, P. J., "Statistical thermodynamics of random networks", *Proc. R. Soc. London, Ser. A* **351**, 351–380 (1976).

Flory, P. J., "Theory of elasticity of polymer networks. The effect of local constraints on junctions," *J. Chem. Phys.* **68**, 5720–5729 (1977a).

Flory, P. J., "The molecular theory of rubber elasticity," *Contemporary Topics in Polymer Science*, Vol. 2, E. M. Pearce and J. R. Schaefgen, Eds., pp. 1–18, Plenum Press, New York (1977b).

Flynn, C. P., *Point Defects and Diffusion*, Oxford University Press (1972).

Ford, G. W., Kac, M., and Mazur, P., "Statistical mechanics of assemblies of coupled oscillators," *J. Math. Phys.* **6**, 504–514 (1965).

Ford, J., "The transition from analytic dynamics to statistical mechanics," in *Advances in Chemical Physics*, Vol. 24, pp. 155–185, I. Prigogine and S. A. Rice, Eds., Wiley, New York (1973).

Fowler, R. H., *Statistical Mechanics*, 2nd ed., Cambridge University Press (1936).

Freed, K. F., "Statistical mechanics of systems with internal constraints: Rubber elasticity," *J. Chem. Phys.* **55**, 5588–5599 (1971).

Frenkel, J., *Kinetic Theory of Liquids*, Oxford University Press (1946); Dover, New York (1955).

Furry, W. H., "Behavior of de Broglie waves and wave packets," pp. 1–137, in *Lectures in Theoretical Physics*, Vol. V, W. E. Brittin, B. W. Downs, and J. Downs, Eds., Wiley-Interscience, New York (1963).

Garber, J. A., and Granato, A. V., "Theory of the temperature dependence of second-order elastic constants in cubic materials," *Phys. Rev. B* **11**, 3990–3997, (1975).

Gibbs, J. W., *Elementary Principles in Statistical Mechanics*, Yale University Press, New Haven, Connecticut (1902); Dover, New York (1960).

Gilder, H. M., and Ganne, J. P., "Isotropic-continuum-model calculation of the thermal expansion of alloys from third-order elastic constants: Application to CuAl," *Phys. Rev. B* **22**, 5628–5634 (1980).

Glauber, R. J., "Coherent and incoherent states of the radiation field," *Phys. Rev.* **131**, 2766–2788 (1963).

Gō, N., and Scheraga, H. A., "On the use of classical statistical mechanics in the treatment of polymer chain conformation," *Macromolecules* **9**, 535–542 (1976).

Goldstein, H., *Classical Mechanics*, 2nd ed., Addison-Wesley, Reading, Massachusetts (1980).

Gottlieb, M., and Bird, R. B., "A molecular dynamics calculation to confirm the incorrectness of the random-walk distribution for describing the Kramers freely jointed bead-rod chain," *J. Chem. Phys.* **65**, 2467–2468 (1976).

Gottlieb, M. and Macosko, C. W., "On the suppression-of-junction-fluctuations parameter in Flory's network theory," *Macromolecules*, **15**, 535–537 (1982).

Grad, H., "Kinetic theory and statistical mechanics," Lecture notes, prepared with assistance of I. Kolodner, Institute for Mathematics and Mechanics, New York University (1950).

Graessley, W. W., "Statistical mechanics of random coil networks," *Macromolecules*, **8**, 186–190 (1975).

Green, A. E., and Zerna, W., *Theoretical Elasticity*, Oxford University Press (1954).

Grindlay, J., "The derivation of the nonlinear elastic equations from a crystal model," *Can. J. Phys.* **41**, 691–695 (1963).

Grüneisen, E., "Theorie des festen Zustandes einatomiger Elemente," *Ann. Phys.* (4), **39**, 257–306 (1912).

Gürsey, F., "Classical statistical mechanics of a rectilinear assembly," *Proc. Cambridge Philos. Soc.* **46**, 182–194 (1950).

Gurtin, M. E., "The linear theory of elasticity," in *Handbuch der Physik*, pp. 1–295, Editor S. Flügge, Vol. VI a/2, Editor C. Truesdell, Springer-Verlag, New York (1972).

Guth, E., "Statistical mechanics of polymers," J. Polymer Science: Part C **12**, 89–109 (1966).

Guth, E. and Mark, H., "Zur innermolekularen Statistik, insbesondere bei Kettenmolekülen I," *Monats. f. Chemie* **65**, 93–121 (1934).

Guttman, L., and Rothstein, J. A., "Computation of elastic moduli from interatomic forces," *Phys. Rev. B* **19**, 6062–6067 (1979).

Halmos, P. R., *Finite-Dimensional Vector Spaces*, D. Van Nostrand, Princeton, New Jersey (1958).

Hedin, L. T., "A microscopic derivation of the Born-Huang relations between the atomic force constants," *Ark. Phys.* **18**, 369–378 (1960).

Heisenberg, W., *The Physical Principles of the Quantum Theory*, C. Eckart and F. C. Hoyt, Trans., University of Chicago Press (1930); Dover, New York (1949).

Heitler, W., and London, F., "Wechselwirkung neutraler Atome und homöopolare Bindung," *Z. Phys.* **44**, 455–472 (1927).

Helfand, E., "Theory of the kinetics of conformational transitions in polymers," *J. Chem. Phys.* **54**, 4651–4661 (1971).

Helfand, E., "Flexible vs. rigid constraints in statistical mechanics," *J. Chem. Phys.* **71**, 5000–5007 (1979).

Hellmann, H., *Einführung in die Quantenchemie*, Franz Deuticke, Leipzig and Vienna (1937).

Hill, R., "On the elasticity and stability of perfect crystals at finite strain," *Math. Proc. Cambridge Philos. Soc.* **77**, 225–240 (1975).

Hill, T. L., "Thermodynamics of small systems," *J. Chem. Phys.* **36**, 3182–3197 (1962).

Hopf, E., "Complete transitivity and the ergodic principle," *Proc. Natl. Acad. Sci. U.S.A.* **18**, 204–209 (1932).

Huang, K., "On the atomic theory of elasticity," *Proc. R. Soc. London, Ser. A* **203**, 178–194 (1950).

Huntington, H. B., "The elastic constants of crystals," pp. 213–351 in *Solid State Physics*, Vol. 7, F. Seitz and D. Turnbull, Eds., Academic Press, New York (1958).

Ikenberry, E., *Quantum Mechanics for Mathematicians and Physicists*, Oxford University Press, New York (1962).

Ishioka, S., "Quantization of Kramers' Rate Theory," *J. Phys. Soc. Jpn.* **48**, 367–376 (1980).

Jackson, E. A., *Equilibrium Statistical Mechanics*, Prentice-Hall, Englewood Cliffs, New Jersey (1968).

James, H. M., "Statistical properties of networks of flexible chains," *J. Chem. Phys.* **15**, 651–668 (1947).

James, H. M., and Guth, E.,   "Theory of the elastic properties of rubber," *J. Chem. Phys.* **11**, 455–481 (1943).

James, H. M., and Guth, E.,   "Theory of increase in rigidity of rubber during cure," *J. Chem. Phys.* **15**, 669–683 (1947).

James, H. M., and Guth, E.,   "Simple presentation of network theory of rubber with a discussion of other theories," *J. Polymer Sci.* **4**, 153–182 (1949).

Jammer, M.,   *The Philosophy of Quantum Mechanics*, Wiley, New York (1974).

Jánossy, L.,   "Zum hydrodynamischen Modell der Quantenmechanik," *Z. Phys.* **169**, 79–89 (1962).

Jaynes, E. T.,   "Information theory and statistical mechanics," **106**, 620–630; **108**, 171–190 (1957).

Jeffreys, H.,   *Cartesian Tensors*, Cambridge University Press (1931).

Johnson, F. A.,   "A bond charge model of lattice dynamics, I," *Proc. R. Soc. London, Ser. A* **339**, 73–83 (1974).

Johnson, F. A., and Moore, K.,   "A bond charge model of lattice dynamics. II," *Proc. R. Soc. London, Ser. A* **339**, 85–96 (1974).

Kaplan, H.,   "Remarks on force-constant models for lattice dynamics," *Phys. Rev.* **125**, 1905–1910 (1962).

Karrer, E.,   "A kinetic theory of the elasticity of highly elastic gels," *Phys. Rev.* (2) **39**, 857 (1932).

Kästner, S.,   "Theorie der Polymernetzwerke mit behinderter Fluktuation," *Coll. Poly. Sci.* **259**, 499–507, 508–513 (1981).

Katz, A.,   *Principles of Statistical Mechanics; The Information Theory Approach*, Freeman, San Francisco, California (1967).

Kellogg, O. D.,   *Foundations of Potential Theory*, Dover, New York (1953).

Kemble, E. C.,   *The Fundamental Principles of Quantum Mechanics with Elementary Applications*, McGraw-Hill, New York (1937); Dover, New York (1958).

Khinchin, A. I.,   *Mathematical Foundations of Statistical Mechanics*, G. Gamow, Trans., Dover, New York (1949).

Khinchin, A. I.,   *Mathematical Foundations of Information Theory*, R. A. Silverman and M. D. Friedman, Trans., Dover, New York (1957).

Kim, H. Y. and Weiner, J. H.,   "Gaussian-wave-packet dynamics in uniform magnetic and quadratic potential fields," *Phys. Rev. B* **7**, 1353–1362 (1973).

Klauder, J. R., and Sudershan, E. C. G.,   *Fundamentals of Quantum Optics*, Benjamin, New York (1968).

Kolos, W., and Wolniewicz, L.,   "Improved theoretical ground-state energy of the hydrogen molecule," *J. Chem. Phys.* **49**, 404–410 (1968).

Kotkin, G. L. and Serbo, V. G.,   *Collection of Problems in Classical Mechanics*, D. ter Haar, Trans. Ed., Pergamon, Oxford (1971).

Kramers, H. A.,   "Brownian motion in a field of force and the diffusion model of chemical reactions," *Physica (The Hague)* **7**, 284–304 (1940).

Kubo, R.,   *Statistical Mechanics*, North-Holland, Amsterdam, and Wiley, New York (1965).

Kuhn, W.,   "Über die Gestalt fadenförmiger Moleküle in Lösungen," *Kolloid-Z.* **68**, 2–15 (1934).

Landau, L. D., and Lifshitz, E. M.,   *Statistical Physics*, 3rd ed., revised by E. M. Lifshitz and L. P. Pitaevskii; J. B. Sykes and M. J. Kearsley, Trans., Pergamon, New York (1980).

Landauer, R., and Swanson, J. A.,   "Frequency factors in the thermally activated process," *Phys. Rev.* **121**, 1668–1674 (1961).

Landsberg, P. T.,   *Thermodynamics*, Wiley-Interscience, New York (1961).

Landsberg, P. T.,   *Thermodynamics and Statistical Mechanics*, Oxford University Press, (1978).

Langevin, P. "Sur la théorie du mouvement brownien," *C. R. Hebd. Séances Acad. Sci.* **146**, 530–533 (1908).

Lax, M., "The relation between microscopic and macroscopic theories of elasticity," pp. 583–596 in *Lattice Dynamics, J. Phys. Chem. Sol.*, Suppl. 1, R. F. Wallis, Ed., Pergamon Press, Oxford (1965).

Leibfried, G., and Ludwig, W., "Theory of anharmonic effects in crystals," pp. 275–444 in *Solid State Physics*, F. Seitz and D. Turnbull, Eds., Academic Press, New York (1961).

Levine, R. D. and Tribus, M., Eds., *The Maximum Entropy Formalism*, MIT Press, Cambridge, Massachusetts (1979).

Lichnerowicz, A., *Elements of Tensor Calculus*, J. W. Leech and D. J. Newman, Trans., Methuen, London, and Wiley, New York (1962).

Louisell, W. H., *Quantum Statistical Properties of Radiation*, Wiley, New York (1973).

Love, A. E. H., *A Treatise on the Mathematical Theory of Elasticity*, 4th ed., Cambridge University Press (1927).

Luban, M., "Role of external surface forces in the statistical mechanics of solids," *Phys. Rev. B* **11**, 4069–4070 (1975).

Luban, M., and Novogrodsky, H., "Statistical mechanics of solids," *Phys. Rev. B* **6**, 1130–1134 (1972).

Ludwig, W., *Recent Developments in Lattice Theory*, Vol. 43 in Springer Tracts in Modern Physics, G. Höhler, Ed., Springer-Verlag, New York (1967).

Mackey, G. W., "Ergodic theory and its significance for statistical mechanics and probability theory," *Adv. Math.* **12**, 178–268 (1974).

Madelung, E., "Molekulare Eigenschwingungen," *Nachr. Ges., Wiss, Gottingen* **20**, 100–106 (1909).

Madelung, E., "Quantentheorie in hydrodynamischer Form," *Z. Phys.* **40**, 322–326 (1926).

Maradudin, A. A., Montroll, E. W., and Weiss, G. H., *Theory of Lattice Dynamics in the Harmonic Approximation*; Suppl. 3 of *Solid State Physics*, F. Seitz and D. Turnbull, Eds., Academic Press, New York (1963).

Mason, W. P., *Physical Acoustics and the Properties of Solids*, D. Van Nostrand, Princeton, New Jersey (1958).

Mazur, J., and Rubin, R. J., "Coefficient of thermal expansion and Young's modulus for a one-dimensional model of a solid," *Am. J. Phys.* **31**, 835–836 (1963).

McConnell, A. J., *Applications of Tensor Analysis*, Dover, New York (1957).

Messiah, A., *Quantum Mechanics*, Vol. I, G. M. Temmer, Trans., North-Holland, Amsterdam (1964).

Meyer, K. H., and Ferri, C., "Sur l'élasticité du caoutchouc," *Helv. Chim. Acta* **18**, 570–589 (1935).

Meyer, K. H., von Susich, G., and Valko, E., "Die elastischen Eigenschaften der organischen Hochpolymeren und ihre kinetische Deutung," *Koll. Z.* **59**, 208–216 (1932).

Miiller, A. P. and Brockhouse, B. N., "Crystal dynamics and electronic specific heats of palladium and copper," *Can. J. Phys.* **49**, 704–722 (1971).

Milstein, F., "Review: Theoretical elastic behaviour of crystals at large strains," *J. Materials Sci.* **15**, 1071–1084 (1980).

Milstein, F., and Hill, R., "Theoretical properties of cubic crystals at arbitrary pressure—III. Stability," *J. Mech. Phys. Solids* **27**, 255–279 (1979).

Mindlin, R. D., "Elasticity, piezoelectricity and crystal lattice dynamics," *J. Elasticity*, **2**, 217–282 (1972).

Münster, A., *Statistical Thermodynamics*, First Engl. Ed., Springer-Verlag, New York (1969).

Neighbors, J. R., and Alers, G. A., "Elastic constants of silver and gold," *Phys. Rev.* **111**, 707–712 (1958).

Nelson, E., *Dynamical Theories of Brownian Motion*, Princeton University Press, Princeton, New Jersey (1967).

Newton, R. G., "Probability interpretation of quantum mechanics," *Am. J. Phys.* **48**, 1029–1034 (1980).

Niedermann, H. P., and Wagner, M., "On the quantum mechanical foundation of classical shell models in lattice dynamics," *Phys. Stat. Sol.* (*B*) **78**, 615–624 (1976).

Nozières, P., and Iche, G., "Brownian motion in a periodic potential under an applied bias: The transition from hopping to free conduction," *J. Phys.* **40**, 225–232 (1979).

Nye, J. F., *Physical Properties of Crystals*, Clarendon Press, Oxford (1957).

Oono, Y., Ohta, T., and Freed, K. F., "Elastic properties of a polymer chain with excluded volume: A renormalization group theory," *Macromolecules* **14**, 880–881 (1981).

Parrinello, M. and Rahman, A., "Strain fluctuations and elastic constants," *J. Chem. Phys.* **76**, 2662–2666 (1982).

Pear, M. R., and Weiner, J. H., "A generalization of Kramers' rate formula to include some anharmonic effects," *J. Chem. Phys.* **69**, 785–793 (1978).

Pear, M. R., and Weiner, J. H., "Brownian dynamics study of a polymer chain of linked rigid bodies," *J. Chem. Phys.* **71**, 212–224 (1979).

Pearson, D. S., and Graessley, W. W., "The structure of rubber networks with multifunctional junctions," *Macromolecules* **11**, 528–533 (1978).

Pechukas, P., "Comment on 'Flexible vs. rigid constraints in statistical mechanics,'" *J. Chem. Phys.* **72**, 6320–6321 (1980).

Peierls, R. E., *Quantum Theory of Solids*, Oxford University Press (1955).

Penrose, O., "Foundations of statistical mechanics," *Rep. Prog. Phys.* **42**, 1937–2006, (1979).

Perchak, D. R., "Brownian dynamics of crystalline and polymeric systems," Ph.D. Dissertation, Brown University, Providence, Rhode Island (1981).

Perchak, D., and Weiner, J. H., "Classical and quantum calculations for short stretched chain models," *Macromolecules,* **15**, 545–549 (1982).

Plancherel, M., "Beweis der Unmöglichkeit ergodischer mechanischer Systeme," *Ann. Phys.* **42**, 1061–1063 (1913).

Rallison, J. M., "The role of rigidity constraints in the rheology of dilute polymer solutions," *J. Fluid Mech.* **93**, part 2, 251–279 (1979).

Richards, E. G., *An Introduction to Physical Properties of Large Molecules in Solution*, Cambridge University Press (1980).

Risken, H., and Vollmer, H. D., "Brownian motion in periodic potentials in the low-friction-limit; Nonlinear response to an external force," *Z. Phys.* B **35**, 177–184 (1979).

Ronca, G., and Allegra, G., "An approach to rubber elasticity with internal constraints," *J. Chem. Phys.* **63**, 4990–4997 (1975).

Rosenthal, A., "Beweis der Unmöglichkeit ergodischer Gassysteme," *Ann. Phys.* **42**, 796–806 (1913).

Rudin, W., *Real and Complex Analysis*, McGraw-Hill, New York (1966).

Saito, N., Okano, K., Iwayanagi, S., and Hideshima, T., "Molecular motion in solid state polymers," in *Solid State Physics*, F. Seitz and D. Turnbull, Eds., Vol. 14, pp. 343–502, Academic Press, New York (1963).

Sanders, W. T., "Peierls stress for an idealized crystal model," *Phys. Rev.* **128**, 1540–1549 (1962).

Schrödinger, E., "Der stetige Übergang von der Mikro-zur Makromechanik," *Naturwissenchaften* **28**, 664–666 (1926).

Schrödinger, E., *Statistical Thermodynamics*, Cambridge University Press (1946).

Seiler, R., "Does the Born-Oppenheimer approximation work?" *Helv. Phys. Acta* **46**, 230–234 (1973).

Shalitin, D., and Imry, Y., "Statistical mechanics of solids," *Phys. Rev. B* **11**, 4065–4068 (1975).

Shannon, C. E., "A mathematical theory of communication," *Bell Syst. Tech. J.* **27**, 379–623 (1948).

Sheard, F. W., "Calculation of the thermal expansion of solids from the third-order elastic constants," *Philos. Mag.* **3**, 1381–1390 (1958).

Shewmon, P. G., *Diffusion in Solids*, McGraw-Hill, New York (1963).

Sinai, Ya. G., *Doklady Akad. Nauk* **153**, 1261–1264 (1963). English translation: "On the foundations of the ergodic hypothesis for a dynamical system of statistical mechanics," *Sov. Math.-Dokl.* **4**, 1818–1822 (1964).

Sirovich, L., *Techniques of Asymptotic Analysis*, Springer-Verlag, New York (1971).

Slater, J. C., *Quantum Theory of Molecules and Solids, Vol. 1: Electronic Structure of Molecules*, McGraw-Hill, New York (1963).

Slater, N. B., *Theory of Unimolecular Reactions*, Cornell University Press, Ithaca, New York (1959).

Smale, S., "On the problem of reviving the ergodic hypothesis of Boltzmann and Birkhoff," pp. 260–266 in *Nonlinear Dynamics*, R. H. G. Helleman, Ed., *Ann. N.Y. Acad. Sci.*, **357** (1980).

Smith, R. A., *Wave Mechanics of Crystalline Solids*, Chapman and Hall, London, (1961).

Stakgold, I., "The Cauchy relations in a molecular theory of elasticity," *Q. Appl. Math.* **8**, 169–186 (1950–1951).

Sussmann, J. A., "A comprehensive quantum theory of diffusion," *Annales de Physique* **6**, 135–156 (1971).

Sutherland, W., "The mechanical vibrations of atoms," *Philos. Mag., 6th Ser.*, **20**, 657–660 (1910).

Tabor, D., *Gases, Liquids and Solids*, 2nd ed., Cambridge University Press (1979).

Takabayasi, T., "On the formulation of quantum mechanics associated with classical pictures," *Prog. Theor. Phys.* **8**, 143–182 (1952).

Takahasi, H., "Eine einfache Methode zur Behandlung der statistischen Mechanik eindeimensionaler Substanzen," *Proc. Phys.-Meth. Soc. Jpn.* **24**, 60–62 (1942).

Terlecki, G., Grün, N., and Scheid, W., "Solution of the time-dependent Schrödinger equation with a trajectory method and application to $H^+ - H$ scattering," *Physics Letters* **88A**, 33–36 (1982).

Thurston, R. N., "Wave propagation in fluids and normal solids," in *Physical Acoustics*, W. P. Mason, Ed., Vol. I, Part A, pp. 1–110, Academic Press, New York (1964).

Treloar, L. R. G., *The Physics of Rubber Elasticity*, 3rd ed., Clarendon Press, Oxford (1975).

Treloar, L. R. G., "The mechanics of rubber elasticity," *Proc. R. Soc. London, Ser. A* **351**, 301–330 (1976).

Tribus, M. *Thermostatics and Thermodynamics*, Van Nostrand, Princeton, New Jersey (1961).

Truesdell, C., and Noll, W., "The non-linear field theories of mechanics," in *Handbuch der Physik*, S. Flügge, Ed., Vol. III/3, Springer-Verlag, Berlin (1965).

Truesdell, C., and Toupin, R. A., "The Classical Field Theories," with an Appendix on Invariants by J. L. Ericksen in *Handbuch der Physik*, S. Flügge, Ed., Vol. III/1, 226–858, Springer-Verlag, Berlin (1960).

Vineyard, G. H., "Frequency factors and isotope effects in solid state rate processes," *J. Phys. Chem. Solids* **3**, 121–127 (1957).

Voigt, W., *Lehrbuch der Kristallphysik*, Teubner, Leipzig (1910).

Volkenstein, M. V., *Configurational Statistics of Polymeric Chains*, S. N. Timasheff and M. J. Timasheff, Trans., Wiley-Interscience, New York (1963).

Völkl, J., and Alefeld, G., "Hydrogen diffusion in metals," pp. 231–302 in *Diffusion in Solids; Recent Developments*, A. S. Nowick and J. J. Burton, Eds., Academic Press, New York (1975).

Vollmer, H. D., and Risken, H., "Bistability effects of the Brownian motion in periodic potentials," *Z. Phys. B* **37**, 343–349 (1980).

Wallace, D. C., *Thermodynamics of Crystals*, Wiley, New York (1972).

Weiner, J. H., "Classical and quantum rate theories for solids," *Phys. Rev.* **169**, 570–577 (1968).

Weiner, J. H., "Thermally activated motion of dislocations," in *Mathematical Theory of Dislocations*, pp. 203–209, T. Mura, Ed., Amer. Soc. of Mech. Engineers, New York (1969).

Weiner, J. H., "Thermal activation and tunneling phenomena in solids," pp. 62–77, *Proc. Sixth U.S. National Congress of Applied Mechanics*, Amer. Soc. of Mech. Engineers, New York (1970).

Weiner, J. H., "Quantum rate theory for a symmetric double-well potential," *J. Chem. Phys.* **68**, 2492–2506 (1978).

Weiner, J. H., "Hellmann-Feynman theorem, elastic moduli, and the Cauchy relations," *Phys. Rev. B* **24**, 845–848 (1981).

Weiner, J. H., "Use of $S = k \log p$ for stretched polymers," *Macromolecules*, **15**, 542–544 (1982).

Weiner, J. H., and Adler, W. F., "Computer simulation of vacancy migration," *Phys. Rev.* **144**, 511–524 (1966).

Weiner, J. H., and Askar, A., "Time-dependent perturbation calculations based on the hydrodynamic analogy to quantum mechanics," *J. Chem. Phys.* **54**, 1108–1113 (1971a).

Weiner, J. H., and Askar, A., "Particle method for the numerical solution of the time-dependent Schrödinger equation," *J. Chem. Phys.* **54**, 3534–3541 (1971b).

Weiner, J. H., and Forman, R. E., "Rate theory for solids. IV. Classical Brownian motion model," *Phys. Rev. B* **10**, 315–324 (1974a).

Weiner, J. H., and Forman, R. E., "Rate theory for solids. V. Quantum Brownian-motion model," *Phys. Rev. B* **10**, 325–337 (1974b).

Weiner, J. H., and Partom, Y., "Quantum rate theory for solids. II. One-dimensional tunneling effects," *Phys. Rev.* **187**, 1134–1146 (1969).

Weiner, J. H., and Partom, Y., "Quantum rate theory for solids. III. N-dimensional tunneling effects," *Phys. Rev. B* (3) **1**, 1533–1539 (1970).

Weiner, J. H., and Pear, M. R., "Computer simulation of conformational transitions in an idealized polymer model," *Macromolecules* **10**, 317–325 (1977).

Weiner, J. H., and Perchak, D., "On Frenkel's governor model for stretched polymers," *Macromolecules* **14**, 1590–1591 (1981).

Weiner, J. H., and Sanders, W. T., "Peierls stress and creep of a linear chain," *Phys. Rev.* **134**, A1007–A1015 (1964).

Weiner, J. H., and Stevens, T. W., "Relative importance of internal pressure and excluded-volume effects in resolution of network collapse problem," *Macromolecules* (in press).

Weinreich, G., *Solids: Elementary Theory for Advanced Students*, Wiley, New York, (1965).

Weisskopf, V. F., "Of atoms, mountains, and stars: A study in qualitative physics," *Science* **187**, 605–612 (1975).

Wert, C. A., and Zener, C., "Interstitial atomic diffusion coefficients," *Phys. Rev.* **76**, 1169–1175 (1949).

Wightman, A. S., "Statistical mechanics and ergodic theory: an expository lecture," pp. 1–32 in *Statistical Mechanics at the Turn of the Decade*, E. G. D. Cohen, Ed., Dekker, New York (1971).

Wilson, A. H., *Thermodynamics and Statistical Mechanics*, Cambridge University Press (1957).

Wolynes, P. G., "Quantum theory of activated events in condensed phases," *Phys. Rev. Letters*, **47**, 968–971 (1981).

Zhdanov, G. S., *Crystal Physics*, Academic Press, New York (1965).

INDEX